he Elements

III	IV	V	VI	VII	O
					2 / **2** / **He** / 4.003
2 3 / **5** / **B** / 10.81	2 4 / **6** / **C** / 12.01	2 5 / **7** / **N** / 14.01	2 6 / **8** / **O** / 16.00	2 7 / **9** / **F** / 19.00	2 8 / **10** / **Ne** / 20.18
2 8 3 / **13** / **Al** / 26.98	2 8 4 / **14** / **Si** / 28.09	2 8 5 / **15** / **P** / 30.97	2 8 6 / **16** / **S** / 32.06	2 8 7 / **17** / **Cl** / 35.45	2 8 8 / **18** / **Ar** / 39.95

28 / **Ni** / 58.71	2 8 18 1	**29** / **Cu** / 63.55	2 8 18 2	**30** / **Zn** / 65.37	2 8 18 3	**31** / **Ga** / 69.72	2 8 18 4	**32** / **Ge** / 72.59	2 8 18 5	**33** / **As** / 74.92

28 Ni 58.71	**29** Cu 63.55	**30** Zn 65.37	**31** Ga 69.72	**32** Ge 72.59	**33** As 74.92	**34** Se 78.96	**35** Br 79.90	**36** Kr 83.80
46 Pd 106.4	**47** Ag 107.9	**48** Cd 112.4	**49** In 114.8	**50** Sn 118.7	**51** Sb 121.8	**52** Te 127.6	**53** I 126.9	**54** Xe 131.3
78 Pt 195.1	**79** Au 197.0	**80** Hg 200.6	**81** Tl 204.4	**82** Pb 207.2	**83** Bi 209.0	**84** Po (210)	**85** At (210)	**86** Rn (222)

63 Eu 152.0	**64** Gd 157.3	**65** Tb 158.9	**66** Dy 162.5	**67** Ho 164.9	**68** Er 167.3	**69** Tm 168.9	**70** Yb 173.0	**71** Lu 175.0

95 Am (243)	**96** Cm (247)	**97** Bk (247)	**98** Cf (252)	**99** Es (254)	**100** Fm (257)	**101** Md (257)	**102** No (255)	**103** Lw (256)

Atomic weights are given to four significant figures and are based on carbon-12; values in parentheses are for the most stable or the most familiar isotope. (Elements 104 and 105 were reported in the late 1960s, but official names and symbols were yet to be designated.)

elements of
general and
biological
chemistry

elements of general and biological chemistry

an introduction to the molecular basis of life

third edition

John R. Holum, Ph.D.

Professor of Chemistry,
Augsburg College

JOHN WILEY AND SONS, INC.
NEW YORK · LONDON · SYDNEY · TORONTO

in that *Manual* a few
proach for a very brie
For a while, my text is
is why I did not limit
time allotted to me.

Acknowledgment
all who have written,
Mickelberg and Neal
Adolphus College, and
aid at important mome

Minneapolis, Minnesot

preface
to the
third edition

The previous edition of this text appeared in print just as the full and awesome extent of what we have been doing to our planet penetrated our collective consciousness. I wrote in the preface to that edition that "our students live in a world populated by people and other living things, and they fancy the notion that illustrations of basic principles of physics and chemistry might just as well be taken from the world of the living as from the world of the dead." The theme of this new edition remains, as before, the molecular basis of life, but the world of the living, alas, is becoming increasingly unhealthy.

Previous editions in various units stressed the *kinship* we have with all living things without saying very much about our *dependence* on the environment. It is that dependence that we have ignored as we have gone our free-wheeling ways in what Garrett Hardin would call the last, remaining public "commons," the waters of the land and the oceans and the air around us. Man, as we are somewhat painfully, somewhat happily learning, does not stand above the great cycles of nature. Some of what is needed to understand those cycles has always been a part of chemistry, and I have made it more explicit in this new edition.

The major change I have made in writing the present edition is the interweaving of chemistry-related material from the environmental sciences to illustrate several facets of the molecular basis of life's dependence on environmental factors. My aim has been to be illustrative, not comprehensive, and to provide students with a vocabulary of topics and terms they may use to pursue in other sources both a deeper and a broader understanding of the environment.

I have discussed environmental topics where they seemed logically to fit. The dangers of thermal pollution, for example, follow very smoothly (and quickly) a discussion of factors that affect rates of reactions. Reverse osmosis and desalination of seawater make the just-prior study of osmosis a good deal more interesting. After describing what a catalyst is and why it is valuable, it takes but a moment to show students how porous beds of catalysts in auto mufflers will make it easier to get cleaner exhaust. The little excursions of earlier editions into "important individual compounds" cannot now ignore such environmentally important substances as gasoline, lead additives, phosphates, and pesticides. The study of oxygen has been completely redone and split into a separate chapter together with other nonmetallic elements of the biosphere. The oxides of oxygen (ozone), sulfur, nitrogen, carbon, and silicon and their roles in healthy and harmful ways in the environment are discussed. Later, in the chapter on hydrocarbons, we return to air pollution to sketch how photochemical smog is formed.

In the struggle to keep the length of the book about the same, I have pruned a number of (now) seemingly minor things (for example, among others, the more

supplemen
mat

preface to th

chapter 1 concerning goals and methods

the care of the Earth and the Earth's people The needs of this planet and her inhabitants must be cared for in hundreds of ways, and this book is written to help you prepare to meet some of those needs. Perhaps you will specialize in the care of human health as a nurse, a dental hygienist, an X-ray technician, a therapist, a dietician, a food technologist, or a home economist. Or maybe you will tend the earth and other human needs—the categories often overlap—as an agricultural specialist, a conservationist, a ranger, an ecologist, a forester, or in one of any number of related vocations. Your goal may be to become a teacher of health and physical education or some other science subject. Whatever you plan to do, you will be a citizen and a voter, one who breathes the air and drinks the water of this land and sups on the harvest of its soils. No doubt you already are deeply concerned about the environment. In the fight to save it, the energy that comes from that concern is certainly important, but energy needs direction or it disappears in smoke and fury. For direction we need goals and values and we need knowledge and understanding. There are goals and values implied all throughout this book, but its main thrust is toward a deeper understanding of the nature and the unity of our world.

seeking unity in the diversity around us Undergirding all of nature and all of life is a remarkable unity. To put it as ecologist Barry Commoner does, everything is tied to everything else. Living things share the same kinds of energy sources within their cells, the same basic kinds of building materials, the same informational systems or hereditary alphabets, and the same planet. This book is about those features of that unity that are seen especially clearly by physical scientists.

our theme: the molecular basis of life. The differences between various living things are dramatic and often beautiful, but no more so than the startling similarities, especially when seen at molecular levels, at the molecular basis of life. Moreover, by dipping to the molecular level and seeing a unity there we understand better the wide-ranging differences and varieties in nature. At the molecular level we see more clearly that good health is intimately related to good body chemistry. Those who tend the health needs of society, as they understand better the molecular basis of life, will function more thoughtfully, more carefully, and with the greater personal satisfaction that comes from going beyond the slavish following of orders through knowing more of what they are doing. At the molecular level we also understand more clearly the corollary to Barry Commoner's "law," if everything is indeed tied to everything else, then in nature it is impossible to do only one thing. The corollary does not summon us to inaction, but rather warns us to know what we are doing and to know it before instead of after the act.

One of the abiding hopes of serious students and teachers is that people with knowledge and understanding will act wisely on what they know. Since the study you are starting involves an uncommon sort of knowledge with a vocabulary and a set of symbols not often used in everyday conversation, we need a plan for our work.

Although life has a molecular basis, the molecules of life are sometimes so complex that they numb the mind, at least at first glance. But the score of a Beethoven symphony, to a beginner, does the same thing. A third-grader, viewing the arithmetic homework of a fifth-grader, quietly despairs of the future. Beginners to any field of study, regardless of age, forget (or have yet to learn) that there are common ways of handling what seems so complex at the start. We look for relations, common features, and we get the most basic things straight from the beginning—definitions, symbols, scales, and the like.

We shall look on the complicated molecules of life as a mountain climber views a contour map. He does not try to commit it to memory. He uses his knowledge of a few signs and symbols with which any number of such maps can be read and interpreted. Complicated molecules also carry "map signs." Once we recognize them and see them in any complex molecule, we need not memorize its structure, but we can still understand and maybe make intelligent predictions of the chemical behavior of the substance in this or that setting. These molecular "map signs" (functional groups) are best introduced among simple substances, and that is why we have a few chapters that include acids, bases, and organic chemicals before we go too far into the molecular basis of life. The most basic principles in our study concern atomic and molecular structure, and we shall start with these in the next chapter.

solving problems—creating others. It is ironic that one of the principal reasons we have so many environmental problems now is that we have tried very hard to solve other problems. The quest for an escape from drudgery and man-killing hours of labor not only gave birth to the yoke, the sail, and various wind and water mills, it also spawned coal- and gasoline-burning engines as well as nuclear power plants. The dread of disease and early death gave rise, in part, to chemicals for killing disease-bearing pests that spread typhus, malaria, and various fevers, chemicals now often feared for reasons not earlier noticed. Fertilizers, weed killers, irrigation projects, extensive roads and railways, and hybrid grains opened up lands that otherwise might not be usable, and they made possible spectacular increases in the world's food supplies.

The fruits of science and technology sometimes, unfortunately, leave a bitter aftertaste. Fertilizers may also kill lakes; weed killers are hard to confine to their targets and they sometimes hit nontarget forms of life; irrigation projects have been known to cause the soil to turn salty; the traffic on the roads brings poisons into the air. Only the hybrid grains seem an unmixed blessing, but even they demand water and extensive fertilization.

do we turn around? It does not seem at all likely that we will turn ourselves around and go back to the pre-1850 or 1890 days when most Americans were living at or below the current poverty level, when life was not only harder but much shorter. Alternatives to that prospect exist, but they require more than technology and science. Few of our current cares can be handled only by improvements in technology. Biologist Garrett Hardin writes of ''no-technical-solution problems,'' issues that will require something in the way of a change in human values. As examples he cites the arms race, the population explosion, urban sprawl, and environmental decay. Yet, there are features to each of these problems that are purely technical and that need the help of scientists and engineers.

scientific method and attitude. There has evolved principally in the sciences a method for handling those technical questions whose solutions depend almost entirely on facts and the use of reason. Called the scientific method, it works only when the facts[1] are mostly of a measurable, reproducible kind, those that can be checked by other scientists. Thus the method works best when the measured changes and events can be made to happen again. It is used most successfully when there is no urgent political or social crisis that demands a decision before a number of supporting facts are gathered and studied. The most important additional feature of the scientific method is the mental attitude that must accompany its use. Used by scholars in all fields, the attitude calls for a strong commitment to be objective and impartial, to describe accurately how the facts were obtained, to report them honestly, and to be open to the implications of new facts.

What is called the scientific method is far from a cut-and-dried procedure. It is no magic, step-by-step set of directions for research. Rather, when we describe the method here, we set down only a more or less general pattern of activity that can be seen to have occurred in many success stories in science. The history of science, however, is full of accounts of men and women who had intuitions, made guesses, had wild dreams, or were seemingly just plain lucky. Great discoveries such as penicillin, aniline dyes, radioactivity, and vulcanized rubber happened by accident. They happened, however, to people with enough scientific training to recognize their significance. Indeed, this is probably the major initial step to scientific success—having a deep awareness of the current state of the knowledge and the theories in your

---

[1] To a scientist, a *fact* is any event, occurrence, or characteristic property he or others can verify by retaking the measurement or by repeating the event. A scientific fact is, thus, only one kind of fact. Some facts are historical, and even though a historical event cannot be exactly repeated the facts surrounding it are no less true, especially if there were independent eyewitnesses and records. Other facts are personal, for example, personal likes and dislikes.

particular branch of science. This knowledge includes awareness of many unexplained observations and several weaknesses in current theories. These deficiencies are attacked. Using what he knows, the scientist works out what he thinks is a better explanation. We could call this his tentative hypothesis, and if it is any good it is suggestive of ways of being checked. In fact, this is one purpose of a hypothesis—to suggest experiments to collect more facts that might bear on the problem. The new facts strengthen or discredit the hypothesis or suggest modifications. If the hypothesis is sound, is thoroughly checked, is productive of explanations and successful predictions, and if it has some breadth, that is, if it concerns a family of observations rather than just one or a few obscure points, scientists may begin to call it a *theory*. If the theory has great scope; if it encompasses a multitude of events and ties together a number of otherwise seemingly unrelated features of nature; if it is virtually a universal experience of mankind; then it may be referred to as a *law of nature*. Thus we have, for example, Newton's law of gravitation that expresses what all scientists now see are universal features of such widely disparate things as the fall of an apple, the pull of the tides, and the motions of the planets. Or we have the first law of thermodynamics, which states our conviction that in all natural events something we call energy is conserved.

taking measurements. Reproducible facts are measurable facts. Science depends on *human* measurement; without it, there is no science. The five senses are the most important tools a scientist has, but they are quite limited. It is easy to tell if an object is hot or cold. To tell with accuracy, however, whether a person's temperature is 98.6°F or 100°F is another matter, and much can depend on the difference. The need for delicate instruments to measure very small differences with great accuracy is obvious. Moreover, we must have ways that make it possible for different people to obtain the same data, thus avoiding arguments. Herein lies the key to scientific progress.

Men used to ask, "*Why* do we get sick?" The answers were arguments and debates that sometimes led to bloodshed and seldom to cures. It was when men began to ask "*How* do people get sick?" that progress began in relieving and curing or even preventing disease. The "how" question demanded observations and measurements, rather than expressions of opinion. Out of it came the realization that blood circulates, the germ theory, vitamins, tailor-made drugs, and all the other factors that comprise modern medicine.

the international system. SI. Instruments of measurement depend on definite measuring standards. The marks and numbers on a thermometer would be meaningless unless the marks and numbers on all thermometers were related to the same thing. The standards used universally by scientists are provided by the metric system, a system now in the process of being further refined, relabeled, and legally adopted throughout the world as the International System of Units, officially abbreviated SI. The designation "SI" may be regarded as the successor to "metric system," but in practical affairs they may be taken as synonyms. Both systems are based on ten; both have nearly identical symbols and prefixes; both are essentially identical in the *sizes* of the reference units; they differ in the ways used to provide *reference standards*.

The great convenience of the SI units or of its predecessor, the metric units are the decimal relations of the subunits. Moreover, these relations are always implied in the names of subunits by suitable prefixes. The prefix "kilo-," for example, means "one thousand." Thus, "one kilometer" is "one thousand meters"; "one kilogram" is "one thousand grams." The prefixes and symbols for multiples and submultiples in the system are in Table 1.1. Below is an illustration of how the prefixes of the system work with units of length.

10 millimeters = 1 centimeter	10 meters = 1 dekameter	
10 centimeters = 1 decimeter	10 dekameters = 1 hectometer	
10 decimeters = 1 *meter* (the base)	10 hectometers = 1 kilometer	

Metric measures were first devised by the Paris Academy of Science at the close of the 18th century. About the middle of the 19th century these measures became legal to use in the United States and Great Britain, where they have yet to become widely used, however, except within scientific communities. Some serious difficulties with the original metric references were

Table 1.1 **Prefixes for Multiples and Submultiples of SI and Metric Units**[a]

	Prefixes	Symbols
1 000 000 000 000 = 10^{12}	tera	T
1 000 000 000 = 10^{9}	giga	G
1 000 000 = 10^{6}	**mega**	**M**
1 000 = 10^{3}	**kilo**	**k**
100 = 10^{2}	hecto	h
10 = 10^{1}	deka	da
0.1 = 10^{-1}	deci	d
0.01 = 10^{-2}	**centi**	**c**
0.001 = 10^{-3}	**milli**	**m**
0.000 001 = 10^{-6}	**micro**	**μ**
0.000 000 001 = 10^{-9}	nano	n
0.000 000 000 001 = 10^{-12}	pico	p
0.000 000 000 000 001 = 10^{-15}	femto	f
0.000 000 000 000 000 001 = 10^{-18}	atto	a

[a]The most commonly used prefixes and symbols are in boldface.

studied by a conference culminating in the Treaty of the Meter (Paris, 1875). Under terms of the treaty, the signatory nations established an International Bureau of Weights and Measures to serve as keeper of the international references and they provided for additional General Conferences on Weights and Measures as needed.

meter. In 1889 the standard of length, the meter, was officially defined as the distance separating two narrow scratches on a bar of platinum-iridium alloy when its temperature is zero degrees centigrade. The reference is kept in a vault at Sevres, France (near Paris). Each nation that signed the treaty has a copy of the prototype bar, and the United States redefined its yard as being 0.9144 meter. See Figs. 1.1 and 1.2. The 11th General Conference on Weights and Measures (1960) adopted the International System (SI), an action that, in part, redefined the meter in terms of something not subject

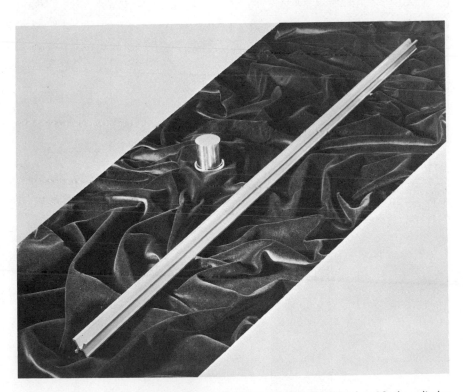

Fig. 1.1 The United States standard of mass, Prototype Kilogram Number 20, the cylinder shown above, is a duplicate of the international standard kept in France. The platinum-iridium bar, Prototype Meter Number 27, also shown above, which served as the United States standard of length, has been replaced by the wavelength of the orange-red light emitted by the krypton-86 isotope. The bar will remain as a secondary standard because of the ease with which it can be used for certain types of measurements. (Courtesy of the National Bureau of Standards, Washington, D. C.)

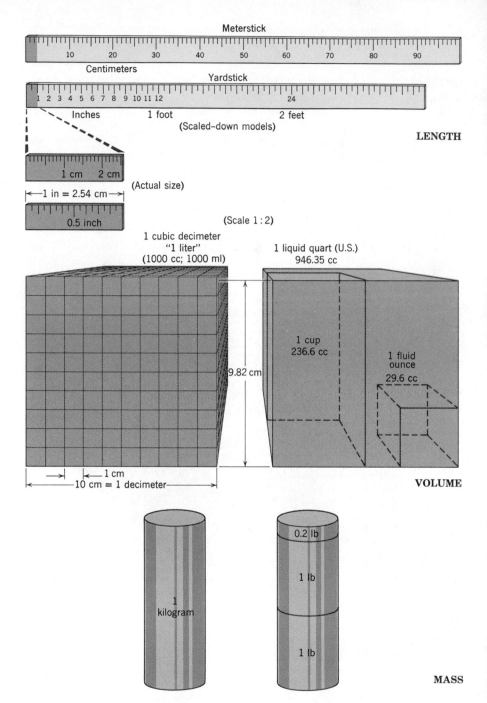

Fig. 1.2 Visual comparisons of relative sizes of units of length, volume, and mass in the SI (metric) and English systems.

concerning goals and methods

to loss by theft, fire, or corrosion. (The change, however, was at considerable loss in understandability to beginners in science.) The international standard meter is defined as 1 650 763.73 wave lengths[2] in a vacuum of the orange-red radiation emitted by the krypton-86 atom when it undergoes a transition between the energy levels $2p_{10}$ and $5d_5$. We shall not try to explain that further. The new definition changes only the way in which the most accurate copies of meter sticks would ultimately be checked. It does not change the actual length of the meter as formerly understood, at least not to any extent of importance in ordinary affairs. The old references, the platinum-iridium bars with their scratches, are still used for routine comparisons. The advantage of the SI meter, of course, is that krypton-86 is not subject to copying errors or to any of the other ravages of environment and time. Moreover, although the prototype-1 metric meter has to be in one place, the SI reference, krypton-86, is available everywhere.

mass. Mass is a measure of the inertia of a body, that is, its resistance to being moved, or to suffering any change in its motion. Mass is therefore a measure of the amount of matter in an object as related to some standard reference mass.[3] The General Conference has yet to find an acceptable reference for mass that is not an artifact. The SI standard mass is the kilogram and the reference is the same metric mass defined in 1889—a block of platinum metal kept by the International Bureau of Weights and Measures in its Sevreś vault in France. The United States Bureau of Standards has an accurate copy. See Figs. 1.1 and 1.2.

volume. In principle, volume may be expressed as (length)^3. There is, therefore, no need for a special reference. The standard meter and its subdivisions and multiples can be used for defining a unit of volume. That unit in the metric system was the liter, and one liter is exactly one cubic decimeter or 1000 cubic centimeters. A very common subunit is the milliliter or one-

[2] In the International System (SI) spaces instead of commas are used to separate groups of numbers by threes. Instead of 1,562 meters, for example, it is written 1 562 meters.

[3] Weight, on the other hand, is strictly a measure of the gravitational attraction the object is said to experience. In going from earth to moon the mass of an astronaut remains the same but his weight undergoes wide changes as he moves in and out of the earth's and the moon's gravitational fields. His weight on the moon is roughly one-sixth of his weight on the earth. Whenever a double beam weighing balance is used, the mass of some object is determined by comparing its weight (gravitational attraction) with the weight (gravitational attraction) of a reference mass at essentially the identical geographical location (thus cancelling any problems associated with small fluctuations in the force of gravity at various places on earth). In chemistry it is common and acceptable in most situations to use the term "weight" when "mass" is meant.

thousandths of a liter. The milliliter (ml) is, therefore, identical with a cubic centimeter (cc).

$$1 \text{ ml} \equiv 1 \text{ cc}$$

The liquid quart is roughly 0.946 liter or 946 ml. (The word "liter" is not on the SI list of official terms, but will undoubtedly be used for all but the most accurate work where the official term for liter, cubic decimeter, is to be employed. We shall use the terms "liter" and "milliliter" frequently and "cubic decimeter" not at all; and we shall use "ml" and "cc" interchangeably. The SI standard of volume is the cubic meter.)

temperature. The SI unit of temperature is the degree Kelvin (K). It is identical with the degree Celsius (°C), formerly called the degree centigrade.[4] The degree most familiar to people in English-speaking countries is degree Fahrenheit (°F).

A temperature *degree* is not the same as a temperature *scale*, but in understanding both this difference and the different degrees, Fig. 1.3 may be helpful. We shall not now discuss in detail how the Kelvin scale is devised. In practical work the scales are fixed by the freezing and boiling points of various pure substances—oxygen, water, sulfur, silver, and gold. The zero on the Kelvin scale corresponds to the degree of cold reached when all movements of the particles of a "perfectly behaved" or ideal gas cease. Since you cannot have less than no motion at all, this degree of cold is understandably called *absolute* zero. Between the freezing and boiling points of water there are (by definition) 100 degrees on both the Kelvin and Celsius scales. On the Fahrenheit scale there are more—180. (For future reference—see equations below—the ratio of 180 to 100 is 9 to 5.) On the Celsius scale the freezing point of water is called (arbitrarily) zero degrees; on the Fahrenheit scale this degree of cold is called (equally arbitrarily) 32°. To convert values of degrees between the Celsius and Fahrenheit scales most scientists reach for a handy table. If that is not available, the following equations may be used:

$$°C \text{ to } °F: \qquad °F = °C\left(\tfrac{9}{5}\right) + 32°$$
$$°F \text{ to } °C: \qquad °C = (°F - 32°)\tfrac{5}{9}$$

(When needed, degrees Kelvin = °C + 273.15)

In some professions, medicine and dietetics, for example, both scales are encountered, and workers in these fields find it useful to have some idea

[4] In official SI usage, the word "degree" and its symbol, (°), are not employed with the Kelvin scale. Thus, you would write 300 K, not 300°K. In any other temperature system the degree sign is always used; 300°C, not 300 C. We shall have almost no occasion to use the Kelvin scale.

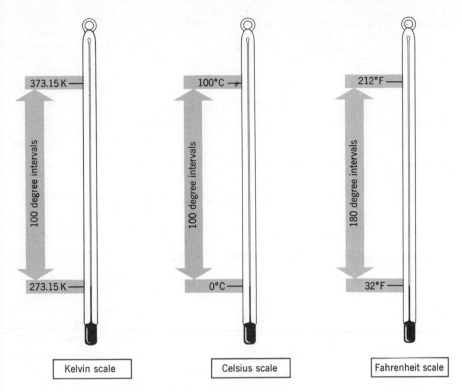

Fig. 1.3   Relations between the Kelvin, Celsius, and Fahrenheit scales.

of how these scales compare in terms of familiar situations. The following data (rounded to whole numbers) are frequently used as reference points, in addition to the data for water:

	°F	°C
Average room temperature	77	25
A very cold day	− 20	− 29
A hot day	100	38
Anesthetic ether boils	94	35
Chloroform boils	142	61
Normal body temperature	98.6	37

The most common SI units with which we shall work are listed in Table 1.2 together with their English equivalents. (The best way to acquire familiarity with the SI system is to use it and to associate various units with approximate equivalents in the English system. For example, there are about 2.5 cm in an inch; a liter and a quart are very nearly the same; a meter is slightly longer than a yard.)

Table 1.2 Some Common SI Units and English Equivalents

Unit	Abbreviation	Definition	English System Equivalents
		Length	
Meter	m	Standard meter (Figs. 1.1 and 1.2)	39.37 in. (slightly over a yard)
Centimeter	cm	$\frac{1}{100}$ meter	0.394 in. (2.54 cm per inch)
		Mass	
Kilogram	kg	Standard kilogram (Fig. 1.1)	2.2 lb
Gram	g	$\frac{1}{1000}$ kg (0.001 kg)	0.035 oz (1 oz per 28.35 g) 453.6 g per pound)
Milligram	mg	$\frac{1}{1000}$ g (0.001 g)	There are 64.8 mg per grain.
		Volume	
Liter[a]	l	1 cubic decimeter	1.057 liquid qt; 33.8 oz[b] (approximately 1 qt)
Milliliter[a]	ml	$\frac{1}{1000}$ liter	29.6 ml per fluid oz (16.231 minims) (volume of 1 gram water at 4° C and 760 mm pressure)
Cubic centimeter	cc	Identical with the milliliter	

Miscellaneous Units of Common Measure

Commercial dry measure (U. S.)
   1 bushel = 4 pecks = 32 dry quarts (qt) = 64 pints (pt) = 35.24 liters

Commercial weight—avoirdupois
   1 pound (lb) = 16 ounces (oz av) = 256 drams (dr av) = 7000 grains (gr) = 453.6 g

Apothecaries' fluid measure (U. S. fluid measure)
   1 fluid ounce (fl oz, or f℥) = 8 fluid drams (fl dr, or f℈) = 480 minim (♍) = 29.6 ml

Apothecaries' weight
   1 ounce (oz ap, or ℥) = 8 drams (dr ap, or ℨ) = 24 scruples (s ap, or ℈)
                                  = 480 grains (gr) = 31.1 g

[a] Not official SI names. See text.
[b] These and other fluid volume measures in this table are for U. S. fluid measures. British fluid measures are slightly different.

energy In some old, period movie you may have viewed a scene in which a hot cannonball teeters precariously on the cornice of a besieged medieval fortress. That cannonball has a variety of abilities or potentials, as both defenders and attackers knew. Because of its mass and its location relative to the earth, the cannonball has a *position-changing capacity*—its own position when it falls and the position of things that get in the way when it falls, including at least small portions of the material where final impact occurs.

Because of its relatively higher temperature, the hot cannonball has a *temperature-changing capacity;* cooler things nearby get warmer.

If the cannonball is so hot that it glows, it has an *illumination-changing capacity*, too. Darker things near it appear brighter, more illuminated.

It would not be too farfetched to imagine that the cannonball has a *noise-level-changing capacity* as well; either as it drops and collides with things or as it cools and contracts unevenly (much as steam pipes crack and groan when they quickly warm up or cool down).

To carry the picture further we have to leap the centuries, but if that hot, glowing cannonball were near the sensing "eye" of a photoelectric device (some supermarket doors operate by means of such devices), it would have an *electric-current-changing capacity*. Light from the cannonball that fell on the photocell's eye would cause a surge of electricity. And once we have electricity, it is also possible to have *magnetism*.

The production of mechanical action, thermal effects, illumination, sound, electricity, and magnetism are all somehow directly or indirectly the capabilities and potentials of that cannonball. (If it dropped into a tub of acid we would add a *material-transforming-capacity* to our list, but that is closer to real chemistry than we want to be at the moment.) The cannonball clearly has something—only what? What do we call that "something" that is not really a "thing" at all? We obviously need a name, and we call it *energy*.

The cannonball has energy. It does not have mechanical work; it does not have heat; it does not have light, or sound, or electricity, or magnetism. (It does not even have chemistry . . . yet.) It has a variety of abilities, of capacities for causing events. Needing a label, we say it has energy. There are several ways by which the cannonball can transfer energy to certain parts of its surroundings. Only when *transfers* of energy occur do we have a way of measuring energy. When we do the measurements carefully we get a highly significant result. Transfers of energy take place *without any net loss* of *total* energy. Provided we have identified and measured all the ways of energy transfer, this result is observed. It is one of the most important laws of nature: energy may be neither created nor destroyed, but it may be transferred in various ways. When the cannonball hits things we say that it transfers *kinetic energy*—energy associated with bodily motion. (The maximum amount it could transfer in this particular way is measurably related to its mass (m) and its velocity (v) at the moment of impact by the equation:

$$\text{kinetic energy} = \text{K. E.} = \tfrac{1}{2}mv^2.)$$

When it transfers energy in such a way that it suffers a drop in its own temperature, we say that a flow of *heat* has occurred. How much energy may be transferred in this way may be measured directly or indirectly by a device called a calorimeter, but we shall not go into that matter. (We shall, however, need to know the common unit of heat, the calorie, to be discussed soon.) For heat to flow there must be a temperature difference between the heat source and the heat "sink."

Heat, as one form of the transfer of energy, is particularly important in scientific work because every other form of energy can be converted *quantitatively* into heat. A measure of the heat generated from other forms of energy therefore provides a quantitative measure for those other forms. (Although we can work it the other way around, by converting heat into the other forms, in practice we can *never* do it quantitatively.)

units of heat. the calorie and the kilocalorie. If one gram of water, initially at 14.5°C, is placed in contact with a warmer object such that the temperature of the water rises exactly one degree Celsius, then we say that one calorie of heat was transferred to the water. The *calorie* (cal) is an amount of heat required to raise the temperature of one gram of water one degree Celsius (specifically the particular degree between 14.5 and 15.5°C). The *kilocalorie* (kcal), of interest to those on diets, is 1000 calories. If you were to raise the temperature of a quart of water (roughly, one liter, or 1000 grams) from room temperature (about 25°C) to the boiling point, you would have to arrange for the transfer of about 75,000 calories (75 kilocalories) of heat into the water. How this is calculated is shown in the example below. You could get 75 kcal from the combustion of only about three-tenths of an ounce of carbon (as in coal), assuming no wastage of heat. It is because the calorie is such a small unit that nutritionists and other scientists prefer to use the kilocalorie as the common unit, but, in a confusion of terms, when a given serving of food is said to have, for example "250 calories," what is meant is 250 kilocalories. A common effort to avoid the confusion (but that only makes it worse) is to call the nutritionist's calorie the "large calorie" and write it with the capital, as in Calorie = 1 kilocalorie = 1000 "small calories." For our study, learn the terms calorie and kilocalorie.

Example. In making morning coffee, it is not uncommon for a cook to bring a liter of water (about four cups) from room temperature (25°C; 77°F) to boiling. How many calories of heat are needed to do this?

Solution
    1. One liter of water is equivalent to 1000 grams.
    2. The total change in temperature is $100 - 25 = 75$ degrees C.
    3. To raise 1 gram 1 degree, we need 1 calorie; to raise 1 gram 75 degrees, we need 75 calories.
    4. For 1000 grams, we need: $1000 \times 75 = 75,000$ calories or 75 kilocalories.

units of density and specific gravity. In many situations, especially clinical work, concepts of density and specific gravity are used. Density is defined as the amount of mass per unit volume:

$$\text{Density} = \frac{\text{mass (weight)}}{\text{volume}}$$

The density of lead, in SI units, is 11.3 grams/cc. The density of aluminum is 2.70 grams/cc. (In these situations, it is often helpful to read the solidus or slash line, /, as "per.") When we say, somewhat carelessly, that lead is heavier than aluminum, we really mean that lead is more dense than aluminum.

Nearly all substances expand in volume with increasing temperature. They do not change in mass, however. Therefore, the density of a substance is different at different temperatures. The change, however, is usually not much; at 0°C, mercury has a density of 13.5955 grams/cc, whereas at 100°C, its density is 13.351 grams/cc. To avoid problems, when a density is stated, the temperature at which it was measured is also stated. For example, the expression: $d^4_{water} = 1.000$ gram/cc means "the density of water at 4°C is 1.000 gram per cubic centimeter." (Incidentally, you should learn that fact about water.)

Specific gravity is the ratio of the mass of any object to the mass of an equal volume of water at the same temperature (unless otherwise specified). This definition automatically makes the specific gravity of water equal to 1. (Why?) Knowledge of the specific gravity of another substance informs us at once whether it is more or less dense than water. The concept of specific gravity is commonly used with liquids.

Specific gravities of liquids and solutions are often conveniently measured by a *hydrometer*. The technique is based on the principle that a floating object displaces an amount of liquid exactly equal to its own weight (Archimedes' principle). Figure 1.4 illustrates a hydrometer and its use.

A urinometer float is simply a hydrometer calibrated for the determination of specific gravities of urine specimens. Normal urine has a specific gravity, at room temperature, ranging from 1.008 to 1.030; it increases with increasing amounts of solid wastes present. An unusually high specific gravity is, therefore, indicative of an abnormal condition in the body.

References and Annotated Reading List

At the end of each chapter there will be an annotated list of books and articles. All are references used in the writing of the text. Some are advanced works that will primarily interest only instructors. Most, however, can be read with understanding

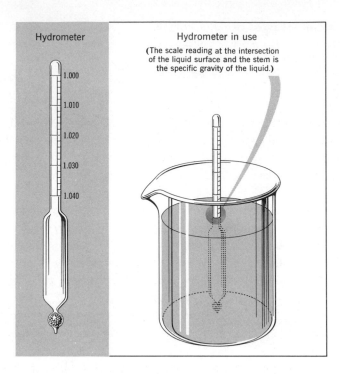

Hydrometer

1.000
1.010
1.020
1.030
1.040

Hydrometer in use

(The scale reading at the intersection of the liquid surface and the stem is the specific gravity of the liquid.)

Fig. 1.4 The hydrometer shown is calibrated to measure the specific gravities of liquids having values greater than 1. If the liquid studied has a specific gravity exactly equal to 1, the hydrometer will sink until the 1.000 mark is at the surface of the liquid. In liquids that are denser than water the hydrometer will displace less volume of liquid and will not sink as far. Hydrometers and urinometer floats are usually calibrated for measuring specific gravities at specified temperatures.

by the students using this text. Nearly all of the books are available in paperback editions; most of the articles have appeared in *Scientific American,* the *Journal of Chemical Education,* and *Chemistry.* (Since some articles and books undoubtedly have been missed, their omission from these lists does not imply adverse judgment of their worth.)

1. A. V. Astin. "Standards of Measurement." *Scientific American,* June 1968, page 50. A brief history of the development of measuring standards with emphasis on the metric system and the SI.

2. G. Socrates. "SI Units." *Journal of Chemical Education,* Volume 46, 1969, page 710. Following a brief survey of how the Systeme Internationale d'Unities (SI) came into being, there are several tables giving basic units, derived units, prefixes, conversion factors, and physical constants. Protocol for using SI is also described.

3. "Brief History and Use of the English and Metric Systems of Measurements." (With a chart of the modernized metric system.) National Bureau of Standards Special Publication 304A, 1969. (Available for 20¢ from the Superintendent of Documents, Washington, D. C.; the full-scale wall chart is available for 50¢ as item C 13.10;304.)

4. Lord Ritchie-Calder. "Conversion to the Metric System." *Scientific American,* July 1970, page 17. Great Britain plans to complete its ten-year changeover to the metric system by 1975. Before describing the problems and progress, the author (Chairman of the Metrication Board) provides a lively discussion of the history of measurement.

Problems and Exercises

1. If you are not too familiar with any system other than the English system for weights and measures, it is more important at the start to gain some impressions of orders of magnitudes than to memorize conversion factors. (These factors can always be looked up.) To get a feel for SI units and how large they are, try the following exercises.

   (a) How long is the nail on your little finger, in cm and in mm? (Don't be fussy about being exact; round your answers off to the nearest whole numbers.)

   (b) If you were buying clothing in, say, France, Italy, or Germany you might get startled looks from the sales ladies if you said your waist was (let's be kind) 22. To them "22" means 22 cm. Just how many inches are 22 cm?

   (c) If the tip of one finger were a cube 1 cm on each side, what would be its volume? How much water, in grams, would it hold? (The density of water is, rounded, 1 g/cc.)

   (d) If a pound of butter can be cut into 64 pats, how much would each pat weigh in grams? In milligrams?

   (e) In addition to two whole pounds of butter, how many pats (part d) would be needed to make up a kilogram of butter?

   (f) If you were to put a cup of mercury (take its density as 13.5 g/cc) into a 1-cup milk carton, how much would it weigh (ignoring the carton) in pounds?

   (g) Some people like water to be 70°F for swimming. What is that on the Celsius scale?

   (h) While camping at a better-than-average hostel in Austria you used the electric stove to bake corn bread. You set the dial at 350 and soon incinerated the corn bread. What happened? What setting should you have used?

   (i) What would be zero K on the Celsius scale?

   (j) There are 5280 feet in a mile. How many kilometers is that?

   (k) If you were traveling on the European continent all the distances would be in kilometers. Figure out what number (or fraction) you would use to change from a distance given in kilometers to the more familiar unit of miles.

   (l) Suppose you brought an American motorcycle to the continent. How would you relabel the following readings on the speedometer: 25, 60?

   (m) Three teaspoonfuls (one tablespoonful) corresponds to 0.5 fluid ounce. How many cubic centimeters are there in a teaspoonful?

(n) Assuming you have access in the laboratory to a balance, the next time you are there weigh a penny, a nickel, a dime, and a quarter using units of grams.

2. If you can read the article by Allen V. Astin mentioned in the Reading List, consider the following questions.

    (a) What was the proposal for the standard of length adopted and used by the Paris Academy in 1790–1799?

    (b) What might have been the reason for Jefferson's failure to urge its adoption in this country?

    (c) What was the adopted proposal for the standard of volume?

    (d) What is the fourth basic physical dimension (not included in our Chapter 1) for which a standard exists?

3. Perform calculations that will tell you if anesthetic ether (boiling point 34.6°C) is a liquid or a vapor (gas) at normal body temperature (98.6°F).

4. Calculate the number of kilocalories required to raise the temperature of 2 liters of water 90° on the Celsius scale.

5. How do the Kelvin and Celsius *degrees* compare?

chapter 2 the nature of matter: the atomic theory

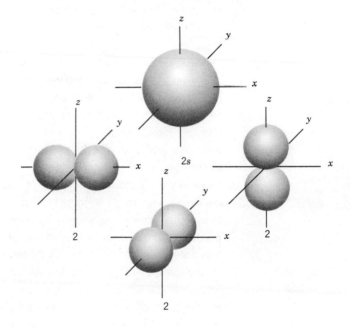

There is a great deal of difference between apples and apple seeds, and we can enjoy an apple while avoiding its core. The fruits of much scientific research are possible because of "seeds" no less strange. We cannot, however, maintain and enjoy a high standard of health and ignore its core. In a manner of speaking, these first several chapters are about the core of health. This chapter is about its peculiar seeds.

Progress in science had many origins. One of them occurred when people began to wonder about what they and their earth were made of. Back a few centuries before the Christian era several Greek philosophers sought a fully rational understanding of the nature of things. Eventually, the question became, how are things in general put together? Thales of Miletus (about 600 B.C.), convinced that there is a unity to all there is, reasoned that there must be one primary matter from which all other things emerged or evolved. He believed this to be water. Anaximenes (about 550 B.C.) thought it to be air. Heraclitus (about 480 B.C.) reasoned that fire had to be the primary matter—fire, the spirit and embodiment of change—because, to this philosopher, the only feature of the world that really exists is change itself. "To be is to change." Credit him with placing some trust in the senses; his senses saw change all about him; and yours do, too. Parmenides of Elea (about 500 B.C.), in the manner of the highly successful mathematicians, trusted his reason more than his senses, and he argued that all that is, taken all together, forms one indivisible, unchangeable being. Change is an illusion.

If Parmenides were right—at least, if everyone believed him to be right—there could be no science, for science is certainly a study of how things change, what they change from and to, and when to expect change. But not even Parmenides' contemporaries were convinced.

Democritus (about 460 B.C.) refused to abandon either his reason or his senses. There are features of the world that endure; there are features that change. How can there be both? That is, how can reason harmonize permanence and change? Democritus believed that there is not one indivisible, unchangeable being but, instead, a number of them. The Greek word for "indivisible" is *atomas*, literally, "noncutable." These "atoms" were thought by Democritus to be infinite in number and identical except for shape and size. When something undergoes a change, its individual atoms change their positions. Thus, even in the midst of change certain features remain permanent—the identity of the individual "atoms." The senses provided some indication that this ancient, largely philosophical atomic theory made sense. These people were familiar with the wearing away of stone steps; with the evaporation of water; with the fact that some substances were more dense than others. They also knew that you could not see, in one brief moment or even in one day, any wearing away taking place. Yet over a long period of time it happened. The existence of exceedingly tiny, invisible "atoms" as the building blocks of the stone step could easily help one understand their slow erosion. The same argument would apply to slow evaporation. And dense objects simply had more of the "atoms" in a given volume than lighter things.

Atoms, as they are known today, are incredibly small. One cubic centimeter of gold contains about 60,000,000,000,000,000,000,000 (6×10^{22}) of them. Yet, in spite of their smallness, they can be "cut" although the procedure is not delicate. Atom-smashing devices are employed, and the use of such instruments has revealed that atoms are made of other, even smaller, *subatomic particles*. Evidence for more than a dozen of these particles has been collected by examination of the "debris" from atom-smashing experiments.

For our purposes, three subatomic particles are of considerable importance: the neutron, the proton, and the electron. Chemists describe all atoms by picturing these three subatomic particles grouped in varying arrangements and varying proportions. These three are to chemists the fundamental building blocks of matter. We shall describe less fundamental building blocks, atoms and molecules, in terms of them. Before doing so, we should know more about what electrons, protons, and neutrons are.

Since we shall not go into advanced nuclear physics, the best statements that we can make about subatomic particles are descriptions of their behavior. They all behave as if they have mass. Two of them, the electron and the proton, behave as if they are electrically charged. Although the charge on a proton is of the same *intensity* as that on an electron, it is of opposite character. This equal but opposite relationship is indicated by the symbols that have been selected to describe the charges. A proton is said to have a $+1$ unit of charge and an electron a -1 unit. The most significant behavior of particles that bear charges of opposite character, or opposite sign, is their tendency to exert a pull or an attraction on each other. Like-charged particles, on the other hand, behave as if they were repelled or pushed apart by each other.

The mass of a proton equals that of a neutron and is about 1.7×10^{-24} gram. Scientists designate this mass as one *atomic mass unit*, abbreviated amu.[1] The mass of an electron is a tiny fraction, $\frac{1}{1823}$, of one atomic mass unit. Data for the three subatomic particles are summarized in Table 2.1.

the bohr model of the atom. In 1913, a 27-year-old Danish physicist, Niels Bohr, provided theoretical and experimental justification for picturing an atom as a miniature solar system. Two years earlier, a British physicist, Lord Rutherford, discovered that atoms contain hard, dense, inner cores, which he called *nuclei*. It is now understood that a nucleus has this density because all neutrons and protons of an atom are clustered tightly together within it. (Just how several protons—like-charged bodies—can be fixed tightly together is beyond

---

[1] More precisely, 1.0000 amu $= 1.6603 \times 10^{-24}$ gram.

Table 2.1 **Three Subatomic Particles**

Name	Mass (amu)	Charge	Common Symbol
Electron	$\frac{1}{1823}$	-1	e^-
Proton	1	$+1$	p, p^+, or simply $+$
Neutron	1	0	n

the scope of our study. Many other subatomic particles are known, however, and they all occur in the nucleus. Some are believed to be involved in binding the components of a nucleus together.)

Although we shall add more later, an atom can now be defined as an electrically neutral particle consisting of one nucleus and enough electrons to balance the nuclear charge. The problem of atomic structure becomes a matter of determining how electrons are arranged relative to their nucleus. In the Bohr model, Rutherford's nucleus is the center of an atomic "solar system." The "planets" of the system are the electrons. In the model, these move at high speeds in circular or elliptical orbits at some distance from the nucleus. These ideas are illustrated by the model in Fig. 2.1.

some modifications of the planetary model. Electron orbits cannot be seen, not even with the most powerful systems of magnification. What types of measurements, then, enable scientists to describe atomic structure in any terms? It is known that, if energy is properly supplied, electrons can be forced to leave atoms, and the energy required can be measured. Since the 1920s, inferences from such data have led scientists to abandon attempts to describe accurately how electrons move, or where they precisely are, relative to a nucleus. Indeed, there are theoretical reasons for believing that precision simultaneously on both these matters is not possible. Speculation about a problem such as the shape of a particular electron "orbit" has been abandoned. The question has instead become one of determining the probability that an electron may be found at any given distance from the nucleus. At certain distances and the corresponding regions, the probabilities are high and at others, low.

Those regions about a nucleus in which the electrons of an atom may most probably exist are called energy levels or shells. The term *shell* indicates geometry. The several regions or shells that an atom may have are roughly concentric with each other and the nucleus in much the same way that onion sections are concentric. The term *energy level* indicates measured facts about energy relations. The first energy level (shell) is the region that, of all the

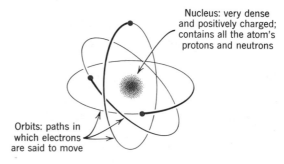

Nucleus: very dense and positively charged; contains all the atom's protons and neutrons

Orbits: paths in which electrons are said to move

Fig. 2.1 Schematic diagram of the planetary model of the atom. Often called the "Bohr atom," it includes basic ideas contributed by Rutherford.

Table 2.2 Energy Levels in Atoms ("Electron Shells")

Level number	1	2	3	4	5	6	7
Shell letter[a]	K	L	M	N	O	P	Q
Maximum number of electrons allowed in theory[b]	2	8	18	32	50	72	98
Maximum number of electrons actually found in nature	2	8	18	32	32	18	8

[a] The decision to assign to the first shell the letter K was arbitrary.
[b] The numbers fit the equation, Max. No. $= 2n^2$, where $n =$ shell number. For shell number 4, for example, $2n^2 = 2 \times (4)^2 = 2 \times 16 = 32$.

energy levels, is closest to the nucleus. It is called the *lowest* energy level because an electron there is harder to remove than one at any higher energy level (that is, in any shell farther away from the nucleus).

Energy levels have been given letters and numbers. The lowest one is called the *first* energy level or the K-shell. The next level is the *second* energy level or the L-shell, and so forth (see Table 2.2). There are limits to the numbers of electrons shells can accommodate, presumably because electrons, being like-charged, resist crowding together. The K-shell, being the smallest one, has a low limit; it can hold a maximum of two electrons. The other limits are summarized in Table 2.2.

The most probable and most stable arrangement of an atom's electrons is called its *electronic configuration*. Only 105 fundamentally different kinds are known. Of these, 81 are stable, 9, although naturally occurring, are unstable (radioactive), and 15 are artificial (and radioactive), including technetium and promethium. All of matter, in all its great variety, is constructed from roughly 100 building blocks. As a group, they are called the *elements*.

An element may be defined, in part, as any substance whose atoms have identical electronic configurations. All atomic nuclei in an element have identical nuclear charges. The atomic nuclei of different elements have different nuclear charges.

Before taking up the question of electronic configuration in detail, it would be useful to learn more about the elements, how they fit into the scheme of things, and how they are symbolized.

elements, compounds and mixtures—a preview. Elements are one kind of "gross substance"; atoms are the exceedingly tiny particles that make up elements. A sample of an element might be a powder, a metallic material, a liquid, or a gas. The point is that except for certain gases you could have a sample of an element that could be seen with the naked eye. The sample could be weighed. An atom is an individual thing; it can neither be seen

substances

nor weighed directly. Since beginning students often have trouble making these distinctions, let us lay out the start of a flow-diagram that may help avoid the problem. We shall not define all the terms here, but we can refer back to this diagram, Fig. 2.2, later. First, let us broadly define ''substance'' as being a synonym of ''matter'': anything that occupies space and has mass. Scientists have found it convenient to classify substances as being three in kind—elements, compounds, and mixtures. Those three categories provide a net large enough to trap anything except for highly unstable nuclear particles.

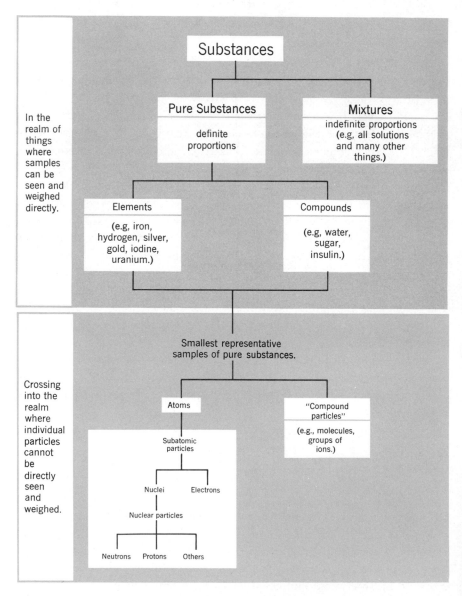

Fig. 2.2 A scheme for classifying matter.

"Substance" is an old term. We may speak of a substance and be totally ignorant of any modern notions of atoms and molecules. We gain little in understanding that way, but it sufficed for centuries.

For centuries an element was just that—"elementary," "simple," a kind of substance that, try as people did, could not be separated into simpler substances. A compound was also just that—something more complex, something compounded of at least two but often more elements. A compound can be broken down into simpler materials. But there is one feature of a compound that is very special. When it is broken into its elements, they are *always* found to have occurred together in the compound in a definite proportion by weight. This was observed so often among so many compound substances that it became the law of definite proportions, a law that distinguishes compounds from mixtures. The components of a mixture do not have to occur together in any particular, definite proportion. The mix of sand, gravel, and shells (and trash) at a beach is an example of a mixture. We shall have much more to learn about compounds and mixtures, but the point here is that they, together with the elements, are the types of *substances* that we have in this world. What these substances are made of, what their building blocks are, is quite another matter to which we now return.

elements. An element is that kind of substance in which all the atomic nuclei present have identical positive charges. This automatically means that in an element all the atoms have identical electronic configurations.[2]

We now add one more distinguishing feature to our definition of an atom, recapitulating the earlier mentioned characteristics.

1. An atom is a very small particle.
2. It has just one nucleus.
3. It is electrically neutral.
4. An atom is the smallest representative sample of an element.

The elements are a diverse assortment. We know several as useful metals: for example, iron, chromium, aluminum, magnesium, nickel, platinum, gold, and silver; others we recognize as nonmetals: sulfur, carbon (e.g., coal), iodine, and phosphorus. Two elements are liquids at room temperature: mercury and bromine. Eleven are gases—the noble gases: helium, neon, argon, krypton, xenon, and radon, in addition to the common gases, oxygen, nitrogen, hydrogen, chlorine, and fluorine. All the other elements are solids at ordinary temperatures.

[2] Strictly speaking, many elements do not consist of individual atoms as such, like so many marbles, but of compound particles made up of atoms. The main point is that in an element the atoms would, if separated, have identical electronic configurations and identical nuclear charges.

Table 2.3 Symbols for Common Elements[a]

Table 2.3 Symbols for Common Elements[a]

C	Carbon	Al	Aluminum	Cl	Chlorine	Ag	Silver (argentum)
F	Fluorine	Ba	Barium	Mg	Magnesium	Cu	Copper (cuprum)
H	Hydrogen	Br	Bromine	Mn	Manganese	Fe	Iron (ferrum)
I	Iodine	Ca	Calcium	Pt	Platinum	Pb	Lead (plumbum)
N	Nitrogen	Li	Lithium	Zn	Zinc	Hg	Mercury (hydrargyrum)
O	Oxygen	Ra	Radium			K	Potassium (kalium)
P	Phosphorus					Na	Sodium (natrium)
S	Sulfur						

[a]*Notes.* The elements of the first column have the simplest symbols, the capitalized first letter of the name. The elements in the second column have symbols consisting of the first two letters. Whenever two letters comprise a symbol, the first is always capitalized and the second is always lowercased. (Beginning students often make mistakes on this point. Consider, however, the two symbols Co and CO. The first, Co, is the symbol for the element cobalt. The second, CO, is the symbol for carbon monoxide, as we shall discuss later.) In some cases, elements have names beginning with the same first two letters, such as magnesium and manganese. The third column lists some examples for which the first letter and some letter other than the second are used. A few important elements were named when Latin was the universal language of educated men. They were given symbols derived from their Latin names, and common examples are listed in the fourth column (with Latin names in parentheses).

symbols for the atoms of the elements. The names of the elements have been reduced to abbreviated "shorthand" symbols. The value of doing this will become clear when we study molecules and compounds. Table 2.3 lists several common elements, together with their symbols. These symbols must be learned.

electronic configurations

Each element has been assigned an *atomic number* that corresponds to the nuclear charge its atoms bear. The atomic number also coincides, therefore, with the number of protons in an element's individual atomic nuclei and to the total number of electrons out in the electronic shells.

Each atom has a characteristic mass. If expressed in atomic mass units, it is numerically equal to the total of the masses of its neutrons and protons. (Electron masses are ignored since they are so small, relative to protons and neutrons.) The characteristic mass of an atom is called its *atomic weight.* (Ultimately, we shall be interested in weighing chemicals, and the verb most commonly used is "to weigh," not "to mass.") If it is said that an element has an atomic weight of 12, this means that each of its atoms has a relative mass of 12 units (and remember that one atomic mass unit *in grams* is extremely small—about 1.7×10^{-24} gram).

The following steps summarize a convenient and accurate way to construct an electronic configuration for any of the first twenty elements:

1. The nuclear charge, given by the atomic number, also tells us the number of electrons to "arrange" to have an electrically neutral atom.

2. Assign the electrons, one by one, to the most stable available energy levels, or shells, within the limits shown in Table 2.2.

    (a) Start with the lowest energy level, the K-shell.

    (b) When that is filled (2 electrons), start filling the next energy level, the L-shell.

    (c) If the L-shell becomes filled (8 electrons), begin to fill the third level, the M-shell.

    (d) A special rule is needed at this point. For atoms of atomic number less than 21, the third level is not occupied by more than 8 electrons, even though, theoretically, it can accommodate more. (This may seem arbitrary. The theory that makes it reasonable is beyond the scope of this book, however.) The application of this rule is illustrated by elements of atomic numbers 19 and 20 (Table 2.4).

3. The number of neutrons in the nucleus is the difference between the atomic number and the atomic weight (to the nearest whole number).

Elements above atomic number 20 require additional rules. Fortunately, for our needs, we shall not have to be too concerned about them. Nearly all substances important to health are made from about 10 elements, and most of these occur among the first 20. The electronic configurations of the first 20 are summarized in Table 2.4.

Electronic configurations may be symbolized in two dimensions (on paper)

Table 2.4   Electronic Configurations of the First Twenty Elements

Element	Symbol	Atomic Number	K-shell	L-shell	M-shell	N-shell
Hydrogen	H	1	1			
Helium	He	2	2			
Lithium	Li	3	2	1		
Beryllium	Be	4	2	2		
Boron	B	5	2	3		
Carbon	C	6	2	4		
Nitrogen	N	7	2	5		
Oxygen	O	8	2	6		
Fluorine	F	9	2	7		
Neon	Ne	10	2	8		
Sodium	Na	11	2	8	1	
Magnesium	Mg	12	2	8	2	
Aluminum	Al	13	2	8	3	
Silicon	Si	14	2	8	4	
Phosphorus	P	15	2	8	5	
Sulfur	S	16	2	8	6	
Chlorine	Cl	17	2	8	7	
Argon	Ar	18	2	8	8	
Potassium	K	19	2	8	8	1
Calcium	Ca	20	2	8	8	2

(a)   (b)

Fig. 2.3   Two ways of representing electronic configurations. (a) "Electron-dot" symbol
of an atom of atomic number 12 and atomic weight 24. (b) A concise representation of
an atom of atomic number 12 and atomic weight 24.

in two ways, as shown in Fig. 2.3. Both are highly stylized methods of
conveying a limited amount of information about an atom. Neither shows
what an atom actually looks like. In this book, the concise representation,
as illustrated in part (b) of Fig. 2.3, will be employed frequently. This symbolism does not try to depict electrons as holding fixed positions, as in part
(a). Moreover, it relieves the reader of counting dots.

atomic orbitals. In the Bohr model, it was the planetary, or solar-system
feature that caught the popular imagination. Bohr's most fundamental contributions were appreciated by only a few physicists and chemists. His basic
postulate, one not suggested or anticipated by classical physics, was that
electrons could "reside" in an atom only in what are called *allowed* energy
states. Electrons could not be anywhere or everywhere—only in certain energy
states. Bohr's second major postulate was that, as long as an electron stayed
in such a state, its movements caused the atom neither to gain nor to give
off energy. If an electron "jumped" from a high energy state to a lower
one, then energy was emitted—in a quantity or *quantum* equal to the difference between the two energy levels. For an electron to go from a lower
to a higher state, the atom had to absorb that precise quantum or "packet"
of energy. In all Bohr's work, the emphasis was on questions of energy for
the fairly simple reason that either emitted or absorbed energy can be
measured. Only with measurements can there be checks between theory about
nature and nature itself.

In the search for equations by which these energies could be better
calculated, physicists during the 1920s found equations that gave, for the
element hydrogen, not only its allowed energy levels but also an improved
picture or model of its structure. Thus far, we have mentioned only principal
energy levels or shells. Sublevels were also found. For each sublevel there
was an equation that could be used to calculate where an electron having
that energy would most probably be in relation to the nucleus. For a particular

sublevel, at certain distances and angles from the nucleus, the probability would be high; at other distances and angles it would be very low. Regions having a reasonably high probability of having an electron of a particular energy were enclosed by imaginary envelopes, and these regions came to be called atomic orbitals.[3]

An atomic orbital is a particularly shaped volume of the space near an atomic nucleus in which an electron having a particular allowed energy most likely might be. Such an orbital does not *have* to have an electron in it; but one *could* be there if it had the energy corresponding to that sublevel. We shall shortly look at shapes of these atomic orbitals, but each shape arises from wrapping an imaginary envelope around just that much of the space near the nucleus within which the probability is arbitrarily high (e.g., at least 80 to 90%) of finding an electron of a particular energy, if an electron is to have such energy at all and be associated with that nucleus.

These shapes have been calculated with great precision only for one very simple system—one proton plus one electron, the hydrogen atom. *Exact* calculations for systems as complicated as one proton and two electrons have not been possible, and there does not seem to be any hope that they can ever be made. (Approximate solutions have been worked out.) There is strong evidence, however, that the orbitals calculated for the hydrogen atom are approximately the same as those in higher atoms. At least the *shapes* and symmetries are believed to be substantially the same.

s orbitals; p orbitals. At the first principal energy level (K-shell), there is only one orbital, the 1s orbital. Its "probability envelope" encloses a sphere with the center at the nucleus, as illustrated in Fig. 2.4. An orbital having such spherical symmetry is called an s orbital.

At the next energy level, No. 2 (L-shell), there are four orbitals. One has spherical symmetry, and it is designated the 2s orbital. The other three, although having identical, "dumbbell" shapes, are oriented differently in space. In all elements except hydrogen, these three are of slightly higher energy than the 2s orbital. Called the 2p orbitals, they are illustrated in Fig. 2.5. Any orbital at whatever main level or shell that has their peculiar symmetry may be called a p orbital. Those at the 2 level are customarily "named" $2p_x$, $2p_y$, and $2p_z$.

As noted earlier, the elements most common to organic chemistry and biochemistry are relatively simple. We shall, therefore, encounter no needs for other types of orbitals at still higher levels, orbitals labeled d and f orbitals. The d orbitals occur in sets of five from level 4 and on; the f orbitals exist in sets of seven from level 6 and on. For nearly all of our work, we can get along very nicely with just the simple, Bohr picture, concentrating our

[3] The expression "atomic orbital" also stands for the *equation* describing the sublevel. This was the original meaning. We shall use the expression in a later usage, one that associates it with the *region in space* that the equation may be used to calculate.

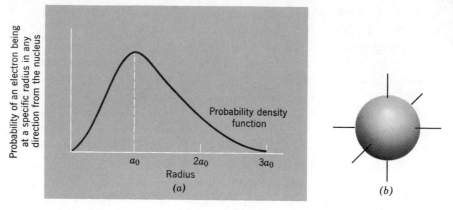

Fig. 2.4 The 1s orbital. (a) Imagine the space surrounding a proton to be made up of layer on layer of infinitesimally thin concentric, spherical shells. What is the probability that an electron can be in each of these? This curve is the answer. At radius equal to a_0 (0.529A), the probability is a maximum. [One Angstrom (A) is defined as $1A = 10^{-8}$ cm.] (b) One of the microspheres in (a) will enclose a space within which the total probability of finding an electron will be 90%. The contour of such a "probability envelope" is shown in (b), and this depicts the shape and symmetry of the 1s orbital. If the electron of a hydrogen atom is going to be in its lowest energy state it will be in a space such as this 90% of the time.

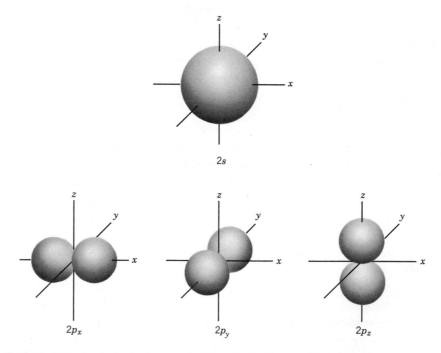

Fig. 2.5 Orbitals at principal energy level number 2 (the L-shell). For the hydrogen atom, the electron may be at the second level in any one of four ways: in the 2s orbital or in one of the mutually perpendicular 2p orbitals.

the nature of matter: the atomic theory

attention only on the total number of electrons at the principal levels without regarding their distribution among the sublevels. That is why our study of this phase of atomic structure has been very brief. Before concluding it, however, we shall see how electronic configurations are handled in the atomic orbital model.

The order of the filling of the orbitals is given by Fig. 2.6. As before, electrons are "fed" into the orbitals of lowest energy first, but there is a definite limit to the maximum number allowed in an orbital. According to the Pauli exclusion principle, an orbital can hold at most only two electrons and then only if the electrons are spinning in opposite directions. Electrons behave as if they spin about an axis, and to designate the two possible ways of spinning, clockwise or counterclockwise, arrows pointing in opposite directions are often used: ↑ and ↓. However, two electrons, even of opposite spin, will not crowd into the same orbital if there is another empty one of the same energy. This is Hund's rule. Table 2.5 shows the distribution of

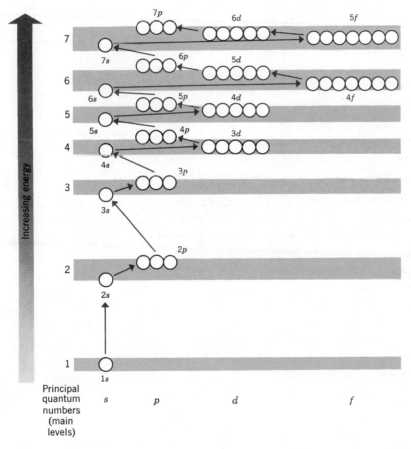

Fig. 2.6 Beginning with the 1s orbital, the general order of filling successive orbitals is shown by the paths of the arrows.

Atomic Number	Element	$1s$	$2s$	$2p_x$	$2p_y$	$2p_z$	$3s$	$3p_x$	$3p_y$	$3p_z$	$4s$
1	H	↑									
2	He	↑↓									
3	Li	↑↓	↑								
4	Be	↑↓	↑↓								
5	B	↑↓	↑↓	↑							
6	C	↑↓	↑↓	↑	↑						
7	N	↑↓	↑↓	↑	↑	↑					
8	O	↑↓	↑↓	↑↓	↑	↑					
9	F	↑↓	↑↓	↑↓	↑↓	↑					
10	Ne	↑↓	↑↓	↑↓	↑↓	↑↓					
11	Na	↑↓	↑↓	↑↓	↑↓	↑↓	↑				
12	Mg	↑↓	↑↓	↑↓	↑↓	↑↓	↑↓				
13	Al	↑↓	↑↓	↑↓	↑↓	↑↓	↑↓	↑			
14	Si	↑↓	↑↓	↑↓	↑↓	↑↓	↑↓	↑	↑		
15	P	↑↓	↑↓	↑↓	↑↓	↑↓	↑↓	↑	↑	↑	
16	S	↑↓	↑↓	↑↓	↑↓	↑↓	↑↓	↑↓	↑	↑	
17	Cl	↑↓	↑↓	↑↓	↑↓	↑↓	↑↓	↑↓	↑↓	↑	
18	Ar	↑↓	↑↓	↑↓	↑↓	↑↓	↑↓	↑↓	↑↓	↑↓	
19	K	↑↓	↑↓	↑↓	↑↓	↑↓	↑↓	↑↓	↑↓	↑↓	↑
20	Ca	↑↓	↑↓	↑↓	↑↓	↑↓	↑↓	↑↓	↑↓	↑↓	↑↓

[a]From 21 to 30, electrons now go into the available $3d$ orbitals until they are filled and then $4p$ orbitals start to fill. Elements 21 to 30 make up the first group of transition elements.

electrons among the various orbitals for the first 20 elements. At element 6, carbon, we see Hund's rule applied. The sixth electron is not placed in the $2p_x$ orbital with the fifth because there is an empty orbital of the same energy available, the $2p_y$ (or $2p_z$). At element 8, oxygen, the last electron is placed in the $2p_x$ orbital rather than the 3s because, even though this crowds two electrons together, it is a more stable situation than if the eighth electron were placed into the higher 3s level. Pauli's principle states that this crowding is permissible if the two electrons are of opposite spin. As seen in Fig. 2.6, the 4s orbital is of slightly lower energy than the 3d. That is why, before the M-shell (level 3) is filled (including the 3d orbitals), two electrons go into the N-shell (level 4) into the 4s orbital. Once this is filled, then the 3d orbitals start to fill (from elements 21 to 30). These constitute the first series of so-called transition elements—all metals.

isotopes The table of atomic weights on the inside back cover reveals that only rarely are atomic weights of elements simple, whole numbers. We should expect them to be whole numbers if all the atoms in a sample of an element were

the nature of matter: the atomic theory

identical in all respects, since in atomic weight units (awu) an atomic weight is simply the sum of the number of protons and neutrons in an atom. However, the atoms in an element are not identical in every respect. Slight variations are usually found in the numbers of neutrons present. If two (or more) atoms have identical nuclear charges (number of protons) but different numbers of neutrons, they are said to be *isotopes*. The existence of isotopes largely explains fractional atomic weights.

The element chlorine (atomic number 17) consists principally of two isotopes called chlorine-35 and chlorine-37. One has an atomic weight of 35 awu (17 protons + 18 neutrons). The other's atomic weight is 37 awu (17 protons + 20 neutrons). In nature, these isotopes occur in the ratio of approximately 4 to 1. The average atomic weight, which is all that can be measured *chemically*, may be calculated as follows:

Four of chlorine-35 $35 \times 4 = 140$ awu
One of chlorine-37 $37 \times 1 = 37$ awu
Total weight of five atoms $= 177$ awu

Average weight of five atoms $= \dfrac{177}{5} = 35.4$ awu

The calculated answer, 35.4 awu, agrees well with the measured value of 35.453 awu.

Isotopes of elements are fairly common. A total of about 250 are known to occur naturally. In massive nuclear reactors, physicists and chemists have succeeded in making about 1100 more, some of which are highly useful in medicine (see Chapter 22).

If two atoms are to be called isotopes, they must have identical nuclear charges. Therefore, *they also must have identical electronic configurations*. Since electronic configurations determine chemical properties, isotopes of an element exhibit identical chemical behavior. (We can see now why it would have been wrong earlier to define an element as a substance in which all atoms are identical. Because of the existence of isotopes we have to be particular and say that in an element all atoms have identical nuclear charges and identical electronic configurations.)

families of elements; the periodic law

The study of 105 elements would be a massive undertaking if each were uniquely different from all others. One of the great simplifying developments in chemistry, however, has been the discovery that elements can be grouped together into a few families. This discovery came slowly over a period of a century. It was the result of the work of many scientists from several countries. Dimitri Mendeleev (Russia) is credited with the greatest contributions. The final form of the periodic law came from the work of H. G. J. Moseley (England) in 1913.

Elements that are members of a family are closely similar in chemical behavior. Since it is just such behavior that we are about to examine, a brief study of how these families are organized will enable us to take advantage of certain unifying principles.

periodic functions. Nature exhibits many types of behavior that may be described as periodic. The seasons are an example. Periodically, we have a winter season, and the "period" here has to do with time. In the language of science, we say that the seasons are a *periodic function* of time. In cities, locations of street intersections are usually periodic functions of distance.

periodic law. *Among the elements, several characteristic properties are periodic functions of their atomic numbers.* This is a statement of the *periodic law:* a universal experience of scientists that, as the elements are arranged in their order of increasing atomic number, every now and then, in a fairly regular or periodic way, properties of lower-numbered elements reappear among those numbered higher.

periodic table. The periodic table inside the front cover is an organization of the periodic relationships of the elements. Each box in the chart contains the following information:

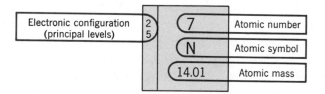

As the elements are tabulated from left to right in order of increasing atomic numbers, rows are interrupted at points that permit elements of similar properties to be placed beneath each other. Thus, each vertical column consists of one family of elements.

Each horizontal row in the table is called a *period*. The vertical columns are called *groups*. The transition elements, a large number of elements in the center of the table, intervene between Groups II and III (see Fig. 2.7). The elements numbered 57 to 71, the *rare earths* or the *lanthanide series*, belong in Period 6, but they are treated separately for reasons of convenience. Elements 89 to 105, the *actinide series*, are similarly treated. One of many examples of periodic behavior is the ionization energies of the elements.

ionization energy and periodicity. If an atom is given enough energy in the right form it can be made to lose one electron. (The atomlike, positively charged fragment left behind is called an ion—but more about those particles

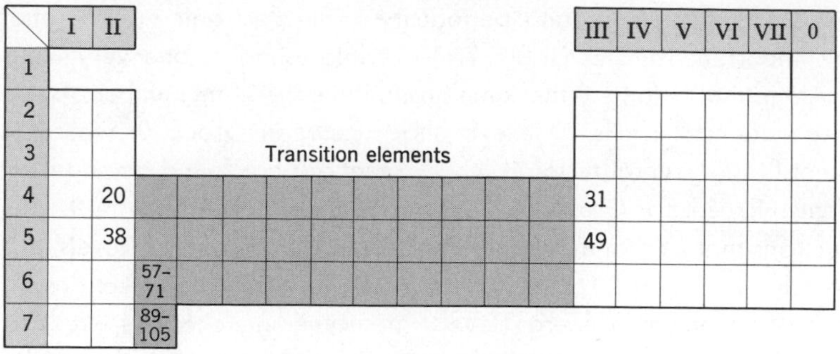

Fig. 2.7 The transition elements and their location in the periodic system.

in the next chapter.) The minimum amount of energy needed to cause loss of an electron from atoms of each of the first twenty elements—the ionization energy—is placed beneath the atomic symbol in the following display:[4]

						(1)					(2)
						H					He
						314					567

(3)	(4)	(5)	(6)	(7)	(8)	(9)	(10)
Li	Be	B	C	N	O	F	Ne
124	215	191	260	336	314	402	497

(11)	(12)	(13)	(14)	(15)	(16)	(17)	(18)
Na	Mg	Al	Si	P	S	Cl	Ar
119	176	138	188	254	239	300	363

(19)	(20)
K	Ca
100	141

At element No. 10 (Ne), instead of continuing on the same horizontal line, a new line is started. At element 10 there seems to be a sharp drop in ionization energy in going to the next element. (See also exercise 8, end of chapter.) The next sharp drop occurs at element 18 (Ar); and there was an earlier drop at element No. 2 (He). The data, displayed in this way, illustrate one periodic function of atomic number—the ionization energies of the elements. Of even greater significance to the chemist is the fact that the vertical columns of elements emerging in this display contain those with quite similar chemical properties.

[4] The numbers in the display are in units of kilocalories per sample of element containing 6×10^{23} atoms. The values of energy refer to loss of electrons from the atoms when the elements are in their gaseous states.

electronic configurations and periodicity. The electronic configurations of a few important families (Table 2.6) are interesting in one very important way. Atoms that belong to the same group have the same number of electrons in their outermost shells. One exception occurs in Group 0, where helium does not fit the generalization. (Other exceptions are found among transition elements.) Except for Group 0, the group number coincides with the number of electrons that exist in the highest occupied principal energy levels of atoms in the family. Group IV elements, for example, have four electrons in their highest occupied main energy levels. In succeeding chapters, we shall see that this correlation of electronic configuration with family membership explains why a number of chemical properties are similar within a family.

metals and nonmetals. If the periodic chart is divided, as illustrated in Fig. 2.8, the elements to the left of the line include all the metals. Those to the right are nonmetals. The borderline is not as sharp as implied. The elements along it have some metallic properties and some nonmetallic properties. Thus,

Table 2.6   Electronic Configurations of Atoms in Several Common Families

Family	Element	Atomic Number	K	L	M	N	O	P	Q
Group I:	Lithium	3	2	1					
The alkali	Sodium	11	2	8	1				
metals	Potassium	19	2	8	8	1			
	Rubidium	37	2	8	18	8	1		
	Cesium	55	2	8	18	18	8	1	
	Francium	87	2	8	18	32	18	8	1
Group II:	Beryllium	4	2	2					
The alkaline	Magnesium	12	2	8	2				
earth	Calcium	20	2	8	8	2			
metals	Strontium	38	2	8	18	8	2		
	Barium	56	2	8	18	18	8	2	
	Radium	88	2	8	18	32	18	8	2
Group VII:	Fluorine	9	2	7					
The halogens	Chlorine	17	2	8	7				
	Bromine	35	2	8	18	7			
	Iodine	53	2	8	18	18	7		
	Astatine	85	2	8	18	32	18	7	
Group O:	Helium	2	2	(filled *K*-level is the *outside* shell)					
The noble	Neon	10	2	8					
gases	Argon	18	2	8	8	(outer "octets")			
	Krypton	36	2	8	18	8			
	Xenon	54	2	8	18	18	8		
	Radon	86	2	8	18	32	18	8	

the nature of matter: the atomic theory

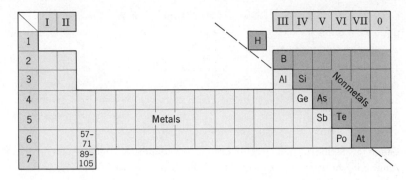

Fig. 2.8 Metals and nonmetals and their general locations in the periodic system.

carbon is very brittle, but it conducts electricity. (Those on the borderline are sometimes called metalloids, or semimetals.) All the gaseous elements are nonmetals. In terms of their electronic configurations, all the metals are characterized by having 1, 2, or 3 electrons at their highest principal energy levels. Among the nonmetals, there are 4 to 8 electrons at these shells.

Among the great variety of properties found in the elements, the most general property of the metals is that they are good conductors of electricity, and this conductivity decreases with increasing temperature. The nonmetals, as a group, are very poor conductors of electricity, but they show an increase in conductivity with rising temperature.

References and Annotated Reading List

Book

1. L. B. Young, editor. *The Mystery of Matter*. Oxford University Press, New York, 1965. Part 2 ("Is Matter Infinitely Divisible?") and Part 3 ("Is Matter Substance or Form?") provide a history of the atomic concept by means of selections from the writings of the scientists who made this history.

Articles

1. G. Feinberg. "Ordinary Matter." *Scientific American*, May 1967, page 126. The author's position is that it is extremely unlikely that the details of elementary particle physics have any bearing on an understanding of natural events that do not involve nuclear transformations. To understand the matter of ordinary experience we need to think in terms of only three particles: electrons, protons, and neutrons.

2. E. G. Mazurs. "Ups and Downs of the Periodic Table." *Chemistry*, July 1966, page 7. There is no such thing as *the* periodic chart. Mazurs describes the many varieties, including one of his own making.

3. J. H. Wolfenden. "The Noble Gases and the Periodic Table. (Telling it like it was.)" *Journal of Chemical Education*, Volume 46 (1969), page 569. The discovery of a new constituent in air came to many chemists as "an unwelcome intrusion upon the Periodic Table." This article tells the fascinating story while it illustrates many of the human sides of scientific progress.

4. Glenn T. Seaborg and J. L. Bloom. "The Synthetic Elements: IV." *Scientific American*, April 1969, page 57. How the new elements are made is described together with the possibilities of going to element 114 and beyond.

Brief Summary

1. Ancient Greek philosophers postulated the existence of atoms as the ultimate, indivisible particles that could not be cut (*atomas*).

2. Modern theory holds that atoms consist of subatomic particles, the most important of which appear to be the electron, the proton, and the neutron.

3. Lord Rutherford discovered the atomic nucleus as a hard, dense, inner core of an atom in which all positive charge and all mass are concentrated. Later work revealed that the nucleus contains all of an atom's protons and neutrons.

4. Niels Bohr postulated that electrons occupied discrete energy levels in atoms and that, as long as they did not change levels, the atom neither gained nor emitted energy.

5. In modern theory, attempts to be precise about where electrons are or how they move are not made. The emphasis is placed rather on the probability of finding an electron at a particular point in space away from a nucleus. Those regions in space where such probabilities are very high are called atomic orbitals. Those close to the nucleus usually represent more stable locations for electrons than those further out. Each orbital can hold up to two electrons.

6. The most stable arrangement of an atom's electrons is called its *electronic configuration*. With the help of certain rules, it may be constructed from a knowledge of the atomic number. (This procedure should be mastered for the first 20 elements.)

7. Elements are defined as those substances consisting of atoms of identical electronic configurations and nuclear charges.

8. The relative mass of an atom, in atomic mass units, is the sum of its protons and neutrons, each weighing one atomic mass unit.

9. Atoms of the same element that have slightly varying numbers of neutrons in their nuclei are called *isotopes*.

the nature of matter: the atomic theory

10. According to the periodic law, properties of elements are periodic functions of their atomic numbers. The existence of this law makes possible a periodic table in which the elements are organized into a few families.

11. With few exceptions, members of a family have the same number of electrons in their highest occupied energy levels. Therefore, they have similar chemical properties.

Problems and Exercises

1. To understand some chemical properties of elements we shall find it useful in future work to be able to figure out an electronic configuration without referring to a table. (We limit this to just the first 20 elements.) Following the example, complete the table using only the atomic number from which to make all other deductions. (The composition of the nuclei cannot be completed without having both the atomic number and the atomic mass. We are interested here only in electronic configurations.)

| Atomic Number | Distribution of the Electrons in: | | Group in Periodic Table | Element is likely a metal or nonmetal? |
	Main Shells [cf. Fig. 2.3 (b)]	Atomic Orbitals		
(Ex.) 6	2 4	$1s^22s^22p_x2p_y$	4	nonmetal
11				
8				
17				
3				
12				
20				
9				
19				

2. Write the electronic configuration (main shells only), including the composition of the nucleus of an atom of atomic number 15 and atomic weight 31.

3. Write the electronic configuration (main shells only), including the nucleus, of an atom that would be a reasonable isotope of the atom described in Problem 2.

4. If an element consisted of just two isotopes, X and Y, in a ratio of 6 to 4, what would be the listed atomic weight for the element if atoms of X had 30 protons and 35 neutrons and atoms of Y had 30 protons and 38 neutrons?

5. What is the most general characteristic of a metal in terms of (a) something that can be directly measured, experimentally? (b) a feature of atomic structure?

6. Data for 2 pairs of atoms are given below. The members of which pair would be expected to have virtually identical chemical properties? Why? (In general terms, only.)
   Pair 1.   A (9 protons and 10 neutrons in its nuclei)
             B (10 protons and 10 neutrons in its nuclei)
   Pair 2.   C (6 protons and 6 neutrons in its nuclei)
             D (6 protons and 7 neutrons in its nuclei)

7. What would be the net electrical charge on a particle if it had:
   (a) 8 protons and 10 electrons
   (b) 11 protons and 10 electrons
   (c) 18 protons and 18 electrons
   (d) 19 protons and 18 electrons

8. Make a graph of the data for ionization energies displayed on page 35. Use the horizontal axis for atomic numbers and the vertical axis for ionization energies. (Units of 100 from zero to 600 would be convenient.) A graphical display brings out strongly the sharp breaks at elements 2, 10, and 18 that were mentioned on page 35.

9. What were the two major ideas that Bohr contributed to our understanding of atomic structure?

10. In connection with a periodic table, what is the difference between a "period" and a "group?"

11. Using illustrations where appropriate, define the following with such precision that each definition applies to nothing else in the world.
    (a) proton   (h) atomic weight
    (b) electron   (i) energy level
    (c) neutron   (j) atomic orbital
    (d) nucleus   (k) Pauli exclusion principle
    (e) atom   (l) Hund's rule
    (f) element   (m) electronic configuration
    (g) atomic number

chapter 3 the nature of matter: compounds and chemical bonds

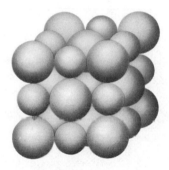

The elements include many interesting substances. Yet millions of things in this universe are compounded from the nuclei and electrons of more than one element. Acids, alkalies, drugs, genes, carbohydrates, fats, and proteins are a few. These consist of chemical compounds. Unlike elements, compounds contain different atomic nuclei and, frequently, many of these are found close to each other in a single representative sample (sometimes called a *molecule*). Somehow these like-charged cores are prevented from flying apart; we say that *bonds* exist between them. In this chapter we shall lay the foundation for a study of compounds by investigating how they derive stability by means of chemical bonds.

compounds A chemical compound is that type of substance whose smallest representative sample contains two or more nuclei from *different* elements. These nuclei are embedded in collections of enough electrons to render the sample electrically neutral. In some compounds, the smallest unit is called a *molecule* (Latin: little mass). In others, it is called an *ion pair* or an *ion group*. A compound is homogeneous; only one unique kind of molecule or one kind of ion group makes up the substance. In terms of what can be measured, compounds are characterized by the *law of definite proportions*: the elements that make up a compound occur in it in definite proportions by weight. That is true because the elements in a compound are always present in definite proportions by atoms.

When chemists say that elements or atoms are "present" in compounds, they understand "present" in a very restricted sense. Compounds are not collections of neutral atoms in the way that gravel is a collection of stones and pebbles. But the *parts* of atoms do make up compounds. Hence, *in a chemical sense only* we can say, for example, that sugar contains carbon. Sugar molecules contain carbon *nuclei* (and other nuclei also), not carbon *atoms,* plus enough electrons, arranged in an electronic configuration distinctive for sugar molecules, to make the molecules electrically neutral.

chemical bonds Whenever any two things are fixed to each other, we say that a bond exists. (Wallpaper, for example, can be bonded to plaster, and it would be proper to say that a paste bond exists.) In chemical compounds, positively charged nuclei from two or more elements become fixed relative to each other. They do not touch. They are simply fixed at some very small distance from each other with enough firmness to say that a bond, a *chemical bond,* is present. Atomic nuclei bear positive charges, and for big nuclei these charges are quite large. The essential problem in understanding a chemical bond is in discovering what prevents nuclei in compounds from flying apart, a behavior we should expect of like-charged bodies. The most general answer would be that somehow the mutual attractions between nuclei and electrons offset the repulsions felt between nuclei (as well as between electrons). We shall examine two of the ways by which this interaction seems to take place among substances: the ionic bond and the covalent bond.

ionic bonds; **chemical reactions and electron transfers.** Sodium and chlorine are not
ionic compounds stable in each other's presence. When sodium and chlorine are mixed, the following changes in electronic configurations occur among billions of sodium and chlorine atoms:

the nature of matter: compounds and chemical bonds

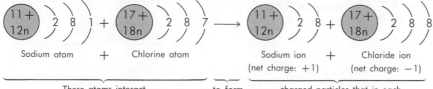

Sodium atom   +   Chlorine atom   Sodium ion   +   Chloride ion
                                          (net charge: +1)   (net charge: −1)

These atoms interact ············· to form ········ charged particles that in each
                                          other's presence are very stable.

In the most general terms, a phenomenon such as this is called a *chemical reaction*. That is the name we give to any event that involves a net rearrangement or redistribution of electrons relative to atomic nuclei. A *physical change*, on the other hand, is our name for all other events, those that leave electronic configurations essentially unchanged. A chemical change always produces new substances. Physical changes do not (e.g., melting ice, tumbling rocks, breaking wooden sticks).

Just as there are types of elements and types of compounds, there are types or classes of chemical reactions. The reaction of sodium with chlorine is in the family of *oxidation-reduction* or *redox* reaction. When a particle (e.g., a sodium atom) loses an electron, the event is called *oxidation*. The gain of an electron (e.g., by a chlorine atom) is called *reduction*. The chemical reactions that use oxygen in the body also involve electron transfers and electron-transport events.

ions. In our example, sodium atoms transferred one electron each to chlorine atoms. The new particles that still have sodium nuclei are now positively charged. The other new particles with chlorine nuclei are negatively charged. These new particles are not atoms. Positively or negatively charged particles at the atomic (or molecular) level in size are called *ions*. Since we shall encounter ions many times, we should start now to learn how they are symbolized.

symbols and names for ions. Table 3.1 shows the names and symbols for several important ions that are derived from single atoms. (Many important ions are derived from clusters of several atoms. They have special names and symbols that are best studied when we see how such clusters are held together.) The positively charged ions in Table 3.1 are named after the parent element. All names of negatively charged ions in the list end in "-ide," with a prefix derived from the name of the parent element. Ionic symbols are the same as the symbols of the original elements except that the electrical charge on the ion is indicated as a superscript on the right side. Even though names and symbols for ions closely resemble those for the atoms from which they are derived, *it cannot be emphasized too strongly that ions have characteristics profoundly different from their corresponding neutral atoms.* Sodium,

ionic bonds; ionic compounds

Table 3.1   **Some Important Ions**[a]

Group	Element	Symbol for Neutral Atom	Symbol for Its Common Ion	Name of Ion
I	Lithium	Li	Li^+	Lithium ion
	Sodium	Na	Na^+	Sodium ion
	Potassium	K	K^+	Potassium ion
II	Magnesium	Mg	Mg^{2+}	Magnesium ion
	Calcium	Ca	Ca^{2+}	Calcium ion
	Barium	Ba	Ba^{2+}	Barium ion
III	Aluminum	Al	Al^{3+}	Aluminum ion
VI	Oxygen	O	O^{2-}	Oxide ion
	Sulfur	S	S^{2-}	Sulfide ion
VII	Fluorine	F	F^-	Fluoride ion
	Chlorine	Cl	Cl^-	Chloride ion
	Bromine	Br	Br^-	Bromide ion
	Iodine	I	I^-	Iodide ion
Transition elements				
	Silver	Ag	Ag^+	Silver ion
	Zinc	Zn	Zn^{2+}	Zinc ion
	Copper	Cu	Cu^+	Copper(I) ion (cuprous ion)[b]
			Cu^{2+}	Copper(II) ion (cupric ion)
	Iron	Fe	Fe^{2+}	Iron(II) ion (ferrous ion)
			Fe^{3+}	Iron(III) ion (ferric ion)

[a] Other common ions, which are derived from more than one element, are listed in Table 3.4.
[b] Names in parentheses represent older practice.

whose symbol is Na (and not Na^+), reacts violently with water. Sodium ions, whose symbol is Na^+ (and not Na), are present in water in every cell of the body and are essential to life.[1]

ionic compounds. The ions formed in our earlier example, Na^+ and Cl^-, being oppositely charged particles, attract each other. In any real situation, of course, hundreds of billions of these ions would form and there would be the problem of how to accommodate both the attractive forces between

[1] One of the annoying sources of confusion and misunderstanding for beginning students is the lingo of all scientists, including doctors and others in medicine and related fields. Between such people there are innumerable "shorthand" ways of talking about various matters, ways of saying things which, if taken literally, make no correct sense. Thus a physiologist may speak of "the sodium requirement" for a certain biological system. He means "the sodium *ion* requirement," and all his colleagues know he means that. They know the absurdity of even thinking of introducing elemental sodium into a living system. The beginner, who should certainly be pardoned for not knowing that right away, will eventually pick this up and realize the situation is not too bad and that the "shorthand" is helpful in his work. However, in this book we shall try to avoid entirely all shorthand of this nature.

the nature of matter: compounds and chemical bonds

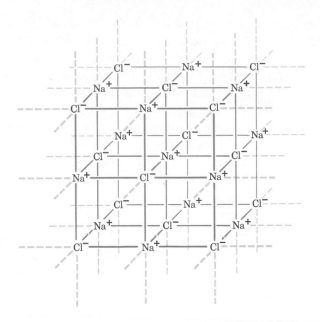

Fig. 3.1 The arrangement of ions in sodium chloride (table salt) is seen in this representation of a tiny fragment from a crystal of salt.

unlike-charged ions and the repulsive forces between like-charged ions. In an alternating stacking together, illustrated in Figs. 3.1 and 3.2, repulsive forces between like-charged ions are shielded. Each positive ion is attracted to and surrounded by negative ions, and each negative ion is attracted to and surrounded by positive ions. When enough ions have aggregated, a visible crystal of an *ionic compound* appears. Ionic compounds, one class of chemical compounds, *are those that consist of orderly aggregations of oppositely charged ions assembled in a definite ratio that assures overall electrical neutrality.*

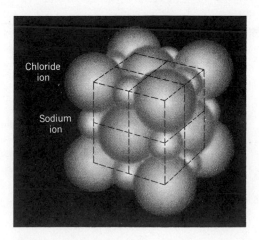

Fig. 3.2 Orderly aggregation of ions in crystalline sodium chloride.

ionic bonds; ionic compounds

names and symbols for ionic compounds. Ionic compounds are named after their constituent ions (with the word *ion* omitted). The name of the positively charged ion, by convention, appears first. Thus, the name of the ionic compound consisting of sodium ions and chloride ions is sodium chloride.

Shorthand symbols for compounds are called *formulas*. Formulas of ionic compounds show what ions are present and in what ratio they occur by a combination of atomic symbols and subscripts following those symbols. Subscript number 1 is understood; that is, it does not appear in formulas. Thus, the symbol for sodium chloride is NaCl. Magnesium ions and chloride ions aggregate in a ratio of $1Mg^{2+}$ to $2Cl^-$. They cannot aggregate in any other ratio, since opposite charges must cancel each other to preserve electrical neutrality for the substance. The $+2$ charge on one magnesium ion is neutralized by the -2 charge on *two* chloride ions. The formula for magnesium chloride is:

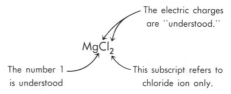

The smallest whole-number ratio is usually used. The ratio of $1:2$ in $MgCl_2$ might also be expressed as $Mg_{0.5}Cl$, or Mg_3Cl_6, or $Mg_{0.33}Cl_{0.66}$, but this is not done. These conventions are illustrated in the examples of Fig. 3.3.

ionic bonds. In terms of our definition of a chemical compound, sodium chloride is an electrically neutral substance whose smallest sample consists of two nuclei, one each from sodium and chlorine, embedded in collections of electrons. Electrons are gathered in two new, more stable, but still separate arrangements about the two nuclei. Physically discrete, oppositely charged ions are present. With the electrons collected in this way, repulsive forces between the nuclei are shielded, and they do not fly apart. The ions attract each other, and a bond, called an *ionic bond*, exists between them. The

Constituent Ions	Ratio of Aggregation (to ensure neutrality)	Compound Formula	Compound Name
Mg^{2+} and Br^-	$1(++):2(-)$	$MgBr_2$	Magnesium bromide
Ca^{2+} and O^{2-}	$1(++):1(=)$	CaO	Calcium oxide
Na^+ and O^{2-}	$2(+):1(=)$	Na_2O	Sodium oxide
Fe^{3+} and O^{2-}	$2(+++):3(=)$	Fe_2O_3	Iron(III) oxide (ferric oxide)
Cu^+ and S^{2-}	$2(+):1(=)$	Cu_2S	Copper(I) sulfide (cuprous sulfide)

Fig. 3.3 Writing names and formulas for ionic compounds.

the nature of matter: compounds and chemical bonds

expression "ionic bond" does not refer to a thing; it is simply a way of talking about a force of attraction between oppositely charged ions in ionic compounds. It is a strong bond and important in many aspects of the chemistry of health. Ionic compounds are found in solution in every cell of living organisms, in nearly all groundwater and in all lakes and oceans.

Shortly after the advent of the Bohr atom model, Kossel in Germany and Lewis in America developed a theory, often called the *octet theory*, that showed how structures of atoms related to their tendencies to enter into chemical bonding. Although considerable refinement in our understanding of the chemical bond has occurred since then, the theory still provides useful rules for predicting formulas.

the octet theory

The octet theory starts with the recognition that an outer octet of electrons, or a filled *K*-shell as the outside shell, is somehow an electronic configuration of exceptional stability. Support for this is the occurrence of such configurations among atoms of the noble gases (Group 0), which have extraordinary chemical unreactivity. It requires an unusual amount of energy to remove or to add an electron to an inert gas atom. They generally do not form stable ions even when an effort is made to give them "counter ions" (ions of opposite charge) to help stabilize them (as in crystalline sodium chloride). Atoms in all other groups are reactive, although to widely differing degrees. None of them has a noble gas configuration in the outermost shell.

Chemical reactions, you will recall, are those events in which there are rearrangements or redistributions of electrons relative to atomic nuclei. The reactions of the reactive atoms of the main groups of the periodic table are such that these rearrangements generally lead to noble gas configurations. This is further support for the octet "rules." Let us see how this applies among the elements that frequently form ionic compounds, particularly those in Groups I, II, VI, and VII. (The transition elements are also prone to participate in the formation of ionic compounds. Their behavior, however, correlates with conditions of electronic stability beyond the intended scope of this textbook.)

When elements of Groups I, II, VI, and VII react by electron-transfer processes, their atoms form ions. Many of these are listed in Table 3.2, which shows their electronic configurations in relation to those of the noble gases. In every instance, the stable ions listed have noble gas configurations.

Opportunities for these ions to form occur whenever Group I or II elements are mixed with Group VI or VII elements. By electron-transfer or redox events, the atoms initially in the mixture adopt electronic configurations that are more stable in their new environment. For illustrations, see Fig. 3.4. Spontaneous chemical events, therefore, share the characteristic common to all spontaneous natural changes; they proceed from a relatively unstable situation to one that is more stable. Rocks fall down rather than up; water flows spontaneously

Table 3.2 Configurations of Ions and Noble Gas Structures

Group	Common Element	Nuclear Charge (Atomic Number)	ATOMS Electronic Configurations						Ion	IONS Electronic Configurations						Comparable Noble Gas
			K	L	M	N	O	P		K	L	M	N	O	P	
I: Alkali metals	Li	3+	2	1					Li^+	2						Helium
	Na	11+	2	8	1				Na^+	2	8					Neon
	K	19+	2	8	8	1			K^+	2	8	8				Argon
II: Alkaline earth metals	Mg	12+	2	8	2				Mg^{2+}	2	8					Neon
	Ca	20+	2	8	8	2			Ca^{2+}	2	8	8				Argon
	Ba	56+	2	8	18	18	8	2	Ba^{2+}	2	8	18	18	8		Xenon
VI:	O	8+	2	6					O^{2-}	2	8					Neon
	S	16+	2	8	6				S^{2-}	2	8	8				Argon
VII: Halogens	F	9+	2	7					F^-	2	8					Neon
	Cl	17+	2	8	7				Cl^-	2	8	8				Argon
	Br	35+	2	8	18	7			Br^-	2	8	18	8			Krypton
	I	53+	2	8	18	18	7		I^-	2	8	18	18	8		Xenon
O: Noble gases	He	2+	2													
	Ne	10+	2	8												
	Ar	18+	2	8	8											
	Kr	36+	2	8	18	8										
	Xe	54+	2	8	18	18	8									

The noble gases do not form stable ions.

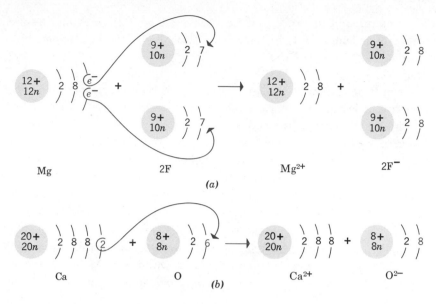

Fig. 3.4 Redox reactions and the formation of ions. (a) Formation of magnesium fluoride, MgF_2. (b) Formation of calcium oxide, CaO.

toward the ocean; reactive elements of the main groups that are without noble gas configurations tend to adopt them, if given the opportunity.

chemical stability, chemical reactivity, and the octet rule. In a general way, the most reactive elements are found among those whose atoms are closest to noble gas configurations. Atoms in Group I need lose but one electron each. Energetically, this is easy if an electron acceptor is available, and if there is subsequent opportunity for oppositely charged ions to aggregate. The "ifs" are important. Ions in relative *isolation* represent *high energy* and unstable situations, especially in the cases of positive ions. Stability is not just a matter of outer octets. It is also a matter of the environment in a crystal of oppositely charged ions where positive ions have negative ions as nearest neighbors and vice versa. Even though charged particles can exist—and the octet theory gives us rules to predict which ones can—such ions always must have as near neighbors particles "rich" in the opposite charge.

Assuming that oppositely charged ions can aggregate after forming, then atoms in Group I (such as sodium and potassium) are more reactive toward an electron acceptor than the atoms in Group II, where an atom must lose two electrons to acquire an octet.

electrovalence. The word *electrovalence* (Latin *valere*, "to have power, to be strong") is frequently used by chemists in describing *relative combining abilities* of those elements that form ions. These elements are given *electrovalence numbers* whose values coincide with the kind and amount of charge on the corresponding stable ions (see Table 3.1 or 3.2). Thus, the electro-valence of sodium is $+1$; of oxygen, -2, etc. All Group I elements have electrovalences of $+1$; Group II, $+2$; Group III, $+3$; Group VI, -2; and Group VII, -1.

Elements in Group IV or Group V form ions only very rarely. (The cost in energy of losing or gaining three or four electrons is very high.) Thus, they are not commonly assigned electrovalence numbers. Yet these groups include some of the most widely occurring elements. Carbon (Group IV) occurs in all organic compounds, and over a million have been studied. Nitrogen (Group V) occurs along with carbon, oxygen, and hydrogen in all living things. It also makes up approximately 80% of the air. Silicon (Group IV) is basic to sands and silicates and therefore is found throughout the earth's crust. To understand how atomic nuclei in these substances are prevented from flying apart (that is, to understand how these substances are stable), we must study the covalent bond. In doing so, we shall build the foundation for our study of organic compounds, the principal kinds of compounds found in the body.

covalent bonds. molecules and molecular substances

diatomic molecules. The types of bonds in organic compounds are also present in some of nature's simplest substances, the reactive, gaseous elements: hydrogen, oxygen, fluorine, chlorine, and nitrogen. Unlike the inert gases, whose smallest stable samples are atoms, these reactive elements exist as minute particles consisting of *two* nuclei and enough electrons to make the particle neutral. Their correct formulas, as chemicals, are H_2, O_2, F_2, Cl_2, and N_2. These uncharged nonionic particles that are regarded as the smallest *stable* samples of the elements mentioned are called *molecules*. Since they consist of two nuclei each, they are sometimes called diatomic molecules.

covalent bond. Electron transfers between like atoms do not take place. Even if one of the atoms were able to accept an electron or two and acquire a noble gas structure, the other, by giving up an electron, would move further away from such a condition of stability. Thus, we cannot understand a chlorine molecule as consisting of Cl^+ and Cl^-. Yet, in a chlorine molecule, two chlorine nuclei are held close to each other.

G. N. Lewis resolved the problem by suggesting that the outer electron shells of two atoms may penetrate each other and some of the outer electrons may, in a sense, be shared between the two nuclei. Instead of electrons transferring between two like atoms, a sharing of electrons takes place. Figure 3.5 illustrates two ways in which this sharing may be depicted on paper. One electron from the outer shell of one chlorine atom is said to *pair* with one electron from the outer shell of the other. The pair of electrons is then said to be shared equally by both nuclei. The net effect is that the outer

the nature of matter: compounds and chemical bonds

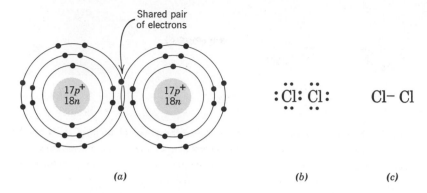

Fig. 3.5 Symbolizing the sharing of a pair of electrons between two chlorine nuclei in a molecule of chlorine. (a) This symbol accounts for all planetary electrons. (b) This "electron dot" symbol accounts only for outershell electrons. All others are "understood." (c) The shared pair, and only this pair, is represented by a straight line.

shells of both original atoms may be said to have acquired octets. The bond that exists because of this cooperative action is called a *covalent bond.*

A representation of the hydrogen molecule is given in Fig. 3.6. Initially, each hydrogen atom had one electron in its outermost shell, in this case a *K*-shell. When two such electrons are paired and shared between two hydrogen nuclei, the *K*-shell for each can be considered to be filled. A filled, *outer K*-shell constitutes, it will be recalled, the configuration of the noble gas, helium.

For years prior to the work of Lewis, chemists had represented a chlorine molecule as Cl—Cl and a hydrogen molecule as H—H. In other words, they had used straight lines to tie atomic symbols together on paper in order to show *structural formulas*—that is, the sequences of atoms within molecules. Lewis was the first to propose that such lines represented shared pairs of electrons. Thus, in the symbol Cl—Cl, a chlorine nucleus and *all* its electrons except the one contributed to the shared pair is represented by the atomic symbol, Cl. The bonding pair, or shared pair, is indicated by the line. Learn to keep the terms straight. The *molecular formula* of chlorine is Cl_2; its structural formula or simply *structure* is Cl—Cl. The molecular formula of

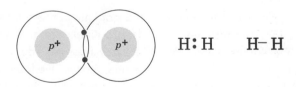

Fig. 3.6 Symbolizing the sharing of a pair of electrons between two hydrogen nuclei in a molecule of hydrogen.

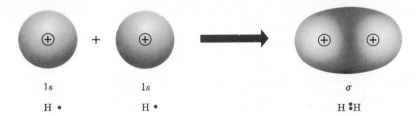

1s   1s   σ

H •   H •   H $\overset{\bullet}{\bullet}$ H

Fig. 3.7 The hydrogen molecule. The formation of the covalent bond in H_2 is depicted as resulting from the overlap or the interpenetration of the 1s atomic orbitals of the hydrogen atoms. The relative darkness of the shading in the molecular orbital gives a qualitative idea of where the "electron cloud" is most dense—between the two nuclei.

water is H_2O; its structure is H—O—H (not H—H—O; not H—O. A molecular formula tells us only the composition of a molecule. A structural formula does this but goes farther; it tells us the nucleus-to-nucleus organization of the molecular parts.

molecular orbitals—another view of the covalent bond. Since the advent of quantum mechanics, the covalent bond has been interpreted as arising from the overlapping of atomic orbitals. The hydrogen molecule, for example, is thought of as arising from the merger of the two 1s atomic orbitals of the separate hydrogen atoms, as illustrated in Fig. 3.7. This merger or overlap of the two atomic orbitals produces a molecular orbital—a region in space surrounding two (or more) nuclei within which shared electrons can be. The shared electrons, in a sense, move with respect to two nuclei instead of one, and this helps account for the greater stability of the molecule as compared with the separated atoms. Each electron is attracted to two oppositely charged centers instead of only one.

The electron distribution in a hydrogen molecule is often symbolized as an "electron cloud." (At least this is one model or interpretation.) Embedded in it are the two nuclei. They cannot fly apart because they are shielded from each other by the relatively high "density" of the electron cloud between the two nuclei. Forces of repulsion (nucleus to nucleus as well as electron to electron) are counterbalanced by forces of attraction, as illustrated in Fig. 3.8, and a bond exists.

Overlapping between atomic orbitals is not limited to s orbitals; p orbitals may overlap, too. The fluorine molecule is a simple case. If you write the distribution of electrons among the orbitals of fluorine, you will see that it is a p orbital that is not fully occupied and that is available for overlap. The covalent bond in the fluorine molecule arises from the overlap of two $2p_z$ atomic orbitals, each initially containing one electron (see Fig. 3.9).

the nature of matter: compounds and chemical bonds

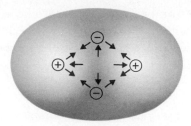

Fig. 3.8   The hydrogen molecule. When the shared pair of electrons is most frequently between the two nuclei, forces of attraction (indicated here by arrows pointing toward each other) are strong enough to counterbalance forces of repulsion (arrows pointing away from each other). This cluster of two protons (two hydrogen nuclei) and two electrons therefore holds together. In chemical terms, we say that a bond—a covalent bond—exists between the two hydrogens.

coordinate covalent bonds.   Each electron in a shared pair need not originate from two separate atoms. Both electrons may be furnished by one of the atoms. A filled atomic orbital (having two electrons) may overlap with an empty atomic orbital. The resulting bond, indistinguishable from a covalent bond, is sometimes called a *coordinate covalent bond*. Mention is made of

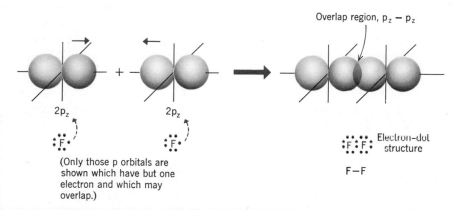

Fig. 3.9   The overlap of the two p_2 orbitals of two fluorine atoms gives a covalent bond between the two fluorines. The shape of the resultant molecular orbital is oversimplified, above. A better model would be more like the following:

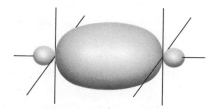

In other words, there is more of a concentration of electron density between the nuclei than indicated in the more simplified picture.

this here only for the sake of completeness. We have to know more about chemical systems to illustrate such a bond, and we shall defer further study until we encounter it among acids and bases where the coordinate covalent bond is extremely important.

polar covalence; polar molecules

The bonding pair of electrons in a chlorine molecule is shared equally between the two nuclei. Since the two nuclei have identical charges, we should expect that the pair of shared electrons would not favor one nucleus over the other. When different nuclei with different nuclear charges are held near each other by a covalent bond, equal sharing is seldom observed. Molecules of the gas hydrogen chloride, H—Cl, illustrate the point.[2]

The shared pair of electrons in a molecule of hydrogen chloride is more frequently in the vicinity of the chlorine nucleus than near the hydrogen nucleus. In other terms, the chlorine nucleus has more than a 50% control over the pair. Although the electrons are shared between the two nuclei, they are not *equally* shared. The net result is that the chlorine end of the molecule carries a fractional excess of negative charge. The electron cloud, so to speak, is denser at the chlorine end than it need be to neutralize the $+17$ charge of the chlorine nucleus located there. At the other end of the molecule, the electron cloud is not quite dense enough to neutralize the nucleus (one proton) located there. Accordingly, the hydrogen end of a hydrogen chloride molecule bears a fractional excess of positive charge. (These fractional excesses of opposite charges at opposite ends of the molecule are equal in magnitude; the molecule, overall, is neutral.) Molecules that have a partial negative charge at one point and a partial positive charge at another are called *polar molecules*.

Another way of looking at this question is to consider that in a particle containing two (or more) plus-charged subparticles (nuclei) there will be some net "center of positive charge." (This would be analogous to a "center of gravity," if we were talking about masses instead of charges.) If minus-charged particles are also present (electrons), then there must be some net "center of negative charge." In a symmetrical atom, these two centers coincide. They are at the same point, and the atom is nonpolar. But if these centers do not coincide, then the particle will be polar. It will have one place where, in effect, there is a partial positive charge and another where there will be a partial negative charge.

The use of the word *polar* in this electrical sense is analogous to its use in a magnetic sense. A polar molecule bears two electrical poles; a magnet has two magnetic poles. And just as two magnets can stick to each other, two polar molecules, if properly oriented, can also cling together. Polarity

[2] Hydrogen chloride is not to be confused with the solution of this gas in water, which is called *hydrochloric acid*.

the nature of matter: compounds and chemical bonds

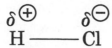

Fig. 3.10 Hydrogen chloride: a polar molecule.

is an important fact about most organic molecules, including those essential to health. Part of the explanation of the strength of a muscle fiber is the fact that the protein molecules in that fiber are quite polar and stick together rather strongly.

Whenever chemists want to emphasize that a certain bond or molecule is polar, they use the symbolism shown in Fig. 3.10. The lower-case Greek letter delta (δ) is a symbol for the word *partial* or *fractional*. An appropriate algebraic sign indicates the kind of charge.

Frequently, in order for two nuclei to be held together covalently, two pairs, sometimes three pairs, of electrons need to be shared between them. The structures in Fig. 3.11 illustrate common instances. Since one shared pair between two nuclei is called a *single bond,* two shared pairs of electrons constitute a *double bond* (e.g., carbon dioxide and ethylene, Fig. 3.11). The electron-dot structures of Fig. 3.11 account for all outer-shell electrons. The "incentive" for forming double and triple bonds appears to be the stability of an outer octet. For example, by sharing three pairs of electrons between them, the nitrogen nuclei in a molecule of nitrogen have, in effect, acquired octets. (We shall not develop the molecular orbital theory of multiple bonds, but in the most general sense, a double bond involves the overlapping of not just one pair of orbitals but two pairs. For our future needs, the simplified treatment of the Lewis theory will easily suffice.)

multiple bonds

The series of compounds:

covalence numbers

$$H-\overset{..}{\underset{..}{Cl}}:\qquad \overset{H}{\underset{\displaystyle .\overset{..}{O}-H}{}}\qquad H-\overset{\displaystyle H}{\underset{\displaystyle ..}{N}}-H\qquad H-\overset{\displaystyle H}{\underset{\displaystyle H}{C}}-H$$

Hydrogen   Water   Ammonia   Methane
chloride

reveals important differences in covalent-combining abilities, or *covalences.* Carbon has four times the covalent-combining ability of hydrogen. Chemists compare these differences by means of covalence numbers, which are listed for several common elements in Table 3.3. They coincide with the number of electrons an atom needs to acquire, by a sharing process, to have a stable outside-shell configuration. (In contrast with electrovalences, covalence num-

55

bers are not given algebraic signs, since electrically charged ions are not involved.) For a working definition, covalence numbers also coincide with the number of straight lines (each representing a shared pair of electrons) that may extend from an atom in a structural formula. (Thus, in Fig. 3.11, each nitrogen with a covalence of three has three lines from it in the structure of a nitrogen molecule.)

complex ions   Many ions are known that involve groups of nuclei held together by covalent bonds. These groups are electrically charged ions because the electronic configurations that give stability to each cluster of nuclei bring together

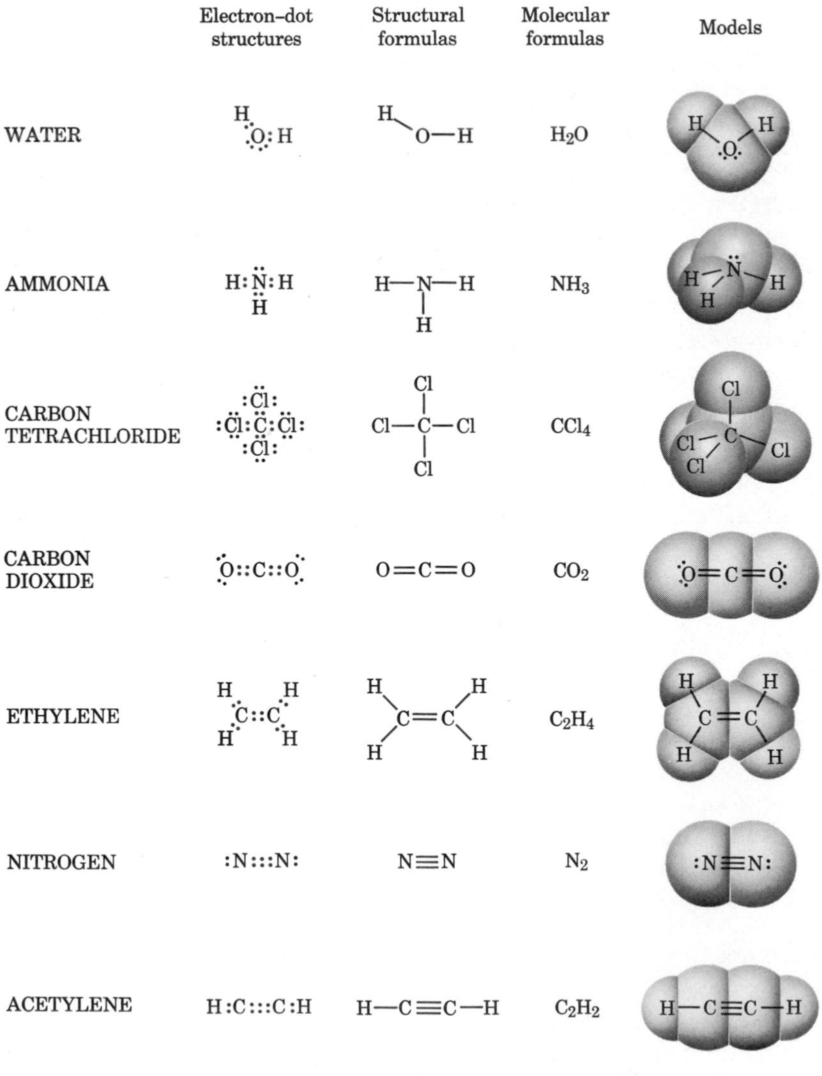

	Electron–dot structures	Structural formulas	Molecular formulas	Models
WATER	H :O:H	H ⟍O—H	H_2O	
AMMONIA	H:N:H H	H—N—H | H	NH_3	
CARBON TETRACHLORIDE	:Cl: :Cl:C:Cl: :Cl:	Cl | Cl—C—Cl | Cl	CCl_4	
CARBON DIOXIDE	O::C::O	O=C=O	CO_2	
ETHYLENE	H H C::C H H	H⟍ ⟋H C=C H⟋ ⟍H	C_2H_4	
NITROGEN	:N:::N:	N≡N	N_2	
ACETYLENE	H:C:::C:H	H—C≡C—H	C_2H_2	

Fig. 3.11   Some common covalent substances.

the nature of matter: compounds and chemical bonds

Table 3.3 Covalences of Common Elements

Element	Atomic Number	Electronic Configuration					Covalence[a]
		K	L	M	N	O	
Carbon	6	2	4				4
Nitrogen	7	2	5				3
Oxygen	8	2	6				2
Hydrogen	1	1					1
Chlorine	17	2	8	7			1
Bromine	35	2	8	18	7		1
Iodine	53	2	8	18	18	7	1
Sulfur	16	2	8	6			2

[a]Only the most common covalence numbers are listed. Some of the elements in the table have multiple covalences.

unequal numbers of electrons and protons. The stabilities of such groups, called *complex ions,* are such that they go through most reactions unscathed. Formulas and charges (electrovalences) for several complex ions are listed in Table 3.4.

When the formula for an ionic compound is to show only one complex ion, no further rules than those stated on page 46 are required. If more than one is to be included in a formula, the symbol of the complex ion must

Table 3.4 Common Complex Ions

Name of Ion	Formula	Electrovalence of Ion
Hydroxide ion	OH^-	-1
Carbonate ion	$CO_3{}^{2-}$	-2
Bicarbonate ion	$HCO_3{}^-$	-1
Sulfate ion	$SO_4{}^{2-}$	-2
Bisulfate ion (or hydrogen sulfate ion)	$HSO_4{}^-$	-1
Nitrate ion	$NO_3{}^-$	-1
Nitrite ion	$NO_2{}^-$	-1
Phosphate ion	$PO_4{}^{3-}$	-3
Monohydrogen phosphate ion	$HPO_4{}^{2-}$	-2
Dihydrogen phosphate ion	$H_2PO_4{}^-$	-1
Cyanide ion	CN^- ·	-1
Permanganate ion	$MnO_4{}^-$	-1
Chromate ion	$CrO_4{}^{2-}$	-2
Dichromate ion	$Cr_2O_7{}^{2-}$	-2
Sulfite ion	$SO_3{}^{2-}$	-2
Bisulfite ion (or hydrogen sulfite ion)	$HSO_3{}^-$	-1
Ammonium ion	$NH_4{}^+$	$+1$

be enclosed in parentheses, and its subscript must be placed outside the parentheses. For example, the formula of ammonium sulfide is written

$$(NH_4)_2S$$

The subscript 4 after H indicates a ratio of H to N only. The subscript 2, however, refers to everything within the parentheses. Thus, in ammonium sulfide, the ratio of ammonium ions, NH_4^+, to sulfide ions, S^{2-}, is $2:1$.

pure substances and mixtures

We saw on page 24 that *elements* and *compounds* constitute the two broad classes of pure substances. Another category of matter, the *mixture*, comprises those materials that consist of two or more pure substances mingled together. Figure 2.2 illustrated the classes of substances. Chemists determine to what category a substance belongs by studying its properties.

properties. The distinguishing characteristics of a substance are referred to as its *properties*. Broadly speaking, there are two types: chemical and physical properties. The former constitute any chemical reactions the substance will undergo. Physical properties are those that can be observed without inducing a chemical change. They include such common aspects as color, luster, physical state (solid, liquid, gas), density, specific gravity, electrical conductivity, melting point, boiling point, ductility (being able to be. drawn into a wire), malleability (being able to be hammered), and transparency. Each pure substance has a unique set of physical properties. Only for this reason can we distinguish one substance from another.

Since chemical reactions, by definition, result in the formation of new substances, these reactions must be accompanied by changes in physical appearances. These changes, moreover, cannot be reversed except by reversing the chemical reaction. Chemists look for changes in physical properties when they try to decide whether a chemical reaction has occurred. Thus, when carbon burns in oxygen to form carbon dioxide, the solid black properties of carbon disappear, and a colorless, odorless gas that will not burn takes its place. When iron filings are mixed with sulfur powder, the physical properties of both the sulfur and the iron are still present and apparent. Moreover, the mixture can be made in any proportion of iron to sulfur. If a mixture of iron and sulfur is heated strongly, however, a chemical reaction takes place. The product of the reaction, iron(II) sulfide, FeS, does not resemble either iron or sulfur and is indifferent to a magnet.

how chemical reactions are symbolized;

The need for a shorthand way of expressing chemical reactions becomes obvious as we go further into our discussion. For this purpose, scientists use chemical equations. In this section, our concern is only to be able to read

and to understand them. In Chapter 4, when we take up weight relations
in chemical reactions, we shall study how to write and to balance them.
As a typical chemical equation, let us consider the following:

$$4Al + 3O_2 \longrightarrow 2Al_2O_3$$

A preliminary "translation" of this would be

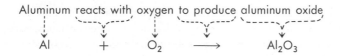

A plus sign ($+$) separates formulas and indicates the addition or mixing of one chemical with another. The arrow always points *to* the products of the reaction. Usually, although not always, the equation is written so that the arrow points from left to right.

The preliminary translation ignored the numbers in front of the formulas. These are called *coefficients*. They indicate the proportions, *in terms of particles* (molecules, atoms, or ion groups), in which the reacting substances interact and the products form. Normally, the smallest whole-number coefficients are used, and the number 1 is always understood. In our example, the coefficients tell us that to carry out this reaction and to avoid having any atoms of aluminum or molecules of oxygen left over, they must be mixed in a ratio of four aluminum atoms (4Al) to three oxygen molecules ($3O_2$). In this way, two unit particles of aluminum oxide ($2Al_2O_3$) form.

balanced equation. Matter is neither created nor destroyed in chemical reactions. Nuclei remain intact. An equation is said to be "balanced," therefore, when all the atomic nuclei of the reactants appear somewhere among the products. In our example, six oxygen nuclei are given as reactants in the form $3O_2$. They appear in the product as part of aluminum oxide: $2Al_2O_3$. Hence, oxygen is said to be balanced. In a similar manner, we note that the nuclei of aluminum are balanced.

Selected Reading List

Articles

1. C. S. Smith. "Materials." *Scientific American*, September 1967, page 68. The entire issue of this magazine is devoted to materials, and this article introduces the subject. After a brief historical survey, the author turns to a discussion of

how properties of materials are understandable in terms of their atomic and molecular structures.

2. K. Lonsdale. "Disorder in Solids." *Chemistry,* December 1965, page 14. Crystalline solids are not perfect arrays of highly ordered aggregations of constituents. The existence of disorder and its importance is discussed.

3. A. H. Cottrell. "The Nature of Metals." *Scientific American,* September 1967, page 90. How atoms in metals are held together is discussed in terms of an electron "sea" or an electron gas model.

4. L. Holliday. "Early Views on Forces Between Atoms." *Scientific American,* May 1970, page 116. Ever since some of the ancient Greek philosophers postulated that atoms exist there has been speculation about what holds atoms together in substances. Holliday surveys various ideas on these forces as they were proposed from early times to the first part of the last century.

Brief Summary

1. The attainment of maximum stability provides at least a major part of the driving force of chemical changes.

2. Electronic configurations in compounds are most stable whenever they involve an outside shell of eight electrons (or a filled *K*-shell as the outer shell).

3. To acquire these conditions of stability, some atoms will sacrifice their electrical neutrality by entering into redox reactions wherein transfers of electrons take place and ions form.

4. Newly formed oppositely charged ions aggregate in a more-or-less orderly fashion and in a ratio that guarantees overall electrical neutrality for the resulting ionic compound. Ionic bonds are said to exist between the ions.

5. Some kinds of atoms, particularly those in Groups IV to VII, may achieve stable electronic configurations by sharing pairs of electrons with other atoms. When this occurs, molecules form.

6. In the molecular orbital theory, this sharing is thought of as an overlapping or partial merger of atomic orbitals.

7. Shared pairs of electrons move in molecular orbitals about more than one nucleus, with one shared pair constituting one covalent bond. Double and triple bonds are possible.

8. Although molecules are electrically neutral, they may be polar if the sharing of electrons is not exactly 50—50; (or if the center of $+$ charge does not coincide with the center of $-$ charge in the molecule.)

9. Complex ions are groups of nuclei held together by covalent bonds but that have too many or too few electrons to render the whole particle neutral.

10. Chemical reactions consist of more-or-less permanent rearrangements or redistri-

butions of electrons relative to atomic nuclei. They are accompanied by marked changes in physical appearance.

11. Physical changes involve no deep-seated disturbance of electronic configurations.

Problems and Exercises

1. From a knowledge of only the atomic number of an element (among the first 20) you should be able to answer the following questions.
   (a) Will the atoms of the element, under suitable conditions, tend to form ions? If so, what charge will each ion bear?
   (b) Will the atoms of the element be capable of entering into the formation of covalent bonds? If so, how many covalent bonds will it ordinarily be capable of forming?
   Without referring to charts or tables, but by constructing and studying electronic configurations (in terms of the principal levels), answer questions (a) and (b) for elements of each of the following atomic numbers. (Tabulate your answers.)
   Elements of atomic number: 17, 8, 5, 9, 2, 20, 13, 19, 6, 12, 7, 16, 3

2. State in your own words, in sentence form, the information conveyed by each of the following equations:

   (a) $2C + O_2 \longrightarrow 2CO$
   (carbon monoxide)

   (b) $CH_4 + Cl_2 \longrightarrow CH_3Cl + HCl$
   (methane)   (methyl chloride)   (hydrogen chloride)

   (c) $N_2 + 3H_2 \longrightarrow 2NH_3$
   (ammonia)

   (Note: this reaction occurs only under special conditions of temperature and pressure. A catalyst is needed. It is called the *Haber process* for the industrial synthesis of ammonia.)

   (d) $2H_2 + O_2 \longrightarrow 2H_2O$
   (water)

3. To test your understanding of chemical equations, consider some purely hypothetical situations wherein we assume we can handle and count individual atoms and molecules. The questions that follow refer to the reactions symbolized in equation form in Exercise 2.
   (a) If 2 atoms of carbon and one molecule of oxygen were mixed and a reaction occurred, how many molecules of carbon monoxide could form? Which reactant, C or O_2, would be used up? How much of the other reactant would be left over?

(b) We wish to make ten molecules of carbon monoxide. What is the minimum number of particles of the reactants, C and O_2, needed?

(c) If 12 molecules of hydrogen were combined with nitrogen to make ammonia, how much ammonia could be made? How much nitrogen would be required?

4. (Optional) Atoms and molecules are so small that there is not the remotest chance that we shall ever be able to pick them up one at a time, transfer them to some container, counting them as we go. This question anticipates what we shall study more systematically in Chapter 4, but it might be useful, just after doing Exercise 3, to lay a foundation here. (If you cannot handle the multiplication of numbers when they involve negative and positive exponential forms, you will not be able to proceed with this question.)

Consider the balanced equation for the reaction of hydrogen with oxygen to form water: $2H_2 + O_2 \longrightarrow 2H_2O$.

(a) Note the coefficients and complete Table 3.5.

For the calculations necessary to complete Table 3.5, you are asked to accept without proof the following facts about molecules of hydrogen, oxygen, and water:

one molecule of H_2 weighs 3.34×10^{-24} gram;
one molecule of O_2 weighs 53.44×10^{-24} gram;
one molecule of H_2O weighs 30.06×10^{-24} gram.

(b) Review the results in Table 3.5, and collect some of them as follows.

6.02×10^{23} molecules of H_2 weigh _____ g
6.02×10^{23} molecules of O_2 weigh _____ g
6.02×10^{23} molecules of H_2O weigh _____ g

(c) If the masses of molecules in atomic mass units are simply the sums of the masses of the individual atoms making up the molecules, then:

What would be the mass of one molecule of H_2
in atomic mass units? __2.01__ amu
What would be the mass of one molecule of O_2
in atomic mass units? _____ amu
What would be the mass of one molecule of H_2O
in atomic mass units? _____ amu

(d) Compare these two sets of answers. In other words, a sample of 6.02×10^{23} molecules of H_2 has a weight in grams that very closely corresponds *numerically* to something important and (eventually) familiar about H_2; what?

(e) And a sample of 6.02×10^{23} molecules of O_2 has a weight in grams that corresponds *numerically* very closely to something important about O_2; what?

(f) Finally, 6.02×10^{23} molecules of H_2O add up to a total weight in grams that corresponds numerically to something important about H_2O; what?

This seemingly awkward number, 6.02×10^{23}, is emerging as a potentially useful number. When we have that many unit particles of any pure substance, the weight of the sample (in grams) numerically equals the formula weight. The number 6.02×10^{23} perhaps should have a name. We shall

Table 3.5

$$2H_2 + O_2 \longrightarrow 2H_2O$$

Showing the relative proportions in terms of the numbers of molecules involved in the reaction (names of the numbers appear in parentheses)			Showing the relative proportions in terms of the weights of the substances involved in the reaction		
Molecules of H₂	Molecules of O₂	Molecules of H₂O	The weight of that many H₂ molecules	The weight of that many O₂ molecules	The weight of that many H₂O molecules
2 (two)	1 (one)	2 (two)	6.68×10^{-24} g	53.44×10^{-24} g	60.12×10^{-24} g
12 (dozen)	6 (six)	12 (dozen)	40.08×10^{-24} g $(12 \times 3.34 \times 10^{-24}$ g)	_____ g	360.72×10^{-24} g
200 (two hundred)	_____	_____	_____ $\times 10^{-22}$ g	53.44×10^{-22} g	60.12×10^{-22} g
2,000,000 (two million)	_____	_____	_____ $\times 10^{-18}$ g	_____ g	_____ g
2×10^{21}	_____	_____	6.68×10^{-3} g	_____ $\times 10^{-3}$ g	_____ g
6.02×10^{23} (name?, see Chap. 4)	3.01×10^{23}	_____	2.01 g	_____ g	_____ g
12.04×10^{23}	_____	12.04×10^{23}	4.02 g	_____ g	_____ g

give it one in Chapter 4, where its usefulness will be examined further as we study formula weights at greater length.

5. (Optional) If you did Problem 4 you can easily do this one. Make two columns. In the first, tabulate the total weights represented by the weights of the H_2 molecules plus the O_2 molecules in one or two *horizontal* lines in Table 3.5. In the second column, simply transfer the corresponding weights of H_2O molecules from the last column in Table 3.5. Compare the data, and note how they "fit" the law of conservation of mass in chemical reactions.

6. What is the total number of atoms of all kinds in one unit particle of each of the following: $Ca(MnO_4)_2$; $(NH_4)_2SO_3$; $Mg(NO_3)_2$; $Al_2(SO_4)_3$?

7. What is the name given to the type of particle that is the smallest stable sample of a covalent compound? Of an ionic substance?

8. Explain why atoms in Groups I and II of the Periodic Table readily form positively charged ions and atoms in Groups IV and V do not.

9. In terms of atomic and molecular concepts and theories of electronic configurations, what is the difference between a physical and a chemical change?

10. In terms of what scientists can observe in experimental work, what are some of the possible features of an event that enable scientists to decide if it is a chemical or a physical change?

11. What is the difference between an *orbit* (Bohr theory) and an atomic *orbital*?

12. Will a molecule necessarily be polar if its individual bonds are polar? Study the structures in Fig. 3.11. Would you, for example, expect the individual double bonds in carbon dioxide to be polar? Would you expect the molecule to be polar? Explain.

13. Why is $+2$ a reasonable electrovalence for magnesium?

14. Why is $+2$ an unreasonable electrovalence for sodium?

15. Why is $+2$ an unreasonable electrovalence for aluminum?

16. Below are the atomic numbers of pairs of elements given hypothetical symbols of X and Y. Predict the *formula* of the ionic compound each pair should be expected to form. If the pair would not be expected to combine, state "no reaction." You should not need to refer to the actual elements having these atomic numbers.

Example: X (No. 4), Y (No. 9).   *Formula:* XY_2
Example: X (No. 8), Y (No. 4).   *Formula:* YX (Why not XY?)
(a) X (No. 19), Y (No. 8)
(b) X (No. 17), Y (No. 13)
(c) X (No. 2), Y (No. 4)
(d) X (No. 3), Y (No. 17)
(e) X (No. 13), Y (No. 16)
(f) X (No. 9), Y (No. 20)
(g) X (No. 5), Y (No. 10)
(h) X (No. 18), Y (No. 7)
(i) X (No. 16), Y (No. 1)
(j) X (No. 11), Y (No. 8)

the nature of matter: compounds and chemical bonds

17. The chart (see below) provides drill in handling electrovalences and in writing formulas and names for chemicals. Across the top and along the side are several formulas of ions. (Their electrical charges have been omitted; you should fill them in.) Write formulas and names for compounds that would be present if ions in the vertical column were combined with those in the horizontal column. The examples illustrate how to do this.

	I	H_2PO_4	SO_4	NO_3	CO_3	OH
Na	NaI Sodium iodide					
NH_4		$NH_4H_2PO_4$ Ammonium dihydrogen phosphate				
Ca						calcium hydroxide $Ca(OH)_2$
Li						
Ba						
Fe (II)			$FeSO_4$ Iron (II) sulfate (ferrous sulfate)			

chapter 4 moles, chemical energy, states of matter

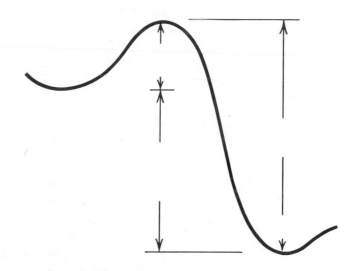

In the chapters to come we shall examine a number of chemical properties. To make this study possible we must first discuss three key ideas or principles of chemistry: the idea of a *reacting* unit of matter; the kinetic-molecular theory (or the "molecule's-eye view" of things and events); and what we mean by the expression "chemical energy."

Quantitative work in science requires usually just one reference standard for each kind of measurement. To measure length we need just the meter, although for convenience we work with fractions and multiples of it (e.g., the centimeter and the kilometer). To measure mass we again need only one reference, the kilogram, together with convenient fractions and multiples of it. When it comes to weighing out chemicals for use in experimental work, however, one, practical, measurable reference for all chemicals will not do. In fact, we find it most convenient to have a separate measured reference for each chemical, a special "reacting unit" for every one. Our next questions are why? And what do we do about it?

chemicals combine as particles. When atoms combine they do so in definite ratios of intact atoms to produce compounds with definite composition. What the individual atoms happen to weigh is quite immaterial. Atoms do not know what they weigh. (They do not *know* anything.) But when they do interact and combine, it is always as whole particles, and the particle-to-particle or atom-to-atom ratio is always expressible in simple, whole numbers. Chemical changes do not split atoms into fractional pieces. Carbon atoms, for example, can combine with oxygen molecules in a ratio of one particle (atom) of carbon to one particle (molecule) of oxygen to form carbon dioxide.

$$C + O_2 \longrightarrow CO_2$$

The coefficients—all 1 in this equation—tell this ratio.

the chemist's dilemma. (but not really.) That an oxygen molecule weighs a good deal more than a carbon atom is unimportant as far as the reaction itself is concerned—unimportant, that is, until the chemist tries to arrange a meeting of carbon atoms and oxygen molecules in an exact particle-to-particle ratio of one to one. (He may be concerned about waste and purity, for instance.) If he took two atoms of carbon and four molecules of oxygen, then two of the oxygen molecules would certainly react but the other two would be left over (and would contaminate the product, besides). But now the chemist has a problem. He knows he must mix the chemicals in one particular ratio of *particles,* but there is no way he can pick and count these particles. Individual atoms and molecules are too small.

Chemists solved this problem long ago by learning how to count particles indirectly by simply measuring samples of the chemicals in particular ratios by their weights. To learn how, ourselves, we need to broaden our idea of an atomic weight and study the more general, but closely related concept of formula weight.

formula weights. When atoms combine to form compounds, the atomic nuclei have not been affected. There has been no net loss of weight. Whatever particle forms, be it a molecule or an ion group, it will have both a formula and a formula weight. The formula weight of any substance is simply the sum of the atomic weights of the atoms that appear in the chemical formula. Consider, for example, carbon dioxide:

$$\text{Atoms:} \quad C + O + O \longrightarrow CO_2$$
$$\text{Atomic weights:} \quad 12 + 16 + 16 = 44$$

(formula weight of carbon dioxide)

If the substance is an element with a simple formula such as Na, or Fe, then the formula weight is identical with the atomic weight. Since "formula weight" is the more general term it is more useful. But what is an atomic weight or a formula weight in terms practical enough for experimental and analytical work? Thus far we have learned only that the atomic weight of an element is the sum of the neutrons and protons in the atomic nucleus, each neutron and proton weighing one atomic mass unit or *amu*. We do not have weighing balances that read in *amu* units and it would be inconvenient to do so.

formula weights are relative weights. A formula weight is not the actual weight of an individual atom or molecule. A formula weight tells us indirectly how the weight of such a particle compares with the weight of one atom of one of the isotopes of carbon, carbon-12. Whatever weight an atom of carbon-12 actually has on a scale of grams, chemists choose to say that its weight is 12 units (exactly) on their special atomic weight scale. They pick this number because they want the lightest of all atoms, the hydrogen atom to have at least one whole unit on their scale. They know from other studies that, whatever the scale, a hydrogen atom is $\frac{1}{12}$ as heavy as a carbon atom.[1] To take another example, sulfur atoms (atomic weight 32) weigh $\frac{32}{12}$ times as much as carbon-12 atoms. Molecules of carbon dioxide (formula weight 44) weigh $\frac{44}{12}$ times as much as carbon-12 atoms. These formula weights, therefore, are really shorthand expressions; they give us a numerator in a fraction having 12 as the denominator. The fraction, formula weight/12, tells us how much more or less a particular *formula unit* (atom, molecule, etc.) weighs in relation to the carbon-12 isotope. Let us call by the name *formula unit* the real or hypothetical particle corresponding to the formula. A formula unit could be an atom (e.g., Na), or a molecule (e.g., CO_2) or an ion group (e.g., NaCl).

[1] Instead of setting up the scale of relative weights that gives a value of 12.0000 to carbon-12, chemists might have assigned this isotope of carbon a value of 6.0000 units. But a hydrogen atom would still weigh one-twelfth as much; hence on such a scale, hydrogen's atomic weight (relative weight) would be 0.50000. There is nothing fundamentally wrong with that, but it is not as neat and it creates other problems.

making formula weights practical. reacting units. The actual values of formula weights for particular substances are not especially familiar to very many people, including beginners, but fortunately these values do not have to be common knowledge. With a table of atomic weights for reference, formula weights can be calculated for any formula by simple addition. In that sense, any formula weight is at least potentially familiar, and we shall exploit any advantages we can. What we need is a practical system for measuring chemicals in known ratios by particles, and we arbitrarily set the practical *reacting unit* of a chemical not at one formula unit, not at one atom or one molecule, but at a large enough number of these tiny particles so that the whole sample weighs, in grams, as much as the potentially familiar formula weight of the substance. (By "practical" we mean something that can be measured in practice, such as a weight.) The "familiar" number for carbon-12 is its atomic weight, 12. Hence, the practical reacting unit for this isotope is 12 grams.

avogadro's number. A pile of carbon atoms weighing exactly 12 grams would be visible, easily weighable, and transferable. There would obviously be some definite number of carbon atoms in the pile—how many is not too important. But scientists do know that number fairly accurately, and we may as well note what it is. In twelve grams of carbon-12 there is not a dozen (12) atoms, or a gross (144), or a million (10^6), or a billion (10^9) or, in fact, any nice, round number of atoms for which we have simple names like billion, million, etc. (Once we arbitrarily pick *grams* as our weight unit and we decide on 12 as the weight of carbon on our scale of relative weights, we cannot expect everything else to come out in simple numbers.) The number of atoms in exactly 12 grams of carbon-12 is 6.0238×10^{23}, a number so huge as to be beyond comprehension.[2] Like many other special numbers it has a special name—*Avogadro's Number*—after an Italian scientist, Amadeo Avogadro, who contributed much to our understanding of atomic weights.

the mole. Suppose we weighed Avogadro's number of hydrogen atoms, a pile of hydrogen atoms numbering 6.0238×10^{23}. What would the pile weigh? If that many carbon atoms would weigh 12 grams, then the same number of hydrogen atoms must weigh $\frac{1}{12}$ as much, 1 gram, which is the "familiar" number for hydrogen (its atomic weight). A pile of sulfur atoms, 6.0238×10^{23} in number, would weigh $\frac{32}{12}$ times as much as the 12-gram pile of carbon atoms. (Sulfur atoms weigh $\frac{32}{12}$ as much as carbon atoms; that

[2] Professors D. H. Andrews and R. J. Kokes (Johns Hopkins University), in their text *Fundamentals of Chemistry* (John Wiley & Sons, 1965) described some rough calculations based on the assumption that 1 cubic centimeter of volume would hold 100 small garden peas. On that basis, 6.0238×10^{23} peas would cover to a depth of four feet not only the entire planet but almost 10 more planets like ours.

Another comparison: The oceans of the world contain about 13×10^{23} grams of water.

moles, chemical energy, states of matter

is what the listing of 32 in the table as the atomic weight of sulfur means.) Any time we take samples of carbon and samples of sulfur in weight ratios of 12 grams carbon to 32 grams sulfur we shall inevitably obtain their atoms in a ratio of 1 *atom* carbon to 1 *atom* of sulfur. We would get that one-to-one *atom-to-atom* ratio (sulfur to carbon) by taking any of the following pairs of samples:

Wt. Carbon	Wt. Sulfur	Wt. Ratio
12 g	32 g	12:32 (=0.375)
6 g	16 g	6:16 (=0.375)
3 g	8 g	3:8 (=0.375)
24 g etc.	64 g	24:64 (=0.375)

Here, then is the solution to the "chemist's dilemma" of a few paragraphs back. Anytime you *weigh* chemicals in proportions according to their formula weights you inevitably obtain those compounds in one-to-one proportions according to their formula units. The practical reacting unit of any pure substance is, therefore, easily calculated; simply compute the formula weight and write the word "grams" after it. Chemists have a name for the practical reacting unit of a chemical: either *gram-formula weight* or *mole*.[3] You may, of course, take fractions or multiples of a mole, just as you may with any measuring unit (e.g., centimeter, milligram, microsecond, millimole), and such smaller or larger portions may be any size you please. But whatever its size, it will contain an easily calculated number of moles:

$$\text{No. of moles in a sample} = \frac{\text{weight of sample in grams}}{\text{weight of one mole (in grams by definition)}}$$

To summarize, the actual reacting unit of a chemical is, at one level, just one particle of it; at a higher level, it is a certain number of particles—Avogadro's number. Because we cannot actually count that number and measure the chemical as with a tweezers, we calculate what that number means in terms of a weight in grams of a sample of the chemical. By picking Avogadro's number instead of some neater number our *practical* reacting

[3] This peculiar word "mole" is chemical shorthand for "gram-molecular weight," a term of diminishing popularity but essentially identical with "formula weight written in grams." In 1965 the Commission on Symbols, Terminology and Units of the International Union of Pure and Applied Chemistry (IUPAC) recommended that the IUPAC endorse the following definition of a mole:

"A mole is an amount of substance, of specified chemical formula, containing the same number of formula units (atoms, molecules, ions, electrons, quanta or other entities) as there are atoms in 12 grams (exactly) of the pure nuclide ^{12}C." By "amount of substance" this definition means gram-formula weight.

unit (the mole) for any pure substance will be its gram-formula weight, i.e., its formula weight in grams. *Equal numbers of moles of different substances will therefore always contain equal numbers of formula units.*

Let us now do some sample calculations to see how the mole concept works.

Example 1. A chemist needs 44 grams of carbon dioxide. He intends to make it by the combustion of carbon. What is the minimum amount of carbon he must take?

Step 1. Nothing can be done without a balanced equation. The first step in any problem involving weight relations must be to determine the balanced equation for the operation. It is only from the balanced equation that the ratio of reagents is evident. Such an equation is obtained in one of several ways: you may remember it from some previous experience; you may look it up in a reference book; you may remember only the reactants and products, and then you write the balanced equation by a trial-and-error juggling of coefficients (as described in the next section); occasionally it may be necessary to work out the actual relations by experimentation (as chemists often do). In our case, it is easy. From above:

$$C + O_2 \longrightarrow CO_2$$

Step 2. Calculate formula weights for the reagents. These must be known before actual weights in grams can be determined. Use an atomic weight table for individual atomic weights, and, except when great accuracy is demanded, round off atomic weights to the nearest one-half unit. Until you gain experience, it will help you if you place formula weights beneath corresponding formulas in the balanced equation. In our example:

$$C + O_2 \longrightarrow CO_2$$
Formula wts.: 12   32   44

Step 3. We need 44 grams of carbon dioxide. This corresponds to one mole. The coefficients of the equation tell us that one mole of carbon dioxide requires one mole of carbon for its preparation. One mole of carbon weighs 12 grams, our answer.

Example 2. How much oxygen would be produced by the decomposition of 2 moles of potassium chlorate, in moles? In grams?

Step 1. The balanced equation:

$$2KClO_3 \longrightarrow 2KCl + 3O_2$$

Step 2.   Formula wts.: 122.5   74.5   32

moles, chemical energy, states of matter

Step 3. The coefficients tell us that 2 moles of potassium chlorate yield 3 moles of oxygen (our first answer). Each mole of oxygen weighs 32 grams. Hence, for 3 moles:

3 moles $\times$ 32 grams/mole = 96 grams of oxygen (our second answer) available from 2 moles of potassium chlorate.

Example 3. A chemist needs 0.1 mole of ammonium phosphate, $(NH_4)_3PO_4$. How many grams must he weigh?

Solution. The formula weight of this compound is 149. Hence, one mole weighs 149 grams: 0.1 mole weighs 14.9 grams, our answer.

balancing equations. The ability to balance equations is useful primarily when weight-relation problems are faced in actual laboratory situations. To balance an equation, you must know the formulas for all reactants and products. Unless all can be written, it is obviously pointless to go further. Moreover, unless the formulas are written accurately, the equation cannot be correctly balanced. Once correct formulas are set down in the conventional pattern (use of $+$ signs and an arrow pointing toward the products), balancing the equation is a trial-and-error juggling of coefficients. (Never change subscripts within a formula once it has been correctly written. If you do, you change the formula into a symbol either for another compound or for one that cannot exist within the rules of valence.)

Probably the only useful trick in balancing equations is to start by balancing the ion or group that is initially most unbalanced. Suppose, for example, you were asked to write the balanced equation for: "sodium hydroxide reacts with phosphoric acid to form sodium phosphate and water."

Step 1. Writing correct formulas in the conventional pattern.

$$NaOH + H_3PO_4 \longrightarrow Na_3PO_4 + H_2O$$

Step 2. Trial-and-error juggling of coefficients. Start by balancing the ion most out of balance, in this case, Na^+. Place a 3 in front of NaOH.

$$3NaOH + H_3PO_4 \longrightarrow Na_3PO_4 + H_2O$$

A quick check shows that:
    Na's are balanced;
    PO_4 is balanced (in your mental checking, do not break up a group if nothing has happened to it in the reaction.)

the reacting units of substances

We have remaining, on the left, 3 O's and a total of 6 H's. On the right, we have, in H_2O, O's and H's in a ratio of 2:1 (the same as 6:3). If we put a 3 in front of H_2O:

$$3NaOH + H_3PO_4 \longrightarrow Na_3PO_4 + 3H_2O$$

the equation will be balanced.

As you gain experience in balancing equations, there will be fewer errors in the trial and error step(s).

kinetic molecular theory; the states of matter and heat Besides its reacting unit or mole, another important feature of a pure substance is its physical state. Is it at a given temperature a solid, a liquid, or a gas? How rapidly a substance will undergo one of its chemical changes often depends on the physical state it is in. To understand reactions and to visualize how they occur we need a "molecule's-eye view" of substances in various states and what effect heat has on them.

motion and heat. Many rather common experiences have taught us to associate heat with motion. On a frosty night at the skating rink, rubbing the ears warms them. A campfire can be started by twirling a stick against a board. When a steel bit bites into iron plate, the heat generated can be intense. Although heat was once thought to be a substance (it was called *caloric*), it is now understood as being the result of motion, and therefore a form of energy. An object becomes hot if its tiny component atoms (or molecules or ions) are made to move or vibrate rapidly. The action of a drill boring into iron makes iron atoms do just that, vibrate more and more rapidly.

The states of matter—solid, liquid, gaseous—may be understood according to the kinds of motions molecules in these states are believed to make. The kinetic-molecular theory gives us a "molecule's-eye view" of what goes on in ordinary chemicals when they are in storage. It also helps us to understand many chemical reactions occurring in the body because it gives us a picture of molecules in violent, often self-destructive collisions.

the gaseous state. According to the kinetic-molecule theory, molecules (or atoms) of a gas are in a state of constant, chaotic, utterly random motion. They do not stick to each other, either because they are not polar enough and electrical forces of attraction are too weak, or because collisions are too violent and elastic. Relatively speaking, there is considerable empty space between molecules in the gaseous state. They touch each other only when they collide (see Fig. 4.1). Each molecule, on the average, moves very rapidly. At room temperature, air molecules, for example, move at an average velocity of about 900 miles per hour! Since billions upon billions of air molecules

moles, chemical energy, states of matter

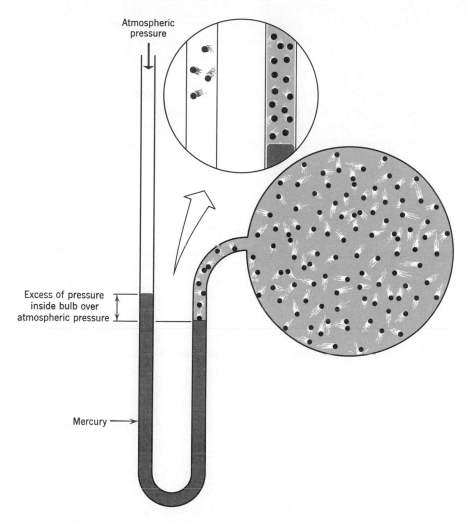

Atmospheric
pressure

Excess of pressure
inside bulb over
atmospheric pressure

Mercury →

Fig. 4.1 The gaseous state; kinetic-molecular theory. The rapid random motions of individual molecules of the confined gas give the effect that the gas occupies the entire volume. Yet, the average distance between molecules is large in comparison with their own diameters. Thus a gas is mostly empty space. The pressure exerted by the gas on the walls of its container and on the mercury column is caused by high frequency collisions at the surfaces. If the temperature of the gas were made to rise, these collisions would occur more frequently and more energetically, and the pressure would rise. In fact, according to the Charles-Gay Lussac Law, the pressure of a confined gas is directly proportional to its absolute temperature.

are present in even one cubic centimeter of air, collisions constantly occur. The *pressure* a gas exerts results simply from the innumerable collisions that its molecules make with its container on each unit of its wall area each second. Each single collision does not amount to much, since molecules are so small; but billions of them per second per square centimeter of container area add up significantly.

When a gas is heated, its molecules simply are made to move faster. Similarly, the molecules move more slowly when the gas is cooled. There is a temperature, called *absolute zero*, at which these molecular motions cease. Its value is $-273.16°C$.

The considerable freedom of motion that molecules of a gas enjoy accounts for the fact that a gas has no definite shape and no definite volume. As any woman who wears perfume knows, a gas or vapor will disperse or diffuse into all parts of a container, whatever its shape or volume.

the liquid state. Slower-moving molecules characterize the liquid state. They are nearly always in contact with each other, in sharp contrast to their situation in the gaseous state. They move about randomly and chaotically with enough energy of motion to prevent them from settling into fixed, rigid patterns. Molecules at the surface of a liquid that happen to be moving upward may escape. If they are not knocked back by collisions with air molecules, their escape is permanent, thus explaining the phenomenon of evaporation. Heat, which makes the molecules of a liquid move more rapidly, therefore increases the rate of evaporation. Enough added heat may produce such vigorous molecular motions in a liquid that its molecules no longer can cling to each other. Violent collisions drive them apart throughout the body of the liquid. Bubbles of vapor (gas) form, and the phenomenon of boiling occurs.

In a liquid, electrical forces of attraction between molecules are effective enough to maintain the liquid in a definite volume. They are not strong enough, however, to hold it to a definite shape (see Fig. 4.2).

the solid state. The motions of molecules in the solid state are vibrations rather than changes in positions. Molecules have fixed positions, fixed neighbor molecules, but they vibrate in all directions about these fixed points. Electrical forces of attraction are able to maintain a definite volume and

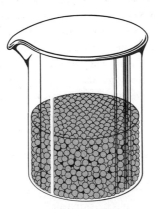

Molecules in the liquid state are densely packed; they have a random arrangement; and they move and slip past each other rather easily.

Fig. 4.2 The liquid state; kinetic-molecular concept.

moles, chemical energy, states of matter

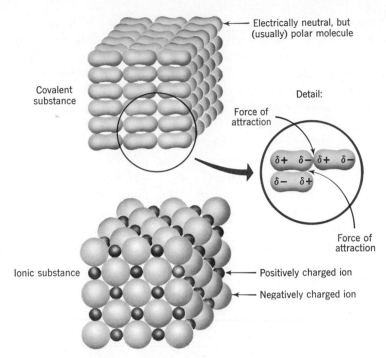

Covalent
substance

Electrically neutral, but
(usually) polar molecule

Detail:

Force of
attraction

$\delta+$ $\delta-$ $\delta+$ $\delta-$

$\delta-$ $\delta+$

Force of
attraction

Ionic substance

Positively charged ion

Negatively charged ion

Fig. 4.3 The solid state. In a covalent substance, the smallest representative "sample"
is an electrically neutral molecule. In most cases, these are polar. This provides for forces
of attraction for holding neighboring molecules together, provided they stack in a reasonably
orderly fashion, as illustrated. In an ionic substance, the individual components are
oppositely charged ions. Forces of attraction can counterbalance forces of repulsion if a
reasonably orderly aggregation of the proper pattern occurs.

a definite shape for a solid (see Fig. 4.3). If a solid is heated, its molecules
move more violently. Since the molecules then need more room, solids
normally expand when they are heated. If the motions become intense
enough, molecules may be unable to hold to fixed positions, and they may
adopt the liquid state. This explains the phenomenon of melting.

To convert a substance from one state into another we usually heat it
(or cool it). Besides the sun, nuclear power and chemicals are our most
important sources of heat. The chemicals in petroleum, wood, coal, and
natural gas burn in air and release heat, which we use to run power plants
and cars, to cook food, and to warm our homes and buildings. We also
use heat to make other chemical events happen faster. There is a close relation
between heat and chemical changes, a relation we must now explore.

Two molecules that are to react with each other usually must collide rather
vigorously. Therefore, heat, which makes collisions between potential reactant
molecules more frequent and more energetic, increases the rates of most
reactions. Let us use the combustion of carbon to illustrate this relation.

**heat and
its chemical
significance**

spontaneous chemical events and molecular structure. We know that certain electronic configurations are more stable than others. One carbon nucleus, two oxygen nuclei, and twenty-two electrons apparently are more stably arranged as a molecule of carbon dioxide than separately as an atom of carbon and a molecule of oxygen. At least, if the opportunity is presented, the rearrangement (chemical reaction) of Fig. 4.4 occurs from left to right rather than from right to left.

Electronic configurations of the chemicals involved, then, are important factors in determining whether a spontaneous reaction will occur. When we say that carbon contains *chemical energy,* we mean that the electronic configuration of a carbon atom is such that it can rearrange into a more stable arrangement, in cooperation, of course, with some other substance such as oxygen. The energy liberated is a measure of the chemical energy initially present, collectively, in carbon and oxygen. Chemical energy, therefore, is a potential energy that exists by virtue of certain relatively unstable kinds of electronic configurations.

spontaneous chemical events and activation energy. The reaction of carbon with oxygen is extremely slow unless the mixture is ignited; that is, unless it is heated to its kindling temperature. (Carbon can be stored indefinitely in air.) In order for the electronic rearrangement, left to right, of Fig. 4.4 to take place, a violent collision must occur between oxygen and carbon. At room temperature, collisions of sufficient energy almost never take place. At higher temperatures, however, they become more frequent. When rearrangements of electrons and nuclei occur, newly formed carbon dioxide molecules emerge moving with more energy on the average than did the reactant particles. In other words, heat is produced. Heat is always a by-product of any chemical reaction wherein product molecules emerge with more kinetic energy than was possessed initially by the reactants. At or above a kindling temperature, enough heat is generated by the reaction to ignite

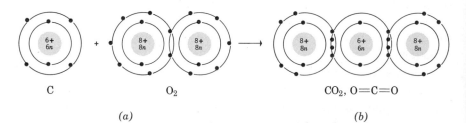

C O_2 CO_2, $O=C=O$

(a)   (b)

Fig. 4.4 Chemical change and molecular structure. Chemical reactions involve rearrangements or redistributions of electrons relative to atomic nuclei. Spontaneous chemical reactions go in the direction of the more stable arrangements. (a) One way of arranging 22 electrons, 1 carbon nucleus, and 2 oxygen nuclei, (b) another way. The arrangement in (b) is more stable than that in (a). Consequently, the spontaneous event is from left to right.

moles, chemical energy, states of matter

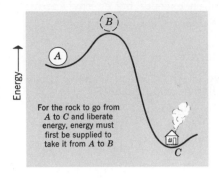

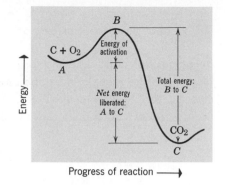

Fig. 4.5

Fig. 4.6

unchanged reactants. These relations can profitably be viewed in another way. Let us consider as an analogy a very common spontaneous event in nature, a falling rock.

Heavy objects tend spontaneously to gravitate in the direction of the center of the earth, the center of gravity. Therefore, we say that rocks at low altitudes represent a more stable arrangement than those at high altitudes. Consider the situation in Fig. 4.5. A rock in either position A or B possesses what physicists call potential energy relative to position C. In B, its potential energy can easily be turned into active or kinetic energy (falling to C). In position A, it is much more difficult. To get the rock from A to C, someone must supply energy to take it from A to B first. This energy is analogous to kindling or ignition energy.

Consider the collection of nuclei and electrons represented by the symbols $C + O_2$ in Fig. 4.6. At position A, there is little chance for a reaction to occur (A to C). The effect of an igniting device (that is, a device that supplies energy), however, is to activate the reactants and to boost them to the top of the "energy hill," B. Now the possibility of going to C is far greater, and once the nuclei and electrons have rearranged into carbon dioxide, CO_2, the chances of returning to B, and thence to A, are nil. In other words, the reaction is irreversible; the reverse reaction is not a natural one.

The energy that must be supplied to reactants to take them to the top of their energy hills on the way to products is called the *energy of activation*. For those familiar with mountains, what we have called "tops of energy hills" are really like saddles in mountains, passes that take energy to climb but are still the lowest energy routes to the other side. In our example, the reaction from B to C (Fig. 4.6) liberates more energy than is needed for activation. The net amount released is observed as heat and some light. This reaction is said to be *exothermic* ("exo-," out; "thermic," heat). The more general term, *exergonic*, is applicable to the release of energy in any form, not just as heat.

An *endothermic* reaction is one that consumes heat. (The more general term is *endergonic.*) Its energy of activation exceeds the energy liberated. The thermal decomposition of potassium chlorate is an illustration.

decomposition of potassium chlorate; catalysis. For the preparation of small amounts of oxygen in the laboratory, the action of heat on potassium chlorate, $KClO_3$, is sometimes used.[4] When this compound is heated to $420°C$, it decomposes into oxygen and potassium chloride:[5]

$$2KClO_3 \xrightarrow[\text{heat to } 420°C]{} 2KCl + 3O_2$$

A sustained high temperature is needed, and Fig. 4.7 illustrates the energy relations of this endothermic reaction.

To generate a temperature of $420°C$ requires a great deal of energy, and energy is expensive. The same decomposition can be accomplished very rapidly at a far lower temperature, $270°C$, if a small amount of manganese dioxide, MnO_2, is added. Nothing permanent happens to the manganese dioxide, which can be recovered unchanged after the reaction. Somehow (in a way we shall not study) manganese dioxide makes it possible for this reaction to occur as rapidly at a lower temperature or more rapidly at the same temperature than when the manganese dioxide was absent. Compounds that perform this service of accelerating reactions are called *catalysts.* The

---

[4] In the hands of beginners, this reaction is potentially hazardous. Hot potassium chlorate explodes when it makes contact with carbon, sulfur, or rubber. At one large university, waste potassium chlorate ignited paper in trash cans. The greatest care must be exercised when this experiment is performed.

[5] Frequently, important experimental conditions for a reaction are summarized on or below the arrow.

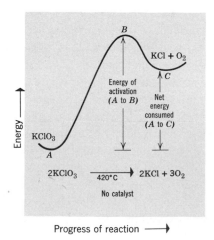

Fig. 4.7 An endothermic reaction.

moles, chemical energy, states of matter

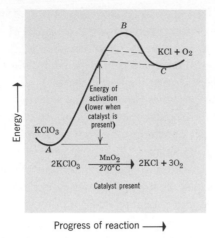

Fig. 4.8 A catalyst lowers the energy of activation.

service is called *catalysis.* In general, any substance whose presence in relatively small amounts will increase the speed of a reaction without itself undergoing permanent chemical change is a catalyst.[6] In the presence of the catalyst (see Fig. 4.8), a lower temperature may be used to cause the same (or faster) rate of reaction *because catalysts in general act by reducing the activation energy required for a reaction.* In effect, a catalyst lowers the height of the energy hill; it might be said that it creates a tunnel through that barrier. Living systems possess thousands of catalysts called enzymes and if anything happens to them life becomes difficult or impossible.

summary of effect of temperature and catalysis on reaction rates. Neither catalyst nor temperature affects the *relative positions* of reactants and products on an energy scale, such as those in Figs. 4.6, 4.7, and 4.8. Both, however, make it easier to get from one side of the energy hill to the other. By increasing the temperature, energy is supplied that increases the rates with which reactants get to the top of their energy barrier. By introducing a catalyst, the height of that barrier is reduced, and crossing it becomes easier.

implications for human health. As a general rule of thumb (one subject to many exceptions, incidentally), raising the temperature of reactants only 10°C often doubles or triples the rate of their reaction! This enormous effect of temperature on reaction rate partly accounts for the seriousness of a very high fever. A change in body temperature from 98.6°F to 106°F is a rise of only about 4.1 degrees on the Celsius scale. Yet this very slight increase can accelerate body reactions to a dangerous extent, as evinced by an increased pulse rate, accelerated respiratory rate, and disturbance in the

[6] Substances that may be used to slow down rapid reactions are called *inhibitors.*

digestive and nervous systems. To be sure, a rise in body temperature during periods of infection is part of the defensive mechanism of the body. Increases in pulse rate and respiration mean faster circulation. Thus, it is not always wise to take medications to reduce a mild fever. However, high fevers over a long period of time are very dangerous.

A fall in body temperature also has important consequences in health. When body temperature drops, reactions slow down dramatically. Use of ethyl chloride as a local anesthetic takes advantage of this principle. When this liquid of low boiling point ($12.3°C$) is sprayed on the skin, its rapid evaporation cools the area to the point where the chemical reactions needed to transmit pain messages along the nervous system do not occur. If a boil at the cooled site is lanced, no pain is felt during the operation.

catalytic mufflers. Special automobile mufflers fitted with porous beds of catalysts are becoming increasingly important in the fight against air pollution. Automobile exhaust passed through such a catalytic muffler brings unburned gasoline and carbon monoxide in contact with a catalyst that permits their complete conversion to carbon dioxide and water in the muffler. The catalyst allows this conversion to go at lower temperatures, which simplifies the problem of designing such an exhaust control and reduces its cost. Up into the early 1970s the chief obstacle to catalytic mufflers was the lead additive in gasoline; lead compounds in the exhaust gases interfere with the catalyst. Once in the atmosphere, compounds of lead constitute a health hazard themselves. (The discussion of lead in gasoline will be resumed in Chapter 10. Lead-free gasoline is possible and it appeared on the U. S. market in 1970.)

effect of temperature on aquatic life. thermal pollution. Thermal pollution is the addition by acts of man of large amounts of heat to any part of the environment such that temperatures rise more than normal. We shall consider one of its effects here in one part of the environment.

When the temperature of a lake or river reaches $95°F$ or thereabouts no known type of fish in the United States can survive. Trout die at an ambient temperature of $77°F$; pike at $86°F$; goldfish and catfish at $95°F$. The thermal death of fish is not yet fully understood, but we do know that heat speeds up chemical changes anywhere. Metabolism is not exempt from this rule. (Metabolism is the total set of chemical reactions in a living system.) To sustain an accelerated metabolism, fish need more oxygen. Unfortunately, warm water holds less oxygen than cold water. To aggravate the problem, the mechanism in fish for transporting oxygen from gills to cells becomes less efficient at higher temperatures. (The hemoglobin in fish blood becomes less able to carry oxygen.) As if this were not enough, pollutants universally present in those rivers and lakes large enough to support power plants are more poisonous to fish at higher temperatures.

Until recently the principal source of heat to rivers and lakes was the sun. As summer temperatures rise and lakes become heated (especially at the surface), fish go to the cooler, more oxygen-rich depths. In the last few decades power plants have become a serious new source of heat for rivers and large lakes.

The turbines of most power plants are driven by hot steam. Heat to make steam from water is generated by burning coal (or oil or gas) or from atomic energy. For maximum efficiency the steam must be superheated and then sharply cooled. Cooling in most power plants is accomplished by drawing cold water from rivers or large lakes. Figure 4.9 gives a general picture of a nuclear power plant and its cooling system. The only essential operating difference in a coal-fired or oil-fired plant is the fuel.

Until the late 1960s most power plants were located along major rivers and near urban, high-power-use areas. But we are running out of rivers conveniently located. According to John R. Clark, if projected power needs were to be supplied by steam-operated power plants, by the year 2000 the entire river flowage in the United States would (in theory) be required to carry off the excess heat during the summer when power demands are high and water levels are low. That is why the power industry has to build power plants more and more by large lakes or the ocean. Sixteen nuclear power plants are presently planned for the shores of the Great Lakes, principally Lake Erie and Lake Michigan, the two lakes least able to withstand environmental shocks. Scientists on the staff of ENVIRONMENT magazine estimate

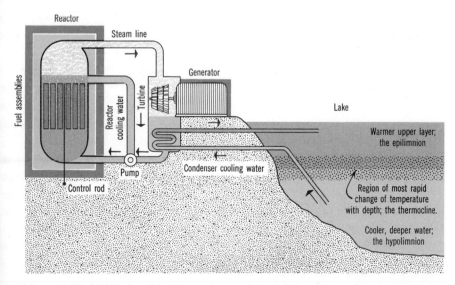

Fig. 4.9 Basic operating parts of a simple nuclear power plant. Nuclear events in the uranium fuel release heat into water circulating in pipes in and around the fuel. The water boils and the steam hits the blades of the turbine and makes it turn the generator. The steam must now be cooled and the water returned to the uranium fuel to begin another cycle. The most economical way to cool the steam is to draw in water, as shown, and discharge it again. The discharged water is normally ten to fifteen degrees warmer than it was, but it is added to the warmer upper layer. (Figure adapted from Environment, January–February, 1970, page 39. Used by permission.)

that the waste heat each day from all these plants would increase the temperature of 18 billion gallons of water 15°F, a volume of water equal to the average daily flowage of the Mississippi River as it empties into the Gulf of Mexico.

When a power plant is by a lake it draws cooling water from the lower, colder depths (the hypolimnion). The plant's effluent, hotter water is discharged into the warmer, surface waters (the epilimnion). If the discharged water is even one or two degrees higher than the normal surface water temperature there are serious ecological consequences. Algae grow faster and when they die they decay, and in the process they use up oxygen that fish need. If the volume of the cooler deep waters is reduced as the volume of the warmer surface waters is increased, marine organisms and fish with high oxygen requirements have a greater struggle for enough living room. It is obvious that this topic (as almost any topic of the environmental sciences) is very large. It involves many scientific and engineering disciplines as well as the arts and science of politics, economics, and last (certainly not least) morality. The literature of the field is enormous and growing. A few selected references are given at the close of this chapter where the interested reader may find more information about thermal pollution, how serious it is, and how the problem might be handled.

In the spring of 1971 vigorous action taken by the federal Environmental Protection Agency won the agreement of pollution control agencies of states bordering Lake Michigan—Wisconsin, Indiana, and Michigan (but not Illinois) —that heated water may not be discharged into Lake Michigan hot enough to raise water temperature 1000 feet from the discharge pipe more than 3 degrees Fahrenheit. Increasingly, new power plants are being built with huge cooling towers to dissipate waste heat directly to the atmosphere instead of into a nearby body of water.

effect of concentration on reaction rate. By "concentration" we mean the amount of a substance present per some given unit of volume.[7]

Higher concentrations of reactants usually mean faster reactions simply because collisions between reactants become more frequent. Combustible

[7] There are many ways of expressing concentration, but the ones we most need right now is the expression *ppm* and the *volume-volume percent* method. When one gas is dissolved in another gas, the latter method is useful for high concentrations. Thus we say that air is roughly 21% by volume oxygen [often written 21% (vol/vol)], meaning that every 100 volumes of air includes 21 volumes of oxygen. Ppm stands for "parts per million," which is a way of expressing the concentration of something when only trace amounts are present in a large volume. "Parts per million" is really a shortened version of "parts per million parts," where "parts" means any unit the user chooses. Thus 1 ppm could mean one volume per million volumes, and this is what is meant when a trace amount of one gas (e.g., sulfur dioxide or carbon monoxide) is intimately mixed with another gas (e.g., ordinary air). For liquid solutions, one part per million would usually stand for one gram per million grams or one milligram per million milligrams; any weight unit will do provided the same one is used twice in the expression. A level of DDT of 0.5 ppm, for example, would mean 0.5 g DDT dissolved in a million grams of water.

moles, chemical energy, states of matter

materials burn far more rapidly in pure oxygen than in air because the oxygen in air is much less concentrated than in the pure material. If a tuft of steel wool, for example, were heated in air [21% (vol/vol) oxygen] it would glow and maybe spark and sputter. But if this hot steel wool were thrust into 100% oxygen, it would burst into flame.

Fish require a minimum concentration of oxygen in the surrounding water. Migrating chinook salmon, for example, will not even enter a river unless its waters contain at least four parts oxygen per million parts of water (4 ppm). The Willamette River in Oregon, with four of that state's major cities and nine paper and pulp mills crowding the 187 miles of its main section, began to deteriorate in the late 1920s. By the early 1960s it was almost an open sewer as it passed Portland Harbor and emptied into the Columbia River. Its average monthly oxygen content in 1957 fell as low as 1.5 ppm. The fish count during the fall salmon run at the Oregon City fishway in 1965 was 79. But citizens, conservation organizations, and newly elected officials teamed together and forced some dramatic changes. By 1969 the lowest monthly average concentration of oxygen in the river at Portland Harbor was 5.6 ppm, and the salmon run rose in the fall of 1969 to a count of 6957.[8] Fish do not need just oxygen but oxygen above a minimum concentration to sustain their metabolism, and concentration of reactants is always an important factor in the rate of any chemical reaction, whether in living organisms or not.

A dramatic if infrequently seen illustration of what a high concentration of oxygen can do to fish is witnessed by fishermen who take minnows for bait on canoe expeditions into the northern Minnesota wilderness canoe country. Faced with the problem of keeping minnows alive during long canoe voyages when the minnow bucket cannot be left in the lake water, fishermen buy their minnows in small, water-tight plastic bags half-filled with water and minnows. Pure oxygen from cylinders at the bait stores is forced into the water, and when the bag is closed the "air" above the minnows is also mostly oxygen. The minnows, by now unusually frisky, stay alive for a few days with this arrangement where, under ordinary circumstances, they would die in hours.

Selected Reading List

Books

1. W. F. Kieffer. *The Mole Concept in Chemistry*. Reinhold Publishing Corporation. N. Y., 1962. A short paperback in which the frequent applications of the concept of a mole of substance are tied together.

[8] Data for the discussion of the Willamette River are from a report in the *New York Times* (Sept. 8, 1970) by E. W. Kenworthy.

2. L. E. Strong and W. J. Stratton. *Chemical Energy*. Reinhold Publishing Corporation. N. Y., 1965. Another paperback, and an excellent introduction to the concepts of energy and their applications to chemical systems.

Articles

1. John R. Clark. "Thermal Pollution and Aquatic Life." *Scientific American*, May 1969, page 19. What thermal pollution does to the aquatic ecosystem is discussed together with ways of handling excess heat from power plants.
2. (Staff Report.) "A New River." *Environment*, January–February 1970, page 36. The "new river" of the title is the flowage of heated water that will come from the many nuclear power plants being planned and built around the Great Lakes.

Brief Summary

1. The reacting units of matter are particles (atoms, ions, molecules), and because they are extremely small and invisible, we have a way of counting them (or ratios of them) by weighing larger, visible samples. That is what the mole concept is about.

2. A formula weight of a pure chemical tells us how relatively heavier or lighter are its individual formula units compared with the atoms in carbon-12. It is calculated by totalling the atomic weights of all the atoms in the formula.

3. The gram-formula weight—the mole—is determined by calculating the substance's formula weight and writing "grams" after that number.

4. A mole of one substance has as many formula units (regardless of their exact identity or their individual, very small weights) as a mole of anything else. (The number of formula units involved in a mole is large—6.023×10^{23}—and has the name Avogadro's number.)

5. There are three states of matter—solid, liquid, and gas—and the kinetic-molecular theory describes the motions of atoms or molecules in these states.

6. When the particles of a substance are made to move with a greater average energy we say that the substance has become heated.

7. Spontaneous reactions that occur rapidly enough are sources of useful energy, including heat.

8. The rate of a chemical change depends on several factors, including the nature of the reactants, their concentration, the presence of a catalyst, and the temperature. (You should be able to make an explanatory statement about each factor.)

9. Most reactions, even spontaneous reactions, require that reactants be activated first, and the minimum energy needed for this is called the energy of activation.

Problems and Exercises

1. In order to solve practical weight-relation problems with ease, you should practice handling certain routine operations. One of these is the calculation of formula weights from formulas and atomic weights. For practice, calculate formula weights for each of the following compounds. Use atomic weights to nearest whole numbers, but for chlorine use 35.5.

Set 1	Set 2	Set 3
(a) H_2O	H_2S	NH_3
(b) BF_3	$AlCl_3$	$MgBr_2$
(c) $(NH_4)_2SO_4$	$Ca(NO_3)_2$	$Ca(H_2PO_4)_2$
(d) $Mg_3(BO_3)_2$	$Mn(H_2PO_4)_2$	$Ca(ClO_4)_2$

Answers to Set 1: (a) 18; (b) 68; (c) 132; (d) 190.

2. Another important operation is the calculation of the number of moles of a compound present in any particular sample size. Calculate the number of moles in the following samples. Use the values of formula weights calculated in Problem 1.

Set 1	Set 2	Set 3
(a) 9 g H_2O	68 g H_2S	34 g NH_3
(b) 17 g BF_3	13.3 g $AlCl_3$	1.84 g $MgBr_2$
(c) 10.56 g $(NH_4)_2SO_4$	98.4 g $Ca(NO_3)_2$	163.8 g $Ca(H_2PO_4)_2$
(d) 285 g $Mg_3(BO_3)_2$	272.8 g $Mn(H_2PO_4)_2$	286.8 g $Ca(ClO_4)_2$

Answers to Set 1: (a) 0.5 mole; (b) 0.25 mole; (c) 0.8 mole; (d) 1.5 mole.

3. A third operation that is useful is the calculation of the number of grams present in any given number of moles of a compound. For practice, calculate the number of grams present in each sample.

Set 1	Set 2	Set 3
(a) 0.2 mole H_2O	0.1 mole H_2S	0.3 mole NH_3
(b) 0.8 mole BF_3	2 mole $AlCl_3$	5 mole $MgBr_2$
(c) 0.001 mole $(NH_4)_2SO_4$	0.03 mole $Ca(NO_3)_2$	0.001 mole $Ca(H_2PO_4)_2$
(d) 2.4 mole $Mg_3(BO_3)_2$	1.6 mole $Mn(H_2PO_4)_2$	2.39 mole $Ca(ClO_4)_2$

Answers to Set 1: (a) 3.6 g; (b) 54.4 g; (c) 0.132 g; (d) 456 g.

4. A situation in which operations such as the above occur might be one of the

industrial syntheses of chlorine. Sodium hydroxide ($NaOH$: "lye") and hydrogen are economically important by-products.[9] The reaction may be written as:

$$2NaCl + 2H_2O \xrightarrow[\text{current}]{\text{electric}} 2NaOH + H_2\uparrow + Cl_2\uparrow$$
$$\text{(electrolysis)}$$

(Use 35.5 as the atomic weight of Cl in working out the following questions.)
   (a) How much sodium hydroxide would form from 2 moles of sodium chloride; in moles? In grams?
   (b) How much chlorine would be produced from 2 moles of sodium chloride; in moles? In grams?
   (c) How much sodium chloride would disappear if 1 mole of hydrogen were produced, in moles? In grams?

5. Consider the reaction of hydrogen with oxygen to produce water:

$$2H_2 + O_2 \longrightarrow 2H_2O$$

   If 2 g of hydrogen were allowed to react with 32 g oxygen
   (a) Would any oxygen be left over, unreacted? (If so, how much in grams?)
   (b) Would any hydrogen go unused? (If so, how much, in grams?)
   (c) How much water would form, in moles? In grams?

6. Consider the reaction of sulfur and oxygen to produce sulfur trioxide, SO_3.

$$2S + 3O_2 \longrightarrow 2SO_3$$

   If 64 g of sulfur were mixed with 64 g of oxygen
   (a) Which reactant could be entirely consumed?
   (b) How much of the other reactant would be left over, in moles? In grams?
   (c) How much sulfur trioxide would form, in moles? In grams?

7. Write balanced equations to symbolize the following reactions:
   (a) Sodium chloride reacts with silver nitrate to form silver chloride and sodium nitrate.
   (b) Sulfur burns in air (oxygen) to give sulfur dioxide.
   (c) Magnesium reacts with nitrogen (N_2) to give magnesium nitride (Mg_3N_2).
   (d) Iron reacts with oxygen to form iron (III) oxide (Fe_2O_3).

8. The following thought questions are based on the principles of the kinetic-molecular theory as we have studied them. Answer them from a "molecule's-eye view." That is, phrase your answers in terms of what individual molecules can be expected to do. Note that all questions are phrased as "how" questions.
   (a) How does warm water evaporate faster than cold water?

[9] From the late 1940s and thereafter the principal industrial technique for this reaction required mercury, and literally thousands of pounds of mercury have "leaked" into the environment from the operation of chlor-alkali plants. Although certainly not the only sources of mercury pollution, these plants were major sources until about 1970 when two plants near Detroit were blamed for mercury pollution of Lake St. Clair and Lake Erie. Mercury pollution will be discussed further in Chapter 16.

moles, chemical energy, states of matter

(b) How does moisture evaporate faster in a breeze than in still air?

(c) How does the evaporation of moisture from the skin cool it?

(*Hint:* Molecules at any given temperature do not all have the same velocities. Some move faster and some slower than the average. Which of these, the faster or the slower, are more likely to escape? Which are left behind?)

(d) How will crushed ice melt faster than the same amount in one block?

(e) How is the energy of the combustion of bunsen burner gas able to make itself felt by melting a chunk of ice in a beaker? That is, how do we get from rapidly moving molecules in the flame to more rapidly moving water molecules?

(f) Explain *how* a mercury column in a thermometer is forced to rise when it is warmed.

9. At room temperature, nitrogen (N_2) is a gas; water is a liquid; and sodium chloride is a solid. What do these facts tell you about the relative strengths of electrical forces of attraction in these three substances?

10. How does the kinetic-molecular theory describe the three states of matter?

11. Explain *how* the pressure of a confined gas increases with increasing temperature. (Use the "molecule's-eye view.")

12. Explain how raising the temperature of a reaction usually accelerates it.

13. What is a catalyst, what does energy of activation mean, and what effect does a catalyst of a reaction have on the energy of activation?

chapter 5 nonmetallic elements of the biosphere

Trace amounts of the ions of several metals are essential to life, but the bulk of matter in plants and animals is made from just a few nonmetallic elements, principally carbon, hydrogen, oxygen, nitrogen, phosphorus, and sulfur. In the last chapter we encountered oxygen, O_2, many times. Oxygen is required for respiration by most animals in its elemental, uncombined form. Certain bacteria "fix" elemental nitrogen, N_2, and change it into nitrogen compounds that are used by plants and then animals. The others cited—carbon, hydrogen, phosphorus, and sulfur—are used in life, together with oxygen and nitrogen, in the molecules of such vital substances as proteins, lipids, nucleic acids, enzymes, and hormones. If we add silicon to our list and combine it with oxygen, we account for an enormous portion of the earth's crust, the rocks composed of silicates.

In this chapter we shall survey some of the chemical properties of those major non-metallic elements that are particularly relevant in both beneficial and harmful ways to the molecular basis of the biosphere, the living individual organisms wherever they are, their communities, ecosystems, and whole environments.[1] Our first, preliminary look at some of the important cycles of nature will occur in this chapter, and to take this look we must consider the major constituents of the great blanket of air above us whose composition is given in Table 5.1.

[1] Excluded from this chapter are the Halogens (Group 7), Noble Gases (Group 0), and hydrogen. The oxide of hydrogen, water, is discussed in Chapter 6, and the hydrides of carbon and related compounds form the subjects of organic chemistry.

Table 5.1 Composition of Clean, Dry Air (near sea-level)

Component	Formula	Concentration[a]
MAJOR COMPONENTS		
Nitrogen	N_2	79.085%
Oxygen	O_2	20.946%
MINOR COMPONENTS		
Oxides of Carbon		
Carbon Dioxide	CO_2	320 ppm
Carbon Monoxide	CO	0.1 ppm
Oxides of Nitrogen		
Nitrous Oxide	N_2O	0.5 ppm
Nitrogen Dioxide	NO_2	0.02 ppm
Oxides of Sulfur		
Sulfur Dioxide	SO_2	1 ppm
Noble Gases		
Helium	He	5.24 ppm
Neon	Ne	18.18 ppm
Argon	Ar	9340 ppm (0.934%)
Krypton	Kr	1.14 ppm
Xenon	Xe	0.087 ppm
Miscellaneous		
Ammonia	NH_3	0 to trace
Methane	CH_4	2 ppm
Hydrogen	H_2	0.5 ppm
Ozone	O_3	0.02 to 0.07 ppm (seasonal variations)

[a] Percents are vol/vol percents; 10,000 ppm = 1%.

the oxygen family   The members of this family and some of their compounds are listed and described in Table 5.2. All the atoms in the oxygen family have outside energy shells of six electrons, which explains how these elements form compounds with similar formulas. For example, their compounds with hydrogen—their *hydrides*—are all of the form H_2X (Table 5.2). Some of their oxides are of the form XO_2, e.g., O_3 (ozone), SO_2, SeO_2, TeO_2, and PoO_2. (Other oxides of these elements are also known, e.g., sulfur trioxide, SO_3.) Our study of this family will be limited mostly to oxygen, sulfur, and some oxides.

oxygen   **occurrence of oxygen.** Oxygen is the most abundant element on our planet. Its nuclei account for almost 50% of the estimated weight of the earth's crust, and they are about one-fourth of the nuclei in living things. The world's lakes and oceans are nearly 90% oxygen by weight. In clean air over the oceans between latitudes 50° north and 60° south the oxygen content is

nonmetallic elements of the biosphere

Table 5.2 The Oxygen Family. Group 6

Element	Symbol	Melting Point (°C)	Boiling Point (°C)	Appearance (at room temperature and atmospheric pressure)	Hydrides		Oxides	
					Formula	B. Pt. (°C)	Formula	B. Pt. (°C)
Oxygen	O	−218	−183	colorless gas	H_2O	100°	O_3 (ozone)	−112°
Sulfur	S	113[a]	445	yellow, brittle solid	H_2S	−61°	SO_2 SO_3	−10° −45°
Selenium	Se	217	685	bluish-gray metal	H_2Se	−42°	SeO_2 SeO_3	m. pt. $>$ 300° (sublimes) m. pt. 118°
Tellurium	Te	452	1390	silvery-white metal	H_2Te	−2°	TeO TeO_3	decomposes decomposes
Polonium	Po	254	962	an intensely radioactive metal (an emitter of α- and γ-rays); a half gram sample in a capsule would heat to 500°C.	—	—	PoO_2	decomposes

[a]Elemental sulfur exists in more than one crystalline form. In rhombic crystals (α-form) it melts at 113°C; in monoclinic needles (β-form) it melts at 119°C; and in a noncrystalline, amorphous form it softens and melts at about 120°C.

20.946% by volume. Essentially no change in this percentage has been detected since 1910, even though an enormous amount of petroleum and coal has been burned since then. Our planet's supply of oxygen is huge. Geochemist Wallace Broecker (Columbia University) estimates that in the air above each square meter of the earth's surface are 60,000 moles of oxygen.

nature's regeneration of oxygen. a preliminary look at photosynthesis. Oxygen is consumed principally in three ways: respiration, decay, and combustion. Respiration is the set of events whereby a plant or animal removes a gas from the surroundings, transfers it to its circulatory system (if there is one), transports it to cells needing it, and exchanges it for waste products. Both animals and higher plants take oxygen from the air or from water (by marine organisms) and deliver carbon dioxide as waste.

Decay, a slow change that also uses oxygen, converts the complex molecules of living things back to "dust," to simple, low-energy molecules.

Combustion or burning, of course, is the rapid reaction of oxygen with organic materials and fuels to produce heat and simple molecules like water and carbon dioxide.

All three changes—respiration, decay, combustion—release carbon dioxide and other substances. Nature recycles its raw materials. Plants that have the green pigment called chlorophyll are capable during daylight hours of taking "waste" carbon dioxide, water, and minerals and making new plant materials and oxygen—more oxygen than they need for respiration. The long sequence of chemical reactions involved is, overall, endothermic. Sunlight is the source of the needed energy, and that is why the change is called *photosynthesis* (light-synthesis). A considerably oversimplified statement of photosynthesis in equation form is

$$CO_2 + H_2O + \text{solar energy} \longrightarrow (CH_2O) + O_2$$

(a building unit for sugars, starch and cellulose)

Respiration, decay, and combustion, in a highly simplified statement, are little more than the reverse of photosynthesis:

$$(CH_2O) + O_2 \longrightarrow CO_2 + H_2O + \text{heat}$$

the oxygen cycle. According to W. S. Broecker, the plants of the world, including oceanic plants such as algae, produce each year an average of eight moles of oxygen per square meter of earth surface. Virtually the entire production is eventually used up again by decay, respiration, and combustion. Broecker estimates that for every 15 million moles of oxygen in the atmosphere, one year's *net* oxygen production is not over one mole. There is a

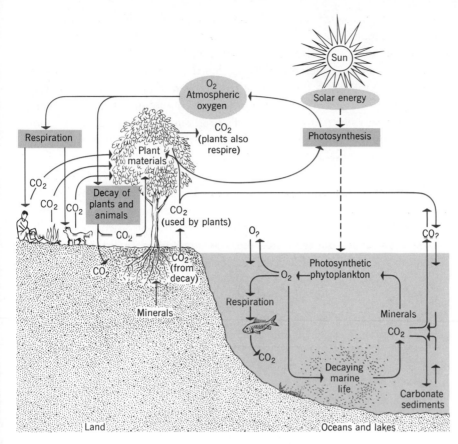

Fig. 5.1 The oxygen cycle. Included in the figure, and inseparable from the oxygen cycle, are the principal natural sources and uses of carbon dioxide. (Not included here, is the production of carbon dioxide by the combustion of fossil fuels.)

nearly perfect balance, then, in oxygen production and consumption that is easily viewed as a cycle, the *oxygen cycle,* in nature, illustrated in Fig. 5.1.

The two equations given above also include carbon dioxide, which makes the oxygen cycle inseparable from a *carbon cycle,* and its main features are given in Fig. 5.1 also.

could we run out of oxygen? One of the questions in circulation during the mounting concern over the environment was "Will we run out of oxygen?" Photosynthesis by oceanic plankton, algae and diatoms is inhibited by trace amounts of DDT. Traces of organic mercury compounds—as low as 1 ppb—also inhibit photosynthesis in plankton. What if the poisons that we send into the oceans were to reduce or stop photosynthesis. The estimates vary, but from 50–80% of the earth's photosynthetic activity is done by the lowly microscopic plants of the oceans. Geochemist Wallace Broecker calculates, however, that our oxygen supply cannot run out. If we burned the entire world's supply of fossil fuels (petroleum materials and coal) we would use no more than 3% of the atmospheric oxygen. Even if photosynthesis were suddenly to cease, while bacteria and animals were to use oxygen to oxidize all carbon-containing material in living things, in soil humus, and in oceanic deeps, less than 1% of the atmospheric oxygen would be used up. What would be most serious about a reduced rate of photosynthesis, says Broecker, is the resulting reduction in the world's food supply, not its oxygen supply, which is reason enough to decry any carelessness about those factors that reduce photosynthesis.

oxidation and reduction. Oxygen is an *oxidizing agent*. Any substance that it successfully attacks, to continue our introduction of terms, we say is *oxidized*. We met the word *oxidation* before, in Chapter 3, where we studied the reaction of sodium with chlorine. We learned there the most general definitions for both oxidation and reduction:

Oxidation: loss of electron(s);

To be oxidized: to lose electron(s) (either the entire control of electrons or part of that control);

Oxidizing agent: a chemical that can cause oxidation;
or an oxidant

Reduction: gain of electron(s);

To be reduced: to gain electron(s) (either fully or partially);

Reducing agent: a chemical that can cause reduction.
or a reductant

It was easy to see these words applied to the chemicals sodium and chlorine because the gain and loss of an electron clearly happens. A full transfer of the electron occurs from sodium atoms, which are oxidized, to chlorine atoms, which are reduced.

Very often, especially in dealing with organic and biochemical materials, it is more difficult in an oxidation-reduction reaction to tell just what is oxidized and what is reduced. For this reason we shall learn two sets of simple rules about this kind of a reaction:

Oxidation: a molecule is oxidized if it
(a) gains oxygen atoms, or
(b) loses hydrogen atoms, or
(c) obviously loses electrons.

Reduction: a molecule is reduced if it
(a) loses oxygen atoms, or
(b) gains hydrogen atoms, or
(c) obviously gains electrons.

nonmetallic elements of the biosphere

Examples

$$2C + O_2 \longrightarrow 2CO$$ carbon is oxidized (it gains oxygen)
                                    oxygen is therefore reduced

$$2N_2 + 3H_2 \longrightarrow 2NH_3$$ nitrogen is reduced (it gains hydrogen)
                                    hydrogen is therefore oxidized

If you identify one reactant in an equation as, say, the oxidizing agent, then another reactant *must* be the reducing agent. A reaction involving the one action *must* involve the other also. (Electrons in chemicals cannot leave something without going to something. They do not disappear into space.)

Oxygen is not the only oxidant in air. In smog some oxygen is converted to the most powerful oxidant in our lower atmosphere, ozone.

smog. The word "smog," a contraction of smoke-fog, was coined in 1911 by Harold Des Voeux some time after a dreadful air pollution disaster killed roughly a thousand people in Glasgow, Scotland. Today the word means polluted air in which visibility is reduced and which contains eye and lung irritants. There are two types of smog, the London type and the Los Angeles type. They share some features but there are important differences. For either to occur there must be a *thermal inversion*. Normally the atmosphere becomes cooler as you go to higher altitudes. In this circumstance, air near the ground, being warmer and therefore less dense, naturally tends to rise (carrying pollutants to higher altitudes where they are dispersed). But if air near the ground is colder than air above it (as in a thermal inversion), the colder, more dense air will stay right there, near the ground, along with its pollutants. One way by which an inversion occurs involves the radiation of earth heat to outer space in hours of darkness when the ground loses heat more rapidly than it gets it (from the sun). The air closest to the ground therefore becomes colder (and more dense) than air higher up. In other words a thermal inversion has been established. If the next day is relatively windless and especially if it is wintertime and the earth with the air nearest it does not become warmed enough, the inversion is not wiped out and on the following night it simply becomes worse. That is why the worst of the London-type smog episodes occur in the months of November through January, months when home-heating units and power plants fueled by coal or heavy oil are especially active in emitting pollutants. It takes the return of winds to terminate the inversion and disperse the pollutants.

An inversion will also occur if a cold (and therefore more dense) mass of air moves into a region resting in a basin-like landform (e.g., the Los Angeles basin; Denver, Colorado). Being more dense, the cold air mass will sink toward ground level displacing warmer, less dense air upwards. Such

Table 5.3 Major Types of Smog

Characteristics	London Type	Los Angeles Type (Photochemical Smog)
When peak intensities occur:	Early in the morning; wintertime	Around noontime
Ambient temperature	30 to 40°F	75 to 90°F
Humidity	Humid and foggy	Low humidity
Thermal inversion	Close to ground	Overhead (varies)
Causes irritation principally to:	Bronchia and lungs (also eyes)	Eyes (but also bronchia and lungs)
Chief irritants	Soot and other particulates; sulfur oxides	Ozone; PAN; aldehydes; oxides of nitrogen. Also sulfur dioxide and particulates. (Carbon monoxide, which has no odor, is also present.)
Major source of irritants	Coal fires	Vehicular traffic
Other Effects	Severe haze	Haze; severe damage to crops, pines, ornamentals; cracking of rubber
General chemical feature	Reducing atmosphere	Oxidizing atmosphere

an air mass may "slide" down the slopes of surrounding mountains or be generated out over the ocean. Either way establishes an inversion.

The two types of smogs are compared and contrasted in Table 5.3. The principal irritants in Los Angeles type smogs are ozone and a family of compounds collectively labeled PAN (which will be discussed in Chapter 10). The death-dealing pollutants in London-type smogs are oxides of sulfur and particulate matter. (These occur in Los Angeles smogs, too.) In the most infamous smog of all time, London's great killer smog of 1952, over 4000 people died. Traffic came to a halt because drivers could not see beyond their windshields!

Los Angeles type smog is called *photochemical smog* because many of its pollutants are produced by sun-powered chemical changes that take place among the primary pollutants—oxides of nitrogen, unburned hydrocarbons, sulfur oxides, particulates, and carbon monoxide. Ozone, in particular, is produced by photochemical changes, and the ozone concentration or "ozone level" is a criterion of severity of Los Angeles type smogs. In the smog emergency plans of the Los Angeles Air Pollution Control District, a First Alert is sounded when the ozone level reaches 0.5 ppm, which happened 17 times in the period of 1966 to 1969.

ozone, O_3. Ozone (from the Greek *ozein*, to smell) is responsible for the peculiar odor sometimes noticed near electrical machines and after severe electrical storms. Electrical discharges convert small amounts of oxygen in air to what might be called the oxide of oxygen, ozone. Ozone's odor can be detected by most people at a level of 0.02 ppm.

effects of ozone on people. It would be hazardous for us to be exposed continuously to an ozone level greater than only 1 ppm. Fortunately, the ozone concentration at ground level seldom becomes high enough to be more than irritating to people, at least on a short-term, day-by-day basis.

In one experiment a human volunteer was exposed for 2 hours to an ozone level of 1.5 to 2 ppm in a warm room. He experienced loss of coordination, inability to express his thoughts, and some respiratory symptoms. At levels more likely to be experienced in smog—at levels of 0.2–0.5 ppm—volunteers experienced no symptoms although they could detect the odor of ozone. (What the long-term effects of ozone on health are is still not known. However, children in Los Angeles County are warned not to run, skip, or jump when the ozone level is 0.35 ppm.)

In one air monitoring survey in Los Angeles in November, 1967, the maximum hourly average ozone level was 0.26 ppm. In the Los Angeles County smog emergency plans, a Second Alert would be called if the ozone level reached 1 ppm. It has not yet happened. Only during the severe smog episode of 1956 did the ozone level in Los Angeles get as high as 0.99 ppm. In contrast, in polar regions where the air is presumably cleanest, the ozone level is between 0.01 and 0.03 ppm.

The ozone in smog is produced by a complex series of reactions that involve the oxides of nitrogen and hydrocarbons (unburned gasoline), which are also important pollutants. When we study the nitrogen oxides later in the chapter we shall see how ozone can be produced at ground level in urban areas. Ozone is routinely made in the stratosphere, where it performs a most beneficial service to us, but stratospheric ozone does not diffuse to our altitudes.

ozone cycle in the stratosphere. In the stratosphere, the region of the atmosphere roughly 7 to 30 miles up, the ozone concentration is higher. When high energy ultraviolet radiation from the sun hits the stratosphere and encounters oxygen molecules, it starts reactions that change oxygen to ozone. The light energy first splits oxygen molecules to atoms:

$$O_2 + \text{ultraviolet light} \longrightarrow O + O$$

These combine with unchanged oxygen molecules to form ozone:

$$O_2 + O \longrightarrow O_3 + \text{heat}$$

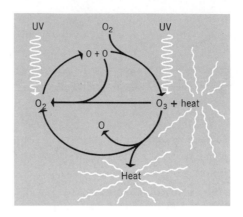

Fig. 5.2   The ozone cycle in the stratosphere which, on balance, converts lethal ultraviolet rays from the sun into heat.

Or they may interact with ozone molecules to produce oxygen:

$$O_3 + O \longrightarrow 2O_2$$

Thus, the ozone does not accumulate and very little if any makes its way
into the lower atmosphere. Eventually, each ozone molecule is struck by
ultraviolet light and broken to oxygen molecules and oxygen atoms. But heat
is also liberated.

$$O_3 + \text{ultraviolet light} \longrightarrow O_2 + O + \text{heat}$$

An ozone cycle therefore exists in the stratosphere, Fig. 5.2, which would
be little else than just interesting except for one thing. This cycle converts
all of the sun's more powerful frequencies of ultraviolet light into heat and
thereby protects life on earth from these lethal rays. Life as we know it would
be impossible without the ozone layer of the stratosphere. As long as the
ozone remains there, it is our friend.

effects of ozone on plants and materials. Plants are very sensitive to ozone
with some being afflicted by an ozone level of only 0.03 ppm for 8 hours.
As is so common with pollutants, one will *potentiate* the other—make the
other more potent. Thus when sulfur dioxide is present, ozone causes injury
to plants more rapidly. Because of ozone some areas of southern California
will no longer sustain crops of leafy vegetables. Whole stands of pines in
the surrounding mountains are succumbing. Crops of certain species of
spinach, radishes, muskmelon, beans, peanuts, potatoes, tomatoes, tobacco,
rye, oats, and buckwheat will suffer at least 20% injury with an 8-hour
exposure at 0.05–0.15 ppm ozone. (The data are from the National Air
Pollution Control Administration.) At levels of 0.10 to 0.35 ppm (for 8 hours)

nonmetallic elements of the biosphere

species of broccoli, corn, beets, onions, peas, cotton, and many others experience 20% injury.

Ozone attacks cotton, nylon, and polyester fabrics when the humidity is high (but not appreciably when the air is very dry). It causes many dyes to fade. Ozone attacks rubber causing rubber hoses and tires to deteriorate and crack (unless they contain antioxidants).

A few cities use ozone instead of chlorine to purify and deodorize their water supplies and to treat sewage. Ozone is highly reactive toward organic substances including, of course, disease and odor-causing microbes.

occurrence of sulfur. Sulfur, a brittle, yellow, nonmetallic element just below sulfur oxygen in the periodic table, was known in ancient times as brimstone ("burning stone"). It ranks 14th in abundance at 0.052 percent in the earth's crust. Large deposits of native sulfur occur in Louisiana, Texas, Sicily, and a few other places. Several sulfur-containing compounds are among the minerals and ores of the earth—substances such as those described in Table 5.4. Sulfuric acid, H_2SO_4, is the most important compound of sulfur commercially. A country's consumption of sulfuric acid is regarded by some economists as as valid a gauge of its economic activity and prosperity as its steel production. About 85% of the sulfur produced in the United States is converted to sulfuric acid of which 50% goes into fertilizers.

Sulfur is a minor but essential constituent in nearly all proteins. The proteins of hair, fur, and feathers are particularly rich in combined sulfur.

To our great discomfiture sulfur compounds are present in both coal and crude oil, and when these fuels are burned their sulfur is converted to sulfur

Table 5.4 **Important Compounds of Sulfur**

SULFIDE ORES		ACIDS	
Pyrite	FeS_2	H_2SO_4	Sulfuric acid
Chalcopyrite	$CuFeS_2$	H_2SO_3	Sulfurous acid (unstable)
Galena	PbS	H_2S	Hydrogen sulfide
Sphalerite	ZnS		

SULFATES (compounds derived from sulfuric acid having either the hydrogen sulfate ion, HSO_4^-, or the sulfate ion, SO_4^{2-}.)

OXIDES

Sulfur dioxide	SO_2		
Sulfur trioxide	SO_3		

Examples: $CaSO_4 \cdot 2H_2O$ gypsum
$BaSO_4$ barite

SULFITES (compounds derived from sulfurous acid having either the hydrogen sulfite ion, HSO_3^-, or the sulfite ion, SO_3^{2-}.)

Examples: $NaHSO_3$ sodium hydrogen sulfite
Na_2SO_3 sodium sulfite

dioxide and traces of sulfur trioxide. Middle Eastern crude is 3.5% to 5% sulfur; Alaskan oil, low in sulfur, is referred to as "sweet" crude. Soft coal has from 0.5 to 5% sulfur; 40 to 60% of this sulfur is present as pyrite (iron sulfide), the rest as organic sulfur. (Only the pyrite sulfur is readily removable.)

the oxides of sulfur and their part in air pollution

Both sulfur dioxide, SO_2, and sulfur trioxide, SO_3, are injurious to living things and materials such as paints, metals, concrete and stone, textiles, leather, and paper. Fortunately, it is sulfur dioxide and not sulfur trioxide that is produced in the greater abundance, because sulfur trioxide reacts rapidly with moisture in the air to form highly corrosive sulfuric acid mists.

$$SO_3 + H_2O \longrightarrow H_2SO_4$$
$$\text{sulfuric acid}$$

Sulfur dioxide also reacts with water, but the acid it forms is not quite as corrosive. (See Chapter 7.)

$$SO_2 + H_2O \longrightarrow H_2SO_3$$
$$\text{sulfurous acid}$$

Both oxides of sulfur have sharp, pungent, irritating odors, but the sulfur trioxide level is normally too low to be smelled (but high enough to be important in the deterioration of metals and building materials). Most people can taste the sulfur dioxide in air when it is at a level or concentration of 0.3 to 1 ppm. Its irritating odor becomes obvious at only 3 ppm. The irritant properties of sulfur oxides are, however, enhanced 2 to 3 times by the presence of the suspended solids in polluted air called *particulates*. Fortunately for human comfort, SO_2 levels almost never exceed 1 ppm except near power plants, refineries, and smelters. (London's terrible smog of 1952 had an SO_2 level of 1.34 ppm, mean daily average, ten times normal.)[2] The levels fluctuate widely according to the city, the time of day, the month, and the season, but Chicago (one of the most SO_2 afflicted of cities) has an SO_2 level above 1 ppm only about 0.2% of the time.

This does not absolve sulfur dioxide. People who live not far down wind from a power plant burning high-sulfur fuel (a decreasing practice among power plants because of new regulations) or near oil refineries or smelters may sometimes breathe air with 3 ppm SO_2 or more. Besides SO_2, smog has many other possible irritants we shall consider later.

If *temporary* human discomfiture were the only result of smog, air pollution would be a less serious problem. Sulfur dioxide, however, is harmful in many ways. It damages any plants having leaves with a high metabo-

[2] The concentration of particulates was 4,500 micrograms per cubic meter (mean daily average), also about ten times normal.

lism—grapes, squash, cotton, alfalfa, grains, apple trees, and white pines, to name a few. In a one to two mile radius around the great Falconbridge nickel smelters of Sudbury, Ontario, Canada, there is scarcely a tree except for some severely damaged (but still living) red oaks and red maples. (Some of the important nickel-bearing ores of our planet are complex compounds of sulfur, often found together with copper and iron. When metals are extracted from these ores, the stack gases contain high levels of sulfur dioxide.) Perhaps the worst property of sulfur dioxide is that in the presence of sunlight, oxygen, and oxides of nitrogen (other pollutants in smog), sulfur dioxide is oxidized to sulfur trioxide. In humid air sulfur trioxide changes to the highly corrosive sulfuric acid mists mentioned earlier.

$$SO_2 + O_2 \xrightarrow[\substack{\text{other pollutants} \\ \text{(e.g., oxides of} \\ \text{nitrogen)}}]{\text{sunlight}} SO_3 \xrightarrow{H_2O} H_2SO_4$$

(In fact, one of the methods for making sulfuric acid industrially, the lead-chamber process, converts sulfur dioxide to sulfuric acid by using as catalysts just those oxides of nitrogen (NO and NO_2) that are also in polluted air.) Much of the damage to materials and property caused by the sulfur compounds of polluted air is the result of the actions of sulfuric acid that forms indirectly from sulfur dioxide.

In the late 1960s and early 1970s Norway suffered from acid rain originating from the burning of high-sulfur coal in other countries. High on the list of suspects were the great industries of England's Midlands and Germany's Ruhr. Tall stacks erected to solve local pollution problems sent acid mists into wind currents that carried them northward where they dumped their moisture load along with the pollutants. Lakes of southern Norway became less habitable to fish, and Norwegian biologists feared that trout could no longer be maintained in Norway's southern lakes.

When humid air is polluted with sulfur oxides it can be more corrosive than sea water. In recent years, about a third of the annual replacement cost of steel rails in England is attributed to the indirect action of sulfur oxides. Some of our best building stones—marble, slate, limestone—are attacked by polluted air. Some of our finest buildings, cathedrals, and monuments are suffering serious deterioration. Cleopatra's Needle, a famous stone obelisk suffered less decay in the 3000 or more years it stood in Alexandria, Egypt, than it has endured in the some 80 years it has stood in the humid, smoggy, acid air of London.

what can be done about the oxides of sulfur in the environment? As long as we continue to use petroleum products and coal as fuel we must contend with sulfur. Most of the coal used to generate electricity in the United States has an average of 2.5% sulfur, but many large Eastern states and cities have or soon will have laws limiting the sulfur content of any fuel to 1% or less.

Some sulfur can be removed from coal, but probably less than half of the coal mined for the eastern market can be desulfurized to such levels (Bureau of Mines survey, 1970). Coal sulfur that is present as iron pyrites (see Table 5.4) can be removed, but roughly half of the sulfur in coal occurs as organic compounds not economically taken out. By 1980 the U. S. Bureau of Mines expects that large-scale coal conversion plants will be operating to change coal to a liquid fuel resembling crude oil or to a gaseous fuel like natural gas. These would be low-sulfur materials.

The sulfur content of petroleum can be reduced at refineries to the low limits being set by city and state laws. It costs 65 to 85 cents a barrel to desulfurize Venezuelan crude from 1.5 to 0.5% at Creole Petroleum's Amuay refinery (Judibana, Venezuela; 500,000 barrels per day capacity).

Oxides of sulfur can be removed from stack gases. In one approach these gases interact with wet limestone (mostly calcium carbonate). Sulfites and sulfates of calcium form and carbon dioxide is sent out.

the nitrogen family The members of this family are given in Table 5.5. We shall study only nitrogen here. Compounds of phosphorus will be studied later when we examine phosphoric acid, H_3PO_4, and its salts, called phosphates.

nitrogen Nitrogen, a gas that we cannot see, smell, or taste, is present in air at a concentration of about 78% (by volume). In its structure ($:N\equiv N:$) each nitrogen has an outer octet, and under ordinary conditions nitrogen reacts with almost no other substances. We need it in air to dilute the oxygen, and we also need it as a source of compounds of nitrogen for plants.

Table 5.5 **The Nitrogen Family. Group 7**

Name	Symbol	M. Pt. (°C)	B. Pt. (°C)	Important Types of Compounds
Nitrogen	N_2	-210	-196	Nitrates (fertilizers, explosives) Oxides (air pollutants) Ammonia (fertilizer). (See Table 5.6.)
Phosphorus	P	44	281	Phosphates and polyphosphates (detergents, fertilizers)
Arsenic	As	815	610	Arsenates (pesticides)
Antimony	Sb	631	1440	Lead-antimony mixtures (alloys) for storage batteries and type metal
Bismuth	Bi	271	1420	In mixtures with other metals: low melting alloys for automatic fire alarms and sprinkler systems

nonmetallic elements of the biosphere

Table 5.6   Important Compounds of Nitrogen

Inorganic Compounds

OXIDES		ACIDS	
N_2O	nitrogen(I) oxide (nitrous oxide;[a] laughing gas)	HNO_2	nitrous acid (unstable)
		HNO_3	nitric acid
NO	nitrogen(II) oxide (nitric oxide[a])	NITRITES (compounds derived from nitrous acid having the nitrite ion, NO_2^-)	
NO_2	nitrogen dioxide		
N_2O_5	dinitrogen pentoxide		
		Example: $NaNO_2$ sodium nitrite	
AMMONIA AND AMMONIUM SALTS		NITRATES (compounds derived from nitric acid having the nitrate ion, NO_3^-)	
NH_3	ammonia		
NH_4NO_3	ammonium nitrate		
		Example: $NaNO_3$ sodium nitrate	

Organic Compounds

Amines (organic derivatives of ammonia)
   Example: $CH_3CH_2NH_2$ ethylamine
Amino acids (building blocks of all proteins)
   One example of about 24: $NH_2CH_2CO_2H$ glycine
Proteins (including all enzymes and many hormones)
Nucleic acids (the chemicals of genes)

[a] These are the commonly used names.

types of nitrogen compounds. Table 5.6 provides a summary of the principal types of nitrogen compounds. Ammonium salts, nitrites, and nitrates all are involved in the lives of plants, and therefore (indirectly), animals. When plants and animals die and decompose, their complex organic nitrogen materials are broken down and returned to the soil and the atmosphere. The nitrogen cycle that exists in nature will be studied in Chapter 20 (Metabolism of Proteins) when we shall be better able to understand how nitrogen nuclei shuttle between the atmosphere and the soils, the seas, the plants, and the animals. In this chapter we shall attend to two of the oxides of nitrogen, NO and NO_2, because they are important pollutants in smog.

When fuels and air are mixed and burned in the cylinders of automobiles or in stationary furnaces (e.g. power plants), very high temperatures result. Under these conditions even normally inert nitrogen (also in the air) will react with oxygen, and the waste gases therefore include nitric oxide, NO. There are several ways by which some nitric oxide is oxidized to nitrogen dioxide. One involves complex interaction with hydrocarbons (as in automobile exhaust). Another uses ozone. In the moments when hot exhaust gases are mixed with and diluted by air, some of the nitric oxide is further changed

the oxides of
nitrogen in the
environment

105

by oxygen to nitrogen dioxide, NO_2. These two oxides are often referred to in the literature of air pollution as the nitrogen oxides and given the general formula, NO_x.

$$N_2 + O_2 \longrightarrow 2NO$$
$$2NO + O_2 \longrightarrow 2NO_2$$

The more villainous of the two is nitrogen dioxide because it is responsible for the production of ozone in the lower atmosphere. It is also the chief cause of the yellowish-brown color normally assumed by the smog over an urban area. Traffic accounts for about 40% and stationary furnaces about 50% of all nitrogen oxides emitted into the air (from data published in 1970 for the United States).

The combined NO_x concentration in severe smog has rarely gone above 3 ppm. One of the remarkable features of smog is the misery caused by such low concentrations of pollutants.

the nitrogen dioxide–ozone cycle. the ozone in photochemical smog. In our earlier study of the Ozone Cycle in the stratosphere we learned that the sun's higher energy ultraviolet rays are converted at those altitudes into heat and do not reach the lower levels where we live. Lower energy ultraviolet rays, however, do filter through, and the nitrogen dioxide molecule is just weakly enough held together that these rays can break it apart to nitric oxide and oxygen atoms:

$$NO_2 \xrightarrow{\text{lower energy UV rays}} NO \ + \ O$$

nitrogen dioxide   nitric oxide   atomic oxygen

The oxygen atoms combine with molecular oxygen to form ozone:

$$O + O_2 + M \longrightarrow O_3 + M^*$$

The letter M stands for any molecule that happens to be nearby; most likely nitrogen or oxygen. M^* stands for an activated, "hot" molecule of M. Without M, the reaction could not produce ozone stable enough to survive even a short time. The newly formed ozone molecule has so much energy that unless it can collide at once with a molecule and transfer some of that energy to the neighbor, the ozone molecule will break apart again to $O_2 + O$.

The newly formed ozone can attack nitric oxide and thereby both are removed:

$$O_3 + NO \longrightarrow NO_2 + O_2$$

nonmetallic elements of the biosphere

The net result would seem to be, again, the conversion of ultraviolet light to heat; but the cycle also establishes a small concentration of ozone. The relations of this cycle are shown in Fig. 5.3.

The cycle, as it stands in Fig. 5.3, does not account for the levels of ozone observed in photochemical smog. These levels probably arise because the hydrocarbons,[3] contributed to smog from unburned gasoline and diesel fuels, indirectly provide a way for newly formed nitric oxide to be re-oxidized to NO_2 without taking out newly formed ozone. If this happens, ozone can accumulate. See Fig. 5.4.

Catalytic amounts of atomic oxygen, known to react very rapidly with hydrocarbons, convert some molecules of the hydrocarbons to very unstable materials. In something of a chain reaction, these unstable intermediates react with the air's more abundant molecular oxygen to produce partly oxidized hydrocarbons. Many of the partly oxidized hydrocarbons are also unstable in air where they form a complex mixture, and some of them can oxidize nitric oxide (NO) to nitrogen dioxide. If nitric oxide is returned to nitrogen dioxide this way, it cannot be returned by reacting with and destroying newly formed ozone and that, roughly, is how the higher ozone levels of photo-chemical smog arise. We have to defer to Chapter 10 ("Hydrocarbons") a more detailed explanation of the reactions of atomic and molecular oxygen with hydrocarbons, and we shall complete our study of smog there.

the carbon family

The members of the carbon family are listed in Table 5.7 together with some of their properties. We shall concentrate our study primarily on carbon and its two oxides and silicon and its various oxides. Certain compounds of lead, which are becoming increasingly serious pollutants, will be discussed in Chapter 10, and how they act as poisons will be described in Chapter 16.

[3] Hydrocarbons are compounds whose molecules are made exclusively of carbon and hydrogen and that comprise gasoline and fuel oil. They will be studied in more detail in Chapter 10. Octane, present in gasoline, has the molecular formula C_8H_{18}.

Table 5.7 **The Carbon Family. Group 4**

Name	Symbol	Density (g/cc; 20°C)	M. Pt. (°C)	B. Pt. (°C)
Carbon	C	3.51 (diamond)	3570	3470 (sublimes)
Silicon	Si	2.33	1414	2355
Germanium	Ge	5.36	959	2700
Tin	Sn	7.29	232	2275
Lead	Pb	11.34	327	1750

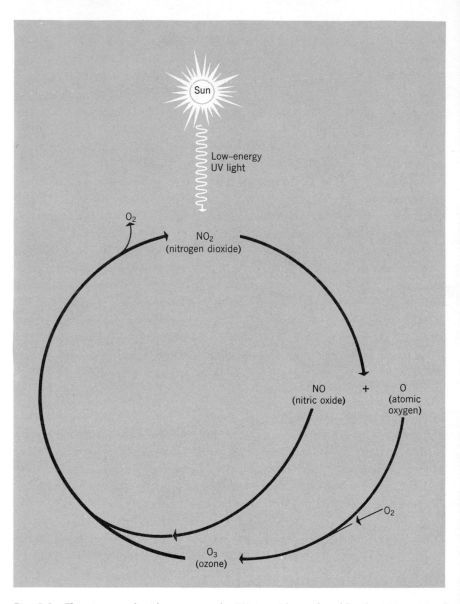

Fig. 5.3 The nitrogen dioxide–ozone cycle. Nitric oxide produced by the UV-energized decomposition of nitrogen dioxide will eventually destroy the ozone produced from the atomic oxygen made in the same decomposition. The arrows are shown of equal thickness to indicate this balance. However, the balance is upset if hydrocarbons are present (Fig. 5.4).

carbon   Pure carbon may exist in principally three forms, as diamonds, graphite, and varieties of carbon black. In hardness these represent a range from one of the hardest to scratch substances known, the diamond, to some of the easiest. These differences are attributed to different crystal structures, illustrated in Fig. 5.5. In a diamond, bonds extend from atom to atom, four single bonds

nonmetallic elements of the biosphere

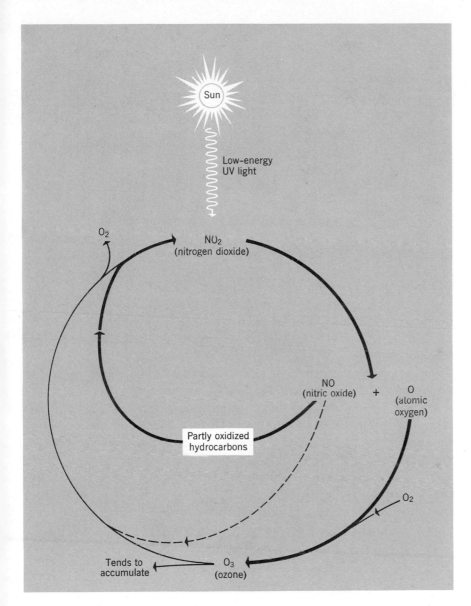

Fig. 5.4 The nitrogen dioxide–ozone cycle when hydrocarbons are present. If oxidation products of hydrocarbons react with newly formed nitric oxide, then newly formed ozone (thicker arrow) cannot as readily be taken out (thinner arrow) and it can accumulate to the levels observed in severe photochemical smog. Automobile exhausts provide much of both the nitrogen dioxide and the hydrocarbons for these events.

from each, each bond equivalent to each other and all very strong. In graphite the carbon atoms are arranged in sheets, and it is relatively easy for slippage between these sheets to occur. Hence, graphite makes an excellent dry lubricant; it is even greasy to the touch. There are many multiple bonds between atoms, and the electrons of these bonds are very mobile.

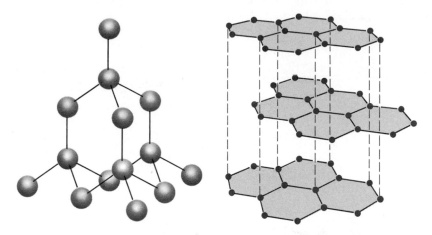

Fig. 5.5   The arrangement of atoms in (a) diamond and (b) graphite.

All outershell electrons in diamond, however, are tied up in bonds. That is why graphite is an excellent conductor of electricity and diamond is not. Sheets and planes of carbon atoms are believed to exist in carbon black, also, but they do not extend as far as in graphite and they are more jumbled together.

Carbon black is made by letting gas burn in an insufficient supply of oxygen and allowing the flame to contact a depositing surface. It is also made simply by heating gas (e.g., methane) to a high temperature in the absence of oxygen. Thousands of tons of carbon black are used each year just for the manufacture of rubber alone, and other uses include the manufacture of paint and printing ink. Sooty smoke also contains carbon particles.

Carbon is a constituent of the molecules of all organic compounds, including, of course, the hydrocarbons found in gasoline and oil. When these are burned in cars, trucks, heating plants, and power plants two oxides of carbon are produced (besides water).

$$\text{Hydrocarbons} + (O_2) \xrightarrow[\text{incomplete}]{\text{if combustion is}} CO_2 + H_2O + CO$$

| (compounds of carbon and hydrogen) | | carbon dioxide (mostly) | | carbon monoxide (traces) |

oxides of carbon

carbon dioxide. CO_2. The principal natural sources of carbon dioxide are the chemical reactions that all plants and animals undergo when they die and decay as well as the reactions of respiration while they are alive, topics introduced earlier (see also Fig. 5.1). Carbon dioxide also enters the atmosphere in large volumes at a few natural gas wells and carbonated springs (e.g., Vichy, France; Geyser Springs, Saratoga). If the gas is cooled and compressed it can be changed into the solid form known as *dry ice*, a solid that vaporizes in air without melting. A familiar use of carbon dioxide is the "CO_2-extinguisher."

Carbon dioxide is not classified as a poison, but since it will not support life, if it is unknowingly allowed to displace oxygen from a room or some other volume (e.g., a silo) living things in there will die.

The principal fates of carbon dioxide in nature are the photosynthetic production of plant materials and the deposition of limestones and dolomites. Until we began to burn fossil fuels at the increasing rates we now use, carbon dioxide released by decay, respiration, and natural fires was largely used up by photosynthesis and any left over went into minerals. The concentration in air was quite steady. The fossil fuels contain carbon photosynthetically fixed eons ago. By our current rate of using these fuels, we add carbon dioxide to the atmosphere more rapidly than it is removed by photosynthesis or by the other great balance wheel of nature, the oceanic-atmospheric exchange. In the last 100 years the amount of carbon dioxide in the atmosphere has increased from an average of 290 ppm to 320 ppm. About 20% of this increase occurred in the 1960s alone. Of the carbon dioxide produced by burning fossil fuels, about one-third has remained, to account for the atmospheric increase, and two-thirds has probably been absorbed by the oceans and (to an entirely unknown extent) by increased vegetation on the planet. (It is known that plants engage in photosynthesis at a more rapid rate when the surrounding air has a higher concentration of carbon dioxide.)

The oceans can help to monitor and control atmospheric carbon dioxide because of the following equilibrium:

$$Ca^{2+} + CO_2 + H_2O \rightleftharpoons CaCO_3\downarrow + 2H^+$$

The ocean is saturated with respect to calcium carbonate ($CaCO_3$), but more calcium ions constantly enter the oceans by way of the rivers of the world whose volumes have come, in part, from water that has percolated through soils and rocks containing calcium ions. Calcium ions can absorb carbon dioxide from the air above the oceans and thus help to keep the carbon dioxide level of the atmosphere down. The ocean's response to an increase in atmospheric carbon dioxide, however, is not swift. The rate is so low that it will take several centuries for the oceans and the atmosphere to come again into equilibrium with respect to carbon dioxide. (The carbon dioxide that goes into coral skeletons as calcium carbonate is produced from organic nutrients metabolized by the living coral and is not taken from the sea water as carbonate ion.)

greenhouse effect. The glass walls and roof of a greenhouse let in sunlight, for photosynthesis, protect the plants from wind, and help to prevent the escape of heat, a factor especially important where winters are cold. One of the effects that carbon dioxide has in the atmosphere is called the greenhouse effect. See Fig. 5.6. While its presence does not stop sunlight from reaching the earth, carbon dioxide does help keep some of the earth's heat

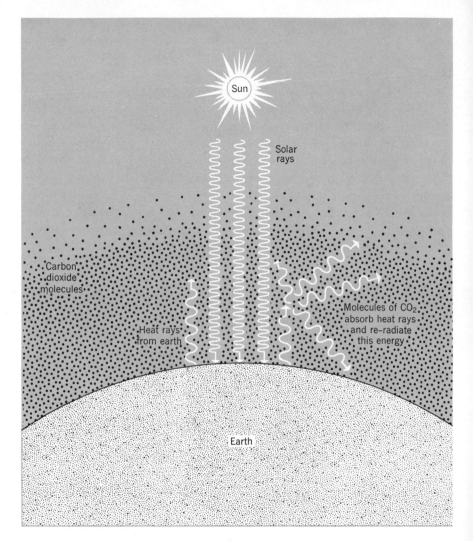

Fig. 5.6   The atmospheric greenhouse effect. The sun's rays are not absorbed by carbon dioxide and they warm the earth. The rays of heat radiated outward from the earth, however, are partly absorbed by carbon dioxide. The now energy-rich carbon dioxide molecules radiate this excess energy equally in all directions, including back toward the earth and out into the lower atmosphere. Thus the lower atmosphere and the earth are kept warmer than they would be in the absence of carbon dioxide. This effect would be (and apparently is being) cancelled—more than cancelled—by the dusts and particulates in air. These reduce by reflection the incoming solar rays before they can warm the earth and its lower atmosphere.

from radiating back to space.[4] The wavelengths of incoming sunlight are not absorbed by carbon dioxide (with minor exceptions), but once the sunlight warms the earth and the earth radiates energy outward, the new wavelengths

[4] Atmospheric carbon dioxide obviously does not protect plants from wind either. The analogy to a greenhouse is really rather poor.

nonmetallic elements of the biosphere

are different. They can be absorbed by atmospheric carbon dioxide, and the molecules of carbon dioxide are made to hold this extra energy momentarily. Then they radiate the energy in all directions, and the earth gets some back. The net effect is that part of the heat escaping the earth is returned and kept within the lower atmosphere. (Atmospheric water vapor also contributes to the greenhouse effect.)

In the period 1885 to 1940, when the rate of consumption of fossil fuels increased drastically, it was presumably the "greenhouse" effect of the added carbon dioxide that raised the average temperature of the earth nearly 1°F. Were this trend to continue and the global temperature average were to rise just a few more degrees, the glacial ice of the Antartic and Greenland would melt, the ocean's levels would rise over 200 feet, and the coastal cities holding half the earth's populations would be flooded. The warming trend stopped, however. Since the early 1940s a sharp cooling trend has set in. In the United States we now have average temperatures about the same as those of the 1830s.

The cooling trend may be caused (at least in part) by a rise in the amount of dust and particles in the stratosphere largely as the result of volcanos. (The stratosphere is the zone roughly between 7 and 30 miles up.) Dust reflects incoming sunlight back to space. According to atmospheric scientist E. W. Barrett (Environmental Science Services Administration), dusts and particles over the entire globe may, on the average, be cutting the planet's available solar energy by one percent.

Dusts created by activities of man (e.g., by the combustion of fuels, or by managing the land so poorly that dust storms can develop) do not reach the stratosphere. The most recent indications are that dusts and particulate matter in the lower atmosphere tend to lower the air temperature. (Of much greater significance are the effects of particulate matter, especially what is emitted from fuel burning devices, on health. In London-type smog disasters, it is the combination of high levels of particulates and sulfur oxides that is particularly hazardous. Sooty particulates, moreover, contain traces of cancer-causing compounds such as benzpyrene (Chapter 10). Over cities the dusts in the air are much more concentrated—10 to 10,000 times—than over rural areas, and it is not uncommon for the central area of a city to receive 30% less sunlight than less populated areas nearby. The monthly dustfall in large cities ranges from 10 to 100 tons per square mile.

carbon monoxide. CO. This colorless, odorless, tasteless gas forms in small amounts when just about anything burns. It is extremely poisonous and it acts without warning. Auto exhaust and poorly vented heating systems are the most dangerous sources of carbon monoxide, which annually kills about 1400 people in the United States, most from space heaters. The idling engine of a small car in a small garage produces a lethal concentration of carbon monoxide in less than 10 minutes. Exposure to a CO-level of 120 ppm for an hour, not impossible in smoke-filled rooms, causes headache, dizziness, and dullness. Inhaled cigarette smoke has 400 ppm carbon monoxide and the smoke from the tip is as high as 20,000 to 40,000 ppm (2 to 5%). It is one factor in the lower average birth weights of babies born of mothers who smoke.

Carbon monoxide levels in major, smog-ridden cities average from 1 to 10 ppm, but they may reach 100 ppm in tunnels, garages, and in densely packed, stalled traffic. In a 1968 study in midtown Manhattan, New York, the average hourly CO-level between 9 A.M. and 7 P.M. at 15 feet above the sidewalk was about 15 ppm. Hour-by-hour levels fluctuated with the traffic density.

How carbon monoxide acts as a poison will be a topic in Chapter 17 where we shall see how red blood cells transport oxygen from the lungs to tissues needing oxygen and how carbon monoxide interferes with this work.

silicon Elemental silicon, a grayish metallic solid when pure, but not found free in nature, is second only to oxygen in natural abundance. It is to the inorganic realm of rocks and minerals what carbon is to the organic world. Its atoms alternate with and are chemically bonded to oxygen atoms in matter such as quartz, sand, granite, clay, mica, asbestos, feldspar, flint, opal, agate, amethyst, and numerous other silicaceous substances including glass. It also occurs in some plants and animals. Many marine organisms are rich in silicon (as the oxide), and the polishing agent and adsorbent known as diatomaceous earth (or kieselguhr, or tripolite) is a porous compound of silicon and oxygen left from the skeletons of long-dead oceanic diatoms and infusoria.

Although it is the oxide of silicon, in a wide variety of forms, that is its most abundant and important compound, other compounds of silicon include the rubberlike silicones. Silicon carbide (SiC), or carborundum, is widely used as an abrasive; it is almost as hard (difficult to scratch) as diamond. Silicon metal has uses in transistors and rectifiers.

silicates The silicates—compounds of silicon, oxygen, and metal ions—make up two-thirds of the bulk composition of the entire earth. The simplest compound of silicon and oxygen is silicon dioxide, SiO_2, called *silica*. Since silicon and carbon each forms a dioxide and both are in the same family, one might guess that silicon dioxide, like carbon dioxide, would be a gas at room temperature. Instead silica is a high-melting solid that exists in about a dozen different crystalline forms. The silicon atom is larger than the carbon atom. There is room about it for more neighboring oxygen atoms. Carbon dioxide consists of separate molecules with two carbon-oxygen double bonds: $O{=}C{=}O$. In silicon dioxide, on the other hand, each silicon atom is bound to four oxygens by single bonds, as illustrated in Fig. 5.7 and each oxygen extends a bond to a different silicon atom, which in turn can bond in different

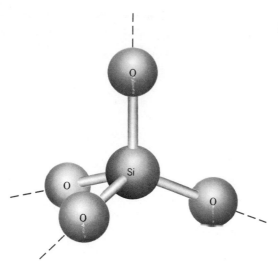

Fig. 5.7 The arrangement of atoms in silica, SiO_2. The dotted lines indicate only that each oxygen is attached to another silicon atom (which, in turn, would be bonded to still other oxygens). This is the arrangement in quartz. The dotted lines should not be interpreted as indicating the geometry of additional bonds. They will be angular, not linear. In the silicates, metallic ions are attached to some of the oxygens, and the possibilities for nearly endless variations become real. The basic silica network shown in its unit, above, need not extend uniformly in all directions. When not all oxygens have to extend to other silicons, but may go to metallic ions instead, then these silica units can bind to each other in long chains (as in the pyroxenes), extensive rings similar to those in graphite (as in mica, another mineral easily cleaved like graphite, or in talc), simple rings (as in emeralds), double rings organized in chains (as in asbestos), to cite some examples.

directions to still other oxygens. Instead of discrete molecules in silica, there is a huge interlacing network of alternating oxygen and silicon atoms. We write the formula as SiO_2 merely to indicate the ratio of atoms. Subtle variations in how this network extends and in the kinds of metallic ions that are trapped in the network account for the varieties of silicates. (See also Fig. 5.7.)

For most minerals it is not possible to ascribe a definite molecular formula. Metallic ions are present in silicates in variable amounts. These ions are responsible for the characteristic colors of the many semiprecious stones found among the silicates: amethyst, onyx, aquamarine, beryl, opal, and agate, for examples.

The feldspars are the most common of all minerals, and their general formula is XY_4O_8, where X may be ions from sodium, potassium, calcium, or barium. Y is silicon and aluminum, and the ratio of Si to Al may vary from $3:1$ to $1:1$. When weathering leaches the metallic ions (X in the formula) from feldspars and replaces them by hydronium ions (H_3O^+) the product is kaolin, the chief component of fine clay. (Ordinary clay is kaolin mixed with sand and iron oxides.) This weathering is accelerated by the acidic materials in smog, and that is why even granite is adversely affected at an accelerated rate in cities plagued by air pollution.

Selected Reading List

The rate of population growth is not nearly as high as the rate of publication of books and articles on the environment. Some of the entries given here will lead to lists as long as you please. At the end of Chapter 10 are several additional references to air pollution. The lists in Chapter 13 and Chapter 20 include articles on the cycles of nature.

Books

1. J. R. Holum and R. B. Boolootian. *Environmental Science: An Introduction to Their Topics and Terms.* Little, Brown & Co., Boston (tentatively, 1972). Additional information about pollutants will be found among the entries (arranged alphabetically) in this book (paperback).

2. H. W. Helfrich, Jr. *The Environmental Crisis.* Yale, New Haven, 1970. Based on a lecture series, the individual chapters are contributions from scientists from the physical, biological and social sciences, government, and economics. Botonist David Gates' chapter goes into the problems of deliberately trying to change our weather.

3. J. C. Esposito. *Vanishing Air.* Grossman, New York, 1970. Ralph Nader's Study Group report on air pollution.

4. S. F. Singer, editor. *Global Effects of Environmental Pollution,* Springer-Verlag, New York, 1970. Global balances of oxygen, carbon dioxide, nitrogen compounds and carbon monoxide are discussed.

5. C. L. Wilson and W. H. Matthews, editors. *Man's Impact on the Global Environment.* MIT Press, Cambridge, Mass., 1970. Climatic effects of man's polluting activities are among the topics.

6. Howard R. Lewis. *With Every Breath You Take.* Crown Publishers, Inc., New York, 1965. Chapter 15, "The Needless Disasters," is a chilling account of how some of man's insults to nature have dealt killing blows in return.

Articles

1. E. Farber. "Oxygen; The Element with Two Faces." *Chemistry,* May 1966, page 17. The occurrence, importance, and the physical and chemical properties of oxygen are discussed.

2. Wallace S. Broecker. "Man's Oxygen Reserves." *Science,* June 26, 1970, page 1537. Estimates of our resources of oxygen are reported.

3. C. J. Pratt. "Sulfur." *Scientific American,* May 1970, page 63. A survey of the sources and uses of sulfur.

4. Available from the Reprint Department of ACS Publications (1155 Sixteenth St., N. W., Washington, D. C. 20036) are the following special reports originally printed in *Chemical & Engineering News*

   "Chemistry and the Oceans" ($1.00)
   "Chemistry and the Atmosphere" ($0.75)

5. A. J. Haagen-Smit. "The Control of Air Pollution." *Scientific American,* January 1961, page 25, The Los Angeles smog is discussed by one of the pioneers of smog research.

6. N. W. Rakestraw. "Controlling Breathing Atmospheres." *Chemistry,* October 1970, page 18. An interesting discussion of the problems of providing people in submarines and spaceships with good air.

7. J. J. Gilman. "The Nature of Ceramics." *Scientific American,* September 1967, page 112. A discussion of how ionic and covalent bonds in the materials of ceramics make them hard, brittle, and resistant to heat.

8. R. J. Charles. "The Nature of Glasses." *Scientific American,* September 1967, page 126. The compositions and structures of various glasses are described together with a discussion of how glasses avoid being crystalline—that is, avoid having an orderly aggregation of constituent particles.

9. S. I. Rasool and S. H. Schneider. "Atmospheric carbon dioxide and aerosols: Effects of large increases on global climate." *Science,* July 9, 1971, p. 138.

Government Publications

The following five large pamphlets were prepared by the National Air Pollution Control Administration and may be purchased from the U. S. Government Printing Office. They are packed with general discussions, tables, explanations, methods of measurement, dangers to materials and living things, summaries and conclusions. They were sources for most of the data in this chapter.

Air Quality Criteria for Particulate Matter, January 1969.
Air Quality Criteria for Sulfur Oxides, January 1969.
Air Quality Criteria for Carbon Monoxide, March 1970.
Air Quality Criteria for Photochemical Oxidants, March 1970.
Air Quality Criteria for Nitrogen Oxides, January 1971.

Environmental Quality. First Annual Report of the Council on Environmental Quality. August 1970. U. S. Government Printing Office.

Brief Summary

1. Members of the Oxygen Family are oxygen, sulfur, selenium, tellurium, and polonium. All form hydrides of the general formula H_2X and oxides of the form XO_2, as well as other oxides.

2. Oxygen, the most abundant element on the planet, supports respiration, decay and combustion and cycles through the biosphere being replenished by photosynthesis. In the stratosphere some oxygen exists as ozone.

3. Ozone is the chief oxidant in photochemical smog and its production depends on the presence of nitrogen dioxide and hydrocarbons.

4. When oxides of sulfur, SO_2 and SO_3, are present in smog it has acidic, corrosive qualities.

5. The Nitrogen Family consists of nitrogen, phosphorus, arsenic, antimony, and bismuth.

6. The oxides of nitrogen found in smog, NO_2 and NO, come from the operation of internal combustion engines. Nitrogen dioxide, NO_2, is involved in the production of ozone in smog and partly accounts for the brownish color of smog.

7. The Carbon Family consists of carbon, silicon, germanium, tin, and lead. Carbon forms the skeletons of all organic compounds. Silicon-oxygen networks make up a large part of the rock in the earth's crust.

8. Carbon cycles through the biosphere as a part of organic compounds made in photosynthesis and carbon dioxide released by respiration, decay, and combustion. While in the atmosphere, carbon dioxide helps maintain the earth's temperature by what is called the greenhouse effect.

9. Because combustion is seldom perfect, carbon monoxide enters the atmosphere.

Problems and Exercises

1. Define each term.
   - (a) smog
   - (b) photosynthesis
   - (c) oxygen-carbon cycle
   - (d) respiration
   - (e) photochemical
   - (f) greenhouse effect
   - (g) oxidation
   - (h) reduction
   - (i) oxidant
   - (j) reductant
   - (k) silica
   - (l) silicates

2. Photosynthesis puts oxygen into the air and yet the concentration of oxygen in air does not change. Explain.

3. How do the oceans help to maintain a fairly even level of carbon dioxide in the atmosphere?

4. Explain how higher and higher levels of carbon dioxide in the atmosphere might, in the long range, affect the level of the oceans.

5. Explain how dusts in the air might contribute to atmospheric cooling.

6. How does the ozone cycle in the stratosphere convert the sun's high energy ultraviolet rays into heat?

7. Not much ozone can accumulate in smog unless hydrocarbons are also present. How is this explained?

8. By what sequence of reactions does the combustion of high-sulfur fuels produce acid mists in smog?

9. How do the nitrogen oxides in smog, NO_2 and NO, arise?

10. What are the principal forms of carbon and how do they differ, structurally?

chapter 6 solutions and colloids

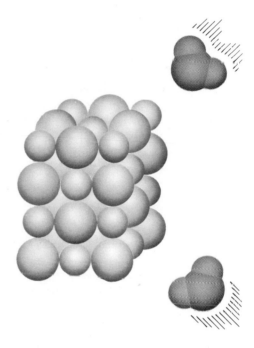

The air you breathe is an intimate mixture of molecules of various gases, and on any given day it will also contain higher or lower concentrations of water vapor, pollutants, and larger particles of dusts and mists. In nearby lakes or rivers or oceans is another intimate mixture of molecules and ions, in this case a mixture in the liquid state, and natural waters also contain solid particles held in suspension by turbulence or other factors. Within you a marvelous river of life, the bloodstream, carries particles of all sizes intimately mixed together—small ions and clusters of ions, small molecules and clusters of molecules, ion-molecule complexes, molecular species so large they are called macromolecules and cannot really be regarded as being in the truly dissolved state. We say, instead, that they constitute a colloidal dispersion; and besides them there are even larger cellular bodies.

There are obviously an enormous number of different mixtures in our environment. Those in which the "things" mixed together have ionic and molecular dimensions, or not much larger, are especially important to us and our environment. These mixtures are solutions and colloidal dispersions. It is not just the identities of the particles mixed together that determines the properties of such mixtures, it is also their sizes. If the particles are very small, on the order of small molecules and ions whose diameters are roughly 0.5 to 2.5 A,[1] then they cannot be seen by optical or conventional electron microscopes. (In 1970 physicists A. V. Crewe, J. Wall, and J. Langmore of the University of Chicago, using a high-resolution scanning electron microscope, obtained pictures of uranium and thorium compounds deposited on carbon films where some of the bright spots were probably caused by single, heavy atoms.)

true solutions

A *true solution* is a uniform, intimate, and stable mixture of the smallest particles—atoms, ions, molecules—from two or more substances. There are nine possible kinds of solutions, and they are listed, with examples, in Table 6.1.

In this chapter we shall be interested chiefly in solutions for which water is the solvent or dispersing medium—*aqueous* solutions. Substances dissolved in a solvent are called *solutes,* and when their diameters are in the range of roughly 0.5 to 2.5 A, then they form a *true solution.* Such solutions are transparent (although sometimes colored), nonfilterable, homogeneous, and stable. The force of gravity cannot bring the solute particles down.

the colloidal state. colloidal dispersions.

At the next higher level of "solute" size are clusters of several hundred to a few thousand particles with cluster diameters ranging from 10 to 1000 A. Clumps of this size are still seldom observable with an optical microscope, but they are now easily photographed by an electron microscope. Matter whose particles have average diameters of 10 to 1000 A is said to be in the *colloidal state.*[2] ("Colloidal" comes from the Greek word for "gluelike." Particles in glue are of colloidal dimension.)

When colloidal particles are scattered and dispersed in water, the product is not a true solution but an example of a *colloidal dispersion.* The dispersed particles still cannot be separated by ordinary filtration, but the dispersion will usually appear cloudy and murky. Very "dilute" dispersions may appear perfectly clear, but if they are placed in a beam of strong light, a cloudiness will be seen. This effect, illustrated in Fig. 6.1, is called the Tyndall effect,

[1] A stands for one angstrom unit of length $= 1 \times 10^{-8}$ cm.

[2] Even though the dimensions given are *average diameters,* the particles need not be spherical to be in the colloidal state. Any shape is possible for this state provided that one dimension is 10 to 1000 A. A soap film in a soap bubble, only a few molecules thick, is in the colloidal state.

Table 6.1 Kinds of Solutions

Kinds	Common Examples
Gas in a liquid	Carbonated beverages (carbon dioxide in water)
Liquid in a liquid	Vinegar (acetic acid in water)
Solid in a liquid	Sugar in water
Gas in a gas	Air
Liquid in a gas	Humid air
Solid in a gas	Certain kinds of smokes
Gas in a solid	Alloy of palladium and hydrogen[a]
Liquid in a solid	Benzene in rubber (for example, rubber "cement")
Solid in a solid	Carbon in iron (steel)

[a]Some doubt exists that this system is a solution.

and true solutions will not give it. Colloidal particles are large enough to reflect and scatter light; solutes in true solution are not.

The several kinds of colloidal dispersions are described in Table 6.2.

If colloidal dispersions of a solid in a gas (smoke) or a liquid are viewed with the aid of a microscope, scintillations that are reflections of light from randomly moving particles may be seen. This behavior was first reported in 1827 by an English botanist, Robert Brown, who observed with a microscope the random, chaotic movements of pollen grains in water. Randomly unequal buffeting of colloidal particles by motions of the molecules of the dispersing

Fig. 6.1 Tyndall effect. The container nearest the light source holds a concentrated sugar solution. The second holds a colloidal dispersion. The light beam is visible in the latter, but it passes through the first unscattered. (Used by permission from Charles W. Keenan and Jesse H. Wood, General College Chemistry, 3rd ed., page 278, Harper & Row, Publishers, New York, 1966.)

Table 6.2 Colloidal Systems

Type	Dispersed Phase[a]	Dispersing Medium[b]	Common Examples
Foam	Gas	Liquid	Suds, whipped cream
Solid foam	Gas	Solid	Pumice, marshmallow
Liquid aerosol	Liquid	Gas	Mist, fog, clouds, certain pollutants in air
Emulsion	Liquid	Liquid	Cream, mayonnaise, milk
Solid emulsion	Liquid	Solid	Butter, cheese
Smoke	Solid	Gas	Dust and particulates in smog
Sol	Solid	Liquid	Starch in water, jellies,[c] paints
Solid sol	Solid	Solid	Black diamonds, pearls, opals, alloys

[a] The colloidal particles constitute the dispersed phase.
[b] The continuous matter into which the colloidal particles are scattered is called the *dispersing medium*.
[c] Sols that adopt a semisolid, semirigid form (e.g., gelatin desserts, fruit jellies) are called *gels*.

phase (e.g., air molecules) creates this phenomenon, now called the *Brownian movement*. The buffeting action partly accounts for the stability of colloidal dispersions, for it overcomes the tendency of larger colloidal particles to settle out.

In the most stable colloidal dispersions the dispersed particles all bear the same kind of electrical charge. Being like-charged, they repel each other and cannot coalesce into particles large enough to settle out. Many proteins in the blood are in electrically charged states, for example. Some common colloidal systems achieve their stability through the mediation of a third substance, a *stabilizing agent* or a *protective colloid*. Oil, for example, can be colloidally dispersed in soapy water, for soap molecules form a negatively charged "skin" about each tiny oil droplet which prevents them from coalescing. Mayonnaise is a colloidal system, an emulsion of olive oil or corn oil in water. It is stabilized by egg yolk, whose protein molecules form a skin around the oil droplets, which keeps them separated. Milk is an emulsion of butterfat in water with the protein casein acting as the stabilizing substance. Agents that stabilize emulsions are called emulsifying agents.

If particles are much larger than 1000 A in average diameter, the force of gravity becomes effective and they settle. Clay shaken in water, for example, forms a *suspension* which is filterable, unstable, and nontransparent.

The distinguishing features of solutions, colloidal dispersions, and suspensions are compared in Table 6.3.

water and aqueous solutions

structure of water

directionality of covalent bonds. If the water molecule were linear, as in H—O—H, its centers of density of positive and negative charges (considering all electrons and nuclei) would coincide; water would be a completely nonpolar substance. But water is very polar, and X-ray studies have helped us see why. There is an angle of 104.5° in water molecules:

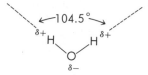

It is therefore impossible for the centers of density of positive and negative charges to coincide.

Covalent bonds, as in water molecules, are always directional. The forces of attraction that give us the covalent bonds are not equally effective in any and all directions from a central atom (e.g., the oxygen atom in water, nitrogen in NH_3, or carbon in CH_4). The bonding forces of covalent bonds are localized to those regions around the central atom where certain of its atomic orbitals are, the orbitals that it can make available to overlap with an orbital of an attached group. We shall see how this directionality arises in a water molecule to illustrate the principles and then for other molecules simply adopt the results as we need them.

The electronic configuration of an oxygen atom is $1s^2 2s^2 2p_x^2 2p_y 2p_z$. The two atomic orbitals of an oxygen atom that can overlap and can furnish electrons for sharing are $2p$ orbitals. Recall that the axes of p-orbitals are perpendicular. According to one theory, illustrated in Fig. 6.2, we imagine

Table 6.3   Types of Dispersions—Solution, Colloidal Dispersion, Suspension

Property	Solution	Colloidal Dispersion	Suspension
Average diameter of dispersed particles	0.5 to 2.5 Å	10 to 1000 Å	Larger than 1000 Å
Behavior toward gravity	Does not separate (kinetic motions)	Does not separate (Brownian movement)	Separates (directed movement under influence of gravity)
Behavior toward light	Transparent	Usually translucent or opaque (Tyndall effect)	Translucent or opaque
Filterability	Nonfilterable	Nonfilterable	Filterable
Homogeneity	Homogeneous	Border line	Heterogeneous
Number of phases[a] present	One	Two	Two
Example	Sugar or salt in water	(See Table 6.2)	Clay in water

[a] A *phase* is defined as any part of a system that is separated by physically distinct boundaries from other parts of the system. Ice in water, for example, is a system consisting of two phases, one solid, the other liquid. Oil in water, likewise, is a two-phase system. In this instance, both phases are liquid.

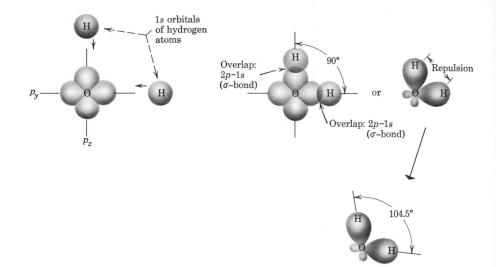

Fig. 6.2 Molecular orbital picture of the water molecule. According to one model, the bonds are created from the overlap of p orbitals in oxygen with s orbitals provided by the hydrogens. Then repulsions between the hydrogen nuclei and repulsions between the electron clouds of the new molecular orbitals spread the bond angle from the "predicted" value of 90° to the actual value of 104.5°.

that the bonds in water form when two hydrogen atoms, each with one electron in a 1s orbital, come in and overlap with the perpendicular 2p orbitals of oxygen. The resulting bond angle should therefore be 90°, but (according to this theory) the two hydrogen nuclei repel each other to spread the angle to the observed 104.5°.[3]

hydrogen bonds. Because of the great polarity of water molecules, they attract each other strongly. Chemists find it convenient to think in terms of an actual bond existing between separate molecules of water, a bond given the special name *hydrogen bond*.

A hydrogen bond is a simple force of attraction that extends from a hydrogen of one water molecule (a site of partial positive charge) to the oxygen of *another* molecule (a site of partial negative charge). (See Fig. 6.3, where dotted lines represent hydrogen bonds.) This "bond" is quite weak, so weak that it barely earns the title. Whereas it takes roughly 90–100 kcal of energy to break Avogadro's number of ordinary covalent bonds, it requires only about 5 kcal to rupture the same number of hydrogen bonds. It is a weak force of attraction resembling an ionic bond in type but certainly not in strength. In an ionic bond there is an attractive force between separate,

[3] In a more sophisticated theory, atomic orbitals are reorganized prior to overlap into new, *bonding* atomic orbitals by an operation called hybridization. Although not difficult, this theory is beyond the intended scope of this book.

oppositely charged ions that bear at least one *whole* unit of charge each. In the hydrogen bond, the force of attraction is between separate, oppositely charged sites of neighboring, neutral (but polar) molecules, each site bearing only a *fraction of a unit* of net charge. It must not be confused with a covalent bond *within* a molecule. (Its name is admittedly misleading on that point.)

The relative weakness of a hydrogen bond does not diminish its importance; it magnifies it. The most important link in a chain is the weakest one. Likewise, in certain key organic compounds of the body—genes, enzymes, proteins, for example—hydrogen bonds are the weak links in their structures that determine much of their stabilities. Hydrogen bonds are not restricted to water molecules. We shall encounter them in many other environments.

surface tension. The great polarity of a water molecule helps explain the phenomenon of surface tension, and thus why detergents are needed for cleansing action in water, and why people who do not produce bile (e.g., after removal of a gall bladder) should have a low-fat diet.

The surface of water in contact with air, or with oils and greases, behaves as if it consisted of an elastic membrane. (For example, if great care is used, a needle can be set afloat on water.) Beneath the surface, water molecules experience electrical forces of attraction (hydrogen bonds) toward other molecules *equally in all directions*. At the surface, however, there are no water molecules outward, nor are there molecules of comparable polarity if air, or oils and greases, are beyond. Hence, a water molecule at a surface cannot experience forces of attraction equally in all directions. It feels a net inward pull (see Fig. 6.4). Since surface molecules cannot really be pulled

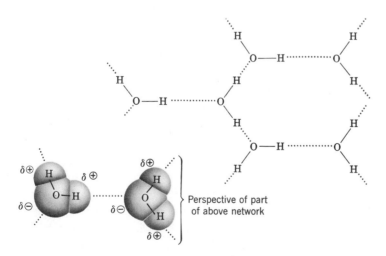

Fig. 6.3   Forces of attraction between polar water molecules are strong enough to make it useful to say that bonds exist between them—hydrogen bonds, represented here by dotted lines. In liquid water, the situation is not as orderly as implied here, but in ice, neighboring water molecules take up orderly positions.

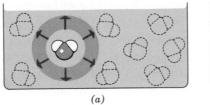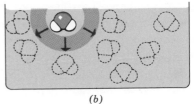

(a)   (b)

Fig. 6.4   The origin of surface tension. (a) In the body of the liquid, molecules of water are attracted by neighbors equally in all directions. (b) Water molecules at the surface experience a net downward attraction, for they have no neighbor molecules of water above them.

very far, they jam together more tightly than do molecules elsewhere in the liquid. This produces the effect of a thin, invisible, elastic membrane at a liquid surface, a phenomenon called *surface tension*.

This surface "membrane" accounts in part for the poor ability of water alone to break up particles of grease or oil. These substances act as "glues" to bind dirt to fabrics and skin. They also tend to coat food particles in the digestive tract. Digestion, which requires the action of water as a solvent and as a chemical, is thereby hindered. Water molecules do not readily break away from their own kind at the surface and penetrate a grease layer to loosen it. However, soaps, synthetic detergents, and bile salts have the common property of reducing the surface tension of water and of easing its penetration of grease or oil. They are all said to be *surface-active agents* or, simply, *surfactants*. When we study their structures, we shall be able to understand how they perform their services.

aqueous
solutions

water and the hydration of solutes.   Since water is such a common solvent, particularly when we consider that aqueous media are found in all plant and animal cells, it is important that we understand how it manages to dissolve various substances. Study the sketch in Fig. 6.5. From a molecule's-eye view, it shows a crystal of sodium chloride in contact with pure water. The kinetic-molecular theory tells as that individual sodium ions and chloride ions in the crystal vibrate about their fixed points, while water molecules constantly bombard the crystal surface. The most probable collisions are those in which opposite electrical charges make contact; that is, those in which a partially positive end of a polar water molecule hits a surface chloride ion, for example. The effect is that, as water molecules bombard the surface, they exert a small attractive force on surface ions. As a result, these ions slip away. A new surface becomes exposed, and the process continues.

hydration.   As each ion leaves the crystal, it is immediately surrounded by several water molecules, as illustrated in Fig. 6.6. This behavior is natural, since unlike charges attract each other. The phenomenon, when water is the solvent, is called *hydration*. The general term, which applies to any solvent including water, is *solvation*. The accumulation of water molecules about each ion effectively shields oppositely charged ions from contact, and they are kept apart in solution.

In contrast with water, air is an extremely poor solvent for most solids and liquids. Sodium chloride, in a sense, does "dissolve" in air when it is boiled, and some separation of unsolvated, oppositely charged ions occurs. However, a temperature of about 1400°C (boiling point of sodium chloride) is needed, thus attesting to the strength of an ionic bond. The tremendous importance of the hydration of ions is seen in the fact that the ions in sodium chloride separate (dissolve) in water at and below room temperature. Water molecules, being very polar, can do something nonpolar air molecules cannot do—make available something besides the neighboring ions in the crystal to which sodium ions and chloride ions can be attracted. Not all ionic substances are very soluble in water, however. Whether they are depends on the relative effectiveness of the solvent versus the neighboring, oppositely charged ions in the crystal lattice to stabilize electrically charged particles.

Covalent substances, those that consist of neutral molecules, can also be solvated by water, provided their molecules are very polar. Sugar is an

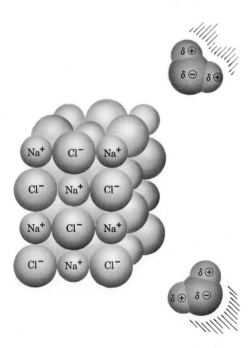

Fig. 6.5 Polar water molecules bombard the surface of the crystal of sodium chloride. A combination of mechanical bumping and electrical forces of attraction dislodges ions on the surface of the crystal and they go into solution; that is, they disperse randomly among the water molecules.

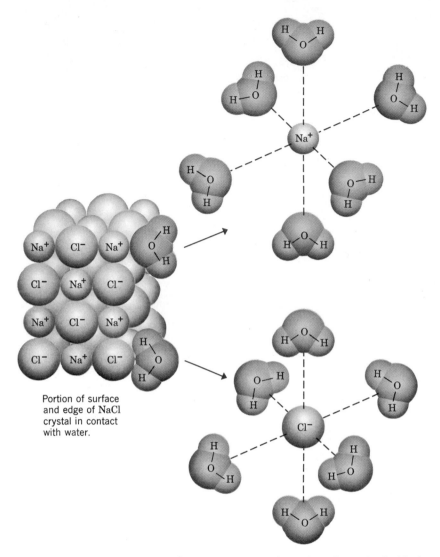

Fig. 6.6 Polar water molecules solvate ions of the solute. This effectively shields these ions from contact with each other, making it hard for them to aggregate into a crystal.

example. In this case, hydration occurs not around fully charged ions, but around partially charged sites on neutral but polar molecules. We shall examine this in more detail when we study organic chemistry.

hydrates. When the aqueous solutions of some ionic substances are carefully evaporated, not all the water molecules are easily driven off. They remain more or less firmly attracted to the ions even as solid, crystalline material forms. There are many common substances in which intact water molecules are held *in definite proportions* within the crystals. They are called *hydrates* and are properly classified as compounds because they "obey" the law of definite proportions. Their formulas, however, are written to indicate that intact molecules of water are present. The formulas of several are given in Table 6.4.

Action of heat on hydrates forces them to release their *water of hydration,* and they change to their *anhydrous forms.* For example,

$$CuSO_4 \cdot 5H_2O \xrightarrow{\text{heat}} CuSO_4 + 5H_2O \text{ (driven off as steam)}$$

Copper sulfate pentahydrate   Anhydrous copper
(deep blue crystals)   sulfate
(nearly white solid)

Some anhydrous compounds readily take up water and reform their hydrates. Plaster of Paris, for example, although not completely anhydrous, contains relatively less water than gypsum. When it is mixed with water, it soon sets into a hard crystalline mass, according to the reaction:

$$(CaSO_4)_2 \cdot H_2O + 3H_2O \longrightarrow 2CaSO_4 \cdot 2H_2O$$

Plaster of Paris   Gypsum

Anhydrous calcium chloride, $CaCl_2$, is a common dehumidifier for damp basements and humid rooms. It forms its hydrate by drawing water molecules from the atmosphere. Any substance that can perform this service is called

Table 6.4 **Some Common Hydrates**

Formulas	Names	Decomposition modes and temperatures[a]	Uses
$(CaSO_4)_2 \cdot H_2O$	Calcium sulfate sesquihydrate (plaster of paris)	$-\frac{1}{2}H_2O$ (163°C)	Casts, molds
$CaSO_4 \cdot 2H_2O$	Calcium sulfate dihydrate (gypsum)	$-2H_2O$ (163°)	Casts, molds, wallboard
$CuSO_4 \cdot 5H_2O$	Copper (II) sulfate pentahydrate (blue vitriol)	$-5H_2O$ (150°)	Insecticide
$MgSO_4 \cdot 7H_2O$	Magnesium sulfate heptahydrate (epsom salt)	$-6H_2O$ (150°)	Cathartic in medicine
		$-7H_2O$ (200°)	Used in dyeing and tanning
$Na_2B_4O_7 \cdot 10H_2O$	Sodium tetraborate decahydrate (borax)	$-8H_2O$ (60°) $-10H_2O$ (320°)	Laundry
$Na_2CO_3 \cdot 10H_2O$	Sodium carbonate decahydrate (washing soda)	$-H_2O$ (33.5°)	Water softener
$Na_2SO_4 \cdot 10H_2O$	Sodium sulfate decahydrate (Glauber's salt)	$-10H_2O$ (100°)	Cathartic
$Na_2S_2O_3 \cdot 5H_2O$	Sodium thiosulfate pentahydrate (photographer's hypo)	$-5H_2O$ (100°)	Photographic developing

[a] Loss of water is indicated by the minus sign before the symbol, and the loss occurs at the temperature given in parentheses.

a *desiccant.* If it acts by forming a hydrate, the substance is said to be *hygroscopic.* Some anhydrous substances are able to draw so much water from moist air that a liquid solution forms. These substances are said to be *deliquescent.*

solubility. There usually is a limit to how much solute a given volume of solvent can hold at a given temperature. This limit varies with the solute, the solvent, and the temperature, as the data in Table 6.5 show. The solubility of a substance is usually (although not always) described in terms of the number of grams of solute that will dissolve in 100 grams of solvent at a stated temperature. When a solution contains all it can of a solute at a given temperature, it is said to be *saturated.* An *unsaturated solution* contains any smaller concentration of solute.[4]

dynamic equilibria and saturated solutions. Consider an experiment in which more solid sodium chloride is placed in water than is needed to saturate it. Solute ions that enter the solution can be expected to travel randomly about. Should such motion bring an ion back to the surface of an undissolved crystal, it might stick. This, of course, would constitute a slight rebuilding of the crystal. The more solute particles in solution, the more likely are such events. Sooner or later, the number that return to a crystal will exactly equal the number that leave it elsewhere. At this point, the rate of crystal regrowth equals the rate of crystal dissolution. In spite of much "coming and going," there is no *net* change, either in the weight of the undissolved crystal or in the amount of solute in solution. The situation is one of *dynamic equilibrium;* dynamic,

---

[4] Other qualitative expressions for concentration are *dilute* and *concentrated.* A concentrated solution is very nearly saturated. The expression, however, is usually reserved for solutions that can hold considerable amounts of solute. A dilute solution is simply one that contains a very small amount of solute per unit volume.

Table 6.5 **Solubilities of Some Substances in Water**

Solute	Solubilities, in grams per 100 grams water			
	0°C	20°C	50°C	100°C
Solids				
Sodium chloride, NaCl	35.7	36.0	37.0	39.8
Sodium hydroxide, NaOH	42	109	145	347
Barium sulfate, $BaSO_4$	0.000115	0.00024	0.00034	0.00041
Calcium hydroxide, $Ca(OH)_2$	0.185	0.165	0.128	0.077
Gases				
Oxygen, O_2	0.0069	0.0043	0.0027	0
Carbon dioxide, CO_2	0.335	0.169	0.076	0
Nitrogen, N_2	0.0029	0.0019	0.0012	0
Sulfur Dioxide, SO_2	22.8	10.6	4.3	1.8 (at 90°C)
Ammonia, NH_3	89.9	51.8	28.4	7.4 (at 96°C)

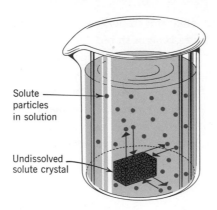

Solute particles in solution

Undissolved solute crystal

Fig. 6.7   In a saturated solution that is in contact with undissolved solute, solute particles (molecules or oppositely charged ions) return to the crystal as rapidly as they leave
the crystal surface elsewhere. In spite of much "coming and going," no net change
occurs either to the concentration of the solution or to the amount of undissolved solute
present. A condition of dynamic equilibrium exists.

because there is a great deal of action; equilibrium, because there is no net
change (see Fig. 6.7). A saturated solution, therefore, is more correctly defined
as one in which a state of dynamic equilibrium exists between the undissolved
solute and its dissolved state. It may be described by means of the symbolism
of a chemical reaction:

$$\text{Undissolved solute} \underset{H_2O}{\rightleftarrows} \text{Dissolved solute}$$

Two oppositely pointing arrows are the chemist's way of stating that a
condition of dynamic equilibrium exists.

   If a saturated solution of a solid, with undissolved solute present, is
heated, molecular motions of all particles increase. Solute particles hold to
fixed positions in the crystal with increasing difficulty, and more go into
solution. It is a general rule that the solubility of a solid in water increases
with temperature. The data for one exception to this rule, $Ca(OH)_2$, are given
in Table 6.5. One explanation is that with calcium hydroxide heat seriously
interferes with the hydration of its ions.

   If a saturated solution of a solid is cooled and the solubility of the material
drops, the rate of crystal regrowth normally exceeds the rate of crystal
dissolution. In other words, dissolved solute precipitates until the opposing
rates again become equal. In situations where there are no crystals to which
to return, there may be no crystal regrowth, and the "excess" solute remains
in solution. The situation is not stable, since a dynamic equilibrium is not
present, and the solution is said to be *supersaturated*. The addition of a "seed"
crystal to a supersaturated solution often results in a swift and dramatic
separation of solute because it provides a nucleus onto which solute can
precipitate.

Honey, jams, and jellies are frequently supersaturated solutions of sugar. If any of these substances remain stored for a long time, excess sugar often leaves the solution in the form of large, beautiful crystals.

Gases, in contrast with solids, become less and less soluble in water (or other liquids) as the temperature rises (see Table 6.5). Heat increases molecular motions for all kinds of solute particles. Gas molecules, however, can escape, whereas molecules or ions of a solid solute normally cannot. One way to prevent the escape of gas molecules from a solution is to increase the pressure of the gas above the solution.

quantitative methods of expressing concentration

One of the chief values of a solvent in the chemistry of health and elsewhere is its ability to bring into intimate contact two or more potential reactants. Ionic substances, in fact, rarely react with each other unless their ions are free to intermingle and collide with each other. They have this freedom in solution.

We have learned that reactants interact on a particle-to-particle basis. The concept of gram-formula weight, or mole, permits us to weigh substances on that basis, but if chemicals are in solution, we need a way of measuring moles of solute by measuring *volumes* of the solution. This is especially important when solutions are used in quantitative analyses, as is frequently done in clinical laboratory work and in quality-control laboratories.

moles per liter; molarity. Chemists define one method of expressing concentration in terms of *molarity, the number of moles of solute per liter of solution.* A solution is said to be 1 *molar* if it contains 1 mole solute per liter of total solution. In a 2 molar solution, the ratio is 2 moles solute per liter of solution.

The student should make a special effort to distinguish between "moles" and "molarity." The mole is a unit for amount of substance, the formula weight expressed in grams; molarity is a way of describing the number of these units per liter of solution.

The term *molar* is usually abbreviated M. Thus, in the symbolism of the field, a "3M NaOH solution" is one that contains 3 moles of sodium hydroxide per liter of solution.[5] Let us now study some examples of problems that involve molarities.

Example 1. A 2M solution of sodium hydroxide is available. A reaction requiring 1 mole of dissolved sodium hydroxide is to be performed. How much of the solution should be measured to obtain this amount of solute?

[5] Some references use the letter F from "gram-formula weight" instead of M from *molar*. This is perfectly all right. A 3F solution and a 3M solution have identical concentrations. The term *formal* is sometimes used as an analog of *molar*.

Solution. Until you gain considerable experience, always say to yourself, or write out on paper, exactly what the expression for concentration means, in full. You should say, "'2M sodium hydroxide' means that there are 2 moles of sodium hydroxide dissolved in every liter of solution." Next, ask yourself how much solute the problem demands—in this case, 1 mole. Next, reason that if there are 2 moles in 1 liter, 1 mole will be found in half a liter, or in 500 cc, of 2M sodium hydroxide.

Example 2. A 0.5M solution of sucrose in water is available. A chemist needs 1 mole of sucrose dissolved in water. How much of the stock solution should be taken?

Solution. The expression of concentration, 0.5M, means that there is half a mole of sucrose dissolved in each liter of solution. To obtain 1 mole of sucrose, the chemist needs 2 liters of the stock solution.

These examples are a way of working such problems by following common sense, after the concept of molarity is thoroughly understood. The expression of this common sense may be shortened by the following equation:

Number of moles solute × number of liters of = number of moles
    per liter of solution   solution taken   of solute obtained

or

Molarity × volume (in liters) = number of moles of solute

It must be emphasized that the concept of molarity refers to unit volume of *final solution,* not unit volume of solvent used to prepare the solution. When you measure the volume of a solution with a graduated cylinder, it is immaterial how much solvent was used to prepare the solution. Fig. 6.8 illustrates the step-by-step procedure for preparing solutions of known molarity.[6]

Often it is not important to know the molarity of a solution, but some idea of concentration is still desirable. In Chapter 4 we learned two such methods— the method of *percent by volume* (vol/vol percent) for gases dissolved in gases (or liquids in liquids), and the method of *parts per million* (ppm),[7] especially useful for very dilute solutions. By converting to different units, the

percent concentration

[6] There is a variation of the concept of molarity that makes the work of analysts much easier. It is the concept of the *normal* solution. Our study of it will come in Chapter 8 when we discuss problems of acid-base analysis.

[7] Obvious extensions of this method often used in discussions of polluted air or water are *parts per billion,* ppb, and *parts per hundred million,* pphm.

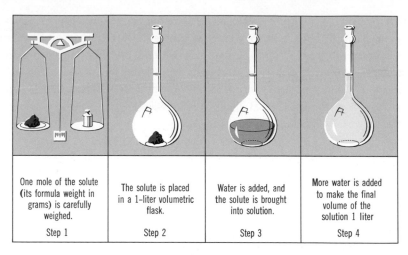

One mole of the solute (its formula weight in grams) is carefully weighed.	The solute is placed in a 1-liter volumetric flask.	Water is added, and the solute is brought into solution.	More water is added to make the final volume of the solution 1 liter
Step 1	Step 2	Step 3	Step 4

Fig. 6.8   The preparation of 1 liter of a 1 molar solution.

number of parts per million *when water is the solvent* is identical with the number of milligrams per liter.

When solids are dissolved in liquids it is frequently useful to know the concentration as a *weight-volume (wt/vol) percent* defined as the number of grams of solute in 100 cc of *solution*. For example, a 10% (wt/vol) solution of glucose would contain 10 grams of glucose in 100 cc of solution. There may be a gallon of this solution or a few drops, but the *ratio* of solute to final volume of solution is 10 grams/100 cc. A 0.9% (wt/vol) salt solution would have 0.9 gram of salt in 100 cc of solution.

Example 3. How would you prepare 500 cc of a 5% (wt/vol) solution of sugar?

Solution. The expression "5%" (wt/vol) tells us that we must have 5 grams in every 100 cc. For 500 cc, we need five times as much, or 25 grams. This amount of sugar would be placed in a volumetric flask that holds 500 cc of liquid when filled to the etched line on its neck. Water would be added, the sugar would dissolve, and the final volume would be made up to the 500 cc mark.

Example 4. How much glucose is present in 50 cc of a 2% (wt/vol) solution?

Solution. A 2% (wt/vol) solution contains 2 grams solute in 100 cc solution. In 50 cc, therefore, there is half as much (50/100), or 1 gram of glucose.

properties of solutions
conductivity

An aqueous solution in which ions are dispersed is a good conductor of electricity. In general, the greater the ionic concentration, the better the solution conducts the current. Nonionic solutions fail to conduct a current. This simple distinction serves to classify substances. Those whose aqueous solutions are conductors are called *electrolytes;* those that do not conduct are called *nonelectrolytes.*

Sugar is often described as a "quick-energy" food. Some athletes, just before a strenuous contest, drink honey to build up a reserve supply. The sugar molecule is swallowed and goes to the muscles and the nervous system. The body's mechanism, if it is healthy, is so constructed that sugar molecules are impelled to go where needed. A phenomenon that plays a small part in understanding this mechanism is *osmosis.*

Your laboratory experience has taught you that filter paper will stop some substances (undissolved solids, for example) and allow others to pass through (solvent and anything in solution). Filter paper is permeable (Latin *permeare,* to go through) to water or to solutions in general. Its pores are very small, but they are more than large enough to permit the passage of atomic- or molecular-sized particles.

Certain membranes in nature are *semipermeable.* They allow water molecules to pass, but they do not permit dissolved solute particles to go through. In one theory, semipermeability is attributed to the extreme smallness of the pores in the membrane. In another theory, it is a matter of water molecules dissolving into the membrane and out again on the other side, without carrying along solute particles. Both theories are useful. (There are others.) The first one is easier to illustrate with a mechanical model, which is why we shall use it (see Fig. 6.9).

In compartment *B* of the device in Fig. 6.9, there is a dilute sugar solution. The solute molecules are quite large. Being uniformly distributed, some are to be found along the membrane. Pure water is in compartment *A.* Since the membrane is semipermeable, water molecules move in both directions through it, from *A* to *B,* and from *B* to *A.* Sugar molecules along the membrane in *B,* however, make it harder for water molecules to go from *B* to *A* than in the opposite direction. As a result, more water molecules move from *A* to *B* than return. Therefore, there is a net flow in that direction; the volume of liquid in *B* increases and its level rises.

If sugar solutions of identical concentration were on both sides of the membrane, a condition of dynamic equilibrium would exist. Water molecules would move back and forth across the membrane, but no *net* change would be noticed. However, if a dilute sugar solution were in *A* and a concentrated solution were in *B,* unequal movements of water molecules would again occur. The net flow would be from the side of the membrane least obstructed by solute molecules; that is, from the dilute solution to the concentrated solution.

The flow of water from a solution that is dilute (or pure water) into a

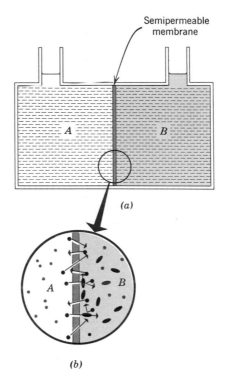

(a)

(b)

Fig. 6.9   Osmosis. (a) Enlarged view of two fluid compartments separated by a semipermeable membrane. (b) Close-up of a small section of membrane and its immediate
environment. Water molecules are represented by dots; sugar molecules in compartment
B, by shaded ovals. In the "sieve" theory of osmosis, the membrane is said to have pores
large enough to permit passage of water molecules but small enough to stop solute molecules (or ions). As drawn, of every five molecules of water that get from A to B, only
three return. Two others are shown colliding with sugar molecules. The result is a net flow
of water from A to B, and level B rises.

solution more concentrated through a semipermeable membrane is known
as *osmosis*.

osmotic pressure.   In the device in Fig. 6.9, the flow of water eventually
will stop when the extra weight of liquid in the rising column becomes heavy
enough to prevent any more water from entering. This extra weight exerts
a pressure downward. The exact pressure needed to prevent the occurrence
of osmosis when a solution is separated from water by a semipermeable
membrane is called the *osmotic pressure* of that solution. Osmotic pressure,
in theory, depends only on the concentration of solute particles of whatever
kind—ions or molecules. It does not matter what origin solute particles may
have; osmotic pressure is determined only by their concentration.

   Osmotic pressures of hundreds of pounds per square foot have been
observed. These pressures are partly responsible for forcing ground water

up to the uppermost branches of the tallest trees. Tree sap behaves as the more concentrated solution; ground water is the dilute solution; the root skins act roughly as semipermeable membranes.

reverse osmosis and desalination of sea water. As the world's needs for potable water[8] grow with its population and industrialization, we are forced more and more to find ways to obtain pure water from the oceans. In the United States we use roughly 350 billion gallons a day (BGD) of water. By 2000, according to the U. S. Department of the Interior, we will need 593 BGD; by the year 2020, 865 BGD. The average runoff of fresh water in the United States is 1200 BGD. While the equivalent of 60 years of the world's rain and snowfall is locked in glaciers (this is about 72% of the world's fresh water supply), this water is not (yet) inexpensively accessible. The oceans, on the other hand, are next door to most of the world's major urban centers.

The technology for purifying sea water is available, but the costs are still too high. One of the methods being studied is *reverse osmosis*. If enough pressure is applied to a salt solution to overcome its natural osmotic pressure, its water but not its ions will be forced back through the osmotic membrane. To work efficiently, the membrane must be very strong yet very thin, and that has been the most serious difficulty. In late 1970 scientists at Gulf General Atomic, Inc. (San Diego, California) reported they had developed a membrane only 2 millionths of an inch thick that kept back over 99.5% of the salt in sea water in one pass. A second pass brings the recovered water to potable standards.

In 1970, according to the U. S. Office of Saline Water, there were 686 desalination plants (with capacities exceeding 25,000 gallons-per day) throughout the world with a total capacity of 247 million gallons per day. About 98% of this was produced by the distillation of seawater or brackish water. (Thus, reverse osmosis and other methods are not yet of much significance.) The larger United States plants are desalting water at a cost of about 50¢ per 1000 gallons. This is still much too high for irrigation purposes for which water costs roughly 2¢ to 3¢ per thousand gallons.

dialysis

The membranes that enclose cells within living systems are not osmotic membranes. They are considerably more permeable. Not only will they permit small solvent molecules to pass through, they also let small ions and molecules pass from one side to the other. If this were not true, the cellular system for life could not work. Nutrient molecules and waste products must be able to go through cell walls. It is important, however, that especially large molecules and particles in the colloidal state be held back.

Membranes that hold back large molecules and colloids but pass small

[8] Potable water is water fit for drinking and cooking.

molecules and ions through are called *dialyzing membranes.* *Dialysis* is this selective passage of small molecules and ions through such membranes, and it obviously resembles osmosis. One feature of the shock syndrome is a dramatic change in the permeability of blood capillaries to large, colloidal molecules. As a result, some blood fluid and protein leave the vascular compartment and enter the interstitial compartment. If left uncorrected, the situation rapidly deteriorates as circulation of oxygen and nutrients declines.

One practical use of dialysis is in the separation of substances in true solution from colloidal particles, a procedure often used in purifying colloidal substances. For this purpose, cellophane, collodian, or an animal bladder may be used as the dialyzing membrane. Thus, if a mixture of colloidally dispersed starch and dissolved sodium chloride is placed in a dialyzing "bag," and water is circulated around it (see Fig. 6.10), the ions soon appear in the water outside the bag while the starch remains behind.

hemolysis. Circulating in the blood stream are millions of red blood cells whose surfaces behave as dialyzing membranes. Within these cells is an aqueous medium containing dissolved and colloidally dispersed substances. Large, colloidally dispersed molecules contribute to determining the direction of dialysis in a manner resembling the way solute concentrations control the direction of osmosis. If red cells were placed in pure water, dialysis would occur. Water would enter the cells in sufficient quantities to rupture them, for dialysis also tends to occur from a dilute solution (or pure water) to a relatively more concentrated solution. Red cells that rupture are said to be *hemolyzed.* The process is termed *hemolysis,* or sometimes "laking" of blood.

If red cells were surrounded by a concentrated salt solution, dialysis again

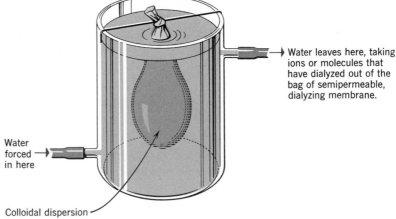

Water leaves here, taking ions or molecules that have dialyzed out of the bag of semipermeable, dialyzing membrane.

Water forced in here

Colloidal dispersion

Fig. 6.10   The apparatus of dialysis.

would occur, this time in the opposite direction—from the cell to the solution (why?). This would cause cells to shrivel and shrink, a damaging event called *crenation*.

In some clinical situations, ions present in body fluids (plasma, interstitial fluid) need replacement. This is usually done by adding salt solutions to the patient's circulation by intravenous drip. For this purpose, it is very important to control the concentration of the salt solutions used in order to prevent both hemolysis and crenation. In other words, the effective concentration of the salt solution must match closely the effective concentration within red cells. A solution 0.9% in sodium chloride has an osmotic pressure equal to that exerted by the solution inside red cells. Red cells bathed in this solution, called *physiological saline solution,* undergo neither hemolysis nor crenation.

Any two solutions that have identical osmotic pressures are said to be *isotonic.* If one of the solutions has a lower osmotic pressure, it is said to be *hypotonic* with respect to the other. (If red cells are placed in a hypotonic environment, therefore, they hemolyze.) When one of two solutions has a higher osmotic pressure, it is said to be *hypertonic* compared with the other. (Red cells, therefore, undergo crenation in a hypertonic solution.)

Selected Reading List

Articles

1. D. F. Othmer. "Water and Life." *Chemistry,* November 1970, page 12. A discussion of the earth's water supply and potential shortages.
2. G. R. Choppin. "Water. H_2O or $H_{180}O_{90}$?" *Chemistry,* March 1965, page 7. An interesting discussion of the molecular structure of liquid water.
3. "The Ocean." *Scientific American,* September 1969. The entire issue is devoted to this major resource.

United States Government Publications

1. *River of Life. Water: The Environmental Challenge.* U. S. Department of the Interior Conservation Yearbook No. 6, 1970.
2. "New Water." Office of Saline Water, U. S. Department of the Interior, 1970.
3. "The A-B-Seas of Desalting." Office of Saline Water, U. S. Department of Interior, 1968.

Brief Summary

1. Particles with diameters of 0.5–2.5 A (the range for atoms, small molecules and ions) can form true solutions but those with a diameter (or at least one dimension) of 10–1000 A are in the colloidal state.

2. A solution is a uniform, intimate, and stable mixture of the smallest particles (ions, molecules, atoms) from two or more substances.

3. The stability of a colloidal dispersion depends largely on the presence of some stabilizing substance (e.g., emulsifying agent) or on a surface electrical charge. The Brownian movement also helps to prevent settling.

4. The covalent bonds in water, the most important solvent in our study, form an angle of 104.5°, which helps to explain one of the most significant facts about a water molecule, its great polarity. Because of this polarity, water molecules tend to stick to each other and hydrogen bonds are said to exist *between* them.

5. The phenomenon of surface tension arises from the polarity of water molecules.

6. The kinetic-molecular theory, the concept of polar molecules, and the principle that unlike charges attract all combine in explanations for the following:
   (a) How water manages to dissolve certain polar or ionic substances.
   (b) How hydration is important to the mechanism of dissolution.
   (Be sure you can describe to yourself just *how* these are explained.)

7. Hydrates are substances in which intact water molecules are held in definite proportions.

8. How concentrated a solution can be depends on the nature of the solute, the solvent, and the temperature. A polar solvent such as water best dissolves very polar molecules or ionic materials.

9. The solubilities of most solids increase with temperature, whereas those of gases decrease with temperature. (Be able to explain how the kinetic-molecular theory helps to explain these generalizations.)

10. Saturated solutions represent instances of dynamic equilibria, situations involving much activity with no net change.

11. The concept of molarity provides a way of expressing concentrations of solutions in terms of moles of solute per liter of solution. Weight-volume percentages state concentrations as grams of solute per 100 cc of final solution.

12. Electrolytes are solutes whose aqueous solutions conduct electricity; nonelectrolytes form nonconducting solutions.

13. Osmosis occurs when there is a net passage of water from a dilute solution (or pure solvent) to a concentrated solution through a semipermeable membrane. (Be able to explain *how* the net flow is in this direction.)

14. Dialysis, a process similar to osmosis, is the migration of small ions and molecules, but not colloidal particles, through dialyzing membranes. Such membranes form an important part of the body, for they separate various fluid compartments from each other.

Problems and Exercises

1. Compare and contrast the three types of dispersions: solutions, colloidal dispersions, and suspensions.

2. Water molecules are polar. What does this mean?

3. Suppose there exists a diatomic molecule, X–Y, and suppose that X is the symbol of an atom of higher atomic number than Y. By writing $\delta+$ and $\delta-$ at appropriate places by the structure, X–Y, indicate the probable polarity of this molecule. (Assume X and Y to be in the same period in the periodic chart.)

4. Ammonia molecules are polar, although not as polar as water molecules. Where would you expect the partial negative charge to be in an ammonia molecule?

5. Predict the bond angle, H—N—H, in the ammonia molecule using the approach illustrated in Fig. 6.2. (The actual value is $106°47'$.)

6. Why are hydrates classified as compounds? How are their anhydrous forms used? Distinguish between the terms *desiccant, hygroscopic, deliquescent.*

7. How would the surface tension of water be affected by raising its temperature? Explain your answer. What do surface-active agents do?

8. Explain in your own words *how* water brings about the solution of sodium chloride.

9. Why is water an effective solvent only for ionic substances or very polar covalent compounds?

10. Molecules of carbon tetrachloride (a common dry-cleaning solvent), CCl_4, are nonpolar. Why will sodium chloride not dissolve in it? (That is, why cannot sodium ions and chloride ions be kept apart and in solution in this solvent?)

11. The speed with which a solid can be dissolved in water increases if we (a) crush the solid to a powder to increase its total surface area, (b) stir the mixture, and (c) heat the mixture.
    Using the kinetic-molecular theory, explain these facts. (This question has nothing to do with *how much* can be gotten into solution, even though heat affects this, too. It has to do only with *how fast* a solution can be made.)

12. Assume the availability of volumetric flasks of the following sizes: 1 liter, 500 cc, 250 cc, 100 cc, and 10 cc. Describe how you would prepare solutions of the following concentrations in the following amounts. State the grams of solute you would weigh and the size of volumetric flask you would select. (Percents are wt/vol percents.)
    (a) 1 liter of 1M NaOH
    (b) 0.5 liter of 0.1M sucrose ($C_{12}H_{22}O_{11}$)
    (c) 100 cc of 0.5M sucrose
    (d) 0.25 liter of 0.1M HCl
    (e) 0.5 liter of 0.9% NaCl
    (f) 0.1 liter of 10% NaOH
    (g) 0.01 liter of 0.1M Na_2SO_4 (State answer in mg.)
    (h) 250 cc of 0.5M LiOH
    (i) 250 cc of 5% NaCl

(i) 0.5 liter of 0.65M NH₄Cl

Ans. (a) 40 g NaOH; 1 liter. (b) 17.1 g sucrose; 500 cc. (e) 4.5 g NaCl; 500 cc.

13. Refer to Fig. 6.9 for this question. In each case below, state which level, A or B, would rise if compartments A and B contained the following solutions:

(a) 10% sucrose in A; 1% sucrose in B.

(b) 0.5% NaCl in A; 0.5M NaCl in B.

(c) 10% NaCl in A; 10% NaI in B (be careful).

14. The chemical stockroom is supplied with the following stock solutions: 0.1M HCl, 0.02M NaOH, 0.05M KOH, 10% HBr, 5% Na₂CO₃. What volume of stock solution would be needed to obtain the amounts of solutes specified in each case below? (Percents are wt/vol percents.)

(a) 0.1 mole HCl

(b) 0.01 mole NaOH

(c) 0.1 mole KOH

(d) 1 g HBr

(e) 2.5 g Na₂CO₃

(f) 1 mole HBr

(g) 0.5 mole Na₂CO₃

(h) 0.75 mole HBr

Ans. (b) 500 cc. (f) 810 cc.

chapter 7 important ionic compounds and their reactions

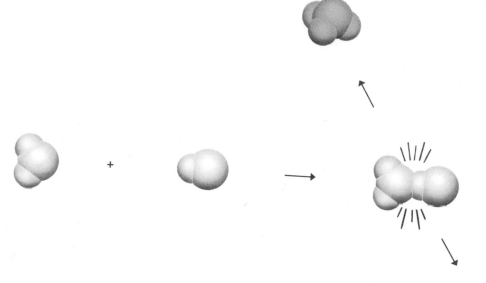

Of the roughly 100 elements, slightly more than a dozen are necessary for building and maintaining living things. These few (C, H, N, O, S, P, Ca, Na, Fe, K, Cl, I, Mg, Cu, and Mo) all serve essential purposes. To ask which is the most important is to ask a meaningless question. If any one were missing, the body could not long survive. Many of these elements are present as their ions. Table salt furnishes two, Na^+ and Cl^-, that have no structural function. They provide no energy. The body needs them to do a few chemical chores—it needs the chloride ion, for example, to make hydrochloric acid for gastric juice—and to maintain osmotic pressure balances. The bloodstream needs a minute trace of hydroxide ions and many other ions. In this chapter, we shall study the behavior of certain key types of ionic substances in aqueous solutions.

ions versus atoms In almost all respects, both chemical and physical, *ions are vastly different from their corresponding neutral atoms*. This must be emphasized. Because symbols for ions and atoms are so nearly alike, beginning students frequently confuse the two kinds of particles. You have observed in the laboratory, for example, the great contrast between copper metal, Cu, and the brilliantly blue copper ion, Cu^{2+}. You are also familiar with the great contrast between sodium metal, Na (violently reactive and viciously corrosive when moisture is present), and sodium ions, Na^+ (extremely stable, necessary for health). This chapter is about *ions* and how they behave toward each other in solution.

Solutions of ions can be made in two ways: first, by dissolving ionic compounds in water and, second, by permitting certain covalent substances or elements to react with water. The first change is called *dissociation*: the separation and diffusion of preexisting ions. The second event is sometimes called *ionization*: the formation or synthesis of ions by chemical reaction.

principal ion-producing substances Substances that can produce ions in water may be classified as follows. Those that liberate hydronium ions in water are called *acids*. Those that liberate hydroxide ions in water are called *bases*. Other substances that liberate other kinds of ions are usually called *salts*. These definitions of acids, bases, and salts are part of a broad theory of ionization formulated in 1887 by a young Swedish graduate student in chemistry, Svante Arrhenius, and modernized slightly for presentation here. Since his time, other more comprehensive theories of acids and bases have been advanced (Brønsted; Lewis; Pearson). We shall study the Brønsted theory later. All these theories, however, include the Arrhenius theory as a special, limiting case. By starting our study with the Arrhenius concepts we cover the most common and familiar acids and bases first. The discussion that follows, therefore, always assumes that water is the solvent because it was primarily this situation with which Arrhenius dealt.

Our discussion will not simply restate the views of Arrhenius. Instead, we shall incorporate from the start one important modification, a change that takes into account the involvement of water molecules in solutions of acids and bases.

ionization of water and dynamic equilibrium In the last chapter liquid water was viewed strictly as a molecular species in which a vast, interlacing, constantly shifting network of hydrogen bonds existed. No hint of the existence of ions in pure water was given. There are ions present, however, but only in exceedingly trace concentrations. The ions are the *hydronium ion*, H_3O^+, and the hydroxide ion, OH^-.

The kinetic-molecular theory taught us the concept of molecules in motion and collision. Hydronium ions and hydroxide ions arise whenever especially

important ionic compounds and their reactions

violent collisions occur between two water molecules that happen to be on a properly oriented collision course:

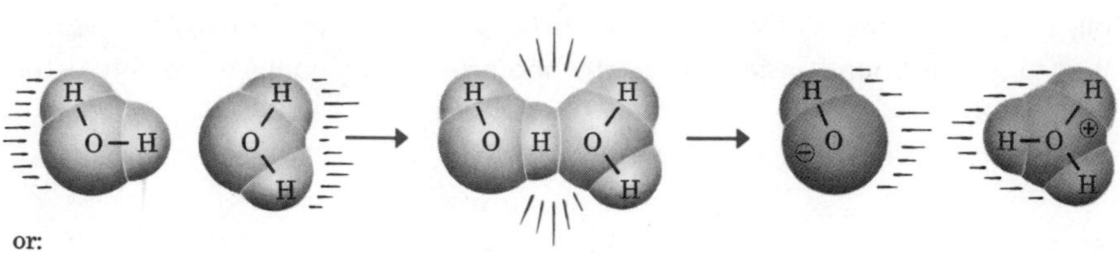

or:

$$H_2O + H_2O \rightleftharpoons HO^- + H_3O^+.$$

Only trace concentrations of ions form because collisions of sufficient violence seldom occur. The two O-H bonds in water are very strong. Moreover, the reverse reaction is energetically very easy if and when a hydroxide ion, a rare species in pure water, does find a hydronium ion, equally rare. The result of these two opposing reactions—forward and reverse—is a steady-state condition, a dynamic equilibrium. It is *dynamic* because there is a considerable coming and going; but it is an *equilibrium* because there is no net change. At equilibrium the concentrations of the ions do not change as time passes. The use of an especially short arrow pointing to the right (toward the ions) in the equation is a simple device to signal that the concentrations of the products at equilibrium are low relative to the concentrations of the reactants. We say that the equilibrium "favors" the reactants, not the products. The longer arrow points toward the particles in greater concentration at equilibrium, the intact water molecules in this case.

The concentration of hydronium ions at room temperature in "pure" water is only about 10^{-7} percent. For every hydronium ion that forms a hydroxide ion *must* also form; its concentration in pure water is therefore also 10^{-7} percent (at room temperature).

If you heat pure water you increase the frequency of violent collisions and produce slightly higher concentrations of the ions. We say that we "shift the equilibrium" in favor of products. Regardless of temperature, however, *in pure water the following relation must be true.*

Concentration of H_3O^+ = Concentration of OH^-

In the Arrhenius theory, modernized for our study, an acid *is any substance that will produce in water a higher concentration of hydronium ions than hydroxide ions.*

A base *is any substance that will make hydroxide ions more concentrated than hydronium ions in water.*

acids and bases

"hydronium ion" versus "hydrogen ion"—where the Arrhenius theory has been modernized. Arrhenius defined acids as substances that liberate hydrogen ions, H^+. He did not and could not realize that these ions (which, after all, are bare protons, the nuclei of hydrogen atoms) cannot exist in water, that they are bound instead to water molecules. We could write this as an equation:

$$H^+ \quad + \quad :\overset{\displaystyle H}{\underset{\displaystyle H}{O}}: \quad \longrightarrow \quad H-\overset{+}{\underset{\displaystyle H}{O}}\overset{\displaystyle H}{:} \qquad \text{Both electrons for this bond were donated by the oxygen.}$$

proton ("hydrogen ion")   hydronium ion

In ordinary conversation between chemists the terms "proton," "hydrogen ion," and "hydronium ion" are used interchangeably, and in many of our later discussions we shall do this, also. But in this chapter we shall stick to the most correct usage—hydronium ion, H_3O^+.

properties of acids   The most important property of acids in water is, to repeat, their ability to liberate hydronium ions. Thus, aqueous solutions of acids have sour tastes, because of the presence of hydronium ions. Organic acids in vinegar, lemon juice, rhubarb, and grapefruit are responsible for their tartness. Solutions that are acidic turn blue litmus paper red, again, because they contain more hydronium ions than hydroxide ions. (See the discussion of Indicators, Chapter 8.)

Some acids liberate one hydronium ion per molecule, and they are called *monoprotic* (one-proton) acids. For example, when gaseous hydrogen chloride is bubbled into water, its molecules react with water to form ions, as illustrated in Fig. 7.1.

In the hydronium ion, the extra proton is attached to oxygen by means of a covalent bond. Note, however, that when that bond forms, *both* electrons for the shared pair are furnished by oxygen. Because of this difference in mode of formation, chemists call such covalent bonds *coordinate covalent bonds* (sometimes, *dative* bonds). Furthermore, it is customary to say that the proton *coordinates* with the water molecule.

Coordinate covalent bonds vary widely in strength. The one in the hydronium ion is not very strong.[1] The proton is easily transferred to any

[1] To say "the *one* (coordinate covalent bond) in the hydronium ion" is to use a manner of speaking. Once that bond forms, the system promptly "forgets" the origin of the bond, and all three O-H bonds in H_3O^+ immediately become equivalent. All three O-H bonds are equally weak in H_3O^+.

important ionic compounds and their reactions

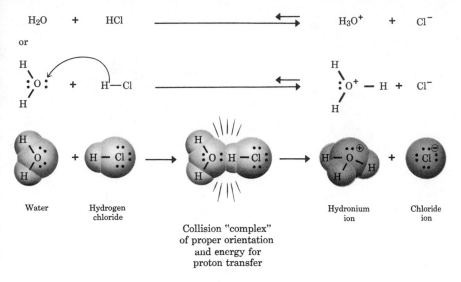

$$H_2O \quad + \quad HCl \quad \longleftrightarrow \quad H_3O^+ \quad + \quad Cl^-$$

or

Water · Hydrogen chloride · Collision "complex" of proper orientation and energy for proton transfer · Hydronium ion · Chloride ion

Fig. 7.1 When molecules of gaseous hydrogen chloride dissolve in water, they react with water molecules to form hydronium ions and chloride ions. The proton initially bound to a chlorine is now more strongly bound to an oxygen.

other group that can bind it more strongly. That is the principal reason why we may take the liberty of speaking of hydrogen ions and H^+ when it would be more correct to say hydronium ions and H_3O^+.

Other important monoprotic acids are the other hydrogen halides dissolved in water—hydrobromic acid (HBr) and hydriodic acid (HI)—as well as nitric acid (HNO_3) and acetic acid.

Nitric acid:[2]

or: $H_2O + HNO_3 \rightleftharpoons H_3O^+ + NO_3^-$

nitric acid   nitrate ion

Acetic acid:[3]

or: $H_2O + H-C_2H_3O_2 \rightleftharpoons H_3O^+ + C_2H_3O_2^-$

acetic acid   acetate ion

[2] In the structures for nitric acid and sulfuric acid the arrows signify coordinate covalent bonds.

[3] Its hydrogens attached to carbon are very strongly bound and will not transfer to water molecules.

Sulfuric acid, H_2SO_4, is *diprotic*. Both its protons are available to furnish hydronium ions:[2]

$$H_2O + H\!-\!O\!-\!\overset{\displaystyle O}{\underset{\displaystyle O}{\overset{\uparrow}{\underset{\downarrow}{S}}}}\!-\!O\!-\!H \;\rightleftharpoons\; H_3O^+ + {}^-O\!-\!\overset{\displaystyle O}{\underset{\displaystyle O}{\overset{\uparrow}{\underset{\downarrow}{S}}}}\!-\!O\!-\!H$$

or:
$$H_2O + \underset{\text{sulfuric acid}}{H_2SO_4} \;\rightleftharpoons\; H_3O^+ + \underset{\substack{\text{hydrogen sulfate}\\ \text{ion}}}{HSO_4^-}$$

The second proton is not as easy to transfer—compare the relative lengths of the arrows—because it has to be pried away from a particle that is already negatively charged, not electrically neutral:

$$H_2O + H\!-\!O\!-\!\overset{\displaystyle O}{\underset{\displaystyle O}{\overset{\uparrow}{\underset{\downarrow}{S}}}}\!-\!O^- \;\rightleftharpoons\; H_3O^+ + {}^-O\!-\!\overset{\displaystyle O}{\underset{\displaystyle O}{\overset{\uparrow}{\underset{\downarrow}{S}}}}\!-\!O^-$$

or:
$$H_2O + \underset{\substack{\text{hydrogen sulfate}\\ \text{ion}}}{HSO_4^-} \;\rightleftharpoons\; H_3O^+ + \underset{\substack{\text{sulfate}\\ \text{ion}}}{SO_4^{2-}}$$

strong and weak acids. Anyone who has ever spilled sulfuric acid on skin or clothing knows that it must be washed away very quickly or it will cause damage. Boric acid, on the other hand, is used in common eyewash preparations. If boric acid shows any of the reactions typical of acids, it must show them very slowly, or under special circumstances. We say that boric acid is a *weak acid*; that sulfuric acid is a *strong acid*. What these useful terms really mean we must find out, for they have important implications both in the chemistry of human health and in understanding some environmental problems.

Hydrogen chloride is acidic in water because a chloride ion simply cannot hold onto H^+ as strongly as can a water molecule. Acetic acid molecules transfer their ionizable protons to water molecules for a similar reason. They furnish hydronium ions by a process similar to that involving hydrogen chloride, and which is illustrated in Fig. 7.2.

However, acetic acid molecules are not nearly as efficient as hydrogen chloride molecules in transferring ionizable protons to water molecules. At room temperature, only about 1% of the acid molecules are ionized in 0.1M acetic acid. It is precisely because such a small percentage are ionized that acetic acid is classified as a weak acid. On the other hand, the percentage ionization of solute in hydrochloric acid is very high. Therefore, it is called a strong acid.

important ionic compounds and their reactions

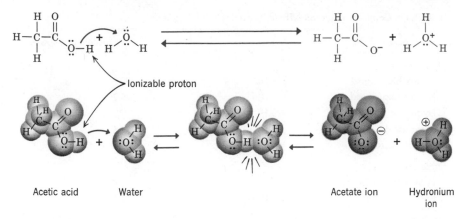

Ionizable proton

Acetic acid   Water   Acetate ion   Hydronium
                                                          ion

Fig. 7.2 When acetic acid molecules dissolve in water, at any given instant a small percent reacts with water molecules to form a low concentration of hydronium ions and acetate
ions. Only the more violent, on-target collisions lead to proton-transfer. The fraction of
all the collisions that are violent enough is much lower for acetic acid than for hydrogen
chloride. The reason is that the proton to be transferred is relatively weakly bound to
chlorine in H-Cl, but more strongly bound to oxygen in acetic acid.

By definition, *weak acids are those that ionize to only a small percentage
in water. Strong acids ionize in percentages well over 50% and approaching
100%*. In Table 7.1 several common acids are listed according to these
categories.

The reactions that are most characteristic of aqueous solutions of the stronger
acids are reactions of their hydronium ions. The weaker acids will give the
same reactions but more slowly. Remember that concentration affects the rate
of a reaction; in aqueous solutions of weak acids the concentrations of
hydronium ions are much less than in solutions of strong acids.

**chemical
properties of
acids**

reaction of acids with active metals. Hydronium ions react with active metals
to generate salts and hydrogen gas. For example, zinc metal reacts with
hydrochloric acid to form zinc chloride, a typical salt, and hydrogen. A *salt*
is any compound consisting of metallic ions (or any positively charged ions
other than H^+ or H_3O^+) together with any *counter-ion*, any negatively
charged ion other than ^-OH. This reaction may be represented in any one
of the following ways:

(a) $Zn + 2HCl \longrightarrow ZnCl_2 + H_2$

This conventional way of writing the
reaction shows the formulas of the
chemicals involved and the proportions in which they interact.

Table 7.1 Common Acids and Their Percentage Ionizations[a]

Acid		Percentage Ionization
Strong acids		
Hydrochloric acid	HCl	92
Hydrobromic acid	HBr	92
Hydriodic acid	HI	92
Nitric acid	HNO_3	92
Sulfuric acid	H_2SO_4[b]	61 (in 0.05M solution)
Moderate acids		
Phosphoric acid	H_3PO_4	27
Sulfurous acid[c]	H_2SO_3	20
Weak acids		
Nitrous acid[c]	HNO_2	1.5
Acetic acid	$H—C_2H_3O_2$	1.3
Carbonic acid[c]	H_2CO_3	0.2
Boric acid	H_3BO_3	0.01

[a]Data are for 0.1M solutions of the acids in water, at room temperature.
[b]*Concentrated* sulfuric acid (99%) is particularly dangerous not only because it is a strong acid, but also because it is a powerful dehydrating agent. This action generates considerable heat at the reaction site, and at higher temperatures sulfuric acid becomes even more dangerous. Moreover, concentrated sulfuric acid is a thick, viscous liquid that does not wash away from skin or fabric very quickly.
[c]An unstable acid. See textual discussion.

(b) $Zn + 2(H_3O^+ + Cl^-) \longrightarrow$
$\qquad (Zn^{2+} + 2Cl^-) + H_2 + 2H_2O$ This expression emphasizes that the reaction involves atomic zinc and ionized hydrogen chloride, and that zinc ions and molecular hydrogen form. Chloride ions do nothing; they are merely passive observers.

(c) $Zn + 2H_3O^+ \longrightarrow Zn^{2+} + H_2 + 2H_2O$ This equation lays bare the essence of the reaction, the only *chemical* event that occurs. Note that it is a redox process.

(d) $Zn + 2H^+ \longrightarrow Zn^{2+} + H_2$ This equation is a common shorthand expression for (c).

Equations of type (c) or (d) are frequently referred to as *ionic equations*. They are used very often to emphasize the essential chemical event of a reaction that involves ions. They leave our view of the chemical event uncluttered by any ions or molecules to which nothing important happens.

In balancing ionic equations, both a *material balance* and an *electrical balance* must be made. Both the number and kinds of nuclei and the *net* number and kind of electrical charge on both sides of the equation must balance.

Metals differ widely in their tendencies to react with hydronium ions. When they do, the atoms of the metal are oxidized; they lose electrons and become metal ions. The electrons are transferred to protons (taken from H_3O^+ ions), which are reduced and made electrically neutral, and which emerge as molecules of hydrogen gas. Elements in the alkali-metal family (Group I of the periodic chart), such as sodium and potassium, include the most reactive metals of all. They not only reduce protons taken from hydronium ions, but they can also reduce protons taken from water. The following reaction of sodium metal is extremely violent:

$$2Na \ + \ 2H_2O \longrightarrow 2NaOH + \ H_2$$

| Sodium metal | Water | | Sodium hydroxide | Hydrogen |

(It would be even more violent in aqueous acids.) Gold, on the other hand, is stable not only toward water but also toward hydronium ions.

The common metals can be arranged in an activity order, an order of their decreasing tendency to become ionic. The result is called the *activity series of the metals*, which appears in Table 7.2. Atoms of any metal above hydrogen in the series will transfer electrons to H^+ particles taken either from

Table 7.2   Activity Series of the Metals

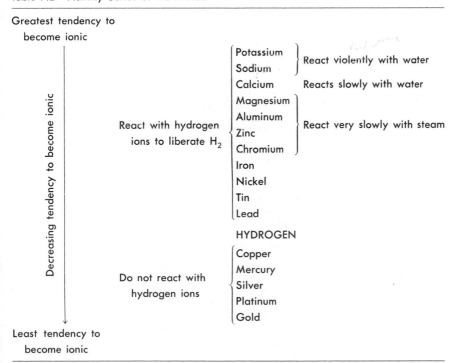

Greatest tendency to
  become ionic

Decreasing tendency to become ionic

Potassium, Sodium — React violently with water
Calcium — Reacts slowly with water
Magnesium, Aluminum, Zinc, Chromium — React very slowly with steam

React with hydrogen ions to liberate H_2: Potassium, Sodium, Calcium, Magnesium, Aluminum, Zinc, Chromium, Iron, Nickel, Tin, Lead

HYDROGEN

Do not react with hydrogen ions: Copper, Mercury, Silver, Platinum, Gold

Least tendency to
  become ionic

H_2O or H_3O^+ to form hydrogen gas, leaving metal ions behind. Tin and lead, however, react only very slowly. The metals below hydrogen on the list do not transfer electrons to H^+ particles.

reaction of acids with metal hydroxides. Hydronium ions in acidic solutions react with metal hydroxides to form salts and water. Sodium hydroxide and nitric acid react as follows:

$$NaOH + HNO_3 \longrightarrow NaNO_3 + H_2O$$

The basic chemical event is given by the ionic equation:

$$OH^- + H_3O^+ \longrightarrow 2H_2O$$
$$\text{or, for short:} \quad OH^- + H^+ \longrightarrow H_2O$$

If the solution resulting from this reaction were evaporated to dryness, crystals of sodium nitrate, $NaNO_3$, a typical salt, would remain.

reaction of acids with carbonates and bicarbonates. To understand these reactions we need to know the structure and one key property of carbonic acid, H_2CO_3, the fact that it is not very stable. It decomposes easily, as follows, and a dynamic equilibrium is established:

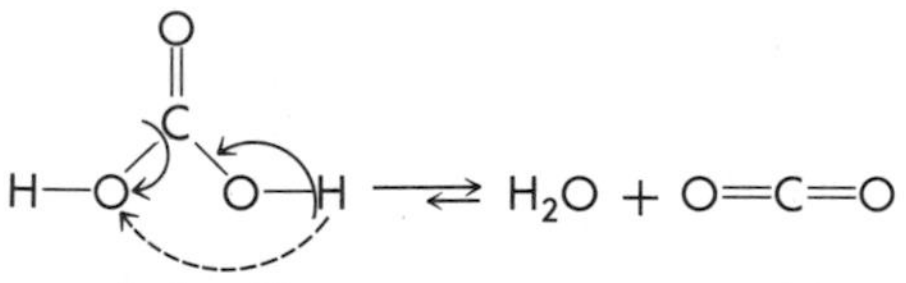

carbonic acid   carbon dioxide

The reverse reaction (with the shorter arrow) occurs to some extent when carbon dioxide is bubbled into water. (If pressure is applied, more CO_2 dissolves in water and more carbonic acid forms.) A solution of carbon dioxide in water, therefore, always contains a small amount of unstable carbonic acid.

Carbonic acid is a *weak* diprotic acid. There are two possible negative ions, the bicarbonate ion and the carbonate ion:

(HCO_3^-) (CO_3^{2-})

bicarbonate ion   carbonate ion

The fact that carbonic acid is a *weak* acid means only one thing, that it holds its protons strongly, more strongly than protons are held in hydronium

important ionic compounds and their reactions

ions. Therefore, if we add hydronium ions by means of a strong acid to a solution of sodium bicarbonate, bicarbonate ions will take protons and carbon dioxide will fizz away.

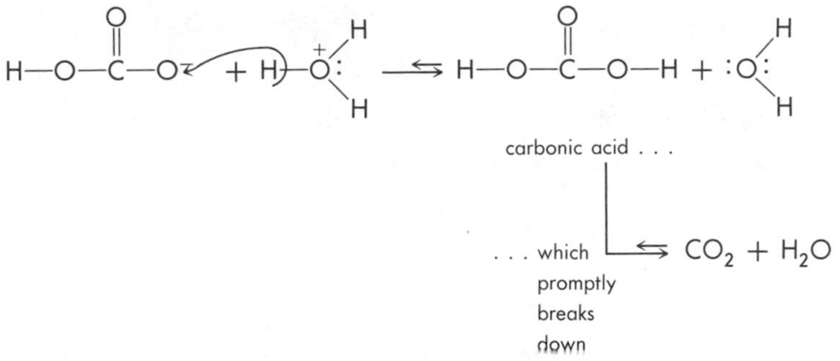

carbonic acid . . .

. . . which promptly breaks down $\rightleftharpoons CO_2 + H_2O$

The full, conventional equation is: (where (aq) means aqueous solution)

$$NaHCO_3 + HCl_{(aq)} \longrightarrow NaCl + H_2O + CO_2\uparrow$$

Sodium carbonate would also react with an acid to liberate carbon dioxide, water, and a salt. Only the mole proportions (the coefficients) are different:

$$Na_2CO_3 + 2HCl_{(aq)} \longrightarrow 2NaCl + H_2O + CO_2\uparrow$$

The ionic equation is:

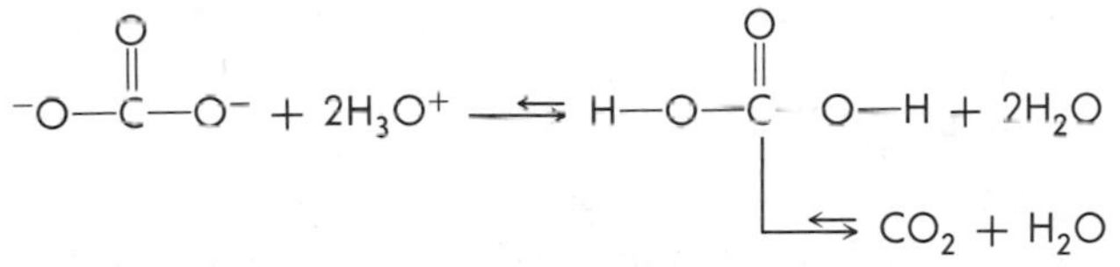

$\rightleftharpoons CO_2 + H_2O$

Both limestone and marble, two important building stones, are mostly calcium carbonate. Calcium carbonate, although insoluble in water, is easily attacked by aqueous acids:

$$CaCO_3 + 2H_3O^+ \longrightarrow Ca^{2+} + H_2O + CO_2\uparrow$$

Monuments and buildings made of marble or limestone are therefore subject to corrosion by the acids in smoggy, polluted air. The oxides of sulfur react with water to generate lower or higher concentrations of the hydronium ion in the aqueous aerosols, mists, and humidity of smog. Sulfur trioxide is the most serious source of acid because it reacts with water to form a strong (highly ionized) acid, sulfuric acid:

$$SO_3 + H_2O \longrightarrow H_2SO_4$$

sulfuric acid

chemical properties of acids

Sulfur dioxide resembles carbon dioxide in its reaction with water, it forms an unstable acid:

$$SO_2 + H_2O \rightleftharpoons H_2SO_3 \quad (H-O-\overset{\overset{O}{\|}}{S}-O-H)$$

sulfurous acid

The difference is that sulfurous acid, although not a very strong acid (see Table 7.1), is much stronger than carbonic acid:

$$H_2SO_3 + H_2O \rightleftharpoons H_3O^+ + HSO_3^-$$

hydrogen
sulfite ion

Both oxides of sulfur, therefore, contribute to the acidity of smog that in some areas is so serious that not only do metals corrode, but people die. The deaths and illness in the air pollution disaster that happened in the valley of the Meuse River, Belgium, in December of 1930 were caused mostly by sulfur oxides. The valley had many industries, including a sulfuric acid plant, a zinc smelter, several coke ovens, and blast furnaces. Over 60 people died and 6000 became ill, mostly from the acidic mists produced by the sulfur oxides. Similar disasters occurred, for essentially the same reasons, in Donora, Pennsylvania, in October, 1948 (20 died; 6000 made ill) and several times in London (e.g., 4000 deaths in the 1952 disaster).

properties of bases The most characteristic property of bases, in the Arrhenius sense, is that they liberate hydroxide ions in water. Solutions containing even a relatively small excess of hydroxide ions over hydronium ions have a bitter taste. They also have a slippery, soapy "feel." Solutions containing more hydroxide ions than hydronium ions turn red litmus blue. (See discussion of Indicators, Chapter 8.) Finally, to review a reaction already discussed under acids, bases react with acids to form salts and water. This reaction, called *neutralization*, is probably the most important chemical property of the hydroxide ion. For example:

$$NaOH + HCl \longrightarrow NaCl + H_2O$$

The ionic equation is:

$$OH^- + H_3O^+ \longrightarrow 2H_2O$$
$$\text{Or, for short:} \quad OH^- + H^+ \longrightarrow H_2O$$

Much of Chapter 8 is devoted to acid-base neutralization.

strong and weak bases. In the Arrhenius sense, a *strong base* is one for which the percentage dissociation in solution is high. The percentage dis-

important ionic compounds and their reactions

Table 7.3 **Common Bases**

Base		Solubility[a]	Percentage Dissociation
Strong bases			
Sodium hydroxide	NaOH	109	91 (in 0.1M solution)
Potassium hydroxide	KOH	112	91 (in 0.1M solution)
Calcium hydroxide (An aqueous solution is called limewater)	$Ca(OH)_2$	0.165	Nearly 100 (saturated solution)
Magnesium hydroxide (A slurry in water is called milk of magnesia)	$Mg(OH)_2$	0.0009	Nearly 100 (saturated solution)
Weak base			
Aqueous ammonia	NH_3	89.9 grams NH_3 at 0°C	1.3 (at 18°C)[b]

[a] Solubilities are in grams of solute per 100 grams of water at 20°C, unless otherwise specified.
[b] The "dissociation" referred to here is the reaction:

$$NH_3 + H_2O \rightleftharpoons NH_4^+ + OH^-$$

sociation of a *weak base* is low. Table 7.3 lists a few bases according to these categories.

The terms *strong* and *weak*, when applied to acids and bases, do not necessarily describe their behavior toward tissue or cloth. Damage by alkalies to certain fabrics and to skin occurs quickly only when fairly concentrated solutions of hydroxide ions are involved. Of the bases in Table 7.3, only sodium hydroxide and potassium hydroxide can be used to prepare such solutions. Calcium hydroxide and magnesium hydroxide are only slightly soluble in water. Hence, it is not possible to obtain concentrated solutions of these that would cause severe damage to the body or to clothing. Indeed, one of them, magnesium hydroxide, as a slurry in water ("milk of magnesia"), is often taken internally as a mild purgative and an antacid. Calcium hydroxide and magnesium hydroxide are listed as strong bases, however, because "strong" here refers to *percent* dissociation of whatever does dissolve in the solution, not to solubility in water.

aqueous ammonia. The great solubility of ammonia in water is attributed to hydrogen bonding. Therefore, we extend our knowledge of hydrogen bonds with this example. Originally we learned that hydrogen bonds can extend from a hydrogen on one water molecule to an oxygen on another. In aqueous ammonia, such hydrogen bonds, of course, occur between water molecules. In addition, however, hydrogen bonds extend from hydrogens on water molecules to nitrogens on ammonia molecules. This situation is illustrated in Fig. 7.3.

An ammonia molecule possesses one unshared pair of electrons in the

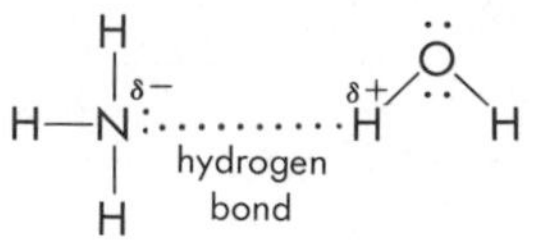

Fig. 7.3 The solubility of ammonia in water is made possible by the existence of opportunities for hydrogen bonding. Ammonia molecules can slip into the hydrogen bond network of water.

outermost shell of the nitrogen. When ammonia is dissolved in water, the following dynamic equilibrium is established:

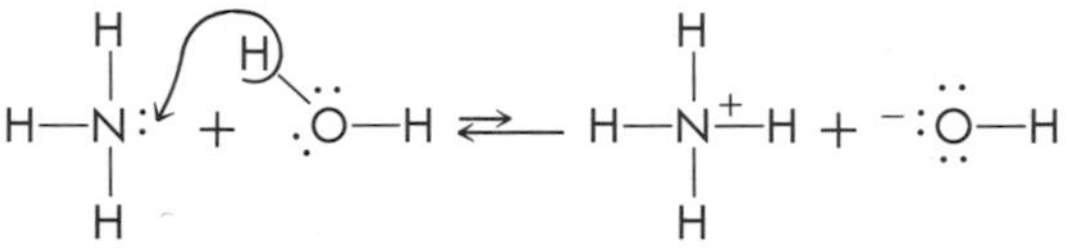

$$\text{or } NH_3 + H_2O \rightleftharpoons NH_4^+ + OH^-$$

As the unequal lengths of the arrows indicate, the dynamic equilibrium favors the species on the left side of the equation. Consequently, in spite of the great solubility of gaseous ammonia in water (see Table 7.3), only a small percentage of hydroxide ions actually forms. That is why aqueous ammonia is often (misleadingly) called "ammonium hydroxide."

The important base in aqueous ammonia is not the hydroxide ion. It is the ammonia molecule. This insight was introduced into chemistry largely by the efforts of Johannes Brønsted, who gave us a broader view of acids and bases, a view to which we now turn.

Brønsted theory of acids and bases

According to definitions introduced in 1923 by Professor Brønsted, a colleague of Niels Bohr, *an acid is any proton donor; a base is any proton acceptor.* A Brønsted acid, therefore, is quite similar to an Arrhenius acid, but the Brønsted concept also applies to situations in which water is not the solvent and hydronium ions are not involved.

The Brønsted definition of a base embraces any species capable of tying up a proton. The hydroxide ion certainly qualifies. Even a water molecule qualifies; when it accepts a proton from a strong acid, it behaves as a Brønsted base, although a feeble one. One of the most important non-Arrhenius bases that qualifies as a Brønsted base is the ammonia molecule. It is an elegant proton acceptor, according to the equation:

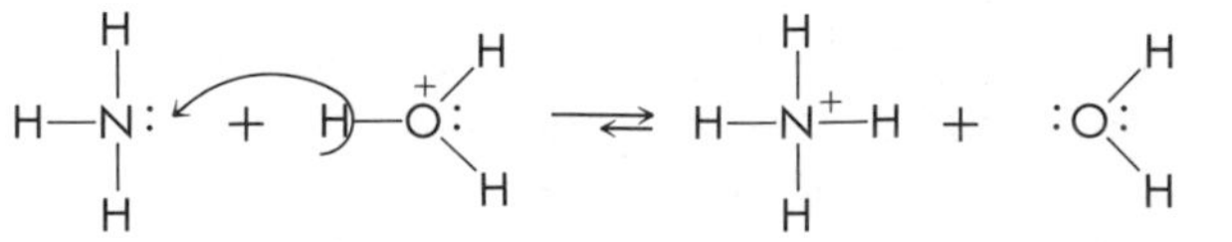

Ammonia	Hydronium ion	Ammonium ion	Water
(stronger base)	(stronger acid)	(weaker acid)	(weaker base)

important ionic compounds and their reactions

It is this ability to neutralize acid that makes the ammonia molecule the most important basic species present in aqueous ammonia.

According to the Brønsted concept, a strong Brønsted acid is one that readily donates a proton; a weak acid is one that has difficulty in releasing a proton. A weak Brønsted base holds a proton only loosely after accepting it. A strong Brønsted base readily accepts and strongly binds a proton. Table 7.4 contains a list of a few common Brønsted acids and bases in order of their strengths.

salts

Salts are prepared whenever an acid reacts with a metal or a metal hydroxide, carbonate, or bicarbonate. If the aqueous solutions from these reactions are evaporated to dryness, crystalline salts collect. All salts are aggregations of oppositely charged ions and are solids at room temperature.

solubilities of salts in water. Salts vary widely in their solubility in water. Some useful "rules of thumb" are the following:

All sodium, potassium, and ammonium salts are soluble.
All nitrates and acetates are soluble.
All chlorides, except those of lead, silver, and mercury(I), are soluble.

Table 7.4   Relative Strengths of Some Common Brønsted Acids and Bases

Brønsted Acid		Brønsted Base	
Name	Formula	Name	Formula
Perchloric acid	$HClO_4$	Perchlorate ion	ClO_4^-
Hydrogen iodide	HI	Iodide ion	I^-
Hydrogen bromide	HBr	Bromide ion	Br^-
Sulfuric acid	H_2SO_4	Hydrogen sulfate ion	HSO_4^-
Hydrogen chloride	HCl	Chloride ion	Cl^-
Nitric acid	HNO_3	Nitrate ion	NO_3^-
HYDRONIUM ION	H_3O^+	WATER	H_2O
Hydrogen sulfate ion	HSO_4^-	Sulfate ion	SO_4^{2-}
Phosphoric acid	H_3PO_4	Dihydrogen phosphate ion	$H_2PO_4^-$
Acetic acid	$H-C_2H_3O_2$	Acetate ion	$C_2H_3O_2^-$
Carbonic acid	H_2CO_3	Bicarbonate ion	HCO_3^-
Ammonium ion	NH_4^+	Ammonia	NH_3
Bicarbonate ion	HCO_3^-	Carbonate ion	CO_3^{2-}
Water	H_2O	Hydroxide ion	OH^-
Methyl alcohol	CH_3-H	Methoxide ion	CH_3O^-
Ammonia	NH_3	Amide ion	NH_2^-
Hydrogen	H_2	Hydride ion	H^-

Increasing acid strength

Increasing base strength

Salts not in the above categories are generally insoluble or, at best, only slightly soluble.

There are exceptions to these rules, but we shall not be wrong very often in applying them. By "solubility" is meant at least to the extent of a 3%–5% solution.

When a salt dissolves in water, to whatever extent, it completely dissociates. In concentrated solutions, however, solute ions may crowd each other so much that many behave as they were stuck together. This gives the appearance of a less than 100% dissociation.

salts from double decomposition reactions. Another way of making salts is by a reaction called *double decomposition or change of partners*. If oppositely charged ions that ordinarily constitute an insoluble salt are mixed together in water, these ions will aggregate and precipitate. This is one of many instances in which the solubility rules are helpful. Consider an experiment in which a solution of sodium sulfate is added to a solution of barium nitrate. Since both these salts are soluble in water, the following ions initially are present in a dissolved state: Ba^{2+}, NO_3^-, Na^+, SO_4^{2-}. Let us now examine all possible combinations of oppositely charged ions from these.

$$Ba^{2+} + 2NO_3^- \xrightarrow{?} Ba(NO_3)_2\downarrow$$ This possibility is obviously out, for barium ions and nitrate ions do not precipitate together from water. ("All nitrates are soluble.")

$$2Na^+ + SO_4^{2-} \xrightarrow{?} Na_2SO_4\downarrow$$ This possibility is also out. ("All sodium salts are soluble.")

$$Na^+ + NO_3^- \xrightarrow{?} NaNO_3\downarrow$$ Again, "all sodium salts are soluble."

$$Ba^{2+} + SO_4^{2-} \xrightarrow{?} BaSO_4\downarrow$$ Barium sulfate is not in any of the categories of water-soluble compounds. We conclude, therefore, that it is insoluble.

We should expect, consequently, that barium ions and sulfate ions will aggregate and precipitate from the solution. We can write the reaction, then, as:

$$Ba(NO_3)_2 + Na_2SO_4 \longrightarrow 2NaNO_3 + BaSO_4\downarrow$$

This way of writing the equation indicates the "change of partners" aspect of the reaction. However, the only event of importance is:

$$Ba^{2+} + SO_4^{2-} \longrightarrow BaSO_4\downarrow$$

Precipitated barium sulfate could be collected on a filter. Evaporation of the clear filtrate would yield pure, crystalline sodium nitrate, provided that correct proportions of reactants were used.

This reaction has been studied in detail because it is important to ask yourself, "What are *all* the possibilities when ions are mixed together in solution?" Knowing a few solubility rules, you can make successful predictions of what to expect, if you follow this advice. Considerable tedious memorization of a multitude of inorganic reactions can be avoided by judicious application of a few generalizations.

some generalizations about ionic reactions. In general, *reactions between ionic substances (or those that can produce ions in solution) will occur if there is the possibility of forming:*

(a) *a gas* (e.g., action of acids on carbonates and bicarbonates);

(b) *an un-ionized, although soluble, species* (e.g., formation of water by the action of acids on metal hydroxides);

(c) *a precipitate* (e.g., action of sodium sulfate on barium nitrate).

salts of medical or commercial importance. Several common salts of practical utility are listed in Table 7.5. Many of them are hydrates. (Because of space limitations, their full formal names as hydrates are not stated.)

detection of strong and weak electrolytes. Solutions containing ions conduct electricity, as we learned in Chapter 6, and how well such a current is conducted depends on the concentration of ions actually present. Figure 7.4

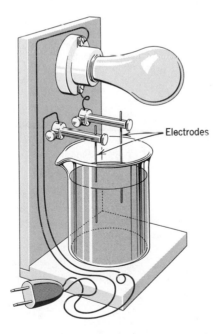

— Electrodes

Fig. 7.4 Device to test for the presence and strength of electrolytes in solution.

Table 7.5 Important Salts and Their Uses

Formula and Name	Uses
$Al_2(SO_4)_3 \cdot 18H_2O$ Aluminum sulfate	Astringent; mordant; water purifier
$(NH_4)_2CO_3$ Ammonium carbonate	Aromatic spirits of ammonia, "smelling salts" (together with ammonium hydroxide and the aromatic oils of nutmeg, lemon, and lavender)
NH_4Cl Ammonium chloride	Diuretic; soldering flux
$BaSO_4$ Barium sulfate (barite)	White pigment for rubber goods, paper, oil-cloth, linoleum; used in X-raying gastrointestinal tract ("barium cocktail")
$(CaSO_4)_2 \cdot H_2O$ Calcium sulfate (plaster of Paris)	Plaster casts; wall stucco; wall plaster
$CuSO_4 \cdot 5H_2O$ Copper sulfate (blue vitriol)	Insecticide; fungicide; used in electroplating copper
$MgSO_4 \cdot 7H_2O$ Magnesium sulfate (Epsom salt)	Purgative; tanning and dyeing
$HgCl$ Mercury(I) chloride (mercurous chloride; calomel)	Purgative; diuretic
$HgCl_2$ Mercury(II) chloride; (mercuric chloride; corrosive sublimate)	Disinfectant, in dilute solutions, for hands, and instruments that cannot be boiled; poisonous
$KMnO_4$ Potassium permanganate	In 0.02% solution—disinfectant for irrigation of urinary tract, vagina, and infected wounds In 1% solution—for local treatment of athlete's foot and poison ivy
$AgNO_3$ Silver nitrate (lunar caustic)	Antiseptic and germicide (used in eyes of infants to prevent gonorrheal conjunctivitis); photographic film sensitizer; indelible ink; hair dyes
$NaHCO_3$ Sodium bicarbonate (baking soda)	Baking powders; effervescent salts; stomach antacid; fire extinguishers
$Na_2CO_3 \cdot 10H_2O$ Sodium carbonate (soda ash; sal soda; washing soda)	Water softener; used in soap and glass manufacture

important ionic compounds and their reactions

Table 7.5 Important Salts and Their Uses (continued)

Formula and Name	Uses
NaCl Sodium chloride (table salt)	Physiological saline solutions; freezing "baths"; flavoring agent
NaClO Sodium hypochlorite (Dakin's solution; commercial bleaches; known only in solution)	Irrigating wounds; bleach
$Na_2SO_4 \cdot 10H_2O$ Sodium sulfate (Glauber's salt)	Purgative; tanning and dyeing; manufacture of glass and paper
SnF_2 Tin(II) fluoride (stannous fluoride; Fluorostan)	Toothpaste additive to combat dental caries
$K_2SO_4 \cdot Al_2(SO_4)_3 \cdot 24H_2O$ Potassium aluminum sulfate (alum)	Astringent in styptic "pencils"; water purification
$Na_2SO_4 \cdot Al_2(SO_4)_3 \cdot 24H_2O$ Sodium aluminum sulfate (sodium alum)	Used in one type of baking powder
$Pb_3(OH)_2(CO_3)_2$ Basic lead carbonate (white lead)	Common pigment in white paint
$Bi(OH)_2NO_3$ Dibasic bismuth nitrate (bismuth subnitrate)	Stomach antacid to promote healing of ulcers

illustrates a laboratory apparatus that can be used to find out quickly, although only approximately, whether a solution contains a weak or strong electrolyte, or a nonelectrolyte. If an electrolyte—the ion producer—is almost completely ionized in solution, it is called a *strong electrolyte*. A *weak electrolyte* is one that exists in solutions almost completely as dispersed molecules with a trace of ions available. A *nonelectrolyte,* for all practical purposes, furnishes no ions, and its solutions are nonconducting.

hard water. Certain salts in groundwater interfere with the use of soap, and water containing them is called *hard water*. One of the minerals in the earth's crust is limestone, a form of calcium carbonate, $CaCO_3$. It is not very soluble in water. Rain water that is rich in dissolved carbon dioxide, however, has a leaching action on limestone that brings calcium ions into the ground-water. The following reaction occurs.

$$CaCO_3 + CO_2 + H_2O \longrightarrow Ca(HCO_3)_2$$

Calcium carbonate
(limestone)

Calcium bicarbonate

The product, calcium bicarbonate, is more soluble in water than is calcium carbonate.

Other ions commonly found in groundwater that interfere with soap are those of magnesium and iron, as well as sulfate and chloride ions. The positive ions, Ca^{2+}, Mg^{2+}, Fe^{2+} and Fe^{3+}, are responsible for "hardness" of water, for they react with soap to form insoluble curds and scums. Soft water lacks these ions (although it may contain others). *To soften hard water, the offending metallic ions must be removed from solution.*

In the home, the most common water-softening procedure is the use of excess soap. Some of the soap is wasted as it precipitates with the positive ions, and the remainder of the soap functions as the cleanser. Synthetic detergents consist of tailor-made molecules that do not precipitate in hard water (see Chapter 14).

Soft water in which the principal *negative* ion is the bicarbonate ion may be softened by boiling. It is designated *temporary hard water*. Boiling provides heat, which decomposes bicarbonate ions according to the equation:

$$2HCO_3^- \xrightarrow{\Delta} CO_3^{2-} + CO_2\uparrow + H_2O$$

(A common symbol for heat is the Greek capital delta, Δ.) As soon as carbonate ions appear they immediately form the far less soluble carbonates of calcium, magnesium, and iron. As these carbonates precipitate, the metallic ions, of course, leave the aqueous solution and no longer can react with soap. Temporary hard water that is circulated in hot boilers, steam pipes, or sterilizers deposits these carbonates as a scaly precipitate that may eventually clog the equipment (see Fig. 7.5).

Permanent hard water lacks sufficient bicarbonate ion to be softened by boiling. Washing soda and household ammonia are common softening agents that precipitate the positive ions of hard water. The following equations illustrate how they work:

$$CaSO_4 + Na_2CO_3 \longrightarrow CaCO_3\downarrow + Na_2SO_4 \text{ (soluble)}$$

Washing soda,
in solution

$$MgSO_4 + 2NH_4OH \longrightarrow Mg(OH)_2\downarrow + (NH_4)_2SO_4 \text{ (soluble)}$$

"Ammonium hydroxide"

Many other techniques are available. One of the most modern takes advantage of the fact that, when hard water trickles through certain naturally

important ionic compounds and their reactions

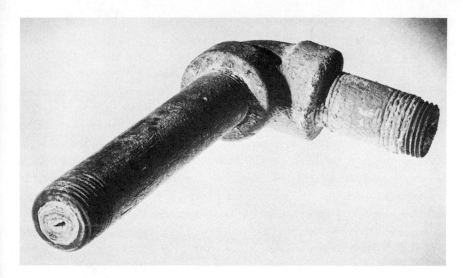

Fig. 7.5 Carbonate scale in a water pipe. The inside diameter of this pipe has been reduced almost to nothing by the accumulation of carbonate scale. (Courtesy of the Permutit Company, a division of Sybron Corporation.)

occurring, porous substances (zeolites) or through synthetic, ion-exchange resins, troublesome calcium, magnesium, or iron ions are exchanged for sodium ions or others not as bothersome.

phosphates in detergents. The "phosphorus" that is said to be in several of the stronger detergents is not elemental phosphorus or even phosphate ion, $PO_4{}^{3-}$. Instead, the most widely used form of phosphorus is sodium tripolyphosphate, or STPP. Some detergents in 1970 had as much as 53% STPP. The fully unprotonated tripolyphosphate ion has the structure shown. In water, this ion will bind 1 to 3 protons; a mixture of ions is present.

tripolyphosphate ion

nitrilotriacetate ion
(NTA)

Tripolyphosphate ions can strongly bind calcium, magnesium, and iron ions *without precipitating,* and this detergent material therefore softens hard water. At the same time it suspends dirt and solubilizes grease. It is altogether a first rate detergent for hard water and tough laundry and dishwasher work.

But, alas, the phosphates from the laundries and kitchens of the country drain into our lakes where they provide a nutrient important to the growth of algae, the one algal nutrient most easily controlled by man. Lake Erie, in the 1960s and early 1970s was receiving about 150,000 pounds of "phosphates" daily. Some comes in from Lake Huron but over two-thirds originates from the wastes of municipalities around Lake Erie. About a third of this phosphate influx leaves each day via the Niagara River. The phosphate level in Lake Erie in the early 1970s was in the range of 0.05–0.15 mg/liter. To stop algal problems, biologists tell us that the phosphate level should be no higher than 0.01 mg/liter. Some beaches of Lake Erie were fouled in 1967 by six inches to three feet of decaying algae, according to a *Science* magazine report (vol. *158*, page 351). French scientists, according to a *New York Times* report (18 January 1970), regard detergent pollution as the single most serious threat to marine life on the Mediterranean Sea.

To reduce phosphate pollution we either stop using it in detergents or remove it in sewage treatment plants. At one of the newer, advanced sewage treatment plants in the United States, the $19 million system at Lake Tahoe, California, over 80% of the original phosphate is removed at an operating cost of 7¢ to 8¢ per thousand gallons. (Total operating cost is about 30¢ per thousand gallons.) Because of this cost, scientists with the detergent industry have sought substitutes for tripolyphosphate, a search no doubt quickened by a rash of local ordinances sharply restricting or banning phosphates in detergents. In the early 1970s, an organic salt, sodium nitrilo-triacetate, or NTA, seemed to be the best substitute for phosphates. Although not as good a cleansing agent, it can also tie up the metal ions in hard water. The largest detergent manufacturers were switching to NTA during 1970. Unhappily, later in 1970 evidence surfaced that NTA might itself be dangerous. It not only ties up the ions responsible for hardness in hard water, it also takes up poisonous ions such as those of mercury and cadmium. In doing so, it greatly increases the toxicity of these ions. Mercury is a common pollutant now (see Chapter 16); the danger as government scientists and public health officials saw it was that the increasing use of NTA would bring NTA-bound mercury and cadmium into well water. The use of NTA as a substitute for phosphate was therefore banned. Following the government's ban several laboratories launched experiments of their own and by mid-1971 some evidence emerged that the dangers of NTA were less than initial experiments had indicated. The future of NTA in detergents (as of mid-1971) was therefore unclear. Complicating the picture was the discovery, reported in mid-1971, that overgrowths of algae in coastal, saltwater marine environments are limited not by phosphates but by nitrogen (as in fertilizers or even NTA). Replacing phosphates in detergents by NTA would therefore be worse than useless as far as coastal waters are concerned, waters that receive about half the sewage of the country (*Environment*, May 1971, page 25).

important ionic compounds and their reactions

Selected Reading List

Book

1. D. E. Carr. *Death of the Sweet Waters.* Berkley Publishing Corporation, N. Y., 1966. What we have done to ruin our waterways, beaches and lakes.

Pamphlet

1. Committee Report. *Phosphates in Detergents and the Eutrophication of America's Waters.* 1970 U. S. Government Printing Office (40¢). The 23rd report to the 91st Congress of the House Committee on Government Operations and based on a study of its Subcommittee on Conservation and Natural Resources, Henry S. Reuss (D., Wisc.), Chairman. The pros and cons of the issue are presented, together with considerable data, as brought out in subcommittee hearings.

Brief Summary

1. It is emphasized that ions differ greatly from their corresponding neutral atoms.
2. The principal ion-producing substances are acids, bases, and salts.
3. In the modernized Arrhenius version, acids liberate hydronium ions in solution; bases liberate hydroxide ions; salts release ions other than these.
4. The characteristic reactions of acids are actually the typical reactions of hydronium ions. These include reactions with metals, metal hydroxides, metal carbonates, and metal bicarbonates.
5. The hydroxide ion is responsible for the typical properties of bases, neutralization of acids being one of the most important.
6. When solutions containing different ions are mixed, a reaction may or may not occur. A reaction can be expected if it is possible and reasonable for a gas, an un-ionized but soluble molecule, or a precipitate to form. Such events usually do not involve all the kinds of ions present. Ionic equations are used to designate exactly which species participate in a reaction.
7. The terms *strong* and *weak,* when applied to acids, bases, or electrolytes in general, designate something about the extent to which these substances can experience a high percent ionization in solution.
8. The dynamic equilibrium that is present when an acid has dissolved in water involves a competition between two species for a proton. Water molecules can bind protons by means of coordinate covalent bonds. Certain negative ions can also bind protons. Those that can do so much better than water molecules (e.g.,

acetate ions) will form weakly acidic solutions. Those that are weaker than water molecules in binding protons (e.g., chloride ion) can form strongly acidic solutions.

9. Ammonia molecules dissolve readily in water because they can participate in hydrogen bonding with water molecules. Some ammonia molecules react with water to form ammonium ions and hydroxide ions.

10. In the Brønsted theory an acid is a proton donor, a base is a proton acceptor. Under these definitions, *strength* and *weakness* refer to relative abilities to release or to bind protons.

11. Salts do not have characteristic chemical properties as do acids and bases. Solubility rules for salts facilitate making predictions about a reaction when solutions of salts are mixed.

Problems and Exercises

1. Write two types of balanced equations (complete equations and ionic equations) for the reaction of hydrochloric acid with each of the following substances. (Where no reaction occurs, state so.)

Set I	Set II	Set III
(a) NaOH	Al	$Mg(HCO_3)_2$
(b) K_2CO_3	KOH	NaBr
(c) Ca	KBr	Mg
(d) NaCl	Na_2CO_3	Li_2CO_3
(e) $NaHCO_3$	$LiHCO_3$	$Ca(OH)_2$

2. Repeat Problem 1 using nitric acid instead of hydrochloric acid.

3. For each salt listed below, write the formula of the acid and of the base needed for its preparation by an acid-base neutralization reaction:

Set I	Set II	Set III
(a) NaBr	Na_2HPO_4	NaI
(b) $NiCl_2$	KCl	KH_2PO_4
(c) KNO_3	$NaC_2H_3O_2$	$Zn(NO_3)_2$
(d) $NaNO_3$	Na_2SO_4	$Mg(HSO_4)_2$

4. Assume that you have separate solutions of each compound in each of the following pairs. Predict what will happen, chemically, if the two solutions in each pair are mixed. Write an ionic equation for the reaction. If no reaction occurs, state so.

Set I	Set II	Set III
(a) K_2SO_4 and	$NaNO_3$ and	$LiCl$ and
$Ba(NO_3)_2$	$CaCl_2$	$AgNO_3$
(b) $NH_{3(aq)}$ and	Na_2S and	Na_2SO_4 and
HCl	$Cu(NO_3)_2$	$BaCl_2$
(c) NH_4BR and	$Pb(NO_3)_2$ and	Na_2CO_3 and
Na_2SO_4	Na_2SO_4	HBr
(d) $CaCl_2$ and	$Hg(NO_3)_2$ and	KOH and
$NaOH$	KCl	H_2SO_4
(e) $NaHCO_3$ and	KOH and	$Pb(NO_3)_2$ and
H_2SO_4	HNO_3	HCl

5. Describe the factor that contributes most to the solubility of ammonia in water.

6. Why is it that acids and bases (in the Arrhenius sense) lend themselves to easy generalizations but salts do not?

7. What would be the principal difference between a 0.1M solution of a weak acid and a 0.1M solution of a strong acid, aside from the formulas of the acids?

8. Why is calcium hydroxide classified as a strong base when it is nearly insoluble in water?

9. List the principal properties of acids and bases according to the Arrhenius concept.

10. What is the difference between a coordinate covalent bond and a covalent bond?
    (a) In the mode of formation?
    (b) After formation of the bonds has occurred?

11. Why is the reaction of an acid with a metal carbonate properly called neutralization of the acid?

12. Would the chemicals that soften permanent hard water also soften temporary hard water? Explain.

13. In each pair below, according to the Brønsted concept, which would be the stronger base?
    (a) Br^- or HCO_3^- (d) NH_3 or NH_2^-
    (b) $H_2PO_4^-$ or HSO_4^- (e) OH^- or H_2O
    (c) NO_2^- or NO_3^- (f) HS or S^{2-}

14. In each pair below, which would be the stronger Brønsted acid?
    (a) $H_2PO_4^-$ or HPO_4^{2-} (d) H_2CO_3 or HCl
    (b) H_2SO_3 or HSO_3^- (e) H_2O or OH^-
    (c) NH_4^+ or NH_3 (f) HSO_4^- or H_3BO_3

15. A solution of ammonium chloride in water has a barely perceptible odor of ammonia, but if a solution of sodium hydroxide is added to it, the odor of ammonia becomes very distinct. Write an ionic equation that would explain this.

16. Define and illustrate each of the following:
    (a) dissociation   (c) hydronium ion   (e) diprotic acid
    (b) acid   (d) ionization   (f) ionic equation

(g) base   (i) strong acid   (k) Brønsted base
(h) strong base   (j) weak electrolyte   (l) neutralization
                (m) coordinate covalent bond
                (n) aqua ammonia (what species are present?)
                (o) hard water (temporary and permanent)
                (p) soften water
                (q) NTA

important ionic compounds and their reactions

chapter 8 acidity: its measurement and control

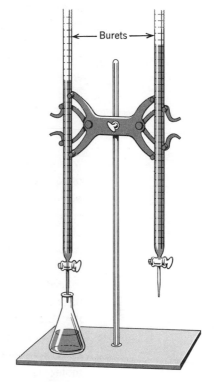

Burets

Protons and proteins are two words taken from the Greek word *proteios,* meaning "first." It is interesting that one of nature's simplest substances, a proton, and one of its most complex, a protein, should rate the common distinction of being "first," of primary importance. Proteins will be studied in three later chapters. Protons deserve at least one chapter, partly because the presence or absence of protons, as hydronium ions, profoundly affects proteins. Protons are blamed for upset stomach or acid indigestion and for tooth decay. Vinegar, containing acetic acid, curdles milk. Meat that, for one reason or another, becomes too acidic is darker than normal, slimy, and difficult to cure properly. Both hydronium ions and hydroxide ions are corrosive. Both are important catalysts that can act in the breaking down of food molecules. Both affect the efficiency of body catalysts, enzymes. These are some reasons we must study ways to detect their presence and to control their concentration.

the pH concept
and dilute
acids or bases

In molar units, the ionization of pure water, at room temperature, furnishes a hydrogen-ion[1] concentration of only 1×10^{-7} mole per liter (and the same concentration of hydroxide ions). Chemists and physiologists have discovered that hydrogen-ion concentrations of this order of magnitude are extremely important, in spite of being so small, partly because hydrogen ions and hydroxide ions act as catalysts for many reactions. Catalysts, you will recall, can exert their influence in very small concentrations. These ions also affect the efficiency of other catalysts, such as enzymes, which are themselves present in small concentrations.

Chemists and technologists routinely make hundreds and thousands of measurements of extremely minute concentrations of hydrogen ions. As a matter of simple convenience, the manipulation of such awkward figures as negative exponents (e.g., 10^{-7}) or their decimal equivalents (e.g., 0.0000001) is tedious, and chemists long ago adopted a shortcut. Instead of using the entire figure with its negative exponent, the exponent itself is used. This exponent is defined as the pH of the solution. Mathematically,

$$[H^+] = 1 \times 10^{-pH}$$

where $[H^+]$ is the concentration of hydrogen ions *in moles per liter*.[2] In other words, the pH of a solution is simply the negative power (the p in pH) to which the number 10 must be raised to express the moles-per-liter concentration of the solution's hydrogen ions (hence the H in pH). For water, at room temperature, $[H^+] = 1 \times 10^{-7}$ mole/liter; therefore, the pH of pure water at room temperature is 7.

A solution that contains more hydrogen ions than hydroxide ions is acidic. In terms of pH units, because of the nature of negative exponents, an acidic solution will have a pH less than 7 (e.g., if $[H^+] = 10^{-6}$, pH = 6, and the solution is acidic). Conversely, a solution that is basic will have a hydrogen-ion concentration less than the hydroxide-ion concentration. Therefore, basic solutions will have pHs greater than 7 (e.g., if $[H^+] = 1 \times 10^{-9}$ mole/liter, pH = 9, and the solution is basic).

Example 1. A blood specimen was found to have a pH of 7.35. Was the blood acidic, basic, or neutral?

Solution. First of all, what do we do with a pH value such as 7.35, that is not a neat whole number? This pH value means that:

$$[H^+] = 1 \times 10^{-7.35}$$

[1] The terms hydrogen ion and hydronium ion will be used interchangeably. See Chapter 7.

[2] Squared brackets [ ] around any formula in chemistry are a symbol that the *moles-per-liter concentration* of the substance in the brackets is specified.

To handle such a number, a mathematical tool, logarithms, is needed.[3] If you do not possess knowledge of logarithms, we shall have to be satisfied with the recognition that 7.35 lies between 7.00 and 8.00. This places the actual value of the hydrogen-ion concentration somewhere between 1×10^{-7} and 1×10^{-8} mole/liter. (The exact value, determined by use of logarithms, is $[H^+] = 4.47 \times 10^{-8}$ mole/liter.) The hydrogen-ion concentration is less than 1×10^{-7} mole/liter; therefore, the specimen is basic.

At equilibrium in any aqueous solution, regardless of *p*H, the values of $[H^+]$ and $[OH^-]$ do not change—that is what equilibrium means. The product of these two concentrations is a constant at any particular temperature. At room temperature:

$$[H^+][OH^-] = 1 \times 10^{-14}$$

Thus, if $[H^+] = 1 \times 10^{-4}$ (a slightly acidic solution) then

$$[OH^-] = \frac{1 \times 10^{-14}}{[H^+]} = \frac{1 \times 10^{-14}}{1 \times 10^{-4}} = 1 \times 10^{-10}$$

In water, in which the following equilibrium is present:

$$H—OH \rightleftarrows H^+ + OH^-$$

if some acid is added to water to make $[H^+] = 1 \times 10^{-4}$, then the equilibrium shifts in that direction that tends to use up the added acid (at least as much as possible). In this case, hydroxide ions tied up some of the acid and as this happened their concentration was reduced to $[OH^-] = 1 \times 10^{-10}$ (from $[OH^-] = 1 \times 10^{-7}$).

detection of hydrogen and hydroxide ions; indicators; *p*H measurements

indicators. To know whether a solution or fluid specimen is acidic or basic is one matter, but to know exactly how acidic or basic is quite another, and usually far more important.

Certain organic dyes show one color above a characteristic *p*H and another color below that *p*H (or *p*H range). Litmus is perhaps the best-known example. In acid, below the *p*H range 4.5 to 8.5, litmus is red; in base, above that range, it is blue. Litmus is usually impregnated into porous paper (litmus paper).

Any dye that will perform the service of indicating the *p*H of a solution is called an *indicator*. Several common indicators and the colors they impart

[3] The equation $[H^+] = 1 \times 10^{-pH}$ may also be expressed as

$$pH = \log \frac{1}{[H^+]}$$

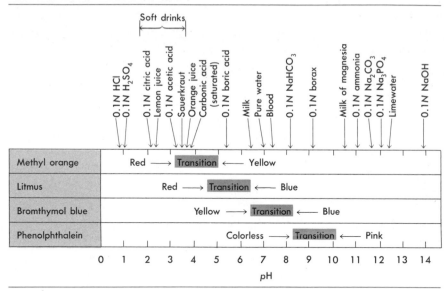

Table 8.1 Colors of Some Common Indicators at Various pH Values and pH Values for Some Common Substances (at 25°C)

to solutions at various pH intervals are listed in Table 8.1. By using two or more of these on test portions of a solution, the pH can be determined to within one pH unit. For example, suppose that a solution is found to be colorless to phenolphthalein. Its pH, therefore, must be some value (it could be any value) less than 9. If this solution, however, is also light blue to bromothymol blue, its pH, while less than 9, cannot be less than 7. It is somewhere between 7 and 9. This example illustrates how two indicators can be used to pinpoint the pH of a solution within a fairly narrow range.

Specially prepared papers containing several indicator dyes are available commercially. When moistened with a test solution, these papers turn a characteristic color that can be compared with a color-pH "code" on the dispenser. With these papers, pHs to within a few tenths of a pH unit are easily and rapidly determined.

If test solutions are highly colored, or if highly precise pH measurements are needed, commercial pH meters are necessary (see Fig. 8.1). These employ specially prepared electrodes that are made to dip into the test solution. Some electrodes are engineered to permit accurate pH measurements of extremely small samples of a test solution. They measure pHs accurately and quickly to within a hundredth of a pH unit.

measurement of total acidity or basicity The pH of a solution tells us indirectly the actual concentration of hydrogen ions in whatever dynamic equilibrium may be present in the solution. It does not, however, tell us anything about the "total acidity," that is, the total concentration of species capable of neutralizing hydroxide ions (or equivalent proton-binders).

ionic equilibria and total acidity. In a 1M acetic acid solution, only slightly more than 0.4% of all acetic acid molecules are ionized at any one time. The pH of this solution is about 2.4. Therefore, it is not strongly acidic, in spite of the fact that its concentration of acetic acid is considered to be fairly high, 1 mole per liter. The pH measurement tells us only that the ionic equilibrium in which acetic acid molecules participate favors un-ionized molecules rather than corresponding ions:

$$CH_3-\overset{\overset{\displaystyle O}{\|}}{C}-O-H + H_2O \rightleftharpoons CH_3-\overset{\overset{\displaystyle O}{\|}}{C}-O^- + H_3O^+$$

acetic acid   acetate ions

The total acidity or the total neutralizing capacity in our sample is still 1 molar, however, since each liter of a 1M solution of acetic acid contains 1 mole of *ionizable hydrogen ions.*

We shall use the expression "ionizable hydrogen ion" to designate one that can be captured by a hydroxide ion to form water. The hydronium ion,

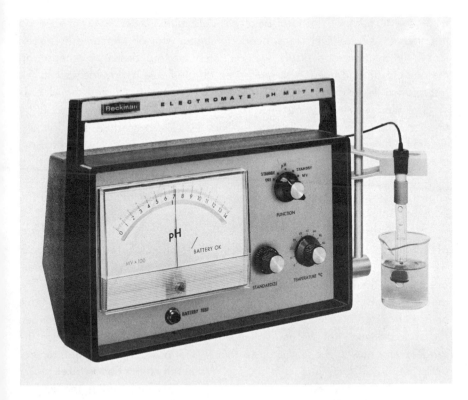

Fig. 8.1   pH meter. (Courtesy of Beckman Instruments, Inc.)

measurement of total acidity or basicity

for example, has an ionizable hydrogen ion. In the neutralization of, say, aqueous HCl, all that occurs is the transfer of a hydrogen ion from the hydronium ion to a hydroxide ion:

$$\underset{H}{\overset{H}{\underset{|}{\overset{|}{O}}}}\!\!-\!\!H + \ddot{O}\!\!-\!\!H \rightleftharpoons \overset{H}{\underset{H}{O}}: + \ddot{O}\!\!-\!\!H$$

Action of hydroxide ions on molecules of acetic acid results in a similar transfer. The ionizable hydrogen in a molecule of acetic acid is the one attached to oxygen. It can be taken by a hydroxide ion, too:

$$CH_3-\overset{O}{\overset{\|}{C}}-\ddot{O}\!\!-\!\!H + \ddot{O}\!\!-\!\!H \rightleftharpoons CH_3-\overset{O}{\overset{\|}{C}}-\ddot{O}: + \overset{H}{\underset{}{O}}\!\!-\!\!H$$

stronger	stronger	weaker	weaker
Brønsted	Brønsted	Brønsted	Brønsted
acid	base	base	acid

Another way of looking at this is to note that any molecule or ion possesses an ionizable hydrogen if it cannot bind one of its hydrogens as strongly as can a hydroxide ion (in the form of water).

acid-base titrations. The total acidity is determined by carefully measuring the amount of base (OH^- ions) needed to react with all ionizable hydrogen ions in the solution. Conversely, we can determine total basicity by measuring the amount of acid needed to react with all available hydroxide ions in the test solution. Hydrogen ions react with hydroxide ions in a mole ratio of $1:1$.

The most common way to conduct a measurement of this type is by *titration*. The apparatus is illustrated in Fig. 8.2. The procedure is as follows. A carefully measured volume of the solution of unknown acidity (or basicity) is placed in a beaker or flask. An indicator is added. If the "unknown" is an acid, a *standard solution* (that is, one whose concentration is accurately known) of a strong base is added to the "unknown" from a buret until the indicator color just barely changes.

If the indicator is properly chosen, this color change occurs when the pH of the solution is what it would be if a solution of the salt that forms were prepared in the same concentration. Methyl orange and phenolphthalein are perhaps the most commonly used indicators for acid-base titrations. The precise point at which all available hydrogen ions (or hydroxide ions) have been neutralized is called the *equivalence point* of the titration. Usually, when the analyst thinks that the equivalence point is close at hand, he adds the reagent very slowly, drop by drop (or fraction of a drop!), until the indicator undergoes its characteristic color change. When this color change takes place, we say that the *end point* has been reached, because that is the end of the titration. Only if the indicator has been carefully selected to give this

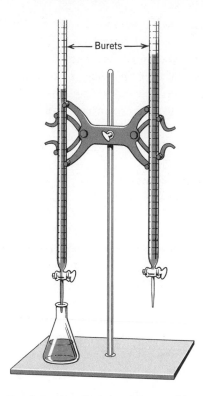

Fig. 8.2   A typical titration assembly.

change of color at the pH of the equivalence point will the end point of
the titration correspond to the equivalence point.

normal solutions; gram-equivalent weights; "equivalents." For purposes of
acid-base titrations, chemists prefer not to deal with concentrations expressed
in terms of molarity. Some acids, for example, consist of molecules each of
which can release more than one hydrogen ion (e.g., sulfuric acid). In titration
analysis, chemists use the more convenient concept of the *normal solution*.
By definition, a 1 normal solution of an acid contains 1 mole of *ionizable*
hydrogen ion per liter.

One mole of sulfuric acid (H_2SO_4; formula weight, 98) contains 2 moles
of ionizable hydrogen ions. Therefore, it takes only half a mole of sulfuric
acid, 49 grams, to supply 1 mole of potential hydrogen ion. This weight,
49 grams, of sulfuric acid is called its *gram-equivalent weight*.

Whatever the acid, its gram-equivalent weight is that amount, in grams,
that will contain one mole of potential hydrogen ion—potential in the sense
that hydroxide ion can get at it in water and neutralize it. By definition:

(1) Gram-equivalent weight of an acid

$$= \frac{\text{gram-formula weight of the acid}}{\text{number of ionizable } H^+ \text{ ions per molecule}}$$

For a monoprotic acid, such as hydrochloric, the gram-equivalent weight coincides with the gram-formula weight.

The gram-equivalent weight of any base is that amount, in grams, that will be capable of neutralizing one mole of hydrogen ion. This definition, of course, applies to the one base in the Arrhenius theory—hydroxide ion—but it also applies to anything that can neutralize hydrogen ion such as carbonate ion, bicarbonate ion, metal oxides, and others that will be discussed later. For the Arrhenius base, by definition:[4]

(2) Gram-equivalent weight of base

$$= \frac{\text{gram-formula weight of base}}{\text{number of available } OH^- \text{ ions per formula unit}}$$

The gram-equivalent weight of sodium hydroxide, $NaOH$, is the same as its gram-formula weight, 40 grams. However, the gram-equivalent weight of calcium hydroxide, $Ca(OH)_2$, is one-half its gram-formula weight, or $\frac{1}{2} \times 74$ grams = 37 grams.

In working with 1 gram-formula weight, we adopted the abbreviation *mole*. Similarly, we shall use the noun *equivalent* as an abbreviation for 1 gram-equivalent weight. Thus, 1 equivalent of sodium hydroxide weighs 40 grams; and 1 equivalent of sulfuric acid weighs 49 grams. In general:

$$(3) \qquad \text{Number of equivalents} = \frac{\text{number of grams of substance taken}}{\text{gram-equivalent weight of substance}}$$

The normality of a solution is the ratio of the number of equivalents of the solute per liter of solution. It is, therefore, analogous to molarity. A 1 normal solution (1N) of an acid contains 1 equivalent of an acid, or Avogadro's number of ionizable hydrogen ions, per liter of solution. A 2 normal solution (2N) of a base contains 2 equivalents of a base, or twice Avogadro's number of available hydroxide ions, per liter of solution.

Example 2. Calculate the weight of sulfuric acid needed to prepare 100 ml of a 1N solution.

Solution. In any problem of this type, until you gain experience, always write out or say to yourself in words exactly what the expression, 1N, really means. It means that our solution must contain a *ratio* of one gram-equivalent weight of sulfuric acid per liter of solution (no matter whether we want a thimbleful or an ocean of it). Hence, to solve this problem, we need to know

---

[4] A more general definition would be:

$$\text{Gram-equivalent weight of base} = \frac{\text{gram-formula weight of base}}{\text{number of available proton-binding units}}$$

the gram-equivalent weight of sulfuric acid. This is found by dividing the gram-formula weight by 2:

$$\frac{\text{Gram-formula weight of } H_2SO_4}{2} = \frac{98 \text{ grams}}{2}$$

$$= 49 \text{ grams, the gram-equivalent weight}$$

Our solution must have a *ratio* of 49 grams of sulfuric acid per liter. But we need only 100 ml of solution. Therefore, we take $\frac{100}{1000}$ or $\frac{1}{10}$ of 49 grams, 4.9 grams (our answer), and dissolve it in water so that the final volume is 100 ml.

The definition of normality can be stated in equation form as follows:

(4) $$\text{Normality } (N) = \frac{\text{number of equivalents}}{\text{number of liters of solution}}$$

By cross multiplying, we derive a useful variant of this equation:

(5) $$\text{Normality } (N) \times \text{volume (liters)} = \text{number of equivalents}$$

In acid-base titrations, the equivalence point is reached when the number of equivalents of base exactly matches the number of equivalents of acid, or, in equation form:

(6) Number of equivalents of acid
$$= \text{number of equivalents of base (at equivalence point)}$$

In view of Eq. 5, we can make some substitutions into Eq. 6, as follows:

(7) Number of equivalents of acid
$$= \text{normality of acid } (N_a) \times \text{volume of acid } (V_a) \text{ in liters}$$

or

(8) $$\text{Number of equivalents of acid} = N_a \times V_a$$

Likewise for the base:

(9) $$\text{Number of equivalents of base} = N_b \times V_b$$

Let us now substitute the information of Eqs. 8 and 9 into Eq. 6:

(10) At the equivalence point:

$$N_a \times V_a = N_b \times V_b$$

It develops that V_a and V_b, although they must always be in the same units, need not be in liters. They can be expressed in milliliters, for example, because the units cancel out in the equation, since they appear on both sides. Ordinarily, units of milliliters are used for volumes.

Example 3. Calculate the normality of a 50 ml hydrochloric acid solution that needed 25 ml of 0.1N sodium hydroxide to neutralize it.

Solution. Collect the known facts as follows:

$$N_a = ? \qquad V_a = 50 \text{ ml} \qquad N_b = 0.1 \qquad V_b = 25 \text{ ml}$$

Therefore,

$$N_a \times 50 = 0.1 \times 25 \text{ ml}$$
$$N_a = \frac{0.1 \times 25 \text{ ml}}{50} = 0.05N \text{ (Ans.)}$$

Example 4. What volume of 0.05N sulfuric acid would be needed to neutralize all the hydroxide ions present in 150 ml of a 0.25N NaOH solution?

Solution. Collect the known facts:

$$N_a = 0.05 \qquad V_a = ? \qquad V_b = 150 \text{ ml} \qquad N_b = 0.25N$$

Thus,

$$0.05 \times V_a = 0.25 \times 150 \text{ ml}$$
$$V_a = 750 \text{ ml (Ans.)}$$

In clinical work, the gram-equivalent weight of a substance is often too large for convenience. For very dilute solutions, concentrations are frequently expressed in *milliequivalents per liter*. There are 1000 meq per liter. A solution that is 0.001N contains 0.001 equivalent per liter or 1 meq per liter.

Another expression often used when dealing with small samples is the *millimole*. There are 1000 millimoles in 1 mole.

Both "equivalent weight" and "milliequivalent weight" are used also with chemicals other than acids and bases. In such cases, however, they obviously must relate to something other than hydrogen or hydroxide ions. This situation is often encountered in certain areas of analysis, where each case must be treated separately.

It has been hinted from time to time that trace concentrations of acids or bases can function to catalyze reactions or to affect other catalysts such as enzymes. We must therefore be aware of any factor that can change the pH of water or that can hold it constant. Acids and bases obviously are major agents for affecting pH. There are many salts, however, that can also change the pH of water, salts whose ions are often found in the fluids of living things.

Solutions of salts, we would expect, should be neutral. Normal salts have neither hydrogen ions nor hydroxide ions even potentially available. Nevertheless, solutions of many salts in water test other than neutral to indicator paper. Sodium carbonate, for example, tests basic. Its solutions, therefore, must contain more hydroxide ions than hydrogen ions. Solutions of ammonium chloride, on the other hand, test acidic and must contain more hydrogen ions than hydroxide ions. Our problem in each case is, where do the "extra" ions come from?

To answer this question we must examine all ions that can be present in these solutions and all possible behaviors of these ions toward each other. Consider a solution of sodium acetate, $NaC_2H_3O_2$. As a crystalline salt it consists of an orderly aggregation of sodium ions, Na^+, and acetate ions, $C_2H_3O_2^-$. When this salt is dissolved in water, these ions separate (and become hydrated). *The solution also tests basic,* which means that $[OH^-] > [H_3O^+]$. The only source of these ions is water. The source of the *imbalance* is the salt, or at least one of the ions of the salt. If, somehow, some few of the already low concentration of hydronium ions in the original water became neutralized by something besides hydroxide ions, the OH^- ions from water would be in excess and the solution would have to test basic. Therefore we reexamine the ions of the salt. Sodium ions, being positively charged, could not take like-charged hydrogen ions H^+ from H_3O^+. (Like charges repel.) Could acetate ions do this? To answer this question, we can use the following train of logic.

1. *If* acetate ions tied up hydrogen ions H^+ (from H_3O^+) what would the product be?

Ans. Slightly ionized molecules of acetic acid, $H-C_2H_3O_2$.

2. *Could* acetate ions do this, even to a slight extent?

Ans. Yes, because we know qualitatively that acetic acid is a *weak* acid.

3. What does this have to do with it?

Ans. If acetic acid is a weak acid, it is by definition capable of retaining the proton. Therefore if it can acquire a proton, it will. (In fact, in a 1M solution of acetic acid only about 0.4% of the acetic acid molecules are ionized.)

Thus from our knowledge of which acids are weak (all of them *except* HCl, HBr, HI, HNO$_3$, and H$_2$SO$_4$), we deduce that the negative ion of *any* weak acid will be a relatively strong Brønsted base—capable of accepting protons from the hydronium ions formed by ionization of water and leaving OH$^-$ in slight excess.

For sodium acetate we deduced that acetate ions would reduce [H$_3$O$^+$], tending to leave OH$^-$ ions (from water) in slight excess. But we have yet to ask whether the sodium ions tie up OH$^-$ ions, offsetting this effect. To answer this question we employ the same logic.

1. *If* sodium ions tied up hydroxide ions, what would the product be?

Ans. Un-ionized "molecules" of sodium hydroxide, NaOH.

2. *Could* sodium ions do this, even to a slight extent?

Ans. No, at least not in the way acetate ions can bind hydrogen ions. We know this because sodium hydroxide is a strong base, and by definition sodium ions readily release hydroxide ions.

On balance, therefore, in a solution of sodium acetate, the acetate ions neutralize some of the hydronium ions (from the ionization of water), leaving hydroxide ions (also from the ionization of water) in slight excess. The solution tests basic. Figure 8.3 summarizes the effects in a diagrammatic way; Fig. 8.4 shows how it can be inferred that a solution of ammonium chloride in water should test acidic; and Fig. 8.5 deals with sodium chloride, which forms a neutral solution. Thus, on the basis of qualitative knowledge concerning strong and weak acids and bases, we may deduce the effect on pH when a particular salt is added to water. If any ion from the salt interacts with water to change its pH, *hydrolysis* is said to occur (Greek: *hydro*, water; *lysis*, loosening).

In general, if a salt is derived from a weak acid and a strong base, its solution in water will be slightly basic. If a salt is derived from a weak base

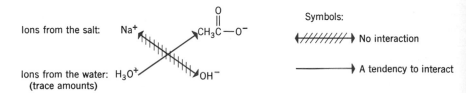

Fig. 8.3   The hydrolysis of sodium acetate. *Inferences.* NaOH is a strong base, with no tendency for Na$^+$ and OH$^-$ to combine. Acetic acid is a *weak* acid; therefore some protons will transfer from H$_3$O$^+$ to CH$_3$CO$^-$.

Conclusion. The solution is slightly *basic* because the transfer of a few protons from H$_3$O$^+$ ions to CH$_3$CO$^-$ ions leaves some of the OH$^-$ ions from water in slight excess.

acidity: its measurement and control

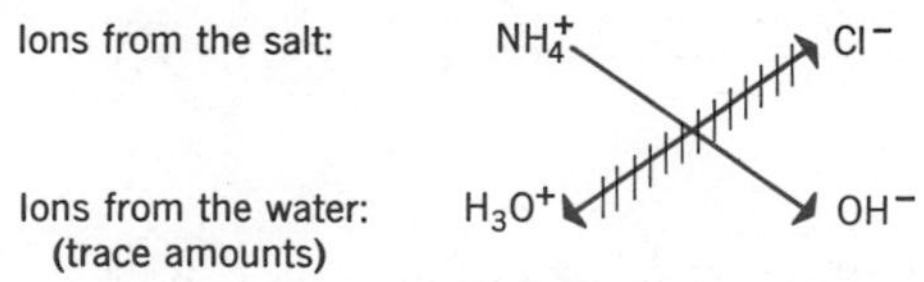

Fig. 8.4 The hydrolysis of ammonium chloride. *Inferences.* HCl is a *strong* acid; there is thus no tendency for protons to be removed from H_3O^+ ions by Cl^- ions. NH_4^+ is a poorer proton binder than OH^-; there is some tendency for the following reaction to occur: $NH_4^+ + OH^- \longrightarrow NH_3 + H{-}OH$.

    Conclusions. If some OH^- ions are neutralized by NH_4^+, a few H_3O^+ ions from the ionization of water will be left in excess. The solution will test acidic.

and a strong acid, its solution will test slightly acidic. But if the salt is made from an acid and a base of matched strengths (both equally strong or both equally weak), its solution will test neutral.

Having seen how some salts can change the pH of water, we shall next study an equally important topic—how certain combinations of salts can protect the pH of a solution from change. Aqueous solutions in the body have characteristic pHs. The pH of blood, as measured at room temperature, not body temperature, normally is within the range 7.0 to 7.9, with an average value of 7.4. If the pH falls outside this range, the blood loses its ability to transport oxygen. Life hinges, therefore, on the blood's ability to control a very small concentration of hydrogen ions within extremely narrow limits. That the blood can do this is all the more significant in view of the fact that many normal body reactions produce acids.

    Among a great variety of substances, blood contains several compounds that can quickly neutralize small amounts of acids or bases. The blood is said to be *buffered* against changes in pH. In general, buffering is accom-

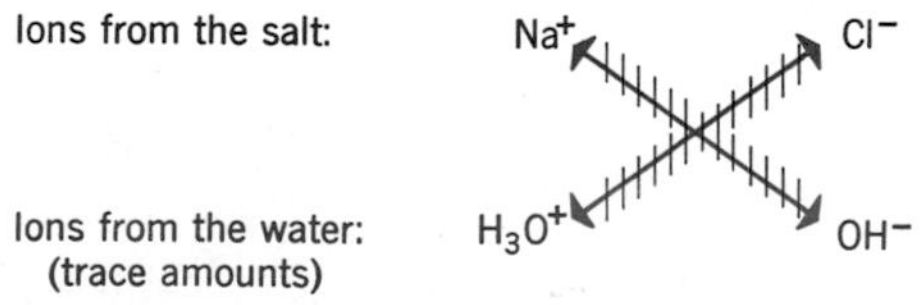

buffers

Fig. 8.5 Sodium chloride does not hydrolyze in water. *Inferences.* NaOH is a *strong* base, with no tendency for Na^+ and OH^- ions to combine to leave H_3O^+ ions from the ionization of water in excess. HCl is a *strong* acid, with no tendency for H_3O^+ and Cl^- to react to reduce the concentration of H_3O^+ and leave OH^- ions in slight excess.

    Conclusion. Since neither of the ions from the slight ionization of water is neutralized by the ions of the dissolved salt, they remain present in equal concentrations. The solution is therefore neutral.

plished by a pair of compounds acting in partnership as a buffer pair, or a buffer system.

the "carbonate" buffer. One of the important buffer systems in blood is the pair HCO_3^-/H_2CO_3, or bicarbonate ion/carbonic acid. Carbonic acid is present because of the interaction of dissolved carbon dioxide with plasma water:

$$CO_2 + H_2O \rightleftarrows H_2CO_3$$

This buffer system functions as follows:

1. One of the pair, H_2CO_3, is capable of handling hydroxide ion:

$$H_2CO_3 + OH^- \rightleftarrows HCO_3^- + H_2O$$

2. The other, HCO_3^-, can neutralize hydrogen ion:[5]

$$HCO_3^- + H^+ \rightleftarrows H_2CO_3 \text{ (a weak acid)}$$

Buffer systems have their limits. Large amounts of either acids or bases overwhelm them. Within their limits, however, they function well and perform crucial services not only in the bloodstream but also in other physiological and clinical situations.

the "phosphate" buffer. Another buffer system in blood is the pair $HPO_4^{2-}/H_2PO_4^-$, monohydrogen phosphate ion/dihydrogen phosphate ion. It functions as follows:

1. The dihydrogen phosphate ion acts as a mild Brønsted acid capable of neutralizing hydroxide ion:

$$H_2PO_4^- + OH^- \rightleftarrows HPO_4^{2-} + H_2O$$

2. The monohydrogen phosphate ion acts as a mild Brønsted base capable of neutralizing hydrogen ion:

$$HPO_4^{2-} + H^+ \rightleftarrows H_2PO_4^-$$

[5] That fact could have been inferred by recalling that the product, H_2CO_3, is a weak acid and has a slight tendency to ionize. Therefore, conversely, it must have a great tendency to form if given the opportunity.

Selected Reading List

Article

1. F. Szabadvary. "Development of the pH Concept." Translated by R. E. Oesper. *Journal of Chemical Education*, Vol. 41. (1964), page 105. A historical survey.

Brief Summary

1. pH is a way of describing the relative acidities of solutions by means of simple numbers. $[H^+] = 1 \times 10^{-pH}$. Solutions with pH's less than 7 are acidic; greater than 7, basic; equal to 7, neutral.

2. For water and its solutions:

$$[H^+][OH^-] = 1 \times 10^{-14} \text{ (at room temperature)}$$

3. Indicators are organic dyes that have a definite pH, or short pH range, at which their color is intermediate between the color they have at more acidic pHs and another they have at more basic pHs.

4. The pH of a solution may or may not be a measure of its total acidity. For dilute solutions of strong acids, it is, since all ionizable hydrogen ions are in an ionized state. For weak acids, however, the total acidity exceeds the measured pH of the solution. The pH is a measure only of the concentration of hydrogen ions actually present. The total acidity, determined by actual titration, measures the total amount of ionizable hydrogen available.

5. Acid-base titrations involve certain calculations. Among important formulas and equations are these:

   (a) Gram-equivalent weight

   $$= \frac{\text{gram-formula weight}}{\text{number of available } H^+ \text{ (or } OH^-\text{) ions per molecule}}$$

   (b) Number of equivalents $= \dfrac{\text{number of grams of substance taken}}{\text{gram-equivalent weight of substance}}$

   (c) Normality (N) of a solution $= \dfrac{\text{number of gram-equivalent weights}}{\text{number of liters of solution}}$

   (d) $N_a \times V_a = N_b \times V_b$ (the condition at the equivalence point)

6. Salts derived from acids and bases of unequal strengths hydrolyze in water. This means that, besides common acids and bases, there are some salts that can change the pH of water. The salt of a weak acid and a strong base gives a basic reaction. The salt of a weak base and a strong acid gives an acidic reaction.

7. A buffer system is capable of protecting a solution against changes in pH that would otherwise occur if small amounts of acids or bases were added. Two important buffer systems present in blood are:

$$HCO_3^-/H_2CO_3 \quad \text{and} \quad HPO_4^{2-}/H_2PO_4^-$$

Problems and Exercises

1. For each of the following pH values, write the concentration of hydrogen ions in moles per liter, and state the condition of the solution: neutral, acidic, or basic.

   Set I: pHs of 14, 2, 12, 6, 7.2 (between what limits?)
   Set II: pHs of 7, 0, 10, 8, 6.7 (between what limits?)
   Set III: pHs of 13, 1, 9, 4, 7.02 (between what limits?)

2. Which solution is more acidic in each of the following pairs? Pay careful attention to units. In all cases, concentrations refer only to hydrogen ions actually present in solution.
   (a) 10^{-3} mole/liter versus 10^{-5} mole/liter
   (b) 10^{-13} mole/liter versus 10^{-8} mole/liter
   (c) 2×10^{-3} mole/liter versus 4×10^{-3} gram/liter

3. What would be the concentration of hydrogen ions in a solution if its pH were -1?

4. What is the concentration of hydroxide ion in moles per liter if the pH of the solution is:

   Set I: 6, 4, 7, 8.2 (between what limits?)
   Set II: 3, 9, 14, 6.3 (between what limits?)
   Set III: 1, 8, 5, 4.2 (between what limits?)

5. One drop of concentrated hydrochloric acid is added to one liter of pure water (pH 7). The resultant change in volume may be ignored. Assume that concentrated hydrochloric acid contains 16 moles HCl/liter and that it takes 16 drops to make 1 cc.
   (a) Calculate the concentration of hydrochloric acid in the resultant solution.
   (b) Calculate the new pH. (You might reflect on the fact that if the pH of your blood were to change this much, you could not live.)

6. Calculate the gram-equivalent weight of each of the following substances:

   Set I: HI, NaOH, H—C$_2$H$_3$O$_2$ (acetic acid, a monoprotic acid), Mg(OH)$_2$
   Set II: HNO$_3$, KOH, H$_2$C$_2$O$_4 \cdot 2H_2O$ (oxalic acid dihydrate, a diprotic acid), HBr
   Set III: H$_2$SO$_4$, HCl, H$_3$PO$_4$ (treat as a diprotic acid only), Ca(OH)$_2$ HClO$_4$ (perchloric acid)
   Ans., Set I: HI, 128 g; NaOH, 40 g; H—C$_2$H$_3$O$_2$, 60 g; Mg(OH)$_2$, 29 g.

7. How many gram-equivalent weights ("equivalents") are in each of the following samples? (See Exercise 6 for names and other pertinent information about unfamiliar formulas.)

Set I	Set II	Set III
(a) 81 g HBr	98 g H_2SO_4	40 g NaOH
(b) 13 g H_2SO_4	4 g NaOH	6.3 g HNO_3
(c) 32.4 g HBr	1.2×10^{-3} g LiOH	10 g $HClO_4$
(d) 1 g KOH	100 g $H\text{-}C_2H_3O_2$	10 g $Ca(OH)_2$
(e) 9.6 g HI	10 g HBr	10 g NaOH

Ans., Set I: (a) 1; (b) 0.27; (c) 0.4; (d) 0.018; (e) 0.075.

8. Individual aqueous solutions were prepared containing the following substances:
    (1) 3.65 g HCl in 500 cc solution
    (2) 8.1 g HBr in 500 cc solution
    (3) 12.8 g HI in 500 cc solution
    (4) 4.9 g H_2SO_4 in 500 cc solution

   (a) What is the normality of each solution?
   (b) What is the molarity of each solution?
   (c) Assuming that the solutes in each case are 100% ionized, what is the concentration of hydrogen ion per liter of solution in each case?

9. If 20 grams of a monoprotic acid (call it HX) in 200 cc of solution gives a concentration of 4N, what is the formula weight of HX?

10. How many equivalents and how many milliequivalents of acid are present in each of the following solutions? (Watch for units of normality, N, and molarity, M.)

Set I	Set II	Set III
(a) 10 cc 1N HCl	1 cc 2N HBr	50 cc 0.2N HI
(b) 100 cc 0.1N H_2SO_4	50 cc 0.1N HNO_3	40 cc 0.25N HNO_3
(c) 1000 cc 0.05M H_2SO_4	25 cc 0.04M H_2SO_4	10 cc 4M HCl

11. How would you prepare each of the following solutions?
    (a) 1 liter 0.4N NaOH
    (b) 100 cc 0.1N H_2SO_4
    (c) 250 cc 0.1N $H_2C_2O_4 \cdot 2H_2O$ (Remember, the water of hydration in this diprotic acid is weighed.)
    (d) 100 cc 1M HNO_3
    (e) 500 cc of a solution containing 154 meq NaCl/liter (isotonic saline solution). Equivalent weight of NaCl is 58.5 grams/equivalent.
    Ans. (e) 4.51 g NaCl.

12. An analyst received the samples in the first column below. He determined their normalities by titration. From the data recorded in the columns, calculate the normality of each solution he titrated (first column).

Samples for Analysis	Volume of Standard Solution Used
(a) 100 cc HCl	50 cc 0.1N KOH
(b) 25 cc acetic acid	20 cc 0.096N NaOH

(c) 36 cc H_2SO_4 32 cc 0.15N KOH
(d) 26.48 cc HBr   25.32 cc 0.112N NaOH
(e) 23.29 cc HCl   24.92 cc 0.132N KOH
Ans. (e) 0.141N.

13. Deduce whether aqueous solutions of the salts listed below would be neutral, acidic, or basic. (Refer to tables in Chapter 7 for lists of the common acids and bases according to strengths. Make the arbitrary assumption that acids and bases not listed as strong are weak.)

Set I	Set II	Set III
(a) Na_2CO_3	$NaNO_3$	$Al(NO_3)_3$
(b) NH_4Br	$KHCO_3$	Na_3PO_4
(c) Na_2HPO_4	Na_3BO_3	K_2SO_3
(d) KCl	KH_2PO_4	KNO_3
(e) $KC_2H_3O_2$	$AlCl_3$	Na_2CO_3

14. Explain how a buffered solution resists small changes in pH. Explain by means of equations and inferences how the buffer pair $H\text{-}C_2H_3O_2/C_2H_3O_2^-$, acetic acid/acetate ion, would buffer a solution.

15. Of the two, which would be the indicator of choice for the titration of acetic acid by sodium hydroxide: methyl orange or phenolphthalein? Why?

chapter 9 introduction to organic chemistry

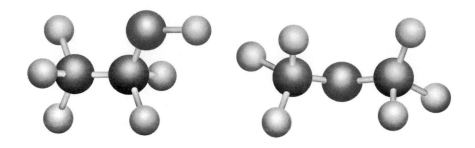

By far the majority of all the compounds in this world contain the element carbon. Excepting only substances that are clearly minerals or of mineral origin—carbonates, bicarbonates, cyanides, and a few others—all the compounds of carbon are classified as organic compounds. They are our muscles and nerves, our foods and natural fibers, our flowers and trees, our drugs and dyes, our plastics and fuels. Alas, they are also many of our poisons and pollutants. We have to live with organic substances; we surely cannot live without them.

The term *organic* was derived from an early belief that compounds of carbon could originate only through the agency of living organisms. This belief began to crumble in 1828, when Friedrich Wöhler, a professor at the University of Gottingen in Germany, discovered that urea, an organic compound, could be prepared simply by heating a substance presumed to be obtainable from mineral sources, ammonium cyanate:

$$NH_4NCO \xrightarrow{heat} NH_2-\overset{\overset{\textstyle O}{\|}}{C}-NH_2$$

Ammonium cyanate   Urea

According to the theory accepted before 1828—the *vital-force theory*—organic compounds could be prepared only with the catalytic help of a mysterious "vital force" believed to reside only within living organisms or within chemicals made by living organisms. According to the theory, inorganic matter lacked this vital force. The theory was firmly established for one simple, most compelling reason: all attempts to synthesize organic substances from demonstrably inorganic matter had failed. Even with Wöhler's experiment it was several years before most of the scientific world was convinced.[1] After that, however, organic chemistry surged forward buttressed by accurate methods to determine molecular formulas and, after August Kekule (1829–1896), useful theories of valence and structure. Literally thousands of organic compounds were synthesized from inorganic sources, many of them substances not hitherto observed to occur naturally.

the nature of organic compounds

The fact that scientists have found it convenient to classify substances as inorganic and organic indicates that these two classes differ in important ways.

they differ in elementary composition. All organic compounds contain carbon, and most inorganic compounds do not. Carbon is basic; it forms the backbones and skeletons of organic molecules. In addition to carbon, all but a small handful of organic compounds also contain hydrogen.[2]

they differ in the kinds of bonds that hold nuclei together. Ionic bonds are more prevalent among inorganic compounds than among organic substances. Many inorganic compounds consist of aggregations of oppositely

---

[1] It is ironic, as George Wald has pointed out, that Wöhler's experiment involved a most important living agency, the chemist, Friedrich Wöhler. All Wöhler demonstrated was that it is possible for chemists to make organic compounds externally as well as internally. (George Wald. *Scientific American*, August 1954, page 48.)

[2] Recall that this is a manner of speaking. Organic substances contain *nuclei* of carbon and *nuclei* of hydrogen and *nuclei* of a few other elements (e.g., oxygen, nitrogen, phosphorus, sulfur, and the halogens), plus electrons, too. Intact carbon *atoms* or hydrogen atoms (or even hydrogen molecules) are not present.

charged ions. Organic compounds are characterized largely by being aggregations of neutral, although usually polar molecules. *Within* each molecule, covalent bonds hold nuclei together. *Between* molecules, electrical forces of attraction experienced by partially charged sites act to hold molecules more or less tightly to each other.

they differ in characteristic ways in physical properties, such as boiling points, melting points, and solubilities. Table 9.1 summarizes these differences.

Some organic substances have molecules so slightly polar that at room temperature they exist as gases; they are not able to stick to each other and, accordingly, they have low melting points and boiling points. For example, methane melts at $-184°C$ and boils at $-161.5°C$. (Among molecules of comparable polarity, however, heavier ones have higher boiling points than lighter ones. Carbon tetrachloride, for example, is as nonpolar as methane, but its molecules weigh nearly ten times as much; CCl_4, formula weight 154, boils at $77°C$ as compared with CH_4, formula weight 16 and boiling point $-161.5°C$.)

Other kinds of organic molecules are more polar. They adhere to each other better, and substances with moderately polar molecules are liquids at room temperature. The most polar of organic molecules comprise solids at room temperature.

Relatively few organic compounds are soluble in water, whereas many inorganic compounds dissolve in water. Water can solvate ions or small polar molecules. However, molecules that are only slightly polar or are very large are not easily solvated, and therefore they do not dissolve in water. Although most organic substances are in this category, the few that do dissolve in water make a tremendous difference. The whole problem of the relative solubilities of organic compounds in water is of crucial importance to health, because foods are organic substances, and the digestive juices and the bloodstream are aqueous systems. The major task of the digestive process is nothing more than breaking large organic molecules present in foods into smaller molecules more soluble in the aqueous systems of the body.

Well over one million organic compounds are known. Several thousand new ones are described each year. How is it that carbon can furnish the basis for so many substances? Its ability to form four covalent bonds is not, by itself, the explanation. Silicon and lead also possess this property. The uniqueness of carbon lies in the fact that it alone among the elements can bond to its own kind, successively, many times *while at the same time* being able to form equally strong bonds to such other nonmetallic elements as hydrogen, oxygen, nitrogen, sulfur, and the halogens. By sharing electrons one carbon nucleus can bond covalently with another carbon nucleus, and this in turn with another, and this with still another, and so on, theoretically an unlimited number of times. Such a linking together, for example, of five carbon nuclei

carbon's uniqueness among the elements

Table 9.1   Characteristics of Ionic and Covalent Substances

A Common Characteristic

In the pure state at room temperature only very rarely will substances of either category conduct electricity. (Metals are omitted from both families; carbon, a nonmetal, does conduct electricity, but it would be classified as covalent.)

IONIC SUBSTANCES	COVALENT SUBSTANCES
Most Significant Differences	
If soluble in water, the solution will conduct electricity	If soluble in water, the solution will not conduct electricity (with only a few exceptions)
If insoluble in water but fusible, the molten mass will conduct electricity	If insoluble in water but fusible, the melt will not conduct electricity
Other Common Differences	
Percent of members of this class that are somewhat soluble in water is relatively high	Small percent soluble in water
Virtually no members dissolve in solvents such as carbon tetrachloride, gasoline, benzene, ether, alcohol, etc. (organic solvents)	Members are generally much more soluble in the organic solvents
Rarely does the element carbon furnish nuclei for these compounds (exceptions: bicarbonates, carbonates, cyanides)	Very common to find carbon nuclei in these compounds. (This class includes virtually all organic compounds)
At room temperature, all are solids	Includes all the gases, all the liquids, and innumerable solids (room temperature being assumed)
Virtually none will burn	Nearly all will burn
Melting points are usually above 350°C and are commonly much higher	Melting points are usually well below 350°C, but some char and decompose before they melt
Examples	
Salts (e.g., sodium chloride, barium sulfate)	Water, alcohols, sugars, fats and oils, lacquers, perfumes, most drugs, and dyes
Metal oxides (sodium oxide, iron oxides)	
Carbonates and bicarbonates	

---

into a "carbon chain" would be symbolized as shown in Fig. 9.1*a*. If the other valence electrons in this chain were to form covalent bonds with hydrogen nuclei, the structure shown in Fig. 9.1*b* would result. (Recall that a straight line represents one shared pair of electrons.) The formula shown here is a *structural formula* or, simply, a *structure*. A structural formula is

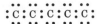

(a) A "chain" of five carbons.

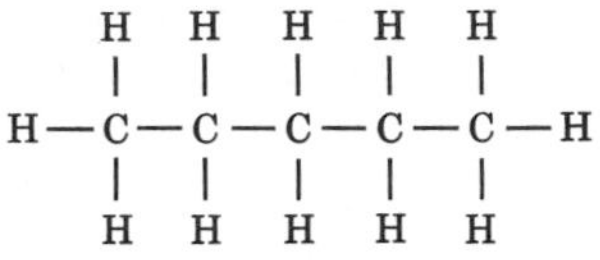

$$H-\underset{\underset{H}{|}}{\overset{\overset{H}{|}}{C}}-\underset{\underset{H}{|}}{\overset{\overset{H}{|}}{C}}-\underset{\underset{H}{|}}{\overset{\overset{H}{|}}{C}}-\underset{\underset{H}{|}}{\overset{\overset{H}{|}}{C}}-\underset{\underset{H}{|}}{\overset{\overset{H}{|}}{C}}-H$$

$CH_3-CH_2-CH_2-CH_2-CH_3$ or $CH_3CH_2CH_2CH_2CH_3$

or $CH_3(CH_2)_3CH_3$

(c) Acceptable ways to write the condensed structure of *n*-pentane.

(b) Structural formula of *n*-pentane.

Fig. 9.1   Pentane, a molecule with a chain of five carbons.

better than a molecular formula (C_5H_{12} in Fig. 9.1) because it tells more than the composition of a molecule. A structure also tells us the basic organization of the parts of the molecule.

condensed structures. Although structural formulas must indicate nucleus-to-nucleus sequences, many of the details of these formulas need not be shown. They may be "understood." The structure of Fig. 9.1b, showing a great number of lines and letters, is cumbersome to write or type. Chemists nearly always condense such a structure and in so doing they agree to certain conventions described in Fig. 9.2 and illustrated there and in Fig. 9.1c.

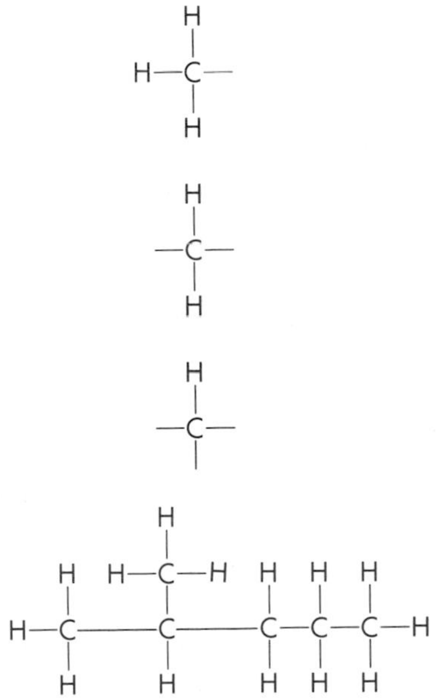

$$H-\underset{\underset{H}{|}}{\overset{\overset{H}{|}}{C}}-$$ condenses to CH_3-

$$-\underset{\underset{H}{|}}{\overset{\overset{H}{|}}{C}}-$$ condenses to $-CH_2-$

$$-\underset{\underset{|}{|}}{\overset{\overset{H}{|}}{C}}-$$ condenses to $-CH-$

E.g. $$H-\underset{\underset{H}{|}}{\overset{\overset{H}{|}}{C}}\overset{\overset{\displaystyle H-\underset{\underset{H}{|}}{\overset{\overset{H}{|}}{C}}-H}{}}{\underset{\underset{H}{|}}{C}}\underset{\underset{H}{|}}{\overset{\overset{H}{|}}{C}}-\underset{\underset{H}{|}}{\overset{\overset{H}{|}}{C}}-\underset{\underset{H}{|}}{\overset{\overset{H}{|}}{C}}-H$$ condenses to $CH_3-\overset{\overset{\displaystyle CH_3}{|}}{CH}-CH_2-CH_2-CH_3$

Equally acceptable is: $CH_3\overset{\overset{\displaystyle CH_3}{|}}{C}HCH_2CH_2CH_3$

or: $(CH_3)_2CHCH_2CH_2CH_3$

Fig. 9.2   Condensing structural formulas.

the tetrahedral carbon atom. In addition to molecular structure, the shapes of molecules, and the shapes into which large molecules can twist or bend, will be important when we try to understand how enzymes work, for example, or how genes do what they do, chemically. Molecules of covalent compounds have characteristic shapes and surface contours in large measure because covalent bonds are directional. In Chapter 6 we learned that the water molecule is angular, not linear. The H-O-H bond angle is 105°, not 180°. Similarly, in organic molecules wherever a carbon atom is involved with four *single* bonds, the axes of those bonds make definite angles with each other. In the very symmetrical molecule of methane, if the ends of these four bonds were connected with straight lines, there would result the outline of a regular tetrahedron (four identical, triangular sides) with the nucleus of the carbon atom at the exact geometric center (see Fig. 9.3). The angle between any two covalent bonds at the tetrahedral carbon atom in methane is 109.5°.

A "ball and stick" model of methane is shown in Fig. 9.3, but the scale model gives a better idea of its shape.

free rotation about single bonds. The structure of pentane, as shown in Fig. 9.1, conveys two kinds of information: the *composition* of a molecule of pentane and the *sequence* of its nuclei. The structure or sequence is usually written horizontally simply because it is convenient to set type that way, but it is known that a considerable amount of internal twisting and bending takes place in a pentane molecule. What is not obvious about the structure of any organic molecule when it is written in a convenient pattern is that *groups connected by a single bond can rotate about that bond without affecting its strength.*

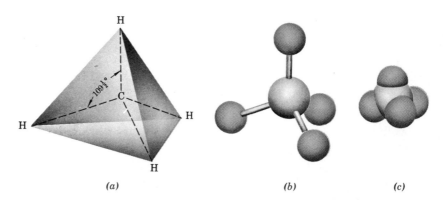

(a)   (b)   (c)

Fig. 9.3 Tetrahedral carbon atom: (a) shows by dotted lines the four covalent bonds of carbon that are directed toward the corners of a regular tetrahedron; (b) is a common "ball and stick" model of methane; (c) is a scale model of methane, a model that attempts to indicate the relative volumes occupied by the various "electron clouds" in the molecule.

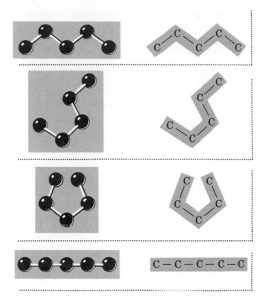

Fig. 9.4 The carbon skeleton of pentane in various conformations. (Only carbon-carbon bonds are shown.)

In the molecular orbital theory, the strength of a covalent bond is related to the extent with which the "parent" atomic orbitals overlap. This degree of overlap in a *single* bond is not appreciably affected by internal twistings and rotations, and such behavior is allowed in terms of the energetics of the situation. A ball-and-stick model of pentane is faithful to experimental fact on this point.

In Fig. 9.4 several conformations of the carbon "skeleton" of pentane are pictured. A sample of pentane contains billions and billions of molecules, and some are in each of the conformations shown and in countless others not shown. Moreover, each molecule twists constantly as it suffers random collisions. The measured physical and chemical properties of pentane reflect an average effect of all the conformations of its molecules on whatever instrument or chemical used on the sample to measure some property. Since no one molecular conformation is unique, we should not read into a structural formula too much about the conformation of the molecule. When we get down to certain specific topics in biochemistry, the shapes of molecules will be as important as their structures. (These two features, of course, cannot really be separated.) For virtually all of our study of the more simple organic compounds, however, we shall be interested only in nucleus-to-nucleus sequences in the conventional structures.

structure determines property. This is true whether the property is physical, chemical, or physiological. Some of the most dramatic examples of this are found in the phenomenon of isomerism.

Table 9.2   Properties of Two Isomers: Ethyl Alcohol and Methyl Ether, C_2H_6O

Property	Ethyl Alcohol	Methyl Ether
Boiling point	78.5°C	−24°C
Melting point	−117°C	−138.5°C
Density	0.789 gram/ml	2 grams/liter
Solubility in water	Completely soluble in all proportions	Slightly soluble
Action of sodium	Vigorous reaction; H_2 evolved	No reaction
Molecular formula	C_2H_6O	C_2H_6O
Structural formula	$H-\overset{\displaystyle H}{\underset{\displaystyle H}{C}}-\overset{\displaystyle H}{\underset{\displaystyle H}{C}}-O-H$	$H-\overset{\displaystyle H}{\underset{\displaystyle H}{C}}-O-\overset{\displaystyle H}{\underset{\displaystyle H}{C}}-H$
Condensed structural formula	CH_3-CH_2-O-H	CH_3-O-CH_3

structural isomerism   Some of the characteristic properties of two well-known organic compounds, ethyl alcohol and methyl ether, are given in Table 9.2. The differences are remarkable. One is a liquid at room temperature and the other is a gas. One reacts vigorously with sodium metal, and the other does not. One is freely soluble in water, and the other is not. In the light of these differences, what is the most remarkable of all is that they have identical molecular formulas. When each is analyzed quantitatively for percent of carbon, hydrogen, and oxygen, and for formula weight, each answers to the same molecular formula: C_2H_6O. Interestingly, when this formula is juggled into a specific structure in which all the rules of covalence are obeyed, not one but two structures are possible. There are two unique ways by which two

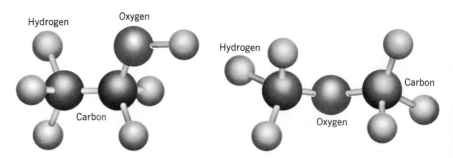

Fig. 9.5   "Ball and stick" models of two isomers, ethyl alcohol and methyl ether. Each isomer has the same molecular formula C_2H_6O, but they have different structures. They differ in the sequences in which their atoms have become joined together.

carbons, six hydrogens, and one oxygen can become linked together. Ball-and-stick models are pictured in Fig. 9.5.

Compounds that have identical molecular formulas but different structures are called *isomers*. The phenomenon of the existence of isomers is called *isomerism*. Ethyl alcohol is said to be an isomer of methyl ether. When molecular formulas involve large numbers of nuclei, the number of potential isomers becomes astronomical. It has been estimated, for example, that the total number of different structures that can be fashioned, within the rules of valence and the geometry of carbon, for the molecular formula $C_{40}H_{82}$ is 6.25×10^{13}! Although very few are actually known (chemists have found neither good reason nor the time to go to the trouble of making them all), clearly the phenomenon of isomerism must be greatly responsible for the huge number of organic compounds possible.

The hundreds of thousands of organic compounds that are known can be classified into relatively few groups on the basis of similarities in structure and, therefore, similarities in chemical properties. Just as zoologists classify animals into families having structural likenesses, so chemists classify organic compounds according to structural similarities. A few such families of compounds are shown in Table 9.3.

how organic chemistry is organized as a subject

In the next few chapters, we shall be doing something very similar to what you once did a long time ago when you learned how to read maps. You learned the meaning of a few simple map signs, and with that knowledge you became able to understand an enormous number and variety of complicated maps. Our study of simple organic compounds and their reactions will be like learning map signs. We shall then use them to understand some of the properties of the more complicated molecules found in living systems.

Selected Reading List

Articles

1. H. A. Bent. "The Tetrahedral Atom." *Chemistry*, December 1966, page 9. A lively sketch of the development of ideas about covalent bonds and molecular shapes from the time of Dalton to the Lewis theory. See also "The Tetrahedral Atom. Part II. Valence in Three Dimensions." *Ibid.*, January 1967, page 9.

2. J. B. Lambert. "The Shapes of Organic Molecules." *Scientific American*, January 1970, page 58. The 1969 Nobel Prize in chemistry was shared by Odd Hassel (Norway) and D. H. R. Barton (England) for work on the concept of conformation in chemistry. This article discusses that work.

Table 9.3 Some Important Classes of Organic Compounds

Class	Characteristic Structural Feature
Hydrocarbons	Composed only of carbon and hydrogen, with many subclasses according to whether single, double, or triple bonds are present. Alkanes: all single bonds (saturated hydrocarbons)[a] Alkenes: at least one carbon-carbon double bond Alkynes: at least one triple bond Aromatic: the cyclic, benzenoid ring system
Alcohols	Contain the —OH group joined to a saturated carbon atom, as in CH_3—OH
Ethers	Contain the grouping $-\overset{\mid}{\underset{\mid}{C}}-O-\overset{\mid}{\underset{\mid}{C}}-$, as in CH_3—O—CH_3
Aldehydes	Contain the grouping $-\overset{O}{\overset{\parallel}{C}}-H$, as in $CH_3-\overset{O}{\overset{\parallel}{C}}-H$
Ketones	Contain the grouping $-\overset{\mid}{\underset{\mid}{C}}-\overset{O}{\overset{\parallel}{C}}-\overset{\mid}{\underset{\mid}{C}}-$, as in $CH_3-\overset{O}{\overset{\parallel}{C}}-CH_3$
Carboxylic acids	Contain the grouping $-\overset{O}{\overset{\parallel}{C}}-OH$, as in $CH_3-\overset{O}{\overset{\parallel}{C}}-OH$
Esters	Contain the grouping $-\overset{O}{\overset{\parallel}{C}}-O-\overset{\mid}{\underset{\mid}{C}}-$, as in $CH_3-\overset{O}{\overset{\parallel}{C}}-O-CH_2CH_3$
Amines	Contain trivalent nitrogen, where all covalent bonds are single bonds, as in CH_3—NH_2
Amides	Contain the grouping $-\overset{O}{\overset{\parallel}{C}}-\overset{\mid}{N}-$, as in $CH_3-\overset{O}{\overset{\parallel}{C}}-NH_2$

[a] Any molecule having all single bonds and no multiple bonds is said to be saturated.

Brief Summary

1. The compounds of carbon are the principal objects of study of organic chemists. The way to synthetic organic compounds was opened by the overthrow of the "vital-force theory." It dominated organic chemistry until Wöhler demonstrated (1828) that a "vital force" was not necessary to make an organic compound from a substance of mineral origin.

2. Organic substances differ from inorganic substances chiefly because the former consist primarily of molecules and the latter largely of oppositely charged ions. Since molecules, even though often quite polar, never carry full electrical charges, as do ions, they are seldom attracted to each other as strongly as are oppositely

charged ions. To a large extent, this explains the differences between the two classes in boiling points, melting points, and relative solubilities in various solvents.

3. Organic substances exist in such huge numbers and varieties because of carbon's ability to form bonds to other carbon nuclei, successively, many times, and because these bonds are directional.

4. When two (or more) compounds have identical molecular formulas but different structures, they are called *isomers*.

5. Condensed structural formulas, by implication, convey the identical information of complete structural formulas—the nuclei-to-nuclei sequences within molecules.

6. Groups joined by single covalent bonds can rotate with respect to each other about that bond.

Problems and Exercises

1. Inorganic compounds have melting points considerably higher than organic compounds. Account for this fact in terms of just what happens when a substance melts, what is needed to cause this, and what forces have to be overcome in the cases of inorganic crystals and organic crystals. Account also for the differences in boiling-point ranges.

2. Write full structural formulas (one line for each covalent bond) for each of the following molecular formulas:

   (a) $CHBr_3$ (d) C_2H_6 (g) NH_3O (j) HCN
   (b) H_2O_2 (e) CH_2O_2 (h) C_2H_2 (k) C_2H_3N
   (c) CH_2O (f) C_2H_4 (i) N_2H_4 (l) CH_4O

3. For each of the following pairs of structures decide whether the two are identical, are isomers, or are related in some other way. With some pairs, the only difference is the relative orientation of the same structure "in space" (that is, on the paper). The purpose of this exercise is, in part, to sharpen your awareness of structures as sequences of nuclei within molecules. Make your decisions by first checking the two to see whether they share identical molecular formulas. If they do, either they are identical, or they are isomers. (Otherwise they are not considered further, here.) Next, see whether they have identical sequences however they may be oriented on the paper. If they do not, they must be isomers (provided your initial checking showed them to have identical molecular formulas).

   (a) CH_3 and $CH_3\!-\!CH_3$
       |
       CH_3

   (b) CH_3
         $\diagdown CH_2$ and CH_2
                  $\diagdown CH_3$ $CH_3 \diagup \quad \diagdown CH_3$

   (c) $CH_3CH_2\!-\!OH$ and $CH_3CH_2CH_2\!-\!OH$

(d) $CH_3CH\!\!=\!\!CH_2$ and $\underset{\underset{\displaystyle CH_2}{\diagdown}}{\overset{}{CH_2\!\!-\!\!CH_2}}$

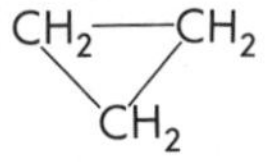

(e) 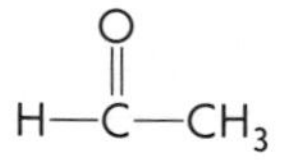 $H\!\!-\!\!\overset{\displaystyle O}{\overset{\|}{C}}\!\!-\!\!CH_3$ and $CH_3\!\!-\!\!\overset{\displaystyle O}{\overset{\|}{C}}\!\!-\!\!H$

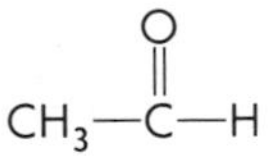

(f) 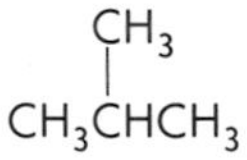 $CH_3\overset{\displaystyle CH_3}{\overset{|}{C}}\!\!HCH_3$ and $CH_3\overset{\displaystyle CH_3}{\underset{\displaystyle CH_3}{\overset{|}{\underset{|}{C}}}}\!\!H$

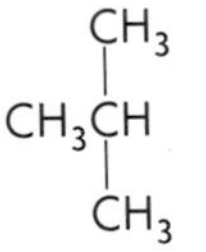

(g) $CH_3CH_2\!\!-\!\!NH_2$ and $CH_3\!\!-\!\!\underset{\displaystyle H}{\overset{|}{N}}\!\!-\!\!CH_3$

(h) $CH_3CH_2\overset{\displaystyle O}{\overset{\|}{C}}\!\!-\!\!O\!\!-\!\!H$ and $H\!\!-\!\!O\!\!-\!\!\overset{\displaystyle O}{\overset{\|}{C}}CH_2CH_3$

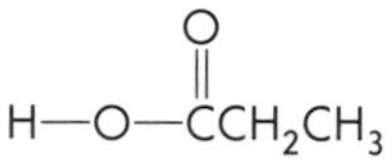

(i) 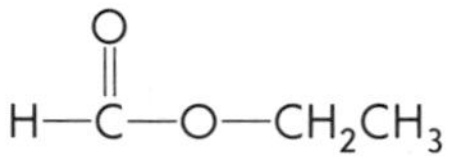 $H\!\!-\!\!\overset{\displaystyle O}{\overset{\|}{C}}\!\!-\!\!O\!\!-\!\!CH_2CH_3$ and $CH_3CH_2\!\!-\!\!\overset{\displaystyle O}{\overset{\|}{C}}\!\!-\!\!O\!\!-\!\!H$

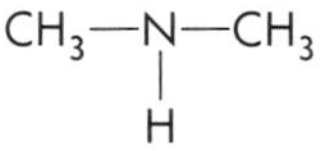

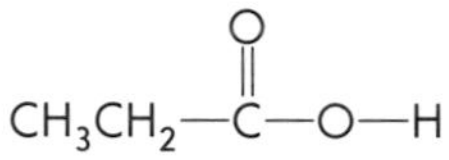

(j) 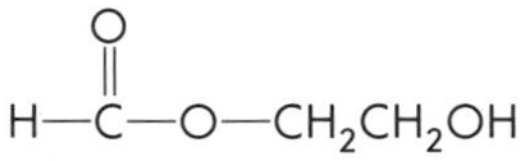 $H\!\!-\!\!\overset{\displaystyle O}{\overset{\|}{C}}\!\!-\!\!O\!\!-\!\!CH_2CH_2OH$ and $HOCH_2CH_2\!\!-\!\!\overset{\displaystyle O}{\overset{\|}{C}}\!\!-\!\!OH$

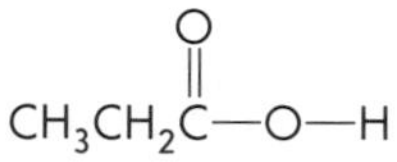

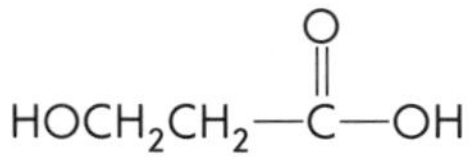

(k) 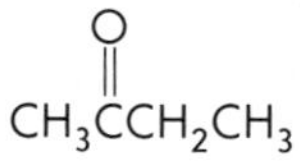 $CH_3\overset{\displaystyle O}{\overset{\|}{C}}CH_2CH_3$ and $CH_3CH_2\overset{\displaystyle O}{\overset{\|}{C}}CH_3$

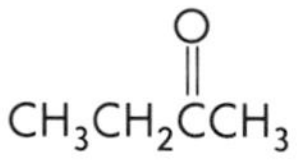

(l) 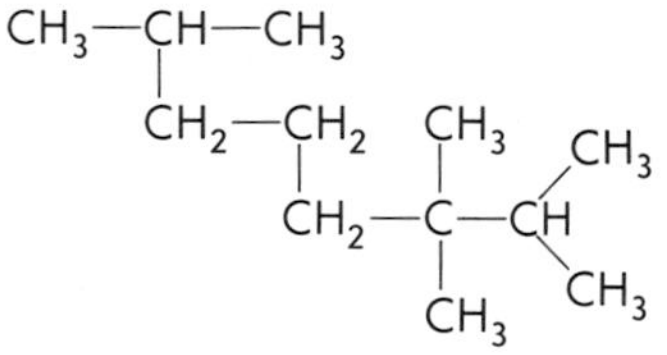 $CH_3\!\!-\!\!CH\!\!-\!\!CH_3$

and $CH_3\!\!-\!\!\overset{\displaystyle CH_3}{\overset{|}{C}}\!\!H\!\!-\!\!CH_2\!\!-\!\!CH_2\!\!-\!\!CH_2\!\!-\!\!\overset{\displaystyle CH_3}{\underset{\displaystyle CH_3}{\overset{|}{\underset{|}{C}}}}\!\!-\!\!\overset{\displaystyle CH_3}{\overset{|}{C}}\!\!H\!\!-\!\!CH_3$

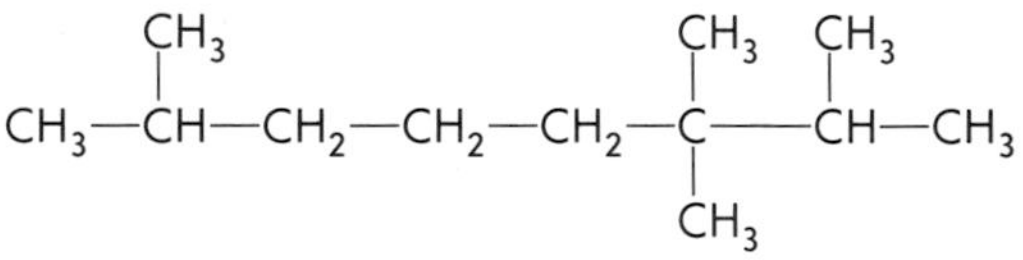

(m) 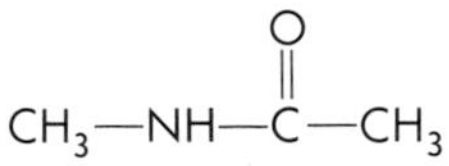 $CH_3\!\!-\!\!NH\!\!-\!\!\overset{\displaystyle O}{\overset{\|}{C}}\!\!-\!\!CH_3$ and $CH_3CH_2\overset{\displaystyle O}{\overset{\|}{C}}NH_2$

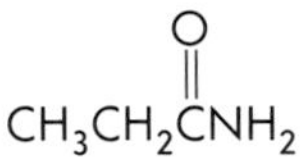

(n) $H\!\!-\!\!O\!\!-\!\!O\!\!-\!\!H$ and $H\!\!-\!\!O\!\!-\!\!H$

chapter 10 hydrocarbons

Petroleum oils and gases are both servants and masters of man: servants because they are useful—they power or lubricate most of the engines of industry and transportation throughout the world; masters, for the very same reason. The molecules found in petroleum are not of major importance in the chemistry of health except for their considerable contribution to the unhealthy aspects of smog. Their study, moreover, is basic to organic chemistry, for they are the simplest of organic molecules.

families of hydrocarbons

The molecules that make up the bulk of crude petroleum belong to the *hydrocarbon class* of organic compounds, whose members contain only carbon and hydrogen. The families in this class, outlined below, are differently characterized by the peculiar kinds of carbon-to-carbon bonds—single, double, or triple—that their molecules contain.

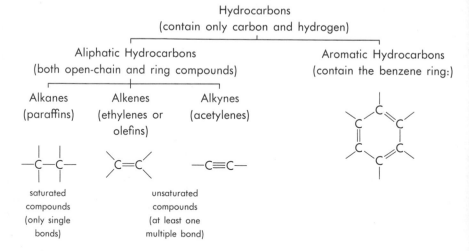

physical properties of hydrocarbons

Molecules of hydrocarbons are virtually nonpolar. This is true of all the families of hydrocarbons. Electrical forces of attraction between their molecules are, therefore, very weak. At room temperature, the lower-formula-weight members of the families of alkanes, alkenes, and alkynes are gases.

Being nonpolar, hydrocarbons are easily soluble in the common, weakly polar solvents, such as carbon tetrachloride, chloroform, benzene, and ether. The hydrocarbons are all insoluble in water. Nearly all are less dense than water.

These properties are reviewed not because they bear directly on important health problems. Hydrocarbons are not usable by the body. However, such important physiological substances as the edible fats and oils have molecules that are very hydrocarbon-like. Huge portions of their molecules consist of *segments* of large hydrocarbon systems. Therefore, these substances have many of the physical properties of hydrocarbons, and the body has to contend with these properties every time it digests, transports, and uses edible fats and oils—all of which activities must occur in aqueous media.

Here is our first important "map sign." *If a structural formula shows a molecule that is substantially hydrocarbon-like, expect the substance to be relatively insoluble in water and less dense than water.* We shall encounter exceptions, but when we do it will be because another structural feature dominates the situation.

alkanes

Molecules in the alkane family are *saturated,* i.e., they possess only single covalent bonds. The structures of the ten smallest, "straight-chain" members

Table 10.1   Straight-Chain Alkanes

Number of Carbon Atoms	IUPAC Name	Molecular Formula[a]	Structure	Boiling Point, in °C
1	Methane	CH_4	CH_4	−162
2	Ethane	C_2H_6	CH_3CH_3	−88.6
3	Propane	C_3H_8	$CH_3CH_2CH_3$	−42
4	Butane[b]	C_4H_{10}	$CH_3CH_2CH_2CH_3$	0
5	Pentane	C_5H_{12}	$CH_3CH_2CH_2CH_2CH_3$	36
6	Hexane	C_6H_{14}	$CH_3CH_2CH_2CH_2CH_2CH_3$	69
7	Heptane	C_7H_{16}	$CH_3CH_2CH_2CH_2CH_2CH_2CH_3$	98
8	Octane	C_8H_{18}	$CH_3CH_2CH_2CH_2CH_2CH_2CH_2CH_3$	126
9	Nonane	C_9H_{20}	$CH_3CH_2CH_2CH_2CH_2CH_2CH_2CH_2CH_3$	151
10	Decane	$C_{10}H_{22}$	$CH_3CH_2CH_2CH_2CH_2CH_2CH_2CH_2CH_2CH_3$	174

[a] Molecular formulas of the open-chain alkanes fit the general formula C_nH_{2n+2}, where n = number of carbon atoms in the molecule.

[b] The common names and the IUPAC names for the first three alkanes are identical. From butane and on through the rest of this list the common name is made from the IUPAC name by affixing the prefix *n-* to the IUPAC name. Thus, *n*-butane is the common name for butane.

are shown in Table 10.1. This sequence of compounds is said to constitute an *homologous series* because members differ from each other in a consistent, regular way. Each member differs from the one immediately preceding or following it by one —CH_2— unit. In the terminology of the field, butane is the next higher *homolog* of propane.

isomerism among the alkanes.   Isomerism occurs among the molecules of alkanes having more than three carbon atoms. The structures of the two isomers of butane and the three isomers of pentane are shown in Table 10.2. As the homologous series is ascended, the numbers of possible isomers rapidly increase, as the data at the bottom of this table show.

Since there are more than a million organic compounds, there must be more than a million names—one unique name for each. Organic chemists throughout the world have reached formal agreements about making up systematic names for any compound now known or yet to be made. The full text of all the agreements concerning all the kinds of organic compounds would occupy a very large book, and it is reasonably safe to say that only a few scientists and librarians who specialize in indexing names of compounds have a mastery of organic nomenclature. Gaining that mastery is complicated by the fact that working chemists employ a variety of different systems of nomenclature, a *common*, a *derived*, and a *formal* system. We shall say nothing more about the derived system. The common system gradually evolved in the simpler (!) days when there were few compounds. "Formic acid," for example, could be named from its source—it was obtained by grinding ants

structural features

organic nomenclature

Table 10.2 Some Isomeric Alkanes

Isomer	Structure and Name[a]	Boiling Point, in °C
Isomeric butanes, C_4H_{10}	$CH_3CH_2CH_2CH_3$ *n*-butane (butane)	0
	$CH_3\overset{\overset{\displaystyle CH_3}{\vert}}{C}HCH_3$ isobutane (2-methylpropane)	−12
Isomeric pentanes, C_5H_{12}	$CH_3CH_2CH_2CH_2CH_3$ *n*-pentane (pentane)	36
	$CH_3\overset{\overset{\displaystyle CH_3}{\vert}}{C}HCH_2CH_3$ isopentane (2-methylbutane)	28
	$CH_3\overset{\overset{\displaystyle CH_3}{\vert}}{\underset{\underset{\displaystyle CH_3}{\vert}}{C}}CH_3$ neopentane (2,2-dimethylpropane)	10

Numbers of Isomers of the Higher Alkanes

Molecular Formula	Number of Isomers of This Formula
C_6H_{14}	5
C_8H_{18}	18
$C_{10}H_{22}$	75
$C_{20}H_{42}$	366,319
$C_{40}H_{82}$	6.25×10^{13}

[a] The IUPAC names are given in parentheses.

with water and distilling the resulting soup, and the Latin name for ant was *formica*. No one dreamed in those days that several hundred organic acids would eventually have to be named. Most of the old, common names are still widely used even though formal names exist. (Formic acid is methanoic acid; but nobody calls it that.) The survival of common names is not just laziness on the part of chemists or even a stubborn refusal to "go along." In everyday communication and even in formal writing it is much easier to write and to talk about *dieldrin* (to take one rather spectacular example) than to use its formal name: 1,2,3,4,10,10-hexachloro-6,7-epoxy-1,4,4a,5,6,7,8a-octahydro-1,4-endo-exo-5,8-dimethanonaphthalene. It cannot be pronounced with one breath nor easily printed on one line.

The formal names of most biochemically important compounds would be as complicated or worse than the example given. That is why we shall emphasize common names of compounds. The common names are nearly always used. However, there may be times when you need some familiarity with formal organic nomenclature. You may have to look something up in an organic text or a chemical handbook. To serve students with those possible needs the fundamentals of the formal system (the IUPAC or "Geneva" system) for simple compounds are included in this text.

In this chapter we shall look at the formal names of some of the hydrocarbons. The rules for these names are the basis of all other formal names. The formal rules for naming other families are in Appendix I. By gathering them all together in one place their simplicity and consistency are more apparent, and it becomes easier to study them as one unit.[1]

The characteristic name ending for all members of the alkanes, regardless of the system of nomenclature, is "-ane." Prefixes to this ending indicate the total number of carbons in the molecule for alkanes with five or more. These prefixes are from the Greek, and they have their traditional numerical connotations. For example, "octa-" refers to eight; octane is an alkane with eight carbons in its molecules.

naming
the alkanes

common names. The alkanes in Table 10.1 are called *straight-chain* alkanes, because the sequences of carbons are continuous; there is no branching in their skeletons. Where isomers are possible, the common name for the straight-chain isomer is preceded by the word *normal,* abbreviated, *n-,* as in *n-*butane or *n-*pentane (see Table 10.2). The isomer that has just one, single, one-carbon branch located on the second carbon from the end of a straight chain has the prefix *iso-* affixed to the name of its corresponding straight chain isomer. Compare in Table 10.2 isobutane with *n-*butane and isopentane with *n-*pentane. These examples illustrate a very important feature of common names of alkanes; they indicate the *total* carbon content. Thus, there are two butanes named *n-*butane and isobutane. The *-but-* word-part tells us that four carbons are present; the *-ane-* signifies the alkane family; and the *n-* or *iso-* prefixes give us the rest of the information we need about their structures.

IUPAC names. the "Geneva" system. The International Union of Pure and Applied Chemistry (IUPAC), sanctioned by professional scientific societies throughout the world, has established the formal rules of nomenclature. The IUPAC's first of several meetings on nomenclature was at Geneva in 1892, and the system is therefore often called the "Geneva system." The following is a summary of the IUPAC rules for alkanes.

1. The general name for saturated hydrocarbons is *alkane.*

[1] In courses where time for the formal names simply cannot be taken, IUPAC nomenclature may be omitted without causing later problems. Only names for alkyl groups (methyl, ethyl, etc.) will be needed later, and they can be taken up when alcohols are studied by referring back to this unit.

2. The names of the straight-chain members of the alkanes are those listed in Table 10.1. (The designation *n-* is not part of the IUPAC system at all. Names going beyond the ten-carbon alkanes are, of course, available, but we shall not need them.)

3. For branched-chain alkanes, base the name on the alkane that corresponds to the longest continuous (i.e., unbranched) chain of carbons in the molecule. For example, in the compound

$$
\begin{array}{c}
\text{CH}_2\text{—CH}_2 \\
| \quad\quad | \\
\text{CH}_2\text{—CH—CH}_2 \quad \text{CH}_3 \\
| \quad\quad | \\
\text{CH}_3 \quad \text{CH}_3
\end{array}
$$

which when "straightened" is

$$
\begin{array}{c}
\text{CH}_3 \\
| \\
\text{CH}_3\text{CH}_2\text{CHCH}_2\text{CH}_2\text{CH}_2\text{CH}_3
\end{array}
$$

the longest continuous chain totals seven carbons. The *last* part of the complete name for this compound will therefore be *heptane*. We next learn how to specify the location of the small CH_3— branch.

4. To locate branches, assign a number to each carbon of the longest continuous chain. Begin at whichever end of the chain will result in the lowest numbers to the carbon(s) holding branches. In our example,

$$
\begin{array}{c}
\text{CH}_3 \\
| \\
\text{CH}_3\text{CH}_2\text{CHCH}_2\text{CH}_2\text{CH}_2\text{CH}_3 \\
\;\;1\quad 2\quad 3\quad 4\quad 5\quad 6\quad 7
\end{array}
$$

if this chain had been numbered from right to left, the carbon holding the branch would have the number 5. By "lowest" is meant the occasion of the first branch.

Example:

$$
\begin{array}{c}
\text{CH}_3 \quad\quad \text{CH}_3 \quad\quad\quad\quad\quad \text{CH}_3 \\
| \quad\quad\quad | \quad\quad\quad\quad\quad\quad | \\
\text{CH}_3\text{CH}_2\text{CH——CHCH}_2\text{CH}_2\text{CH}_2\text{CH}_2\text{CHCH}_3 \\
10\;\;9\;\;8 \quad\;\; 7\;\;6\;\;5\;\;4\;\;3\;\;2\;\;1
\end{array}
$$

By numbering this chain from right to left the occasion of the first branch is 2 and the other branches are at 7 and 8. If the chain had been numbered from left to right the first branch would have been at 3 with the other branches at 4 and 9. Even though the sum, $2 + 7 + 8 = 17$, is a *larger* number than the sum $3 + 4 + 9 = 16$, it is the occasion of the first branch that the rule says must have the lowest number.

Having located where the branch(es) are, we must now be able to name the group(s) attached at these locations.

5. **Alkyl Groups.** If a side chain or branch consists only of carbons and hydrogens linked to each other by just single bonds, it is called an *alkyl group*; "alkyl" comes from changing the "-ane" ending of "alkane" to "-yl." This change is the key to making up names for alkyl groups, and Table 10.3 lists the names and structures for the most common ones. Their structures (at least the first five) must be learned so well that they can be recognized written backward, forward, and upside down. Each is derived (on paper) by taking an alkane and removing a hydrogen to leave an unused bond represented by a line. The site of this unused bond must be clearly known, for it is at this point that the alkyl group is attached to a chain. In learning the names and structures of the alkyl groups in Table 10.3, again the best advice is to associate the total number of carbons in the group with the prefix portion of the name of its "parent" alkane. The table shows, for example, four butyl groups, two related to *n*-butane and two to isobutane. All are butyl groups because each has four carbons. To distinguish them from each other, addi-

Table 10.3 **Common Alkyl Groups**

Parent Alkane	Structure of Parent Alkane	Structure of Alkyl Group from Alkane	IUPAC Name of Alkyl Group
Methane	CH_4	CH_3-	Methyl
Ethane	CH_3CH_3	CH_3CH_2-	Ethyl
Propane	$CH_3CH_2CH_3$	$CH_3CH_2CH_2-$	Propyl
		$\begin{array}{c} CH_3 \\ \diagdown \\ CH- \\ \diagup \\ CH_3 \end{array}$	Isopropyl
n-Butane	$CH_3CH_2CH_2CH_3$	$CH_3CH_2CH_2CH_2-$	Butyl
		$\begin{array}{c} CH_3 \\ | \\ CH_3CH_2CH- \end{array}$	sec-Butyl (Secondary-butyl)
Isobutane	$\begin{array}{c} CH_3 \\ | \\ CH_3CHCH_3 \end{array}$	$\begin{array}{c} CH_3 \\ | \\ CH_3CHCH_2- \end{array}$	Isobutyl
		$\begin{array}{c} CH_3 \\ | \\ CH_3-C- \\ | \\ CH_3 \end{array}$	t-Butyl (Tertiary-butyl)

Any normal alkane: If the "free valance" extends from the end of the chain, change the "-ane" ending of the alkane to "-yl."

For example: $CH_3CH_2CH_2CH_2CH_2CH_2CH_2-$ → Heptyl (*n*-heptyl for the common name)

| Any alkane | R—H | R— | Alkyl |

tional word parts are affixed. The words "secondary" and "tertiary" (abbreviated *sec-* and *tert-* or simply *t-*) denote the condition of the carbon in the group having the unused bond. In the *sec*-butyl group this carbon is directly attached to *two* other carbons and is therefore classified as a *secondary* carbon. In the *t*-butyl group this carbon has direct bonds to three other carbons and is classified as a *tertiary* carbon. When a carbon is attached directly to only one other carbon, it is classified as a *primary* carbon. These classifications of carbons should be learned. In our study we shall on only two occasions use the names for the classes to make names for specific groups. Among the butyl groups, one is *sec*-butyl (a name) and one is *t*-butyl (a name). The other two butyl groups are primary (a class), and the class name therefore cannot be used to name either, for it would be ambiguous to do so. But one has a straight chain with the unused bond at the *end;* it is therefore called the *n*-butyl group (or, simply, butyl). The other is called the isobutyl group.

Having learned rules for locating and naming side chains, we next consider situations in which identical groups are located on the same carbon of the main chain.

6. Whenever two identical groups are attached at the same place, numbers are supplied for each group. For example,

$$CH_3CCH_2CH_2CH_2CH_3$$

with CH_3 above and CH_3 below the second carbon.

Correct name: 2,2-dimethylhexane
Incorrect: 2-dimethylhexane
2,2-methylhexane

Note carefully the use of hyphens and commas in organizing the parts of names. Hyphens always separate *numbers* from *word parts;* commas always separate *numbers* from *numbers.* The intent is to make the final name one word.

7. Whenever two or more different groups are affixed to a chain, two ways are acceptable for organizing all the name parts into the final name. The last word part is always the name of the alkane corresponding to the longest chain.

(a) The other word parts can be ordered by increasing complexity of side chains (e.g., in order of increasing carbon content): methyl, ethyl, propyl, isopropyl, butyl, isobutyl, *sec*-butyl, *t*-butyl, etc.

(b) They can be listed in simple alphabetic order. (This corresponds to the indexing system of *Chemical Abstracts,* a publication of the American Chemical Society.)

8. The formal names for several of the more important nonalkyl substituents are as follows:

—F	fluoro	—NO_2	nitro
—Cl	chloro	—NH_2	amino
—Br	bromo		
—I	iodo		

Several examples of compounds correctly named according to these rules are given below. In parentheses are shown some common ways in which incorrect names are often devised. As an exercise, describe how each incorrect name violates one or more of the rules.

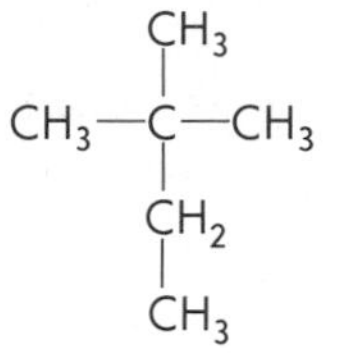

2,2-Dimethylbutane
Not 2-methyl-2-ethylpropane

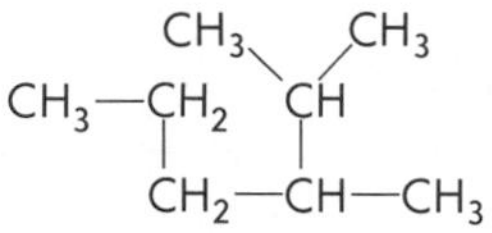

2,3-Dimethylhexane
Not 2-isopropylpentane

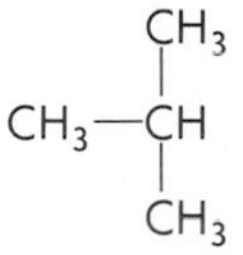

2-Methylpropane
Not 1,1-dimethylethane
Not isobutane, which is its common name

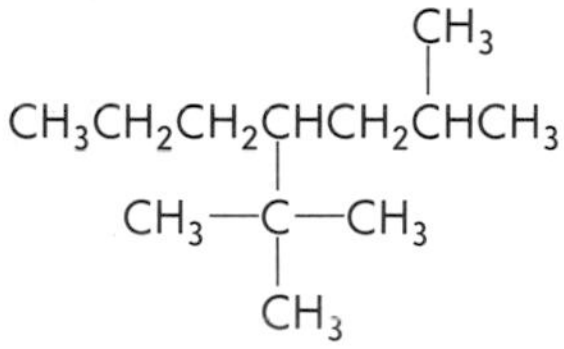

2-Methyl-4-t-butylheptane
Not 4-t-butyl-6-methylheptane
But 4-t-butyl-2-methylheptane is acceptable

cycloalkanes

The alkanes we have considered thus far have been *open-chain compounds*. The structures shown in Fig. 10.1, however, reveal that the rules of valence can be obeyed even if the carbon chain is "coiled back" on itself and closes to form a *cyclic compound*. Cyclic organic compounds that contain only carbon and hydrogen and that involve only single bonds are called *cycloalkanes*. Their names are obtained by placing the prefix "cyclo-" before the name of the corresponding open-chain alkane. Two or more substituents attached to atoms in the ring are given location numbers by numbering the ring atoms. Begin at the site of one substituent and number in whatever

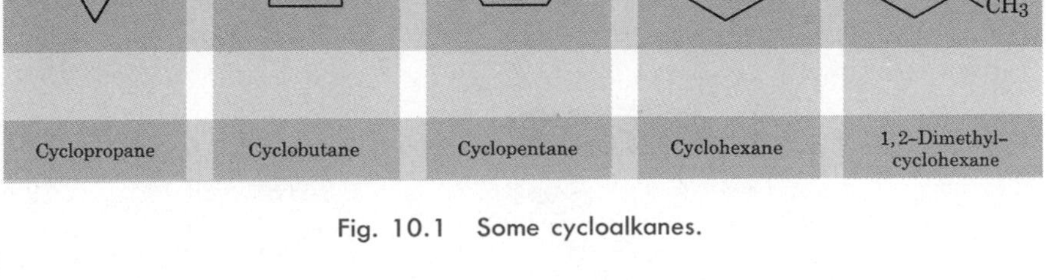

Fig. 10.1   Some cycloalkanes.

direction around the ring that will give the next nearest substitutent the lower number.

Since there are only carbon-carbon single bonds and carbon-hydrogen bonds, cycloalkanes are like their open-chain cousins in both chemical and physical properties.

cyclopropane. Cyclopropane is a sweet-smelling, colorless gas that is used in many types of major and minor surgery as an anesthetic. Mixed with oxygen or air, cyclopropane easily explodes unless the most rigorous efforts are made to avoid the occurrence of a spark.

chemical properties of alkanes and cycloalkanes

As a class, alkanes are the most chemically inert of all organic compounds. Carbon-to-carbon single bonds are extremely sturdy and very difficult to attack chemically. Carbon-to-hydrogen bonds, *as they occur in an alkane environment,* are also exceptionally resistant to chemical attack. Concentrated sulfuric acid, sodium metal, and strong alkalies do not affect alkanes under normal circumstances (e.g., room temperature).

Because of the general inertness of the alkanes, they have been nicknamed "paraffins," from the Latin *parum,* little; *affinis,* affinity. Ordinary household paraffin is a mixture of alkanes having about twenty carbons per molecule.

Here is our second important "map sign." We shall soon turn our attention to families of compounds whose molecules react with a variety of reagents. When such reactions occur, *they usually leave the alkane-like portions of the molecules unchanged.* As an example *n*-pentane does not react with sodium, but *n*-pentyl alcohol does:

$$CH_3CH_2CH_2CH_2CH_3 + Na \longrightarrow \text{no reaction}$$

n-Pentane

$$2CH_3CH_2CH_2CH_2CH_2{-}O{-}H + 2Na \longrightarrow 2CH_3CH_2CH_2CH_2CH_2O^-Na^+ + H_2\uparrow$$

n-Pentyl alcohol · · · · · · · · · · · · · · · · Sodium *n*-pentoxide

(The reaction is very much like the reaction of sodium with water: $2H{-}O{-}H + 2Na \longrightarrow 2HO^-Na^+ + H_2\uparrow$.) The shaded portion of *n*-pentyl alcohol is the alkane-like section, and in this reaction nothing happens to it.[2]

[2] In the shading of the alkane-like portions in this example, more was shaded than really should have been. It works in this case, but in general, a carbon bearing a functional group ($-OH$ in the example), plus at least one if not two of the carbons in the chain next to it, should be excluded from the alkane-like section. Thus, in *n*-pentyl alcohol, only the three carbons:

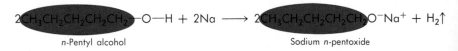

$$CH_3{-}CH_2{-}CH_2{-}CH_2{-}CH_2{-}OH$$

comprise the strictly alkane-like portion. As we shall learn, a functional group has an influence on at least the closely neighboring sections of the molecule.

combustion. Oxygen is the only common chemical that will attack alkanes, and combustion is the most useful chemical reaction of alkanes. The most important product is heat. Bunsen burner gas is largely methane; propane is a common home-heating and cooking fuel; heptane and octane (especially their isomers) are found in gasoline. The combustion of propane proceeds according to the following equation:

$$CH_3CH_2CH_3 + 5O_2 \longrightarrow 3CO_2 + 4H_2O + 531 \text{ kcal/mole of propane}$$

When the supply of oxygen is inadequate, then carbon monoxide (Chapter 5) is another product. Furthermore (as also discussed in Chapter 5), oxides of nitrogen form during the combustion of fuels.

Ozone, which at lower altitudes is made by the interactions of nitrogen oxides with oxygen (Chapter 5), will attack any organic compound. The reactions are extremely complex, especially when they involve unburned alkanes and alkenes in auto exhaust. We shall return to this aspect of smog after we have studied other families of hydrocarbons.

alkenes ("olefins") structural features

If a hydrocarbon molecule contains a carbon-to-carbon double bond, its chemical properties differ so much from those of alkanes that it is convenient to create a new family formally called the *alkenes* and nicknamed *olefins* ('ōləfəns). Names and structures of a few simple alkenes are shown in Table 10.4. Molecules with two double bonds are called *dienes* (two "-ene" linkages, or di-ene). Two dienes, both important in the manufacture of artificial rubber, are listed in Table 10.4.

naming the alkenes

Common names for simple alkenes end in "-ylene." Prefixes, derived from names for the corresponding alkanes, indicate the total number of carbons in the molecule. The names of the simple alkenes in Table 10.4 illustrate these principles. The various butylenes are differentiated arbitrarily by the prefixes α, β, and "iso-." In the homologous series the common system loses most of its practicality above the butylenes, and the IUPAC system is used.

IUPAC names. The IUPAC rules for naming the alkenes are as follows.

1. The characteristic name ending is "-ene."
2. The longest continuous chain *that contains the double bond* is selected. This chain is named by selecting the alkane with the *identical* chain length and changing the suffix in its name from "-ane" to "-ene."
3. The chain is numbered when necessary to give the *first* carbon of the double bond the lowest possible number (e.g., $CH_3CH_2CH=CH_2$ is 1-butene, not 1,2-butene and not 3-butene).

Table 10.4   Representative Alkenes

Number of Carbons	Names	Molecular Formula[a]	Condensed Structural Formula	Boiling Point, in °C
2	Ethylene (Ethene)	C_2H_4	$CH_2\!\!=\!\!CH_2$	-104
3	Propylene (Propene)	C_3H_6	$CH_3CH\!\!=\!\!CH_2$	-47
4	α-Butylene (1-butene)	C_4H_8	$CH_2\!\!=\!\!CHCH_2CH_3$	-6
	β-Butylene (2-butene)	C_4H_8	$CH_3CH\!\!=\!\!CHCH_3$	(See Table 10.5)
	Isobutylene (2-methylpropene)	C_4H_8	$\overset{\overset{\displaystyle CH_3}{\vert}}{CH_3C}\!\!=\!\!CH_2$	-7

Dienes

Number of Carbons	Names	Molecular Formula[a]	Condensed Structural Formula	Boiling Point, in °C
4	1,3-Butadiene	C_4H_6	$CH_2\!\!=\!\!CH\!-\!CH\!\!=\!\!CH_2$	-3
5	Isoprene (2-methyl-1,3-butadiene)	C_5H_8	$\overset{\overset{\displaystyle CH_3}{\vert}}{CH_2\!\!=\!\!C}\!-\!CH\!\!=\!\!CH_2$	34

[a] Molecular formulas of simple alkenes fit the general formula C_nH_{2n}, where n = number of carbons in the molecule.

4. The locations of the groups attached to the main chain are identified by numbers. The word parts are then assembled in a manner analogous to that in alkane nomenclature.

The names in parentheses in Table 10.4 as well as the following examples illustrate correct application of these rules. Study them, noting especially the placing of commas and hyphens. Because Rule 3 gives precedence to the double bond rather than to the side chains, positions bearing side chains will sometimes have larger numbers than they would if an alternate numbering were used.

$$\overset{\overset{\displaystyle CH_3 \qquad\qquad\quad CH_3}{\vert \qquad\qquad\qquad\ \vert}}{CH_3CH_2CHCH_2CH\!\!=\!\!CCH_3}$$

2,5-Dimethyl-2-heptene

$$\overset{\overset{\displaystyle\ \ \ \ \ \ \ \ \ \ \ \ \ \ \ CH_3}{\ \ \ \ \ \ \ \ \ \ \ \ \ \ \ \vert}}{\underset{}{\overset{\overset{\displaystyle CH_3 \quad CHCH_2CH_3}{\vert \qquad\ \ \vert}}{CH_3CHCH_2CH\!\!=\!\!CH_2}}}$$

2-Isobutyl-3-methyl-1-pentene

geometric or *cis-trans* isomerism

Four isomeric alkenes having the formula C_4H_8 are known. Their structures are

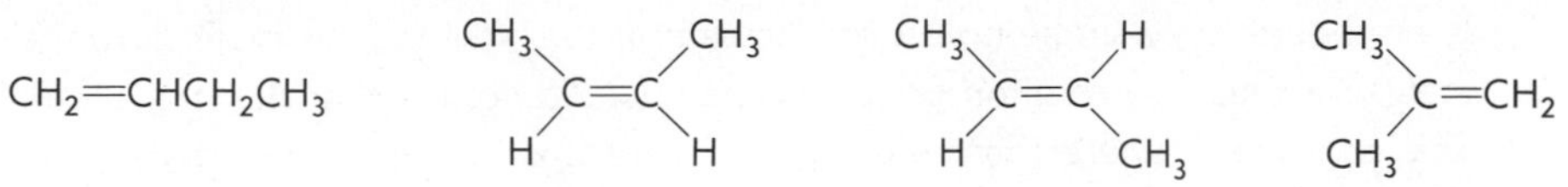

$$CH_2{=}CHCH_2CH_3$$

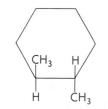

| 1-Butene | cis-2-Butene | trans-2-Butene | 2-Methyl-1-propene |
| (α-butylene) | (cis-β-butylene) | (trans-β-butylene) | (isobutylene) |

In 1-butene the double bond is between the first and the second carbon. In both of the 2-butenes it is between the second and third, but because *there is not free rotation about a double bond* a new type of isomerism is possible among the alkenes. The physical properties of all the butenes are listed in Table 10.5, which is included to demonstrate that differences in structure, however subtle, do mean differences in observable properties. The chemical properties of these butenes are similar, however, since each has the double bond.

Table 10.5 **Physical Properties of the Butenes**

Isomer	Bp (°C)	Mp (°C)	Density (in g/cc)
2-Methylpropene	−6.90	−140.4	0.640 (−20°C)
1-Butene	−6.26	−185	0.641
trans-2-Butene	+0.88	−105.6	0.649
cis-2-Butene	+3.72	−138.9	0.667

The pair of 2-butenes, which differ only in geometry and not in basic nucleus-to-nucleus sequence, illustrates *geometric isomerism*. When the two groups are on opposite sides of the double bond, they are said to be *trans* to each other; if on the same side, they are *cis*.[3]

cis-trans isomerism among cycloalkanes. Two isomeric 1,2-dimethylcyclohexanes are known.

trans-1,2-dimethylcyclohexane
b.p. 123.7°C
m.p. −89.4°C
density 0.777 g/cc

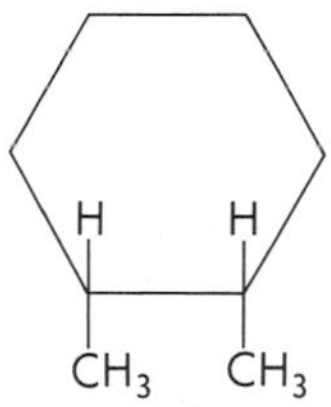

cis-1,2-dimethylcyclohexane
b.p. 130°C
m.p. −50.1°C
density 0.796 g/cc

[3] Those interested in further details should consult not only any text in organic chemistry but also a paper in the *Journal of Organic Chemistry* (Vol. 85, p. 2849, 1970). The paper discusses proposals by the IUPAC for designating *cis* and *trans* relations as *Z* (from the German word *zusammen* or together) and *E* (from the German word *entgegen*, opposite).

Even though only single bonds are present in the isomers, the cyclic arrangement prevents free rotation about the bonds holding together the ring atoms. The *cis*-isomer, where the methyl groups are on the *same* side of the ring, cannot convert to the *trans*-isomer by rotation about a bond. We see, therefore, that the cycloalkanes will, like the alkenes, give rise to many examples of geometrical isomerism.

Nearly all the important reactions of the alkenes occur at the double bond, and most of them occur in such a way that the double bond disappears, and the single bonds remain.

Because the double bond is a structural group that functions chemically, it is called a *functional group*. The characteristic differences between families of organic compounds are differences of functional groups.

There are principally two types of reactions of alkenes of interest in our study—addition reactions and polymerizations. In the former, some reagent is said to add across the double bond, and we shall study two examples, the addition of water and the addition of hydrogen to a double bond.

addition of water to a carbon-carbon double bond. hydration of alkenes. In the presence of an acid, the elements of water can be made to add to a double bond. The —OH group in H—OH becomes attached to a carbon at one end of the double bond and the remaining H— from H—OH goes to the carbon at the other end. The double bond disappears; only a carbon-carbon single bond remains. But the molecule is now a member of the family of alcohols.

in general:

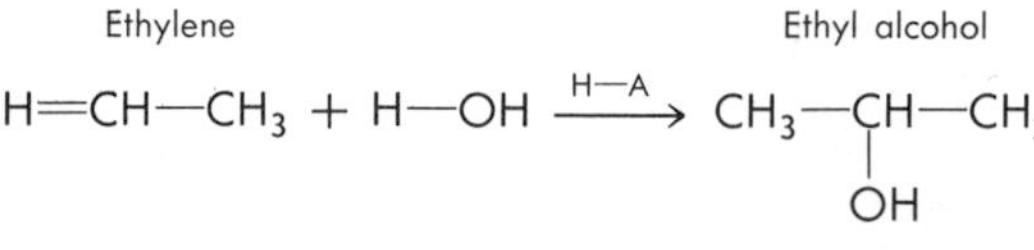

$$\ce{>C=C< + H-OH <=>[H-A^4] -\underset{H}{C}-C-OH}$$

specific examples:

$$\ce{CH2=CH2 + H-OH ->[H-A] CH3-CH2-OH}$$
Ethylene   Ethyl alcohol

$$\ce{CH3-CH=CH-CH3 + H-OH ->[H-A] CH3-\underset{OH}{CH}-CH2-CH3}$$
β-Butylene   sec-Butyl alcohol

[4] H—A is a symbol for some strong acid. Sulfuric acid is commonly used, but there are advantages in keeping the discussion general. The reaction is written as reversible. We are concerned here only about the forward reaction—making the alcohol. But it is possible to get the elements of water back out.

The addition of water to a double bond is an important reaction in several metabolic pathways in living organisms. A different catalyst (an enzyme) is used, but the result is the same. An alkene system is converted to an alcohol system.

The reaction is believed to occur approximately as follows, illustrated by the hydration of ethylene to ethyl alcohol.

Step 1. A proton, H^+, transfers from the catalyst to form a stronger carbon-hydrogen bond.

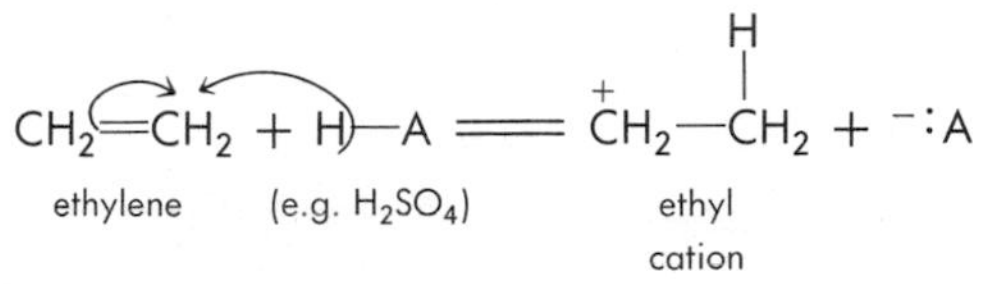

$$CH_2\!\!=\!\!CH_2 + H\!\!-\!\!A \rightleftharpoons \overset{+}{C}H_2\!\!-\!\!CH_2 \overset{\overset{H}{|}}{} + {}^-\!:\!A$$

ethylene   (e.g. H_2SO_4)   ethyl cation

The product, the ethyl cation, is an example of a carbonium ion, a group with a positively charged carbon having only six electrons in its outside shell. Carbonium ions are not very stable. In step two the positively charged carbon regains an outer octet.

Step 2. A carbon-oxygen bond forms.

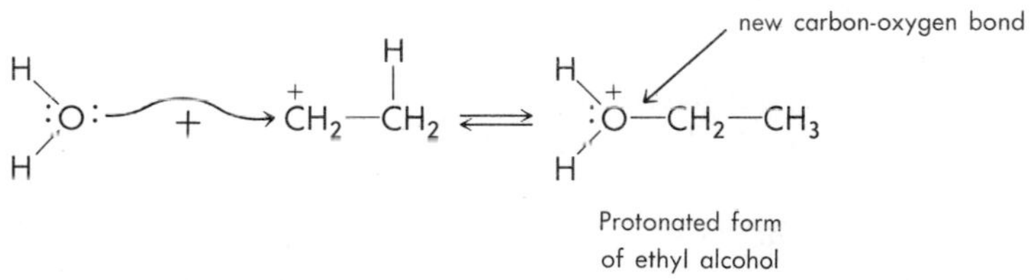

new carbon-oxygen bond

$$\overset{H}{\underset{H}{}}\!\!O\!: \;+\; \overset{+}{C}H_2\!\!-\!\!CH_2\overset{\overset{H}{|}}{} \rightleftharpoons \overset{H}{\underset{H}{}}\!:\!\overset{+}{O}\!\!-\!\!CH_2\!\!-\!\!CH_3$$

Protonated form
of ethyl alcohol

Now the positive charge is on an oxygen, which is acceptable because the oxygen has an outer octet. This new product is really nothing more than an organic derivative of a hydronium ion. One of the Hs in H_3O^+ has been replaced by an alkane-like group. Viewed in a different way, this new product is nothing more than a protonated alcohol molecule. To obtain the final product, the alcohol, all that has to happen is the transfer of this "extra" proton to some acceptor (e.g., $A\!:^-$ or H_2O). Step 3, the last step, may therefore be written as shown on the next page.

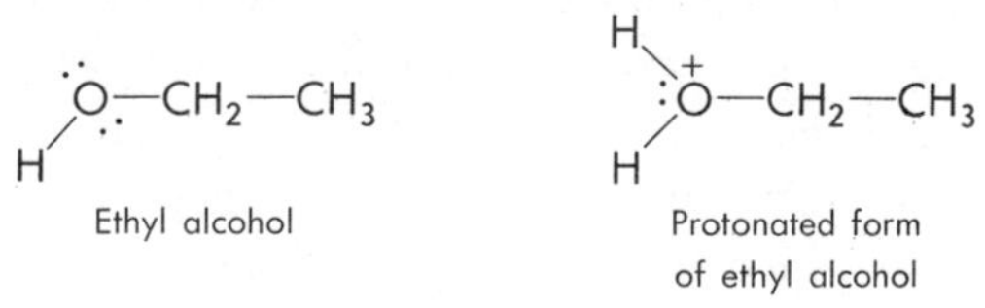

$$\overset{..}{\underset{H}{}}\!O\!\!-\!\!CH_2\!\!-\!\!CH_3 \qquad\qquad \overset{H}{\underset{H}{}}\!:\!\overset{+}{O}\!\!-\!\!CH_2\!\!-\!\!CH_3$$

Ethyl alcohol   Protonated form
of ethyl alcohol

Step 3. The alcohol is liberated and the catalyst is regenerated.

$$\overset{H}{\underset{H}{:O}}-CH_2-CH_3 \; + \; \overset{..}{:}A \; \rightleftharpoons \; \overset{..}{\underset{H}{:O}}-CH_2-CH_3 \; + \; H-A$$

(or H$_2$O) ·· Ethyl alcohol (or H$_3$O$^+$) Recovered catalyst

addition of hydrogen: hydrogenation.

in general:

$$\underset{/}{\overset{\backslash}{}}C=C\underset{\backslash}{\overset{/}{}} \longrightarrow -\overset{|}{\underset{|}{C}}-\overset{|}{\underset{|}{C}}-$$

$$+ \qquad\qquad \overset{}{\underset{H \; H}{}}$$

$$H-H$$

specific examples:

$$CH_2{=}CH_2 + H-H \xrightarrow[\Delta,\text{ pressure}]{\text{Ni or Pt}} \overset{|}{\underset{H}{C}}H_2{-}\overset{|}{\underset{H}{C}}H_2 \text{ or } CH_3{-}CH_3$$

Ethylene   Ethane

$$CH_2{=}CHCH_2CH_3 + H-H \xrightarrow[\Delta,\text{ pressure}]{\text{Ni or Pt}} CH_3CH_2CH_2CH_3$$

α-Butylene   *n*-Butane

$$CH_3CH{=}CHCH_3 + H-H \xrightarrow[\Delta,\text{ pressure}]{\text{Ni or Pt}} CH_3CH_2CH_2CH_3$$

β-Butylene   *n*-Butane

As the examples indicate, a catalyst is necessary for this reaction, as well as heat and pressure. Usually, powdered nickel or platinum is used. "Hydrogenated vegetable oils" (e.g., Crisco, Spry, Fluffo, Mixo) are made by hydrogenating double bonds in molecules found in vegetable oils.

polymerization. A *polymer* is a very-high-formula-weight substance whose structure consists of several repeating units or parts ("polymer" from the Greek *poly-*, many; *meros*, parts). It is made by causing its unit parts, as separate molecules or *monomers,* to react with each other in such a way that they link to each other successively, many, many times. This linking together of hundreds and thousands of monomers is called *polymerization.* Industrially, it is a most important reaction because it is the source of all plastics, resins, and synthetic lacquers. The features of polymerization occur in nature also, whenever plants or animals synthesize molecules of cellulose, starch, gums, rubber, and even proteins and nucleic acids. Some very simple alkenes, abundantly available from petroleum, are important monomers for the plastics industry.

polymerization of ethylene; polyethylene.

$$nCH_2{=}CH_2 \xrightarrow[\text{pressure}]{O_2 \text{ (trace), heat}} {-}(CH_2{-}CH_2)_n^{5} \qquad (\text{where } n = 100 \text{ to } 1000)$$

Main feature of polyethylene

Some polymerizations occur by means of carbonium ions that the catalyst helps to generate, as illustrated for the case of polyethylene as follows.

Catalyst $+ CH_2{=}CH_2 \longrightarrow$ catalyst$-CH_2-CH_2^+$ (a carbonium ion)

Catalyst$-CH_2-CH_2^+ + CH_2{=}CH_2 \longrightarrow$ catalyst$-CH_2-CH_2-CH_2-CH_2^+$

Catalyst$-CH_2-CH_2-CH_2-CH_2^+ + CH_2{=}CH_2 \longrightarrow$

catalyst$-CH_2-CH_2-CH_2-CH_2-CH_2-CH_2^+$ (growing polyethylene chain)

Catalyst$-(CH_2-CH_2)_2CH_2-CH_2^+ + CH_2{=}CH_2 \longrightarrow$ etc.

When the growing carbonium ion picks up some negative fragment (from the catalyst, for example), it stops growing and a finished polyethylene molecule has been made.

Polymerization of ethylene, like all polymerization reactions, does not produce one pure, homogeneous substance. When billions of ethylene molecules polymerize, some very long chains and some shorter chains form. Polyethylene, therefore, is really a mixture of molecules, but all have the same structural feature: repeating ethylene units. Since polyethylene is essentially a mixture of very-long-chain alkanes, it has the chemical inertness of alkanes. That is why it is useful in making such a variety of plastic household articles (icebox dishes, wastebaskets, drinking glasses, funnels, bowls, and pans), laboratory apparatus, and hospital equipment (for instance, tubing for intravenous feeding and transfusions).

A number of other common plastics with their sources and uses are given in Table 10.6. Polyvinyl chloride, or PVC, became a source of controversy in 1970. This plastic is one of the most widely used for disposable plastic household bottles and containers. Some 200 million PVC bottles were made in 1969. U. S. consumption of PVC in 1970 was 1,120,000 tons. When PVC (or any chlorinated plastics) are burned in municipal incinerators, one product is hydrogen chloride. In moist air this becomes hydrochloric acid, which not only does no good in the outside air to plants or animals, it also corrodes metal parts in the incinerators.

The controversy was about the seriousness of the problem and had not been resolved as late as 1971. There were growing signs, however, that alternatives to the chlorinated plastics would have to be found.

[5] The symbolism used here is common. The arrangement of parentheses with a subscript indicates that the units in parentheses are strung out in a row. The "unused" valences or bonds that appear in this symbol are occupied with binding small fragments, some from the catalyst used. Virtually all of the molecule, however, is as indicated.

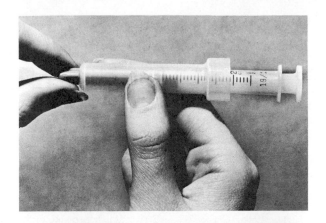

Fig. 10.2 Polypropylene is widely used in a great variety of situations ranging from hospitals to homes. (Photographs courtesy of Enjay Chemical Company.)

alkynes
structural
features

Compounds in which carbon-to-carbon triple bonds occur are called *alkynes*, nicknamed *acetylenes*. The smallest member of this family is acetylene. Although these compounds show many of the typical

$$H-C\equiv C-H$$

Acetylene

addition reactions of the alkenes, the triple bond is not important to substances in the body insofar as we shall study them, and we shall not discuss alkynes further.

Table 10.6   Vinyl Plastics

Plastic	Monomer	Uses
Polyvinyl chloride (PVC)	$CH_2{=}CHCl$ (vinyl chloride)	bottles and other containers; insulation; plastic pipe
Saran	$CH_2{=}CCl_2$ and vinyl (dichloro- chloride ethylene)	packaging film; fibers; tubing
Teflon	$F_2C{=}CF_2$ (tetrafluoroethylene)	nonsticking surfaces for pots and pans
Orlon	$CH_2{=}CHC{\equiv}N$ (acrylonitrile)	fabrics
Polystyrene	—CH$=$CH$_2$	foam plastics and molded items
Lucite, Plexiglas	$\overset{\displaystyle CH_3}{\underset{\vert}{CH_2{=}C}}{-}CO_2CH_3$	coatings; windows; molded items

Natural Polymer

Natural rubber	$\overset{\displaystyle CH_3}{\underset{\vert}{CH_2{=}C}}{-}CH{=}CH_2$ (isoprene)	tires, hoses, boots

As organic chemists gradually unraveled the structures of naturally occurring compounds, it became apparent that many distinctively fragrant or aromatic substances possessed a unique structural feature. This was the flat, hexagonal ring of six carbon atoms that occurs in the hydrocarbon benzene and is called the *benzene ring*.

aromatic hydrocarbons structural features

The structure of benzene is given in Fig. 10.3, together with the most common condensed symbols. Although benzene is highly unsaturated, it does not behave at all like an alkene. It does not, for example, show any addition

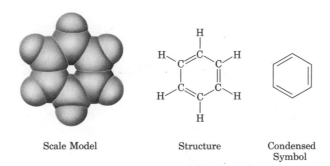

Scale Model   Structure   Condensed Symbol

Fig. 10.3   Benzene.

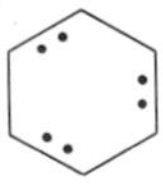

Fig. 10.4

Fig. 10.5

reactions, except under the most drastic conditions. At room temperature it is quite indifferent to concentrated sulfuric acid; it is remarkably stable. This stability may be explained in terms of the molecular orbital theory of the covalent bond we have used.

The second bond in each of the double bonds implied by the conventional structure of Fig. 10.3 involves, of course, a shared pair of electrons. We could, then, write the structure shown in Fig. 10.4 for our benzene molecule. The conventional structure of Fig. 10.3 or that shown in Fig. 10.4 allege that each of these pairs of electrons moves in a molecular orbital about only two carbon nuclei. This is not believed to be true. All three pairs move in a relatively gigantic molecular "shell" about all six carbon nuclei. All six carbons share all six electrons which move, so to speak, in one big circular shell around the benzene ring. This is hard to symbolize with our simple system of a straight line for each shared pair, although many chemists use the symbol of Fig. 10.5.

With this much room in which the six electrons may move, the benzene molecule is quite stable; it strongly resists any chemical event that would disrupt this "closed circuit" of electrons. Thus, when chemists use the conventional symbols of Fig. 10.3 for benzene, they are careful not to read into them any alkene characteristics.

properties of benzene

Benzene is a nonpolar compound. It boils at $80°C$ and it is insoluble in water. In spite of its great flammability, it is often used as a dry-cleaning solvent.

The characteristic reactions of benzene are *substitution reactions*. Certain reagents can displace one of the hydrogens attached to the benzene ring; and this, of course, does not affect the closed-circuit character of the large molecular electron shell.

1. Action of *hot* nitric acid (catalyzed by concentrated sulfuric acid).

$$+ \text{H—O—NO}_2 \xrightarrow[\Delta]{\text{H}_2\text{SO}_4} \text{Nitrobenzene} + \text{H}_2\text{O}$$

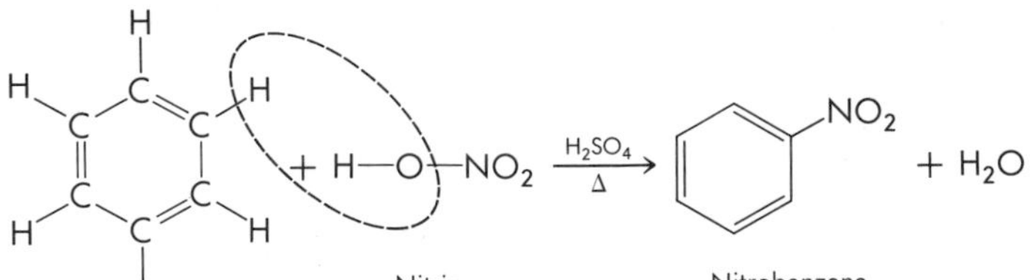

Nitric acid → Nitrobenzene

2. Action of *hot* sulfuric acid.

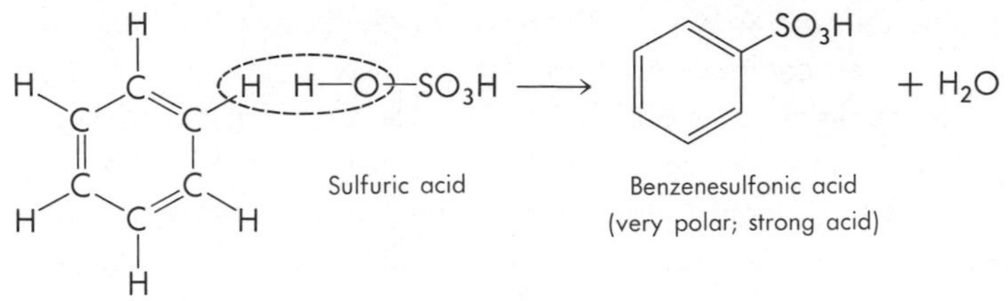

Sulfuric acid → Benzenesulfonic acid (very polar; strong acid) + H_2O

3. Action of bromine in the presence of iron (no reaction without this catalyst, in contrast to the rapid reaction of alkenes with bromine).

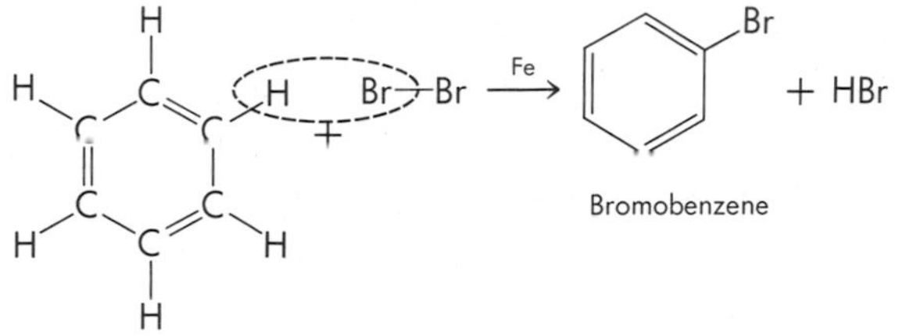

Bromobenzene + HBr

Some of the most important simple derivatives of benzene are listed in Table 10.7, together with statements about their uses.

Table 10.7   Important Aromatic Compounds

Name	Structure	Uses
Toluene	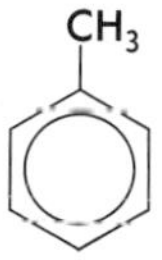 CH_3	Solvent; raw material for other aromatic compounds
Phenol	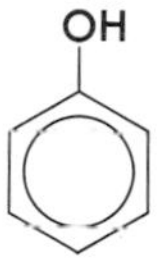 OH	Bactericide (Lister's original antiseptic); (a general protoplasmic poison; toxic action on skin)
Aniline	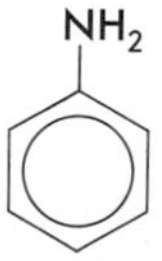 NH_2	Building block for aniline dyes; synthesis of many pharmaceuticals
Benzoic acid	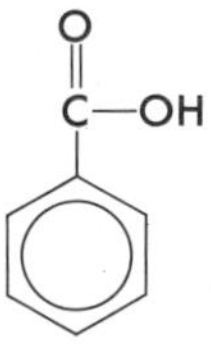 C—OH (with =O)	Starting material for many organic chemicals; used in some ointments designed to soften the epidermis

polynuclear aromatic hydrocarbons

Many compounds are known in which two or more benzene rings are "fused" together. The most common is naphthalene, which contains two benzene rings. Compounds containing several benzene rings are often carcinogenic; that is, they possess cancer-producing activity. Benzo[a]pyrene, a compound that is known to cause gene mutations and lung cancer in some organisms, is a product of incomplete combustion of tobacco, coal, and petroleum fuels. It is one of the trace pollutants in the air of every urban center tested. It even forms on steaks broiled over charcoal when hot fat drips onto the hot coals. A well-done steak may have as much benzo[a]pyrene as the smoke of 600 cigarettes. (Of course, steaks are eaten, not inhaled, but before they are broiled as much fat as possible should be trimmed off.) According to H. R. Lewis, a nonsmoker in Cincinnati, Ohio breathes in each day an amount of benzo[a]pyrene equivalent to 26 cigarettes. (The figures for Detroit, are 37 cigarettes; for Birmingham, Alabama, 50 cigarettes. Birmingham has one of the nation's highest rates of lung cancer.) Methylcholanthrene is another carcinogenic compound isolated from coal tar.

Naphthalene ($C_{10}H_8$)　　Benzo[a]pyrene　　Methylcholanthrene

petroleum

Petroleum (*petra*, rock; *oleum*, oil) is a complex mixture of organic compounds of which nearly all are hydrocarbons. When this mixture is distilled, it can be separated into the "fractions" shown in Table 10.8. Each fraction is a mixture of hydrocarbons having an overall volatility that makes it useful in certain kinds of engines or heating devices. The residues that do not distill are used as residual fuel oil ("resid") or made into asphalt and coke.

cracking

The gasoline fraction of crude petroleum is not large enough to supply even current needs. Organic chemists have solved this problem by discovering ways to break or "crack" larger molecules found in the kerosene range and higher into molecules small enough to be usable as gasoline. This is done by thermal as well as catalytic "cracking" procedures. Much of the gasoline consumed in the world is obtained this way.

Many unsaturated hydrocarbons are obtained from crude petroleum or from cracking operations. They serve as cheap raw materials for a host of useful products, including nearly all plastics, lacquers, resins, organic solvents,

Table 10.8 **Petroleum Fractions**

Boiling Point Range, in °C (a Measure of Volatility)	Number of Carbons in Molecules of the Fraction	Uses
Below 20	C_1-C_4	Natural gas; heating and cooking fuel; Bunsen burner fuel; raw material for other chemicals
20–60	C_5-C_6	Petroleum "ether"; nonpolar solvent and cleaning fluid
60–100	C_6-C_7	Ligroin or light naphtha; nonpolar solvent and cleaning fluid
40–200	C_5-C_{10}	Gasoline
175–325	$C_{12}-C_{18}$	Kerosene; jet fuel; tractor fuel
250–400	C_{12} and higher	Gas oil; fuel oil; diesel oil
Nonvolatile liquids	C_{20} and up	Refined mineral oil; lubricating oil; grease (a dispersion of soap in oil)
Nonvolatile solids	C_{20} and up	Paraffin wax (purified solids that crystallize from some oils); asphalt and tar for roads and roofing

and synthetic rubber. As times goes on and the energy crisis is intensified by the technological revolution in underdeveloped countries and by man's desire to supplant natural fibers and building materials by synthetics, the fossil fuels will be valued more as raw materials for organic synthesis than as fuels.

We have already studied several of the chemicals in smog—ozone and the oxides of nitrogen, sulfur and carbon, and their corresponding acids. Hydrocarbons also contribute to photochemical smog, and we are now in a position to understand how.

the hydrocarbons and photochemical smog

According to figures by Public Health Consultant Howard R. Lewis, every thousand gallons of automobile gasoline burned releases 200 to 400 pounds of unburned (or partly oxidized) hydrocarbons. In the United States roughly 75 billion gallons of gasoline and diesel fuel are used each year. On an average day, therefore, the national atmosphere is treated to over 25,000 tons of hydrocarbons. These contribute to haze and are changed into serious eye irritants and plant killers. The major cities suffer the most.

Hydrocarbons are attacked by both atomic oxygen and ozone. The formation of both of these oxidizing agents, recall, requires solar energy and nitrogen dioxide besides oxygen.

$$NO_2 + \text{sunlight} \longrightarrow NO + \underset{\text{atomic oxygen}}{O}$$

$$O + O_2 + M \longrightarrow \underset{\text{ozone}}{O_3} + M$$

(where M, any neighbor molecule, carries off excess energy)

Unchanged alkanes in auto exhaust are especially vulnerable to atomic oxygen, and they are broken to aldehydes, alkyl radicals, and other products not shown.   (We shall not always show balanced equations in the following discussion.)

$$\text{Alkanes} + O \longrightarrow \underset{\substack{\text{alkyl} \\ \text{radicals}}}{R\cdot} + \underset{\text{aldehydes}}{R-\overset{\displaystyle O}{\overset{\|}{C}}-H}$$

A radical is any atomic or molecular species having one or more unpaired electrons. The oxygen molecule, $\cdot\ddot{O}\!:\!\ddot{O}\cdot$, with two unpaired electrons is a diradical. A chlorine atom, $\cdot\ddot{\underset{..}{C}l}\!:$, is a radical. The methyl radical, one example

of an alkyl radical, would have the structure $H-\overset{\displaystyle H}{\underset{\displaystyle H}{C}}\cdot$. It is electrically neutral,

but its carbon has only seven electrons in its outside shell, six being shared to the three hydrogens, and one "odd" electron unshared (and unpaired) with anything. The symbol for any alkyl radical, therefore, is simply $R\cdot$.[6]

Alkyl radicals are highly reactive. They may combine with oxygen to produce a new radical:

$$R\cdot + O_2 \longrightarrow \underset{\text{peroxy radical}}{R-O-O\cdot}$$

This, in turn, may attack either a water molecule or a hydrocarbon and abstract a hydrogen atom:

[6] In a great deal of chemical writing the word "radical" is carelessly used. It should not be used, for example, to label a complex ion. The hydroxide ion is $^-\!:\!\ddot{O}H$; the hydroxyl radical is $H\ddot{O}\cdot$ (Frequently ^-OH is called (incorrectly) the hydroxide radical.) It is common practice to abbreviate structures of radicals; thus we write $HO\cdot$ instead of $H\ddot{O}\cdot$ for the hydroxyl radical.

$$R\!-\!O\!-\!O\cdot + H\!-\!O\!-\!H \longrightarrow R\!-\!O\!-\!O\!-\!H + \cdot OH$$

an alkyl   hydroxyl
hydroperoxide   radical

There are a number of other possibilities and, given the fact that R— may be quite a number of hydrocarbon-like systems known to be present in unburned gasoline, the organic chemistry of smog is exceedingly complex. It is beyond the scope of not just this text but any full organic text.

PAN. There is one reaction of the alkene family of hydrocarbons in photochemical smog that accounts for the formation of the most potent eye irritants in smog—a family of compounds called the peroxyacyl nitrates, or PAN for short.

PAN can form from a variety of hydrocarbons and most easily from simple alkenes. First, ozone, which readily attacks alkenes at their double bonds, splits an alkene molecule in two.

$$\text{E.g.,}\quad R\!-\!CH\!=\!CH\!-\!R' + O_3 \longrightarrow R\!-\!\overset{\displaystyle O}{\overset{\|}{C}}\!-\!O\cdot + R'\!-\!\overset{\displaystyle O}{\overset{\|}{C}}\!-\!H$$

carboxyl   aldehydes
radicals

Nitric oxide, also in smog, strips an oxygen atom from a carboxyl radical:

$$R\!-\!\overset{\displaystyle O}{\overset{\|}{C}}\!-\!O\cdot + NO \longrightarrow NO_2 + R\!-\!\overset{\displaystyle O}{\overset{\|}{C}}\cdot$$

acyl radicals

Acyl radicals then react with both oxygen molecules and nitrogen dioxide (two steps) to form the peroxyacyl nitrates.

$$NO_2 + R\!-\!\overset{\displaystyle O}{\overset{\|}{C}}\cdot + O_2 \longrightarrow R\!-\!\overset{\displaystyle O}{\overset{\|}{C}}\!-\!O\!-\!O\!-\!NO_2$$

peroxyacyl nitrate
PAN

Besides alkenes, aromatics and aldehydes in smog can also be converted to PAN. The principal member of the family is peroxyacetyl nitrate (R = CH_3).

PAN, first identified in smog in 1961, is now recognized as the agent in smog most toxic to plants. In conifers it causes needle blight; in broad leaf plants, an underleaf silvering or bronzing; and in grasses a bleaching.

As an eye irritant, human volunteers report sensing PAN after only 12 minutes exposure at a level of only 0.5 ppm. PAN affects the whole heart-lung network. College student volunteers experienced a significant increase in oxygen consumption when exercising in an atmosphere with only 0.3 ppm PAN.

Other eye irritants in photochemical smog are a simple aldehyde, formaldehyde ($CH_2{=}O$), and an unsaturated aldehyde, acrolein ($CH_2{=}CHCH{=}O$).

The noxious soup of poisons breathed each day by residents in major urban areas has dramatic effects on health. People who both smoke cigarettes and breathe smoggy air are doubly hit. Inhaled cigarette smoke has about 400 ppm of carbon monoxide, which ties up hemoglobin in blood making it unable to carry oxygen. The average smoker has about 5–6% of his hemoglobin inactivated versus 0.4% for the nonsmoker. Whereas NO_2 levels as high as 3 ppm have been noted in Los Angeles smog, cigarette smoke may have an NO_2 level as high as 5 ppm. There is also hydrogen cyanide in cigarette smoke—a concentration of about 1600 ppm. Long-term exposure to hydrogen cyanide levels above 10 ppm is dangerous.

In the decade of the 1960s, there was a 500% increase in emphysema deaths in New York City, making emphysema the most rapidly growing cause of death in that area. Chronic bronchitis increased 200% in New York City in the same period.

Sixty members of the medical school faculty at the University of California, Los Angeles stated in 1968 that air pollution had become a major health hazard to most of Los Angeles during much of the year.

Economists L. B. Lave and E. P. Seskin have calculated that in terms of decreased morbidity and mortality a 50% reduction in air pollution levels in major urban areas would give a saving of over two billion dollars annually.

What are the prospects of licking air pollution? Not very good without a far more determined effort on the part of all citizens. The graphs in Figure 10.6 tell the dismal story better than words. The estimates used to construct the graphs were based on assumptions that major improvements would be made in controlling emissions from both vehicular traffic and stationary combustion devices. Thus the stringent limits on emissions from automobiles called for by the late 1970 Clean Air Amendments (PL 91-604) to the 1963 Clean Air Act are built into the graphs. Also assumed is the development of so-called "breeder" reactors. See Chapter 22.

The emission of pollutants from automobiles will be substantially reduced by 1980 if provisions of the 1970 Clean Air Amendments are carried out. Compared with vehicles of the 1960s having no control devices, the emissions from automobiles of the 1980 model year will be reduced 98% for hydrocarbons, 96% for carbon monoxide and 91% for nitrogen oxide. Much of this control depends on the development of the catalytic muffler (Chapter 4) and on finding ways to obtain the effects of high octane gasoline without using lead additives.

leaded gasoline. Tetramethyl and tetraethyl lead are the principal compounds of lead added to gasoline to produce knock-free combustion. There is an average of 2.5 ml of these compounds per gallon of leaded gasoline

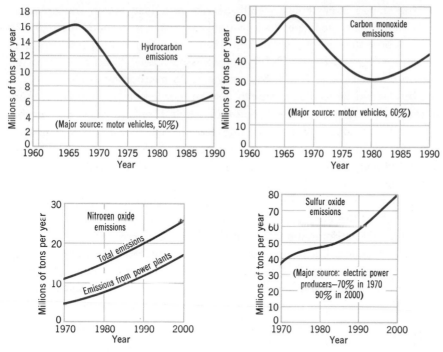

Fig. 10.6 Tomorrow's levels of air pollutants. (Sources of data: For emissions of hydro-carbons and carbon monoxide, National Air Pollution Control Administration Publication No. AP-73, "Nationwide Inventory of Air Pollutant Emissions, 1969" (published August 1970). For nitrogen oxide and sulfur oxide emissions, data compiled by P. W. Spaite and R. P. Hangebrauck and published in "Fuels and Energy," Hearings, 91st Congress, 2nd session, Sept, 1970, Committee on Interior and Insular Affairs. The projections for nitro-gen oxides may be quite conservative. Based on 1968 data of the National Air Pollution Control Administration, the 1970 nationwide emissions of nitrogen oxides would be estimated at about 21 million tons, half coming from power plants and 40% from trans-portation.)

sold in the United States. About three-fourths of the lead appears in the exhaust. Scientists R. L. Metcalf (University of Illinois) and J. N. Pitts, Jr. (University of California, Riverside) estimate that since 1923, when the use of tetraethyl lead began, 2.6 trillion grams (roughly 3 million tons) of lead has poured from exhaust pipes into the atmosphere. Scripps Institute scientists T. J. Chow and J. L. Earl reported in late 1970 that the concentration of lead aerosols in San Diego, California air was increasing by 5% a year. Food fish in nearby waters had 2 to 3 times as much lead in their livers as normal. Lead poisoning hits the nervous system, the digestive system, the tissues that form blood, and the kidneys.

$$(CH_3)_4Pb \qquad (CH_3CH_2)_4Pb$$

Tetramethyl lead   Tetraethyl lead

227

the hydrocarbons and photochemical smog

The United States Public Health Service has ruled that a concentration of 50 micrograms lead per liter in drinking water is grounds for rejecting it. The concentration of lead in San Diego rainwater over a test period of three years ranged from 3–300 micrograms per liter with an average of 40 micrograms per liter. (The U. S. average is 36 micrograms per liter.)

The United States Public Health Service warns that prolonged exposure to relatively small quantities of lead may result in serious illness (irreversible brain injury) or death. If the daily intake of an adult male is no higher than 0.32 mg, his body can get rid of the lead compounds by excretion. At higher levels, the body begins to accumulate lead. Lead enters our bodies from food, dusts, drink, and air. The amount from lead-polluted air may be as much as 10 to 20% of the daily intake. (The cigarette smoker gets a bonus; there is as much as 0.3 micrograms of lead in each puff.)

What will be done about lead in gasoline? Some companies are offering lead-free gasoline, but the president of one of the major manufacturers of lead additives predicted a "bright future" and a "strong demand" for these additives in the decade of the 70s. The issue will no doubt be resolved before the 1980s. It has to be resolved if efficient catalytic mufflers are ever to be installed on exhaust lines of cars (Chapter 4), mufflers that could be crucial to the control of all other pollutants from cars.

Many serious cases of lead poisoning occur among children who eat lead-based paint flaking from walls and woodwork of deteriorating housing. Lead poisoning was labeled by a New York city health official (late 1970) as the most serious pediatrics problem in New York City; evidences of lead poisoning were found in roughly half of a group of 30,000 children tested.

halogen derivatives of the hydrocarbons The simplest organohalogen compounds are those in which one or more halogen atoms have replaced hydrogens of hydrocarbons. A few examples are shown in Table 10.9. They include aerosol propellants, solvents, and the most persistent insecticides discovered.

organochlorine insecticides. DDT, no doubt the most famous and infamous of any insecticide, is in this family. It seemed to be such a great blessing to mankind when it was first employed in 1944 in Naples to stop a raging typhus epidemic that the discoverer of its insecticidal properties, Paul Mueller, was awarded one of the 1948 Nobel Prizes. DDT wiped out the malarial mosquitoes on the island of Sardinia soon after. Public health officials, understandably awed by the potential of this compound, which seemed to be very safe to use around people, were confident that some of mankind's greatest scourges—typhus, malaria, yellow fever—would become, like the Black Death of the 14th century, a dark memory. But some mosquitoes and flies survived the chemical attacks, survived apparently with genes for developing offspring who could also resist DDT. Resistance to DDT first appeared

Table 10.9 **Some Simple Halogen Derivatives of the Hydrocarbons**

Name	Structure	Boiling Point, in °C	Uses
Ethyl chloride	CH_3—CH_2—Cl	12.5	External local anesthetic ("freeze" technique); total anesthetic if breathed (may cause death)
Chloroform	$CHCl_3$	61	Powerful, rapid-acting anesthetic; nonflammable
Carbon tetrachloride	CCl_4	77	Fire extinguisher; nonflammable dry-cleaning solvent (ample ventilation is essential)
Iodoform	CHI_3	(m.p. 119)	Antiseptic wound dressing (releases iodine slowly)
Tetrachloroethylene	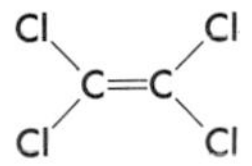 (Cl)(Cl)C=C(Cl)(Cl)	121	Treatment of hookworm infections caused by Necator americanus
Fluorocarbon-12	CCl_2F_2	−30	First fluorocarbon aerosol propellant and still widely used; also widely used as a refrigerant in refrigerators and air conditioners

in the late 1950s. Pest control scientists, impressed by the work of one organochlorine, sought among similar compounds pesticides to which insects would not be resistant. For awhile they were successful, but the new materials, besides leading to resistant species themselves, created environmental problems with which we are still struggling. Several examples of the newer organchlorines are in Table 10.10.

How these compounds kill insects and how they cause problems will be studied in Chapter 16 when we learn more about enzymes and hormones and how poisons affect them.

Selected Reading List

References to Air Pollution

Books

1. Howard R. Lewis. *With Every Breath You Take*. Crown Publishers, Inc., New York, 1965. For the laymen to science, this very informative book is probably the best single book on air pollution. After an interesting survey of the history

Table 10.10 Some Important Organochlorine Insecticides

Name	Structure	LD$_{50}$ (orally in rats; mg per kg of body weight)[a]
Diphenylethane Group		
DDT	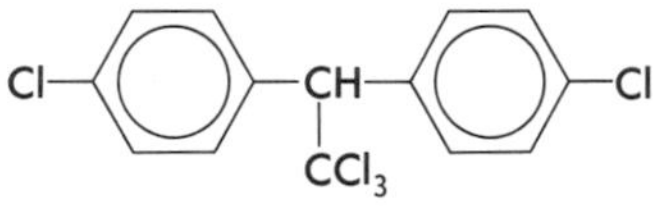	113
Methoxychlor	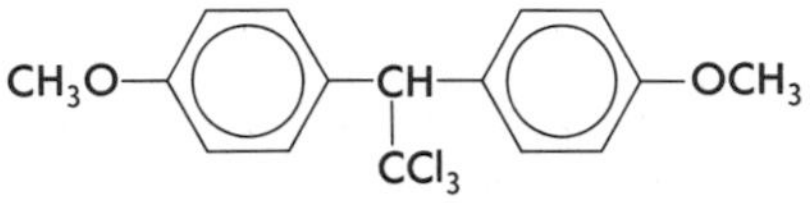	6000
Cyclodiene Group		
Endrin	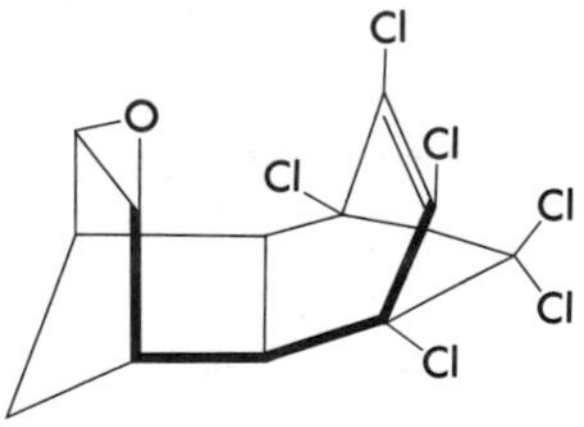	39
Chlordane (a mixture)	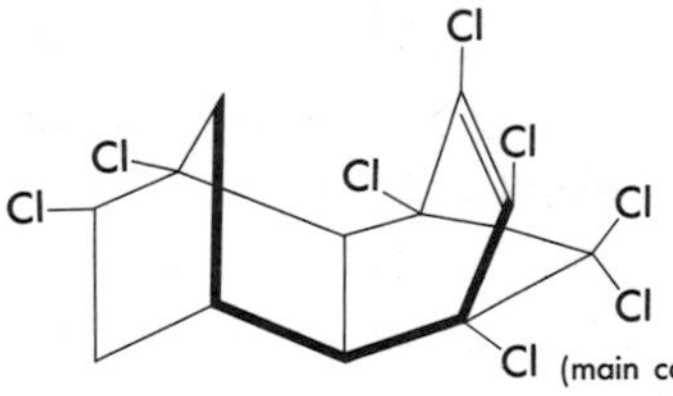 (main component)	350
Dieldrin	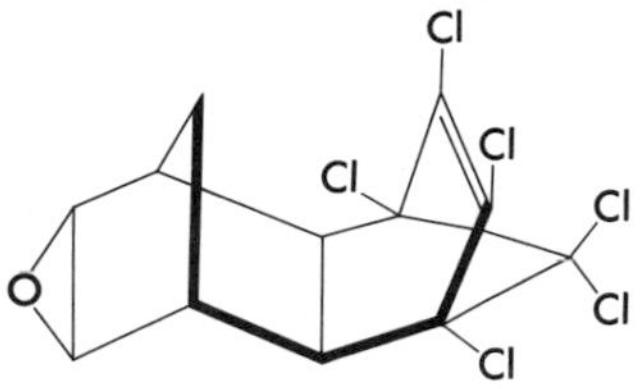	46
Aldrin	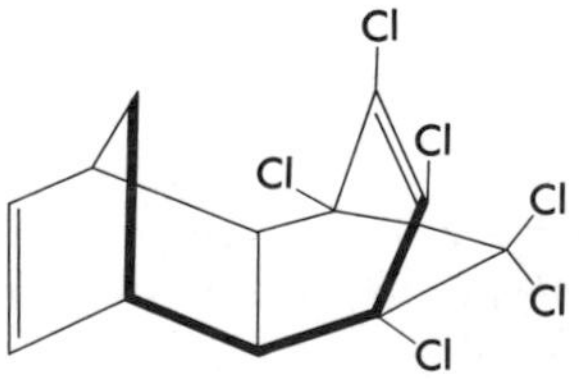	10–12

Table 10.10 Some Important Organochlorine Insecticides (continued)

Name	Structure	LD$_{50}$ (orally in rats; mg per kg of body weight)[a]
Heptachlor		90
Miscellaneous		
Toxaphene	A mixture of polychlorinated terpenes, particularly camphene	70
Lindane		90

[a] The milligrams of pesticide that in one dose, given by mouth to a statistically significant population of rats, will kill 50% of the group. Toxicities vary from species to species and also vary according to the mode of entry into the target (e.g., oral, dermal, subcutaneous, etc.). A number of other factors affect toxicity, too; hence these data do not furnish precise data for man, but they do warn him and give a way of comparing relative toxicities. Toxicity data are from D. E. H. Frear. *Pesticide Index,* 4th edition, 1969. College Science Publishers, State College Pennsylvania.

of the problem it ranges through causes, costs, consequences, and avenues for change. It has a good discussion of benzo[a]pyrene and other carcinogens.

2. J. C. Esposito. *Vanishing Air.* Grossman Publishers, New York, 1970. The Ralph Nader Study Group report on air pollution. The book concentrates on government action and inaction.

3. R. Rienow and L. T. Rienow. *Moment in the Sun.* Ballantine, New York, 1967. A Sierra Club book that touches on several aspects of pollution.

4. Louis J. Battan. *The Unclean Sky.* Anchor Science Study Book; Doubleday, New York, 1966. Written by a meteorologist, this short, easy-to-read book is also outstanding for its clarity in explaining fundamentals of atmospheric science.

5. J. R. Holum and R. A. Boolootian. *Environmental Sciences. An Introduction to Their Topics and Terms.* Little, Brown and Company, Boston, 1972. (Title and date are tentative.) Individual entries on fuels, pollutants, energy, and a number of other topics are sources of supplementary information and data.

6. Ron M. Linton. *Terracide—America's Destruction of Her Living Environment.* Little, Brown and Company, Boston, 1970. Linton gives an overview of the mess we are in; his chapter "Breathing" is breathtaking.

7. *Air Pollution—A Scientists' Institute for Public Information Workbook* (Available for $1.00 (discounted for quantities) from SIPI, 30 East 68th St., N. Y., N. Y. 10021.)

Government Publications

Available at modest cost from the U. S. Government Printing Office, Washington, D. C. are many booklets and pamphlets on air pollution and related topics. All are very well illustrated. The following are a few examples.

1. *The Sources of Air Pollution and Their Control.* Public Health Service Publication No. 1548, 1969 (40¢).

2. *Nationwide Inventory of Air Pollutant Emissions, 1968.* National Air Pollution Control Administration Publication No. AP-73. 1970 (30¢).

3. *Environmental Quality.* First Annual Report of the Council on Environmental Quality, August 1970 ($1.75).

4. *The Effects of Air Pollution.* Public Health Service Publication No. 1556, 1966 (45¢).

5. *Emphysema—The Battle to Breathe.* Public Health Service Publication No. 1715 (35¢).

6. *Report of the Secretary's Commission on Pesticides and Their Relationship to Environmental Health. Parts I and II.* U. S. Department of Health, Education, and Welfare, December 1969. ($3.00). The report of the Mrak Commission led by Emil M. Mrak.

Articles

1. L. B. Lave and E. P. Seskin. "Air Pollution and Human Health," *Science,* August 21, 1970, p. 723. A study of the quantitative effect of air pollution in terms of the dollar benefit of controlling it.

2. J. J. Chisolm, Jr. "Lead Poisoning." *Scientific American,* February 1971, page 15. A thorough discussion of chronic and acute lead poisoning, its origins, and prospects for controlling it.

3. M. H. Hyman. "Timetable for Lead." *Environment,* June 1971, page 14. How lead could be removed from gasoline by 1973 at an inconsequential cost to the buyer.

Brief Summary

Our study of the hydrocarbon families provides the following generalizations that will apply to all families:

1. The structural features of any hydrocarbon (only carbon and hydrogen present) give to a molecule low polarity, low solubility in water, high solubility in nonpolar solvents, and low density (less than 1 gram/cc).

2. The special feature of alkane hydrocarbons—only single bonds—contributes chemical inertness, at least at any alkane-like *portion* of a molecule.

3. If an alkene double bond is present in a molecule, that site will undergo addition reactions (e.g., hydrogenation, hydration).

4. If the "double bonds" are part of an aromatic benzene ring system, substitution reactions occur more readily than addition reactions.

5. Unburned hydrocarbons in auto exhaust are converted by oxidants in the exhaust and in smog to compounds such as PAN, aldehydes, and peroxides that irritate eyes, nose and lungs, kill plants, and contribute to haze.

Problems and Exercises

1. Write the structures for the products to be expected in each of the following situations. If no reaction is to be expected, state so. This exercise will help you learn how to apply the chemical facts about functional groups you studied in this chapter. To work this kind of exercise you have to be able to do three things:

   (a) Classify a specific organic compound into its proper family (or, in many cases in later chapters, several families). If you were studying a new language—and to beginners, that is what organic chemistry is—classifying a compound into its family or families would be like knowing the meaning of a foreign word and its part of speech; i.e., it is a matter of basic vocabulary.

   (b) Recall the short list of chemical facts about the family to see if the reagent given in the question is on that list. This is akin, in studying a language, to thinking about how a particular word with its particular part of speech (noun, or verb, etc.) can be used in a sentence.
   If the reagent given is not on the list, we assume that no reaction occurs.

   (c) On the basis of the chemical fact recalled, apply the fact by writing the specific reaction.

   Example:

   $$CH_3CH_2CH_2CH_3 + H_2SO_4 \longrightarrow ?$$

   Step (a). The organic compound is an *alkane.*
   Step (b). On the list of reactions or chemical facts about alkanes we have . . . nothing, except that they will burn.
   We assume, therefore, that alkanes do not react specifically with sulfuric acid.
   Step (c). We write "no reaction" as the answer.

   Example:

   $$CH_3CH{=}CHCH_3 + H_2O \xrightarrow{\text{H}^+} ?$$

Step (a). The organic compound is an *alkene*.

Step (b). On the list of reactions or chemical facts about carbon-carbon double bonds are the following:

1. They add water (in the presence of an acid) to form alcohols.
2. They add hydrogen (in the presence of a metal catalyst) at high pressure and temperature to change to a saturated system (an alkane).
3. They can polymerize.

Step (c). Since water is the given reagent, together with an acid catalyst, we know we have to write an alcohol for our answer. The skeleton of the alcohol will be identical with the skeleton of the alkene (at least in all our examples), but the double bond will disappear and at one of its carbons will be an —OH group and at the other carbon of the former double bond, another —H.

Answer: $CH_3CH_2CHCH_3$
$\qquad\qquad\qquad\quad |$
$\qquad\qquad\qquad\quad OH$

(a) $CH_3CH_3 + H_2 \xrightarrow[\text{heat, pressure}]{\text{Ni}}$

(b) $CH_2{=}CH_2 + H_2O \xrightarrow{H^+}$

(c) $CH_3CH_3 + H_2O \xrightarrow{H^+}$

(d) $CH_2{=}CHCH_3 + H_2 \xrightarrow[\text{heat, pressure}]{\text{Ni}}$

(e)  ⬡ $+ Br_2 \xrightarrow{\text{Fe}}$

(f) $CH_3CHCH_2CH_3 + \text{conc. } H_2SO_4 \longrightarrow$
$\qquad\ |$
$\qquad CH_3$

(g) $CH_2{=}CHCH_2CH{=}CH_2 + 1\ H_2 \xrightarrow[\text{heat, pressure}]{\text{Ni}}$

(h) 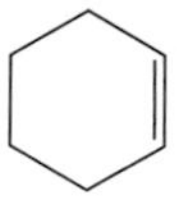 ⬡ $+ H_2O \xrightarrow{H^+}$

(i) $CH_3CH_3 + O_2 \xrightarrow[\text{combustion}]{}$

(j)  ⬡ $+ H_2O \longrightarrow$

2. What would be the name and structure of the monomer unit for the following polymer that has found use as a material for indoor-outdoor carpeting.

$\qquad\quad CH_3 \qquad\quad CH_3 \qquad\quad CH_3 \qquad\quad CH_3$
$\qquad\quad | \qquad\qquad\ | \qquad\qquad\ | \qquad\qquad\ |$
etc.$-CH-CH_2-CH-CH_2-CH-CH_2-CH-CH_2-$etc.

3. Write condensed structural formulas for the members of the following sets of isomers. Check the sets to see that there are no duplications.
   (a) The two isomers of C_3H_7Cl
   (b) The four isomers of C_4H_9Br
   (c) All of the isomers of C_7H_{16} (One is *n*-heptane)

4. (a) Write both the common and the IUPAC names for the compounds of 3-(a).
   (b) Write both the common and the IUPAC names for the compounds of 3-(b).
   (c) Write the IUPAC names for the compounds of 3-(c).
   (d) Identify by its IUPAC name the compound of 3-(c) that would have the common name, *isoheptane*.

5. A chemist was handed a vial containing a liquid. He was told that the substance was chemically pure (not a mixture). He deduced at once that it was not an ionic substance. Why was this reasonable?

6. Define each of the following
   (a) alkane   (g) PAN
   (b) alkene   (h) Geneva system
   (c) hydrogenation   (i) carbonium ion
   (d) polymerization   (j) radical
   (e) photochemical   (k) cis-isomer
   (f) cycloalkane   (l) geometrical isomerism

7. Give an IUPAC name for

(a) 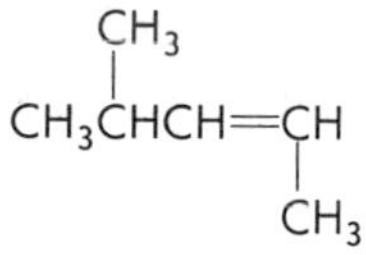
$$\overset{\displaystyle CH_3}{\underset{\displaystyle |}{CH_3CHCH}}=\overset{\displaystyle CH}{\underset{\displaystyle |}{}}\\ CH_3$$

(b) 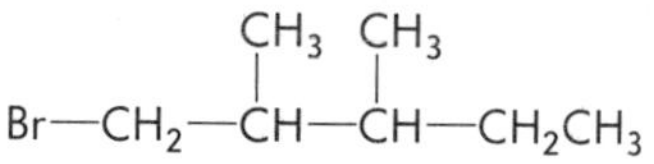
$$Br-CH_2-\overset{\displaystyle CH_3}{\underset{\displaystyle |}{CH}}-\overset{\displaystyle CH_3}{\underset{\displaystyle |}{CH}}-CH_2CH_3$$

(c) if 1,3-butadiene is $CH_2-CH-CH=CH_2$
    what is the name of $CH_2=CH-CH_2-CH=CH_2$

(d) 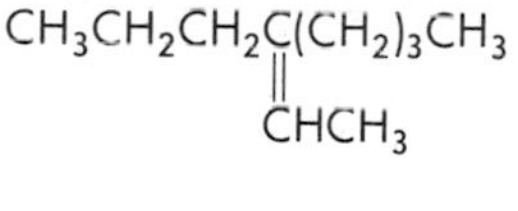 $CH_3CH_2CH_2\overset{\displaystyle }{\underset{\displaystyle \|}{C}}(CH_2)_3CH_3$
    $CHCH_3$

(e)

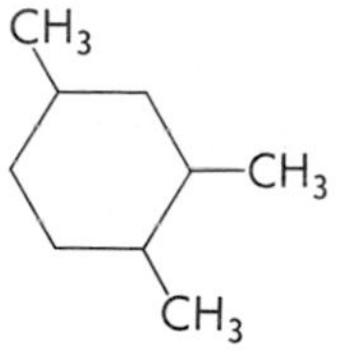

8. Predict which of the following could exhibit *cis-trans* isomerism.

(a) $CH_3CH=CH_2$ (c) 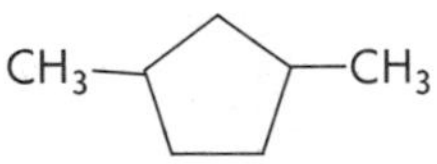 $CH_3-\!\!\!\bigcirc\!\!\!-CH_3$ (e) $(CH_3)_2C=CH_2$

(b) $CH_3CH=CHCH_2CH_3$ (d) $Cl-CH=CH-Br$ (f) $CH_3CH_2CH=CH-Cl$

chapter 11 organic derivatives of water, hydrogen sulfide, and ammonia: alcohols, ethers, mercaptans and amines

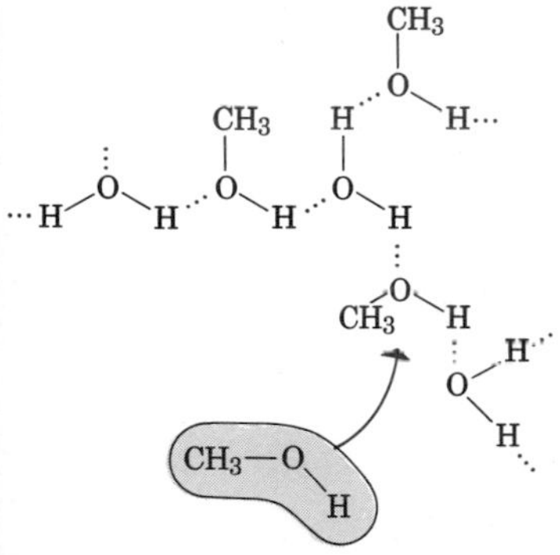

By replacing one or more of the hydrogens of such simple compounds as water, hydrogen sulfide, and ammonia by one or more organic groups, not all the old properties disappear. The alcohols (e.g., CH_3—O—H) are still somewhat water-like; the amines (e.g., CH_3—NH_2) are still partly ammonia-like—still basic; the mercaptans (e.g., CH_3—S—H) still possess nauseating odors. Many properties, of course, have changed by this transition from the inorganic to the organic. Essentially all physiological properties are profoundly different. Biochemically important molecules have all these systems, but we shall study simple cases first in this chapter.

Table 11.1 Some Organic Relatives of Water, Hydrogen Sulfide, and Ammonia

						H
						|
	H—O—H		H—S—H			H—N—H

						H
						|
Alcohols	R—O—H	Mercaptans	R—S—H	Amines[c]		R—N—H
						H
						|
Ethers	R—O—R	Sulfides[a]	R—S—R			R—N—R'
						R''
						|
		Disulfides[b]	R—S—S—R			R—N—R'

[a] Not studied in this chapter.

[b] This, strictly, is not a derivative of hydrogen sulfide but it is readily made from mercaptans as we shall see.

[c] All are classified as amines. The prime (as in R') and the double prime signify that the alkyl groups need not be (but may be) identical.

alcohols
structural
features of
alcohols

The characteristic feature of an alcohol molecule is a *hydroxyl group* (—O—H) *attached covalently to a saturated carbon atom*—one from which radiate only single covalent bonds. Several common alcohols are listed in Table 11.2.

Only single
bonds may go
from this carbon.

"Alcohol carbon"

Alcohol system

subclasses of alcohols. Properties of alcohols vary somewhat, depending on the condition of the alcohol carbon atom—the one that holds the hydroxyl group. For this reason, subclasses of alcohols have been created (see Table 11.2). A *primary* (1°) *alcohol* is one in which the alcohol carbon atom carries only one carbon-to-carbon bond. In a *secondary* (2°) *alcohol,* the alcohol carbon atom carries two and only two carbon-to-carbon bonds; in a *tertiary* (3°) *alcohol* it carries three.

A simple, or *monohydric,* alcohol is one in which one —OH group is attached to an alkane-like chain. If two —OH groups are attached, the substance is classed as a *dihydric* alcohol or a *glycol.* When three —OH groups are present, the compound is a *trihydric* alcohol; glycerol is the most common example.

When the —OH group is attached to any kind of aromatic system (benzene or polynuclear aromatic hydrocarbon residue), the substance belongs to the *phenol* family, named after its simplest member, phenol (see Table 11.2). In many respects, phenols are like alcohols, but enough properties

organic derivatives of water, hydrogen sulfide, and ammonia: alcohols, ethers, mercaptans and amines

Table 11.2 Some Common Alcohols

Structure	Common Name	Subclass	Boiling Point, in °C
CH_3OH	Methyl alcohol	—	65
CH_3CH_2OH	Ethyl alcohol	1°	78.5
$CH_3CH_2CH_2OH$	n-Propyl alcohol	1°	97
CH_3CHCH_3 $\quad$ OH	Isopropyl alcohol	2°	82
$CH_3CH_2CH_2CH_2OH$	n-Butyl alcohol	1°	117
$CH_3CH_2CHCH_3$ $\qquad$ OH	Secondary butyl alcohol (sec-butyl alcohol)	2°	100
CH_3 $\qquad$ CHCH_2OH CH_3	Isobutyl alcohol[a]	1°	108
$\qquad CH_3$ CH_3—C—OH $\qquad CH_3$	Tertiary butyl alcohol (t-butyl alcohol)	3°	83
CH_2—CH_2 OH $\quad$ OH	Ethylene glycol ("glycol")	Dihydric (two 1°)	197
CH_3CH—CH_2 $\quad$ OH $\quad$ OH	Propylene glycol	Dihydric (one 1°; one 2°)	189
CH_2 $\;$ CH—CH_2 OH $\;$ OH $\;$ OH	Glycerol	Trihydric (two 1°; one 2°)	290
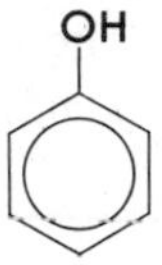 OH ⬡	Phenol	Phenol	182 (m.p. 41°C)

[a]Note that similar names do not necessarily mean similar classification. Isopropyl alcohol is a secondary alcohol whereas isobutyl alcohol is primary. Iso- means only that $(CH_3)_2CH$— is present.

are different to make it useful to have a separate class for them. Thus, alcohols are neither acids nor bases in the Arrhenius sense; but phenols are weak acids.

In common names for simple alcohols, the word *alcohol* refers to the —OH group; preceding this word is the name of the *alkyl group* to which the —OH is attached. The symbol ROH enables us to talk and write in general terms

Table 11.3 Influence of Alcohol Group on Boiling Point

Name	Structure	Formula Weight	Boiling Point (in °C)	Difference in Boiling Point
Ethane	CH_3CH_3	30	-89	154°
Methyl alcohol	CH_3OH	32	65	
Propane	$CH_3CH_2CH_3$	44	-42	120°
Ethyl alcohol	CH_3CH_2OH	46	78	
n-Butane	$CH_3CH_2CH_2CH_3$	58	0	197°
Ethylene glycol	$HOCH_2CH_2OH$	62	197	

about any one member or all members of the family. (For IUPAC names, see the Appendix.)

physical properties

polarity. Alcohol molecules are quite polar. To demonstrate this, we need only compare boiling points of alkanes with alcohols of about the same formula weight (see Table 11.3). Forces of attraction between alcohol molecules obviously must be much greater than between molecules of alkanes. Hydrogen bonding accounts for this.

Water (formula weight 18) boils even higher than methyl alcohol, in spite of the fact that its molecules are lighter. Our picture of liquid water, you will recall, involves a vast interlacing (and constantly shifting) network of hydrogen bonds between water molecules. Alcohol molecules have one of the oxygen-to-hydrogen covalent bonds of water molecules left. This is a very polar bond, and hydrogen bonding *between* alcohol molecules, therefore, is possible. It cannot, however, occur in three directions from one molecule (see Fig. 11.1). Therefore, molecules of an alcohol are not as strongly attracted to each other as molecules of water. Although alcohol molecules are quite polar, they are not as polar as those of water.

solubility. *The —OH group, wherever it is found in molecules of organic compounds, is a water-solubilizing group.* Methane is insoluble in water, but methyl alcohol is completely soluble. Molecules of methyl alcohol dissolve in water readily because they can slip into the hydrogen-bonding sequences in water, as illustrated in Fig. 11.2.

As the molecular weight of an alcohol increases, that is, as the carbon skeleton lengthens, its molecules become more and more alkane-like. In *n*-decyl alcohol:

$$CH_3CH_2CH_2CH_2CH_2CH_2CH_2CH_2CH_2CH_2—OH$$

the small, water-like hydroxyl group is virtually overwhelmed by the long hydrocarbon chain. Water molecules have no attraction for this part of the

organic derivatives of water, hydrogen sulfide, and ammonia: alcohols, ethers, mercaptans and amines

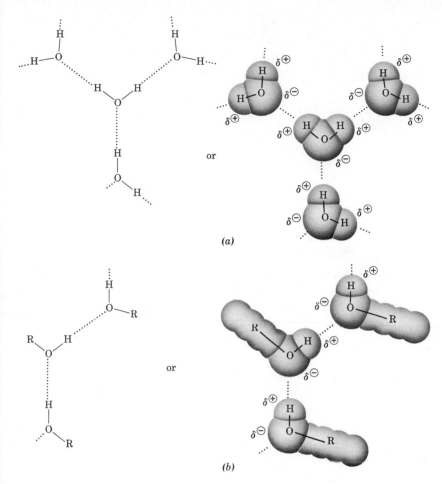

Fig. 11.1 Hydrogen bonding in water and alcohols. (a) Hydrogen bonding in water may occur in three directions from a water molecule. (b) Hydrogen bonding in liquid alcohol is limited to two directions from a molecule. (The drawings are misleading in that they suggest that there is considerable order in liquids. There is some, but molecules in a liquid move about constantly.)

molecule. The flexings and gyrations of this chain interfere too much with hydrogen-bonding sequences necessary for the formation of the solution. This alcohol is insoluble in water (as are most monohydric alcohols having five or more carbon atoms).

The presence of any substantial hydrocarbon chain in any molecule always tends to reduce its solubility in water and to increase its solubility in nonpolar solvents (e.g., benzene, ether, carbon tetrachloride, chloroform, petroleum ether, ligroin, and gasoline). In fact, even molecules of methyl alcohol dissolve in most nonpolar solvents.

To generalize, water tends to dissolve water-like molecules; nonpolar solvents tend to dissolve hydrocarbon-like molecules. Even more generally

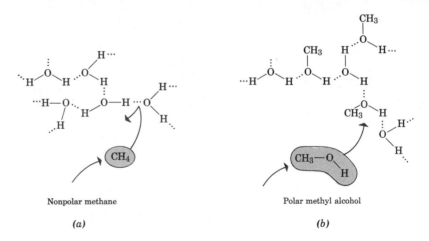

Nonpolar methane

(a)

Polar methyl alcohol

(b)

Fig. 11.2   Solubility of small alcohol molecules in water. (a) A nonpolar alkane molecule cannot break into the hydrogen-bonded sequence in water; hence it cannot dissolve. (b) A polar alcohol molecule, capable of hydrogen bonding, can slip into the sequences in water and thus dissolve.

speaking, polar solvents (such as water) tend to dissolve polar molecules;
nonpolar solvents tend to dissolve nonpolar (or moderately polar) molecules.
The rule of thumb among organic chemists is, "Likes dissolve likes" (where
"likes" refers to relative polarities).

Our discussion of water solubilities has been rather extensive. We are
interested in any factor that helps organic molecules to dissolve in water
(or hinders them from doing so), for nearly all important reactions in the
body occur between organic molecules in aqueous fluids.

Increasing the number of —OH groups per molecule increases the polarity
of the molecule, increases its opportunities to hydrogen-bond to neighbors,
and therefore raises its solubility in water (as well as its boiling point). Ethylene
glycol, propylene glycol, and glycerol (Table 11.2) are all infinitely soluble
in water, and they all have very high boiling points.

chemical
properties

The important reactions of alcohols occur at the —OH group or the carbon
holding it. Like water, alcohols are neither acids nor bases. They release
neither hydrogen ions nor hydroxide ions in solution.

dehydration of alcohols; formation of alkenes or ethers. The elements of
water, H—OH, can be removed from most alcohols:

—OH from the alcohol carbon, and
—H from the carbon attached to the alcohol carbon.

Concentrated sulfuric acid, the most common reagent to bring this change

organic derivatives of water, hydrogen sulfide, and ammonia: alcohols, ethers, mercaptans and amines

about, acts as a catalyst. The product is a compound with a carbon-carbon double bond.

in general:

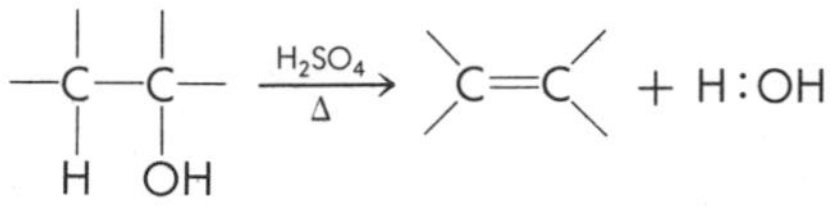

$$-\overset{|}{\underset{H}{C}}-\overset{|}{\underset{OH}{C}}- \xrightarrow[\Delta]{H_2SO_4} \underset{\diagdown}{\overset{\diagup}{C}}=\underset{\diagup}{\overset{\diagdown}{C}} + H:OH$$

specific examples:

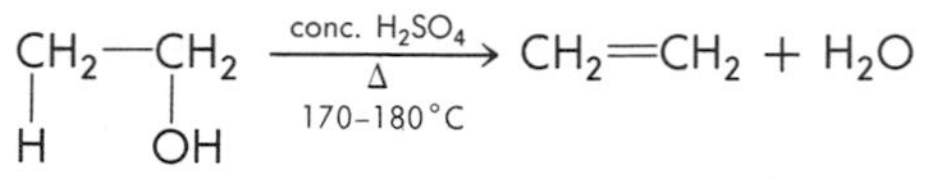

$$\overset{CH_2}{\underset{H}{|}}-\overset{CH_2}{\underset{OH}{|}} \xrightarrow[\underset{170-180°C}{\Delta}]{conc.\ H_2SO_4} CH_2{=}CH_2 + H_2O$$

Ethyl alcohol   Ethylene
(a 1° alcohol)

$$CH_3CH_2\overset{|}{\underset{OH}{C}}HCH_3 \xrightarrow[100°C]{60\%\ H_2SO_4} CH_3CH{=}CHCH_3 + CH_3CH_2CH{=}CH_2 + H_2O$$

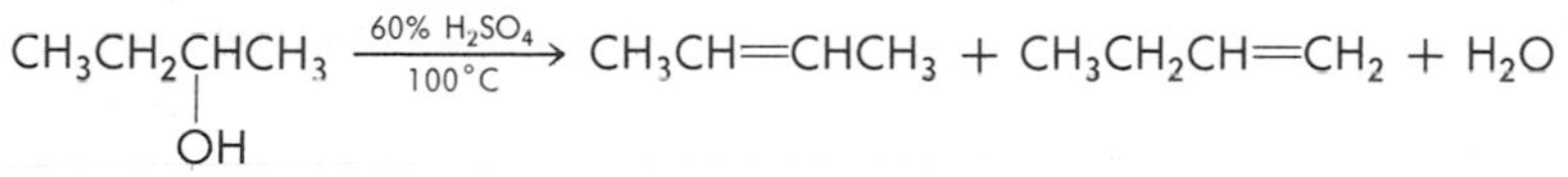

 sec-Butyl alcohol   β-Butylene   α-Butylene
 (a 2° alcohol)   (principal product)

$$CH_3-\overset{CH_3}{\underset{CH_3}{\overset{|}{\underset{|}{C}}}}-OH \xrightarrow[80-90°C]{20\%\ H_2SO_4} CH_2{=}C\overset{\diagup CH_3}{\diagdown CH_3} + H_2O$$

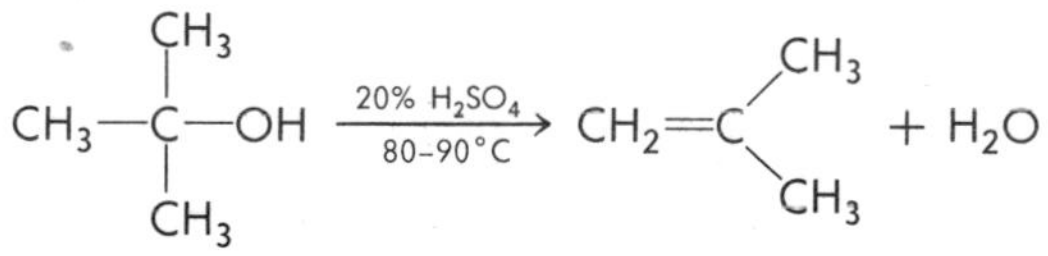

 t-Butyl alcohol   Isobutylene
 (a 3° alcohol)

The data summarized on each arrow show that the best conditions for the dehydration of an alcohol vary from alcohol to alcohol. In general, the order of the ease of dehydrating alcohols to alkenes is $3° > 2° > 1°$. This experimental fact is noted, but its explanation will be left as an exercise for discussion in class, if time permits.

There is another reaction open to alcohols, besides alkene formation, when they are heated in the presence of a mineral acid. The elements of water may form from two different molecules, instead of from within one molecule. The result is the formation of a member of another family of compounds, *ethers*.

in general:

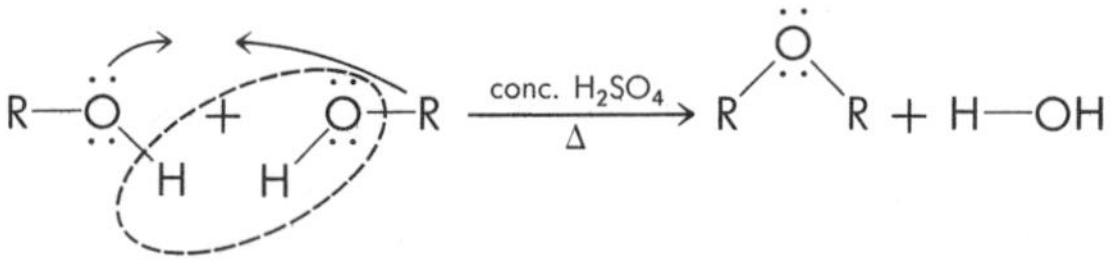

$$R{-}\overset{..}{\underset{..}{O}}\diagdown + \diagup\overset{..}{\underset{..}{O}}{-}R \xrightarrow[\Delta]{conc.\ H_2SO_4} R\overset{\overset{..}{\overset{O}{.}}}{\diagup\diagdown}R + H{-}OH$$

specific examples:

$$CH_3-CH_2-O\underset{H}{} + \underset{H}{}O-CH_2-CH_3 \xrightarrow[140°]{conc.\ H_2SO_4}$$

Ethyl alcohol

$$CH_3-CH_2\overset{O}{\diagdown\diagup}CH_2-CH_3 + HOH$$

Ethyl ether

$$CH_3-O\underset{H}{} + \underset{H}{}O-CH_3 \xrightarrow[\Delta]{conc.\ H_2SO_4} CH_3\overset{O}{\diagdown\diagup}CH_3 + H_2O$$

Methyl alcohol   Methyl ether

At a temperature of 140° C, ethyl alcohol may be converted to ethyl ether. (The presence of concentrated sulfuric acid is assumed in this discussion.) At a higher temperature, 170 to 180°, ethyl alcohol is dehydrated internally, and ethylene is the product. It is generally true that when one system of reagents can lead to the production of two or more products the experimental conditions determine which forms in the predominant amount. It is also true about most organic reactions, that side reactions occur. Thus, in the conversion of ethyl alcohol into ethyl ether, the side reaction is the formation of ethylene. Inevitably, this forces careful attention to techniques of isolating and purifying the desired products. Methods such as distillation, crystallization, extraction, and others have been developed for this purpose. In some cases, side reactions arise when some intermediate is formed in the reaction that has chances, both statistically and in terms of the energetics of the situation, to be changed in more than one way.

oxidation of alcohols; formation of aldehydes and ketones. As a reminder, in the field of organic chemistry, an *oxidation reaction* is any reaction that results in either a *gain in the number of oxygens* or a *loss in the number of hydrogens* in a molecule. A *reduction reaction* is one in which a molecule suffers either a *gain in hydrogens* (e.g., hydrogenation of alkenes) or a *loss in oxygens.*

Controlled oxidation of alcohols (i.e., *not* combustion) involves removal of the pieces of the element hydrogen, H—H:

one —H from the —OH group, and
the other —H from the alcohol carbon

Potassium dichromate, $K_2Cr_2O_7$, and potassium permanganate, $KMnO_4$, are two reagents (oxidizing agents) that can accomplish this. They remove the pieces of elemental hydrogen and convert them into a molecule of water.

organic derivatives of water, hydrogen sulfide, and ammonia: alcohols, ethers, mercaptans and amines

in general:

$$\overset{\displaystyle |}{\underset{\displaystyle |}{-\text{C}}} \overset{\textstyle \curvearrowright}{\text{—O}} + (O)^1 \longrightarrow \overset{\displaystyle |}{-\text{C}}{=}\text{O} + \text{H}_2\text{O}$$

specific examples:

Case I: Oxidation of *primary alcohols;* formation of aldehydes.

$$\text{CH}_3{-}\overset{\text{H}}{\underset{\text{H}}{\text{C}}}{-}\text{O}\diagdown\text{H} + (O) \longrightarrow \text{CH}_3{-}\overset{\text{H}}{\text{C}}{=}\text{O} + \text{H}_2\text{O}$$

Ethyl alcohol   Acetaldehyde

Case II: Oxidation of *secondary alcohols;* formation of ketones.

$$\text{CH}_3{-}\overset{\text{O—H}}{\text{CH}}{-}\text{CH}_3 + (O) \longrightarrow \text{CH}_3{-}\overset{\text{O}}{\text{C}}{-}\text{CH}_3 + \text{H}_2\text{O}$$

Isopropyl alcohol   Acetone

Case III: Behavior of *tertiary alcohols.* Tertiary alcohols have no —H on the alcohol carbon atom. Hence, they cannot be oxidized in this simple way.

We shall not go into the mechanism of the oxidation of 1° and 2° alcohols. As far as an alcohol molecule is concerned, it has lost the elements of hydrogen. By *elements of hydrogen* is meant $\text{H}{:}^-$ and H^+, hydride ion and hydrogen ion. (*If* these formed, they would combine to produce molecular hydrogen: $\text{H}{:}^- + \text{H}^+ \longrightarrow \text{H}{:}\text{H}$.) They do not form as discrete entities. The hydride ion cannot exist in water because it reacts as follows:

$$\text{H}{:}^- + \text{H—OH} \longrightarrow \text{H}_2 + \text{OH}^-$$

But the *net effect* is still their removal.

$$\text{R}{-}\overset{\displaystyle |}{\underset{\text{H}}{\text{C}}}{-}\text{O}\diagdown\text{H} \cdots \rightarrow (\text{H}^+) \overset{(O)}{\searrow} \text{H}_2\text{O}$$
$$\cdots \rightarrow (\text{H}{:}^-) \nearrow$$

Elements
of hydrogen

---

[1] The symbol (O) represents any chemical oxidizing agent capable of effecting the reaction. The ''equations'' shown should be spoken of as ''reaction sequences.'' Specific equations are difficult to balance without devoting more space than is intended.

The removal of the elements of hydrogen from an organic molecule is one of the most important *kinds* of chemical events in living cells. When the elements of hydrogen are removed, they are passed along a whole "chain" of compounds (the respiratory enzymes) until one is reached which catalyzes the combination of these elements with molecular oxygen brought in by breathing. Normally, when hydrogen and oxygen combine, a great deal of heat is released. But in the body, this potential energy is used in synthesizing certain high-energy compounds that are needed directly for running muscles, nerves, and so on. One of the intermediates in the citric acid cycle—a series of reactions in cells that provides the elements of hydrogen—is malic acid. Its conversion to oxaloacetic acid is but one illustration of an oxidation of an alcohol in living things. (Malic acid is also a member of the family of carboxylic acids.)

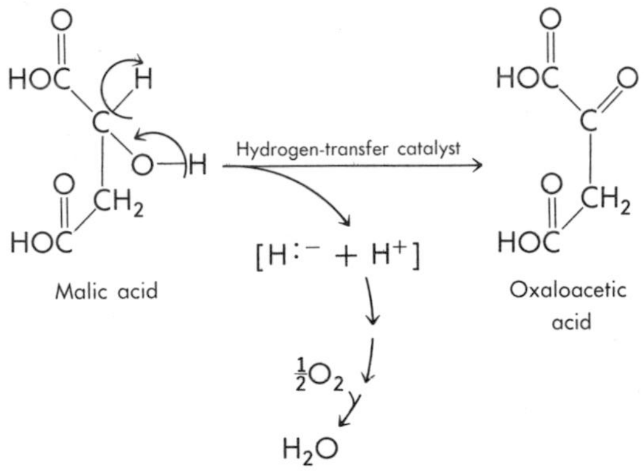

Alcohols undergo other important reactions. Since these involve members of classes not encountered thus far, we shall complete our study of alcohols in the next chapter.

important individual alcohols
methyl alcohol. ("wood alcohol;" methanol). Most methyl alcohol is made by the reaction of carbon monoxide with hydrogen under extremely high pressure and temperature:

$$2H_2 + CO \xrightarrow[\substack{temp. = 350-400°C \\ catalyst = ZnO-Cr_2O_3}]{3000\ lb/sq\ in.} CH_3-OH$$

It acquired its nickname, wood alcohol, from the fact that it is obtainable when wood is heated in the absence of air during the manufacture of charcoal.

Taken internally in sufficient quantity, methyl alcohol produces either blindness or death. It is used primarily as the raw material for the industrial

organic derivatives of water, hydrogen sulfide, and ammonia: alcohols, ethers, mercaptans and amines

synthesis of formaldehyde, as a (temporary) radiator antifreeze, as a solvent, and as a denaturant for ethyl alcohol.

ethyl alcohol. ("grain alcohol," ethanol). Some ethyl alcohol is obtained by fermentation of sugars, but most is synthesized by the hydration of ethylene in the presence of a catalyst. Industrially, it is used as a solvent and in the compounding of pharmaceuticals, perfumes, lotions, tonics, and rubbing compounds. For these purposes, it is adulterated (denatured) by poisons that are very difficult to remove. This is done to prevent its use as a beverage, for nearly all governments derive considerable revenue by taxing potable alcohol. In the United States, ethyl alcohol sells for about 70¢ a gallon, but the tax is close to $20.

The drinkability of (dilute) ethyl alcohol is unique among the alcohols. The body possesses enzymes that act to destroy it rapidly by oxidation. The illusion that alcohol is a stimulant derives from the fact that its first effect is to depress activity in the upper-most level of the brain, the center of judgment, inhibition, and restraint.

isopropyl alcohol. Isopropyl alcohol is a common substitute for ethyl alcohol as a rubbing compound. It is twice as toxic as ethyl alcohol.

ethylene glycol, CH_2CH_2; **propylene glycol,** CH_3CHCH_2
$\qquad\qquad\qquad\quad\;$ OH OH $\qquad\qquad\qquad\qquad\quad$ HO OH

These two glycols serve as the base for all permanent-type antifreezes. Their great solubility in water and their very high boiling points make them ideal for this purpose.

glycerol, $CH_2{-}CH{-}CH_2$ **(glycerin)**
$\qquad\qquad\;$ OH $\quad$ OH $\quad$ OH

Glycerol is a colorless, syrupy liquid with a sweet taste. It is freely soluble in water and insoluble in nonpolar solvents. It is a product of the digestion of simple fats and oils.

sugars. All carbohydrates consist of polyhydroxy compounds. They will be studied in Chapter 13.

In molecules of simple ethers, two alkyl groups are attached to one oxygen atom: R—O—R. The ethers are dialkyl derivatives of water. These alkyl groups may be the same or different. A few simple ethers are listed in Table 11.4.

ethers
structural
features

Table 11.4 **Common Ethers**

Structure	Common Name	Boiling Point, in °C
$CH_3—O—CH_3$	Methyl ether	−24
$CH_3CH_2—O—CH_2CH_3$	Ethyl ether (ether) ("anesthetic ether")	34.6
$CH_2=CH—O—CH=CH_2$	Vinyl ether (vinethene) (another anesthetic)	35
	Anisole (methyl phenyl ether)[a]	154

[a]The hydrocarbon group derived by formally removing one hydrogen from benzene, — is called the *phenyl group.*

naming the ethers The principles for naming ethers are illustrated by the compounds in Table 11.4. The word *ether* specifies the so-called "ether group."

$$-\overset{|}{\underset{|}{C}}—\overset{..}{\underset{..}{O}}—\overset{|}{\underset{|}{C}}-$$ Neither carbon may have a double bond to another oxygen.

Ether group
(carbon-oxygen-carbon)

If the two alkyl groups are identical, their name precedes the word ether; for example, ethyl ether. If they are not identical, both are named; for example, methyl ethyl ether. Anesthetic ether, ethyl ether, is nicknamed simply "ether."

physical properties Ether molecules are not capable of hydrogen bonding with each other, for they possess no —O—H group (nor N—H group). Molecules of ethers are only slightly polar, but the presence of the oxygen with its unshared pairs of electrons means that ethers can *accept* hydrogen bonds from molecules having —OH (or $>$NH) groups. Ethers, therefore, are slightly more soluble in water than alkanes. The absence of any hydrogen-bond-donating ability means that ethers boil at temperatures much lower than alcohols of equivalent formula weight (e.g., ethyl ether, formula weight 74 and boiling point 35°C, and *n*-butyl alcohol, formula weight 74 and boiling point 117°C). Ethers are generally soluble in nonpolar solvents.

organic derivatives of water, hydrogen sulfide, and ammonia: alcohols, ethers, mercaptans and amines

At room temperature, the ether function is stable to acids, bases, oxidizing agents, reactive metals (e.g., sodium), and reactive nonmetals (e.g., bromine). Ethers are highly flammable. Ethyl ether is particularly dangerous, for its vapors are denser than air and tend to accumulate along the floor, where chance sparks (e.g., from shoe cleats) can detonate the ether-air mixture.

chemical properties

What few reactions ethers do undergo are of small consequence in the chemistry of health. However, the ether function does occur in some types of molecules in the body. Therefore, it is important to know that the ether group is chemically very stable, and that physically it is *not* a good water-solubilizing group.

ethyl ether ("ether"). Ethyl ether is a colorless, volatile liquid with a pungent, somewhat irritating odor. Widely used as an anesthetic, it is regarded as having one of the largest safety factors. Although it was first used for this purpose in 1842 by Long in Georgia, word of the results was not published, and the medical profession did not profit. (This illustrates the importance of publicizing scientific discoveries among the appropriate people. To a professional in any field, the value of having and using professional journals must never be overlooked.) Four years later, in 1846, a Boston dentist, Morton, rediscovered the anesthetic properties of ether and successfully demonstrated them in an actual operation.

important individual ethers

Ethyl ether is a depressant for the central nervous system and is, at the same time, somewhat of a stimulant for the sympathetic system. It exerts an effect on nearly all tissues of the body.

vinyl ether, CH_2=CH—O—CH=CH_2 ("vinethene"). This ether is another anesthetic, being more rapid in its action than ethyl ether. It forms an explosive mixture with air.

Sulfur analogs of alcohols are important in the chemistry of proteins. Generically, they are called *thio alcohols* or *mercaptans,* and they have the general structural formula:

mercaptans and disulfides structural features

$$R—S—H$$

The general structure for a *disulfide is*

$$R—S—S—R$$

The common names and structures of a few simple mercaptans are listed in Table 11.5. The word *mercaptan* specifies the —SH group; preceding this word is the name of the alkyl group to which it is attached.

naming the mercaptans

Table 11.5   Common Mercaptans

Structure	Common Name	Boiling Point in °C
CH_3—SH	Methyl mercaptan	6
CH_3CH_2—SH	Ethyl mercaptan	36
$CH_3CH_2CH_2$—SH	n-Propyl mercaptan	68
$CH_3CH_2CH_2CH_2$—SH	n-Butyl mercaptan	98
$HS—CH_2\overset{\overset{\displaystyle O}{\|}}{C}H—\overset{\underset{\displaystyle NH_2}{\|}}{C}OH$	Cysteine (an amino acid, a building block of proteins)	(Solid)

properties   It is rather astonishing that the simple, formal replacement of oxygen by sulfur in an alcohol should produce such a dramatic change in odor. Mercaptans possess the most disagreeable odors of all organic compounds. n-Butyl mercaptan is responsible for the odor of skunk. Most proteins contain the —SH group, but we are spared the odor because proteins are generally nonvolatile. Their molecules ordinarily cannot reach the nose, as they must to be smelled.

The one important reaction of the —SH group is its behavior toward mild oxidizing agents, a reaction that is important in protein chemistry. Mild oxidizing agents abstract the elements of hydrogen from the —S—H groups of two molecules:

$$CH_3—S—(H + H)—S—CH_3 + (O) \longrightarrow CH_3—S—S—CH_3 + H_2O$$

The product is a disulfide. Mild reducing agents easily convert the disulfide back into separate —S—H groups.

$$CH_3—S—S—CH_3 \xrightarrow{\text{Reducing agents}} 2CH_3—S—H$$

amines structural features   Alkyl derivatives of ammonia are called *amines*. One, two, or all three of the hydrogens on a molecule of ammonia may be replaced by alkyl groups. For example:

$$\overset{\overset{\displaystyle H}{\|}}{CH_3—\underset{..}{N}—H} \qquad \overset{\overset{\displaystyle H}{\|}}{CH_3—\underset{..}{N}—CH_3} \qquad \overset{\overset{\displaystyle CH_3}{\|}}{CH_3—\underset{..}{N}—CH_3}$$

Methylamine   Dimethylamine   Trimethylamine

Table 11.6 **Some Common Amines**

Common Name	Structure	Boiling Point, in °C	Solubility in Water
Methylamine	CH_3—NH_2	−8	Very soluble
Dimethylamine	CH_3—$\overset{\underset{\mid}{H}}{N}$—$CH_3$	8	Very soluble
Trimethylamine	CH_3—$\overset{\underset{\mid}{CH_3}}{N}$—$CH_3$	3	Very soluble
Ethylamine	CH_3CH_2—NH_2	17	Very soluble
Diethylamine	CH_3CH_2—$\overset{\underset{\mid}{H}}{N}$—$CH_2CH_3$	55	Very soluble
Triethylamine	CH_3CH_2—$\overset{\underset{\mid}{CH_2CH_3}}{N}$—$CH_2CH_3$	89	14 grams/ 100 grams H_2O
n-Propylamine	$CH_3CH_2CH_2$—NH_2	49	Very soluble
Aniline	⬡—NH_2	184	4 grams/ 100 grams H_2O
Glycine	NH_2—$CH_2\overset{\overset{O}{\|\|}}{C}$—$OH$	m.p. 233	Very soluble

Among di- and trialkylamines, the alkyl groups need not be alike. For example:

Methylethylamine   Dimethylaniline

Several representative amines are listed in Table 11.6.

The compounds in Table 11.6 illustrate the usual method giving common names to amines. The term *amine* is associated with the ammonia-like part of the structure. Alkyl groups attached to nitrogen are named as prefixes to that term. (Exceptions to this rule, such as aniline, involve compounds named before chemists realized the need to systematize nomenclature.)

naming the amines

Molecules of amines are moderately polar. For this reason, they find a polar solvent such as water a compatible atmosphere, and the low-formula-weight amines are readily soluble. The nitrogen-to-hydrogen bond found in mono- and dialkyl amines is polar enough so that it can participate in *hydrogen bonding*. We have encountered this phenomenon previously in connection with water and ammonia. We now extend the concept to amines (and later to amides). Figure 11.3 illustrates how a hydrogen bond can extend from a hydrogen on one amine to the nitrogen on another, or to an oxygen on water.

To summarize what we have learned about the phenomenon of hydrogen bonding, the following generalizations are possible.

1. In general, when a hydrogen is attached by a covalent bond to

$$
\text{nitrogen, as in } -\overset{|}{\text{N}}-\text{H, or}
$$
$$
\text{oxygen, as in } -\text{O}-\text{H,}
$$

it can participate in hydrogen bonding, either to

a nitrogen or to
an oxygen in another molecule.

2. The hydrogen bond is simply a force that is said to be acting to hold very polar molecules together.

3. The hydrogen bond is not a strong bond. It is considerably weaker than either

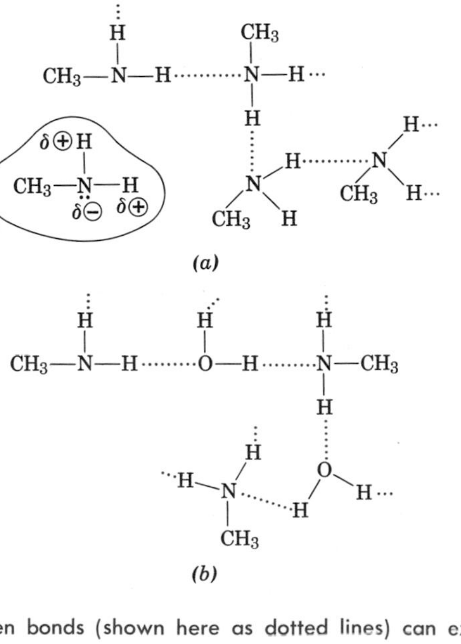

(a)

(b)

Fig. 11.3 (a) Hydrogen bonds (shown here as dotted lines) can exist between molecules of an amine. (b) Low-formula-weight amines are soluble in water because they can slip into the hydrogen-bonding network of water.

ionic or covalent bonds. Yet it is very real and vitally important to the chemistry of the substances (e.g., proteins) in which it occurs.

4. When hydrogen is attached to oxygen, it usually gives rise to a stronger hydrogen bond than when it is attached to nitrogen.

basicity. A molecule of ammonia has an unshared pair of electrons in the outer shell of its nitrogen. It can share this pair with a hydrogen *ion* (bare proton) without giving up the stability of its outer octet. By doing this, it provides a great measure of stability to the proton. This explains how an ammonia molecule behaves as a proton acceptor, a base in the Brønsted sense.

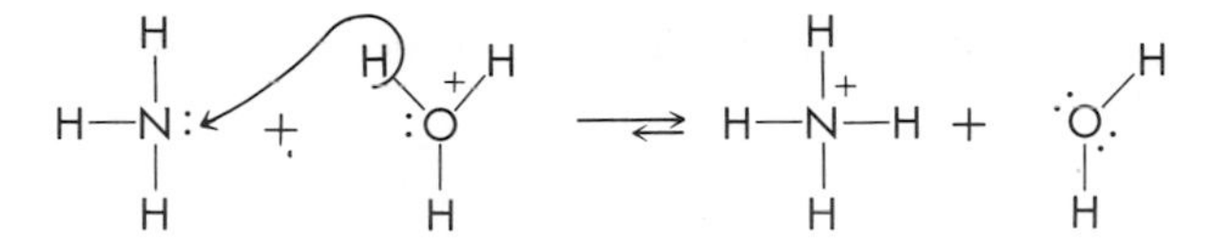

| (Stronger base) | (Stronger acid) | (Weaker acid) | (Weaker base) |
| Ammonia | Hydronium ion | Ammonium ion | Water |

Alkyl derivatives of ammonia, the amines, are basic for the same reason that ammonia is basic. Their molecules also possess an unshared pair of electrons on their nitrogens. They are as efficient proton acceptors or proton binders as ammonia—often, more so.

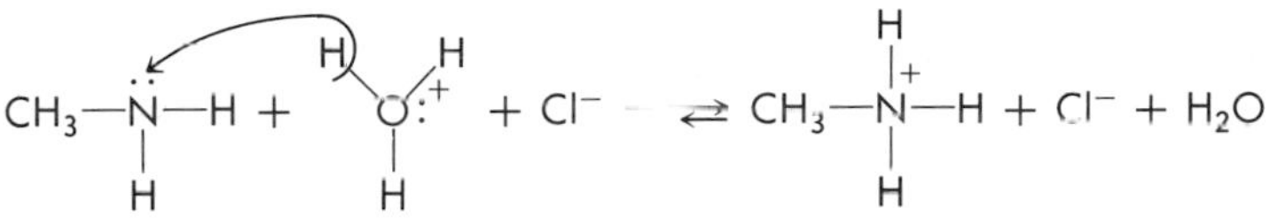

Methylamine   Methylammonium chloride

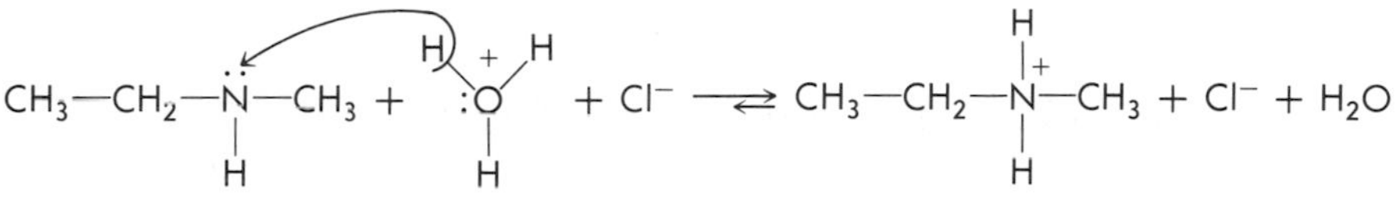

Methylethylamine   Methylethylammonium chloride

The interaction of amines (or ammonia) with organic acids from which amides form will be studied in the next chapter.

properties of amine salts. Protonated amines are really alkyl-substituted ammonium ions (and they are named accordingly). Being ionic, they are soluble in water, for they are capable of being well solvated by water molecules.

$$CH_3(CH_2)_6CH_2NH_2 + HCl_{(aqueous)} \longrightarrow CH_3(CH_2)_6CH_2\overset{+}{N}H_3Cl^-$$

Insoluble   Soluble in water
in water

Since proteins have amino groups, this reaction of amino groups provides a way of greatly affecting protein solubilities in water merely by adjusting the pH of the solution. For this reason, living organisms depend on well-functioning methods for controlling the pHs of their internal fluids—a matter to be studied in Chapters 15 and 17.

If a stronger proton binder than nitrogen (e.g., OH⁻ ion) is added to a solution of an amine salt, the "extra" proton is pulled off nitrogen, and the amine is liberated:

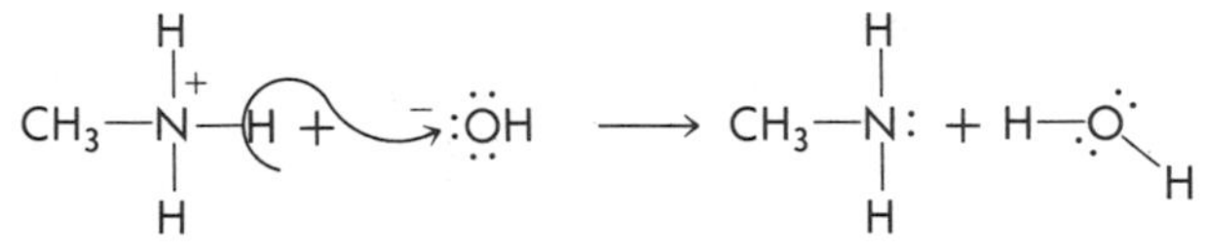

| Methylammonium ion | Hydroxide | Methylamine | Water |

some important heterocyclic compounds

Cyclic compounds (for instance, benzene and cyclopropane), in which all the members of the ring are alike (e.g., all are carbons) are designated as *homocyclic compounds*. Ring compounds in which all the ring members are not alike are called *heterocyclic compounds*.

Among the most important heterocyclic compounds are those whose molecules contain one or more nitrogens in a ring. The structures of a few of the simplest heterocyclic nitrogen compounds are as follows:

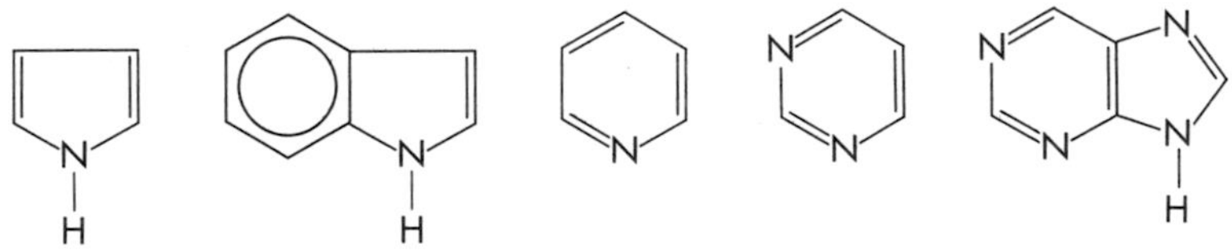

| Pyrrole | Indole | Pyridine | Pyrimidine | Purine |

| Quinoline | Isoquinoline | Piperidine |

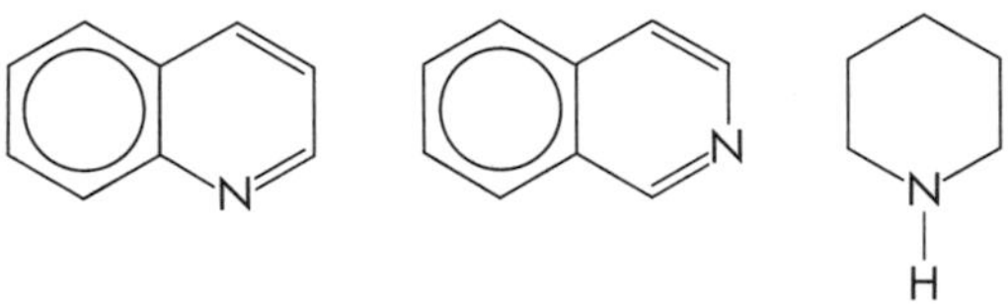

The pyrimidine and purine systems are important in the molecules of genes (Chapter 21).

alkaloids

Alkaloids are basic, nitrogen-containing compounds that are produced by plants and that have a marked physiological activity. Many of them are important drugs. The group includes *opium alkaloids* (morphine, codeine and papaverine) and a synthetic derivative of morphine, heroin; the *tropane*

organic derivatives of water, hydrogen sulfide, and ammonia: alcohols, ethers, mercaptans and amines

alkaloids (e.g., atropine and cocaine); the Cinchona alkaloids (quinine); and the *ergot alkaloids* (e.g., LSD).

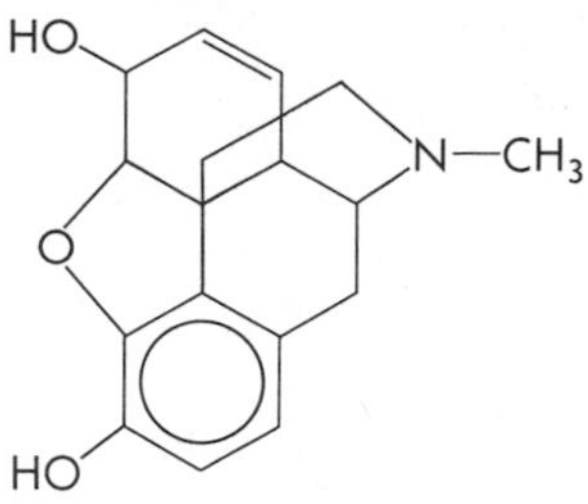

Morphine

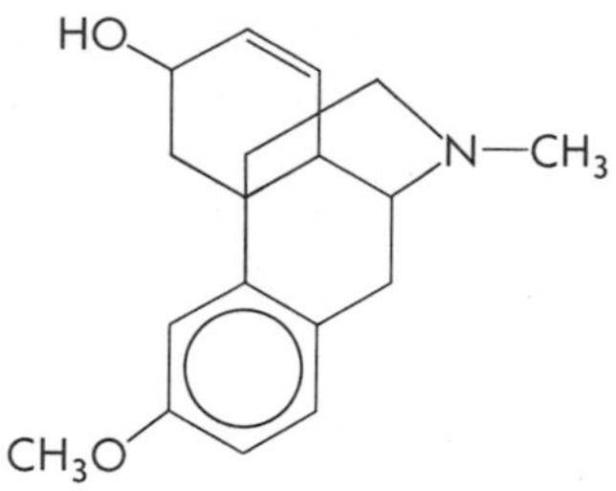

Codeine

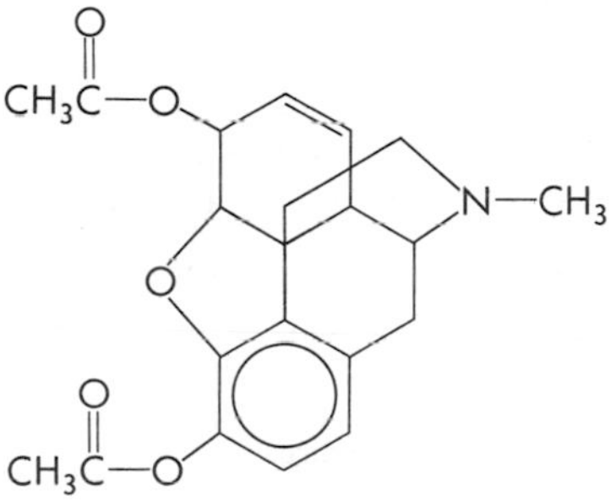

Heroin
(a synthetic derivative of morphine)

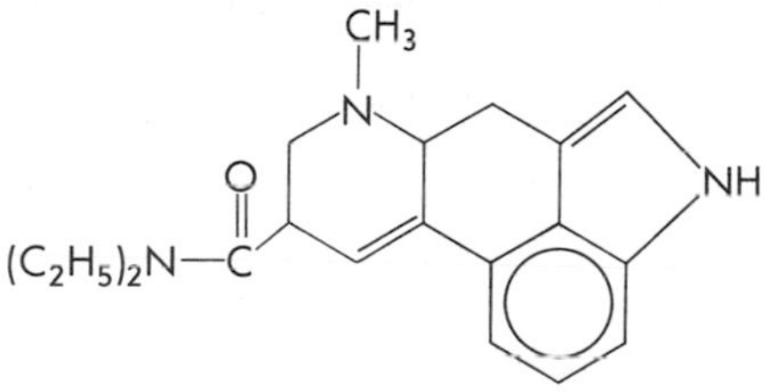

LSD
(lysergic acid diethylamide)

Selected Reading List

Article

1. B. E. Schaar. "A Strange Chapter in Anesthetics." *Chemistry,* October 1966, page 18. The abolishment of pain in surgery is recounted in this story of the discoveries of nitrous oxide ("laughing gas") and ether as anesthetics.

Brief Summary

Our study of alcohols and ethers furnishes the following correlations of structures and properties that will apply wherever their functional groups occur:

1. The —O—H group *tends* to make molecules more soluble in water and less soluble in nonpolar solvents.

2. The presence of an —O—H group on a molecule opens it to attack by
   (a) concentrated sulfuric acid:
      dehydration to alkenes or to ethers, depending on the conditions; and
   (b) oxidizing agents:
      oxidation of 1° alcohols to aldehydes and of
                    2° alcohols to ketones, while
                    3° alcohols are stable.

3. The ether linkage is chemically quite stable toward most reagents at room temperature.

4. Ethers are only slightly more polar than alkanes, as their relative solubilities in water and their boiling points indicate.

5. The mercaptan linkage, —SH, is susceptible to ready oxidation to the disulfide group, —S—S—; a mild reducing agent reverses the reaction.

Our study of amines permits the following correlations of structure with properties that will apply wherever the amino group, —ṄH$_2$ or —ṆH or —N—, occurs:

1. The amino group is a polar group that helps solubilize molecules in water. Amines are also soluble in nonpolar solvents, however.

2. The amino group can participate in hydrogen bonding.

3. The amino group is an electron-rich group that can bind a proton (H$^+$), although it is not as good at this as a hydroxide ion. The hydroxide ion (that is, in the form of water, where the discrete ion is no longer present) is the strongest proton acceptor that can exist in water. However, because amines are proton acceptors also, they are Brønsted bases.

4. Amine salts are ionic substances that are easily soluble in highly polar water and insoluble in nonpolar solvents (the so-called hydrocarbon solvents). An amino group that has accepted a proton (H$^+$) can carry large molecules into solution in water.

Problems and Exercises

1. Write the structure of the principal organic product which, on the basis of what has been studied, would be expected to form in each of the following situations. If no reaction would occur, state "no reaction." (Note: to differentiate between alkene-formation and ether-formation, a coefficient of 2 will be placed before the structure of an alcohol if it is intended that you write the structure of the ether that could form. Otherwise, it is assumed that you would write reactants and products *before* you try to balance equations.) The subscript "aq" as in "HCl$_{aq}$" means aqueous solution. To review how to handle problems such as these see problem 1, Chapter 10.

organic derivatives of water, hydrogen sulfide, and ammonia: alcohols, ethers, mercaptans and amines

(a) $CH_3CH_3 \xrightarrow[\Delta]{H_2SO_4}$

(b) $CH_3CH_2OH \xrightarrow[\Delta]{H_2SO_4}$

(c) $2CH_3CH_2OH \xrightarrow[\Delta]{H_2SO_4}$

(d) $CH_3SH + (O) \longrightarrow$

(e) $CH_3CH_2OH + (O) \longrightarrow$

(f) $CH_3\underset{\underset{\displaystyle OH}{|}}{C}HCH_3 \xrightarrow[\Delta]{H_2SO_4}$

(g) $CH_3\underset{\underset{\displaystyle OH}{|}}{C}HCH_3 + (O) \longrightarrow$

(h) $CH_3CH{=}CHCH_3 + H_2O \xrightarrow{H^+}$

(i)  $+ H_2 \xrightarrow[\text{pressure}]{\text{Ni, heat}}$

(i) $CH_3OCH_3 + H_2O \longrightarrow$

(k) 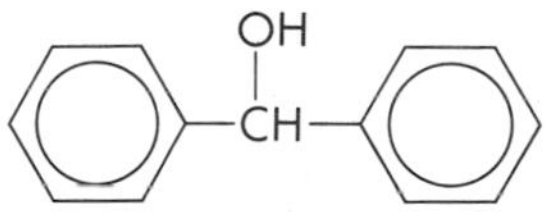 $\xrightarrow{H_2SO_4}$

(l) 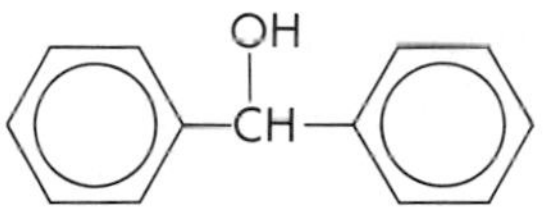 $+ (O) \longrightarrow$

(m) $2CH_3OH \xrightarrow[\Delta]{H_2SO_4}$

(n) 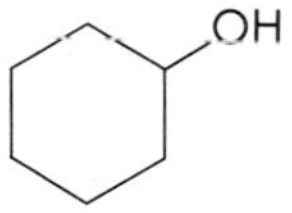 $\xrightarrow[\Delta]{H_2SO_4}$

(o) $CH_3{-}\underset{\underset{\displaystyle CH_3}{|}}{\overset{\overset{\displaystyle CH_3}{|}}{C}}{-}OH + (O) \longrightarrow$

(p) $CH_3S{-}SCH_3 \xrightarrow[\text{agent}]{\text{reducing}}$

(q) $CH_3CH{=}CHCH_2OH + H_2 \xrightarrow[\text{pressure}]{\text{Ni, heat}}$

(r) $NH_3 + HCl_{aq} \longrightarrow$

(s) $CH_3\overset{\overset{\displaystyle CH_3}{|}}{C}HCH_2OH \xrightarrow[\Delta]{H_2SO_4}$

(t) $CH_3\overset{+}{N}H_3Cl^- + OH^- \longrightarrow$

(u) $CH_3CH_2CH_3 + H_2O \xrightarrow{H^+}$

(v) $CH_3\overset{\overset{\displaystyle OH}{|}}{C}HCH_3 \xrightarrow[\Delta]{H_2SO_4}$

(w) $CH_3\!-\!O\!-\!CH_2CH_2\!-\!OH + (O) \longrightarrow$

(x) $CH_3NHCH_3 + HCl_{aq} \longrightarrow$

(y) $CH_2\!=\!CHCH_2\!-\!O\!-\!CH_2CH\!=\!CH_2 + 2H_2 \xrightarrow[\text{pressure}]{\text{Ni, heat}}$

(z) $HOCH_2CH_2NH_2 + HCl_{aq} \xrightarrow[\text{temperature}]{\text{room}}$

(aa) $CH_3OH + (O) \longrightarrow$

(bb) $CH_3\!-\!O\!-\!CH_2CH_2OH \xrightarrow[\Delta]{H_2SO_4}$

(cc) 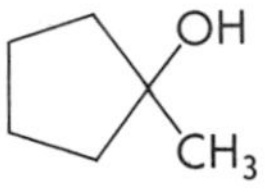 [cyclopentane ring with $\overset{\displaystyle OH}{\underset{\displaystyle CH_3}{|}}$ substituent] $+ (O) \longrightarrow$

(dd) $CH_3CH_2SH + H_2O \longrightarrow$

2. Write the structure of the organic compound that could be used to synthesize each of the following in one step. Then write the equation, including the reagent and conditions, in the manner we have followed in our study.

Ex. 1. $CH_3\overset{\overset{\displaystyle O}{||}}{C}CH_3$ Ans: $CH_3\overset{\overset{\displaystyle OH}{|}}{C}HCH_3$ (by oxidation)

Ex. 2. $CH_2\!=\!CH_2$ Ans: CH_3CH_2OH (by dehydration)

Ex. 3. CH_3SH Ans: $CH_3S\!-\!SCH_3$ (by reduction)

(a) $CH_3CH\!=\!CH_2$

(b) $CH_3\overset{\overset{\displaystyle O}{||}}{C}H$

(c) $CH_3CH_2OCH_2CH_3$

(d) $CH_3CH_2CH_3$

(e) $H_2C\!=\!O$

(f) $CH_3S\!-\!SCH_3$

(g) $CH_3CH_2\overset{\overset{\displaystyle O}{||}}{C}CH_3$

(h) $CH_3CH_2\overset{\overset{\displaystyle OH}{|}}{C}HCH_3$

(i) $CH_3\!-\!\overset{\overset{\displaystyle CH_3}{|}}{C}\!=\!CH_2$

organic derivatives of water, hydrogen sulfide, and ammonia: alcohols, ethers, mercaptans and amines

(i)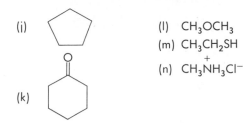

(k)

(l) CH_3OCH_3

(m) CH_3CH_2SH

(n) $CH_3\overset{+}{N}H_3Cl^-$

3. Account for the great differences in boiling points as you go from *n*-butane (b.p. 0°C, formula wt. 60), to *n*-propyl alcohol (b.p. 97°C, formula wt. 60), to ethylene glycol (b.p. 197°C, formula wt. 62).

4. *n*-Propyl alcohol is very soluble in all nonpolar solvents, whereas ethylene glycol and glycerol are insoluble. Explain.

5. Arrange the following compounds into what would be the most reasonable order of increasing solubility in water. Give the number 1 to the least soluble and number 4 to the most soluble.

$CH_3(CH_2)_5CH_2OH$ $CH_3(CH_2)_5CH_2NH_2$
        A   B

$CH_3(CH_2)_4CHCH_2OH$ $CH_3\overset{+}{N}H_3Cl^-$
              |
              OH

        C   D

6. The decidedly fishy odor of a solution of *n*-propylamine in water is removed by adding an equivalent amount of hydrochloric acid. Explain, using an equation to support your explanation.

7. The fishy odor of the solution of Problem 6 can be restored (after the addition of the acid) if an equivalent amount of sodium hydroxide is added. Explain, using an equation to support your explanation.

8. A solution of ethylamine in water tests basic to litmus. Account for the obvious excess of hydroxide ions over hydrogen ions in this solution. (Write an equation showing how ethylamine would interact with water.)

chapter 12 carbonyl compounds: aldehydes and ketones, carboxylic acids, esters and amides

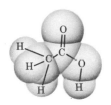

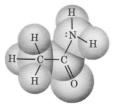

The carbon-to-oxygen double bond, —C—, occurs in the widest variety of nature's most interesting and most useful compounds, including all foods, enzymes, hormones, genes, and many vitamins. What groups are attached to the carbon in this structural unit are all important. In this chapter, we shall investigate several cases that relate to the chemistry of health.

The carbon-to-oxygen double bond, as a functional group, is called the *carbonyl group*.

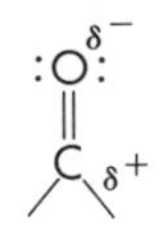

Carbonyl
group

To understand many of the properties of molecules having it, we need simply note one feature. It is polarized such that the carbonyl oxygen bears a partial negative charge and the carbonyl carbon a partial positive charge. An electron-poor species such as H^+ will be attracted to the oxygen; an electron-rich particle such as ^-OH will be attracted to the carbon. Whether anything can come of such collisions depends on what else is attached to the carbonyl carbon. Several families of organic compounds are based on the carbonyl group, each family differing in the groups that are attached to the carbon. These families are outlined in Table 12.1.

Except for the ketones, the common names of carbonyl compounds are related and are best studied together. The word parts for their names are given and

Table 12.1 The Carbonyl Group in Various Families of Organic Compounds

Family Name	Generic Family Structure[a]
Aldehydes	(H)R—C(=O)—H
Ketones	R—C(=O)—R′
Carboxylic acids	(H)R—C(=O)—O—H
Esters	(H)R—C(=O)—O—R′
Amides	(H)R—C(=O)—NH₂ or (H)R—C(=O)—NH—R′ or (H)R—C(=O)—N(R″)—R′

[a]When the symbol for hydrogen is placed in parentheses before (or after) R [e.g., (H)R— or —R(H)], it means that the specific R— group may be either an alkyl group or hydrogen. When an R— group is "primed" (e.g., R′— or R″—) in a generic symbol, it means that the two or more R— groups shown in the symbol may be identical or they may be different.

carbonyl compounds: aldehydes and ketones, carboxylic acids, esters and amides

Table 12.2 *Table 12.2* Giving Common Names to the Aldehydes, Carboxylic Acids and Their Salts, and Esters, and Amides

Class	Characteristic Name Ending of the Class	Characteristic Prefix in the Acid Name			
		C_1 Form-	C_2 Acet-	C_3 Propion-	C_4 Butyr-
Aldehydes	-aldehyde	Formaldehyde	Acetaldehyde	Propionaldehyde	Butyraldehyde
Carboxylic acids	-ic acid	Formic acid	Acetic acid	Propionic acid	Butyric acid
Ion from acid	-ate (ion)	Formate (ion)	Acetate (ion)	Propionate (ion)	Butyrate (ion)
Ester	-ate	(Alkyl) formate[a]	(Alkyl) acetate	(Alkyl) propionate	(Alkyl) butyrate
Amides	-amide	Formamide	Acetamide	Propionamide	Butyramide

[a] A specific group would, of course, be named in place of the general "alkyl" to designate any specific ester (cf. Table 12.7).

put together in Table 12.2. The formal names are taken up family by family in the appendix.

carboxylic acids (and their salts), esters, and amides

The structures of a few aldehydes, each having in common the *aldehyde* group,

$$\overset{\text{O}}{\underset{}{\overset{\|}{-\text{C}}}}-\text{H},$$

are shown in Table 12.3. Nearly all reactions of aldehyde molecules occur at the aldehyde group which is frequently abbreviated —CHO, as in CH_3CHO (acetaldehyde).

aldehydes structural features

In Chapter 11, we saw that the oxidation (i.e., dehydrogenation) of a primary alcohol yields an aldehyde:

preparation

$$R-CH_2-OH + (O) \longrightarrow R-\overset{\text{O}}{\underset{}{\overset{\|}{C}}}-H + H_2O$$

There are many more ways to make aldehydes, but none of them is especially relevant to our goals. The method given, indeed, is far from being the best. The reason is that aldehydes themselves are more easily oxidized than alcohols. If aldehydes are to be made this way, they must be removed from the reaction mixture as they form to prevent their being attacked by unchanged oxidizing agent (see page 265).

Table 12.3 Some Common Aldehydes

Structure	Common Name	Boiling Point, in °C
H—C—H (with O double bonded to C)	Formaldehyde	−21
CH₃C—H (with O double bonded to C)	Acetaldehyde	20
CH₃CH₂C—H (with O double bonded to C)	Propionaldehyde	49
CH₃CH₂CH₂C—H (with O double bonded to C)	Butyraldehyde	76
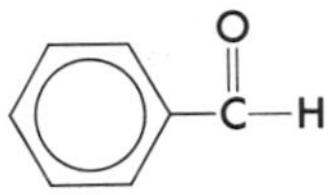 (benzene ring)—C—H (with O double bonded to C)	Benzaldehyde	178

physical properties The presence of the aldehyde group confers only moderate polarity to a molecule, as revealed by the low boiling points of aldehydes (relative to the alcohols). Low-formula-weight aldehydes are soluble in water. Hence the aldehyde group is a moderate water-solubilizing group.

The low-formula-weight aldehydes all have extremely unpleasant odors.

chemical properties *oxidation; formation of carboxylic acids.* At room temperature, molecular oxygen (from air) is not considered to be a vigorous oxidizing agent. Yet the aldehyde group is sensitive enough to oxidation that it is difficult to store aldehydes exposed to air for long periods. They are slowly converted to members of a new class of compounds, the carboxylic acids.

in general:

$$R-\overset{O}{\underset{\|}{C}}-H + (O) \longrightarrow R-\overset{O}{\underset{\|}{C}}-O-H$$

specific examples:

$$CH_3-\overset{O}{\underset{\|}{C}}-H + (O) \longrightarrow CH_3-\overset{O}{\underset{\|}{C}}-O-H$$

Acetaldehyde   Acetic acid

$$(benzene\ ring)-\overset{O}{\underset{\|}{C}}-H + (O) \longrightarrow (benzene\ ring)-\overset{O}{\underset{\|}{C}}-O-H$$

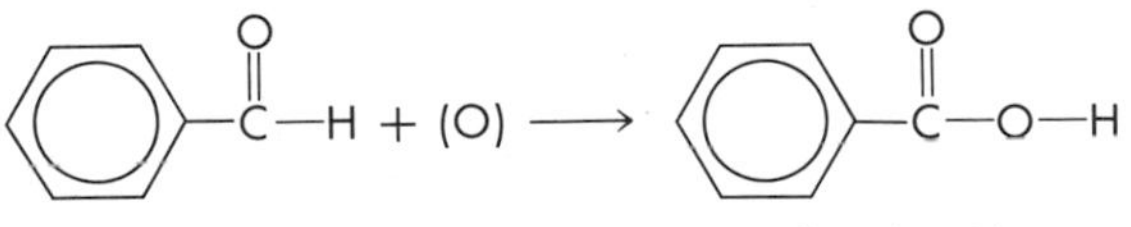

Benzaldehyde   Benzoic acid

When aldehydes are oxidized in aqueous media, the reaction may be understood in a familiar way, as follows. We learned that a carbon-carbon double bond can be made to add the elements of water. So can a carbon-oxygen double bond. The principal difference is that, in the second case, the products are rarely stable. They cannot be isolated and purified. They break down too readily to the original aldehyde and water. But there is compelling evidence that they do form in solution and that an equilibrium mixture is present:

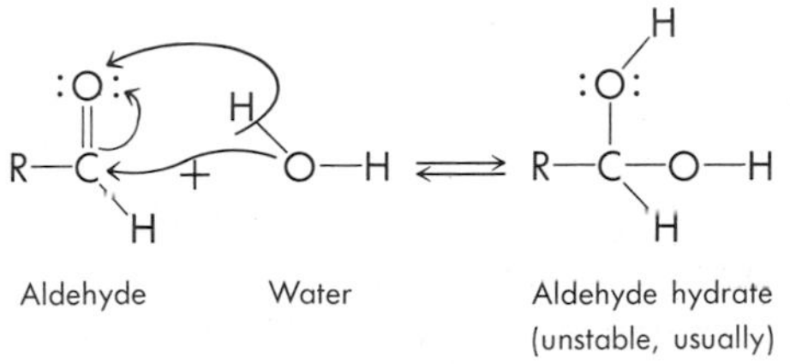

| Aldehyde | Water | Aldehyde hydrate (unstable, usually) |

If the aldehyde is in the form of its hydrate, then the oxidation may be viewed as the dehydrogenation of one of its alcohol groups:

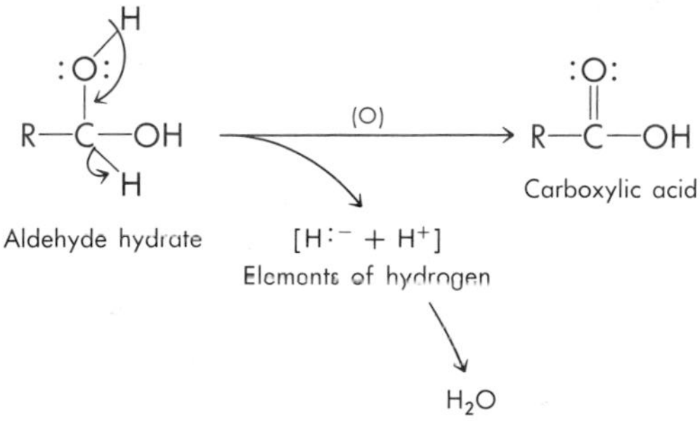

The ease with which the aldehyde group is oxidized makes it possible to detect its presence by reagents that leave other groups unaffected.

tollens' test; silvering mirrors. Tollens' reagent is a solution of silver nitrate in dilute aqueous ammonia. The silver ion and ammonia molecules form a complex, $Ag(NH_3)_2^+$, which is stable in the presence of base. (Otherwise, silver oxide, Ag_2O, would form and precipitate.) This reagent is a mild oxidizing agent, and it can be used to detect the aldehyde group (or any other *easily* oxidized group). As the silver ion acts to oxidize, it is itself reduced to metallic silver. The balancing of the equation is unnecessarily complicated, and we shall settle for the following "equation."

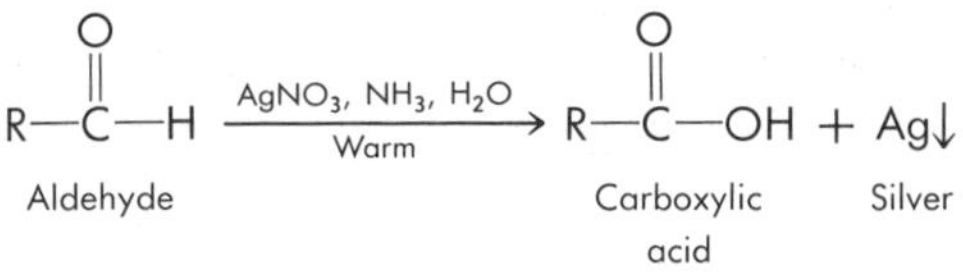

If the inner wall of the test vessel is clean and grease-free, the silver deposits to form a beautiful mirror, and this reaction serves as the basis for silvering of mirrors. (If the glass surface is not clean, the silver separates as a gray, finely divided, powdery precipitate.)

benedict's test and fehling's test.[1] Benedict's solution and Fehling's solution both consist of solutions of copper(II) hydroxide in aqueous media. In each case, a special solubilizing agent is present, for copper(II) hydroxide is otherwise insoluble in water. The solubilizing agent in Benedict's solution is sodium citrate; in Fehling's solution it is sodium tartrate. Benedict's solution is used more frequently, primarily because it can be stored for long periods without deterioration. Fehling's solution decomposes when it is stored and therefore should be freshly prepared each time it is used.

The essential feature of both solutions is the presence of solubilized copper(II) hydroxide, $Cu(OH)_2$, a mild reducing agent. Because of the presence of the Cu^{2+} ion, both solutions are bright blue in color. A positive Benedict's test or Fehling's test consists of the reduction of $Cu(OH)_2$ to Cu_2O, copper(I) oxide (or cuprous oxide). This oxide is brick red in color (sometimes yellowish, depending somewhat on its state of subdivision). It is also insoluble in the medium of the test. Hence, if a test is positive, the blue color of the solution disappears and a reddish solid appears. This change takes place in a few minutes if the test solution is heated, and if the compound tested contains one of the structural features shown in Fig. 12.1.

Some ordinary aliphatic aldehydes react with these reagents, but the changes are complex. A dark, gummy precipitate may form, which apparently is not Cu_2O, while the color of the test solution may remain blue or may become anything from yellow to green to brown. Aromatic aldehydes, in general, fail to give the test.

The structural feature of Fig. 12.1a occurs among several sugars, and Benedict's test is commonly used to detect the presence of glucose in urine. Normally, urine does not contain glucose, but in certain conditions (e.g.,

[1] R. Daniels, C. C. Rush, and L. Bauer. "Textbook Errors, 24. The Fehling and Benedict's Tests." *Journal of Chemical Education*, Vol. 37, page 205 (1960).

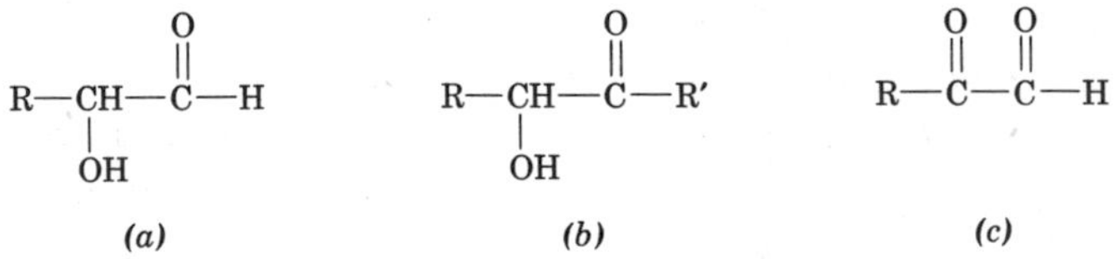

Fig. 12.1   Types of compounds that give positive tests with Benedict's or Fehling's solution, a positive test consisting of disappearance of the blue color of the test solution and the appearance of a precipitate consisting of copper(I) oxide, Cu_2O (usually brick red in color).

diabetes) it does. Glucose molecules contain the feature of Fig. 12.1a, and their rapid detection by Benedict's test is of great diagnostic importance. A positive test for glucose in urine may vary from development of a bright green color (0.25% glucose), to yellow-orange (1% glucose), to brick red (over 2% glucose) when the proportions are 5 cc of Benedict's reagent to 0.5 cc of urine.

behavior of aldehydes toward alcohols; hemiacetals; acetals. An aldehyde group will add the elements of an alcohol in a reaction that resembles the addition of water to the aldehyde.

in general:

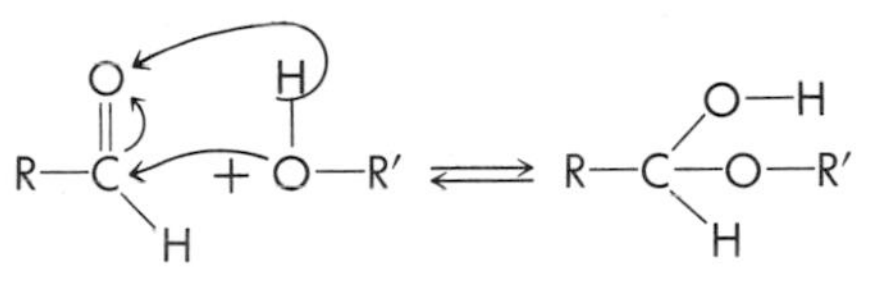

| Aldehyde | Alcohol | A hemiacetal |

specific example:

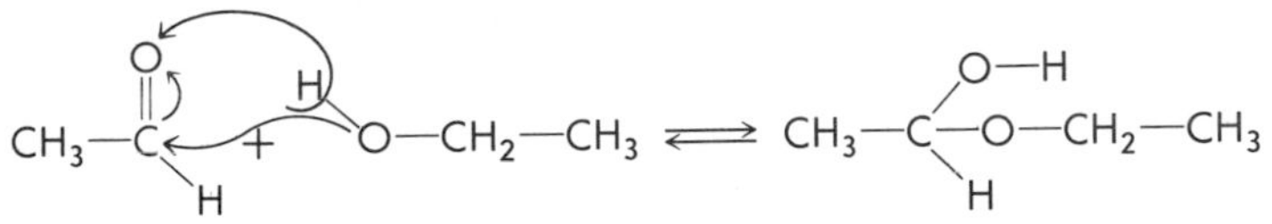

The reaction is reversible, and *hemiacetals are noted for the extreme ease with which they break down into the original aldehyde and alcohol.* In fact, hemiacetals are known primarily only in alcohol solutions. Attempts to isolate them usually fail. The exceptions, however, are important to our goals, for the exceptions occur mainly among the sugars.

The hemiacetal linkage:

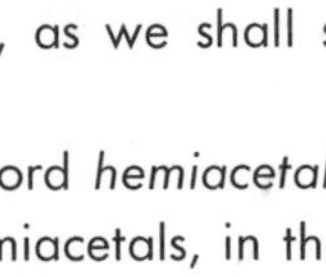

(one carbon, bold-faced, carrying both an alcohol and an ether linkage) occurs in several of the nutritionally important sugars. It is often called a *potential aldehyde* group and, as we shall study in detail in Chapter 13, glucose possesses one.

The "hemi-" part of the word *hemiacetal* suggests that we are halfway to something, and we are. Hemiacetals, in the presence of an acid catalyst, react with alcohols and form *acetals.*

in general:

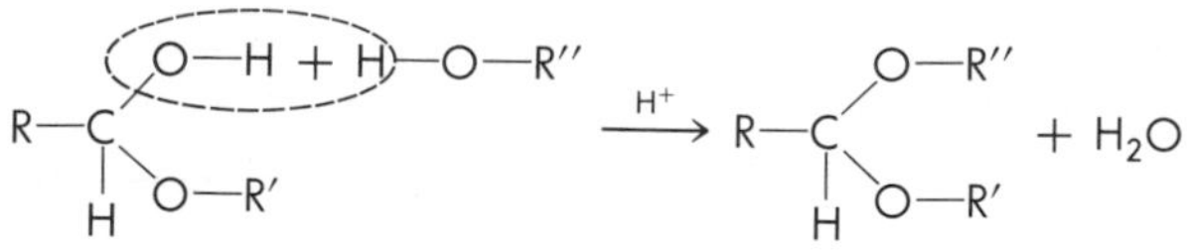

$$R-\underset{\underset{H}{|}}{\overset{\overset{\text{(O—H + H)—O—R''}}{}}{C}}\overset{}{\underset{}{O-R'}} \xrightarrow{\;H^+\;} R-\underset{\underset{H}{|}}{\overset{\overset{O-R''}{}}{C}}\underset{}{O-R'} \;+\; H_2O$$

specific example:

$$CH_3-\underset{\underset{H}{|}}{\overset{\overset{\text{(O—H + H)—O—CH}_2CH_3}{}}{C}}\underset{}{O-CH_2CH_3} \xrightarrow{\;H^+\;} CH_3-\underset{\underset{H}{|}}{\overset{\overset{O-CH_2CH_3}{}}{C}}\underset{}{O-CH_2CH_3} \;+\; H_2O$$

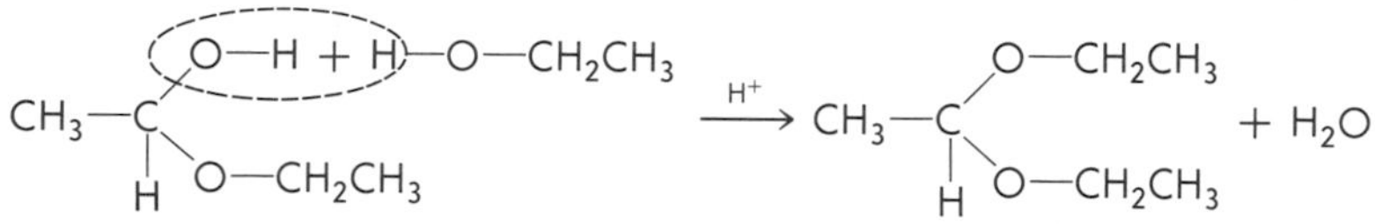

Acetal formation is very similar to ether formation. However, the latter requires high temperatures; the former occurs at room temperature because the —OH in a hemiacetal is *activated* by the presence of the ether linkage attached at the same site. It is generally true among organic compounds that, if different functional groups are situated close to each other on the same molecule, one modifies the properties of the other. This generalization applies to acetals, too. The characteristic feature of an acetal is the presence of two ether linkages joining to the same carbon (bold-faced):

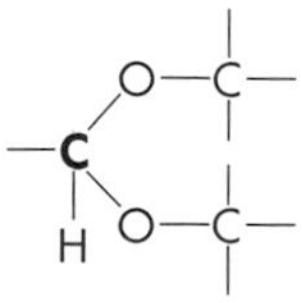

$$-\mathbf{C}\underset{\underset{H}{\diagdown}}{\overset{\diagup}{}}\begin{matrix} O-\overset{|}{\underset{|}{C}}- \\ \\ O-\overset{|}{\underset{|}{C}}- \end{matrix}$$

(Note that the bold-faced carbon originates from the carbonyl carbon of the parent aldehyde from which the acetal ultimately is made.)

As a result, neither behaves as a simple, ordinary ether (characterized by great stability). *In the presence of a trace of acid, acetals undergo easy disintegration all the way back to the original aldehyde and alcohol. However, an acetal is stable in base.* These two facts about acetals are important in sugar chemistry, for both the hemiacetal and the acetal groups constitute weak and therefore important elements in the structures of carbohydrates. The enzyme-catalyzed hydrolysis of acetal linkages is the basic chemistry of the digestion of carbohydrates.

important individual aldehydes

formaldehyde. Formaldehyde, one of the irritants in photochemical smog, is a gas with a most disagreeable and distinctive odor. It is used as a germicide and fungicide, and for these purposes, its common commercial form is a 37 to 40% solution in water (formalin). Its biggest use is for making Bakelite and melamine plastics, and such high explosives as cyclonite and PETN. Bakelite has been widely used in molding items such as telephone casings. The melamines are used in plastic dinnerware.

aldehydes in smog. Trace amounts (as high as 1.9 ppm) of low-formula-weight aldehydes have been often found in smog. They irritate the eyes and the mucous membranes even in periods of light smog. They arise from very complex reactions between unburned hydrocarbons (from gasoline) and the oxidants in smog: ozone and the nitrogen oxides.

Table 12.4 lists several ketones. They have in common the *ketone group*. **ketones** structural features

$$-\overset{|}{\underset{|}{C}}-\overset{O}{\overset{\|}{C}}-\overset{|}{\underset{|}{C}}-$$

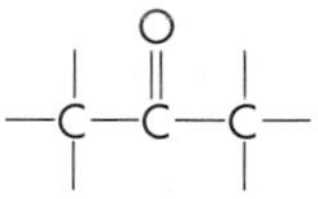

Ketone system
(carbon-carbonyl-carbon)

In Chapter 11 we learned that ketones can be made by the oxidation of secondary alcohols. This reaction is very useful in syntheses, for ketones, in contrast to aldehydes, are very resistant to further oxidation. preparation

in general:

$$R-\overset{OH}{\underset{|}{CH}}-R' + (O) \longrightarrow R-\overset{O}{\overset{\|}{C}}-R' + H_2O$$

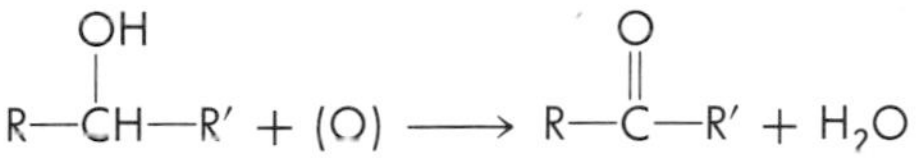

Table 12.4 **Some Common Ketones**

Structure	Common Name (Boiling Point in Parentheses)	Use
$CH_3-\overset{O}{\overset{\|}{C}}-CH_3$	Acetone (56°C)	Solvent; raw material for smokeless powder; one of the "ketone bodies" (cf. Chapter 19)
$CH_3-\overset{O}{\overset{\|}{C}}-CH_2CH_3$	Methyl ethyl ketone (80°C)	Solvent; fingernail polish remover
$\langle\bigcirc\rangle-\overset{O}{\overset{\|}{C}}-CH_3$	Acetophenone (202°C) (phenyl methyl ketone)	Organic synthesis

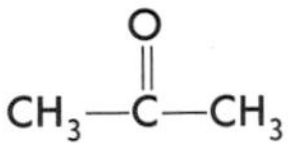

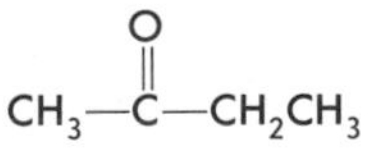

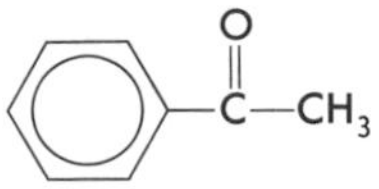

specific examples:

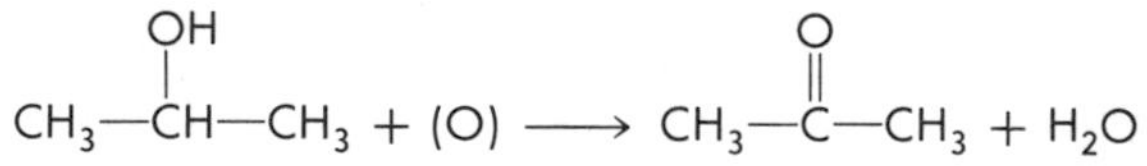

$$CH_3-\underset{\underset{OH}{|}}{CH}-CH_3 + (O) \longrightarrow CH_3-\underset{\overset{O}{\|}}{C}-CH_3 + H_2O$$

Isopropyl alcohol   Acetone

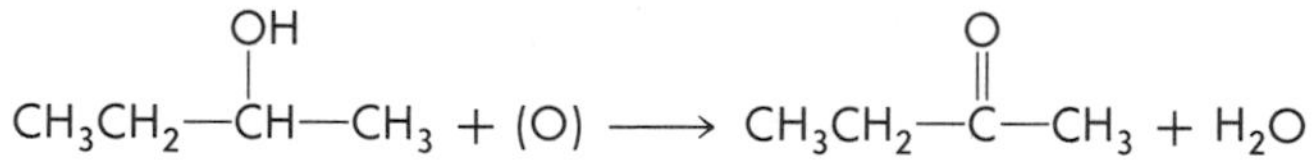

$$CH_3CH_2-\underset{\underset{OH}{|}}{CH}-CH_3 + (O) \longrightarrow CH_3CH_2-\underset{\overset{O}{\|}}{C}-CH_3 + H_2O$$

sec-Butyl alcohol   Methyl ethyl ketone

physical properties

Ketones resemble aldehydes in physical properties. Ketone molecules are of moderate polarity because of the polarity of the carbonyl group. Their odors are far more pleasant than those of the aldehydes.

chemical properties

The most important chemical property of ordinary ketones, for our purposes, is their general stability toward oxidizing agents. Benedict's reagent, Fehling's solution, and Tollens' reagent leave ketone groups unaffected. In accord with the generalization about the effect of neighboring functional groups on each other, the ketone group activates a hydroxyl group on a neighboring carbon. Although ordinary alcohols are stable toward *mild* oxidizing agents such as Tollens' or Benedict's reagents, the —OH group in the system

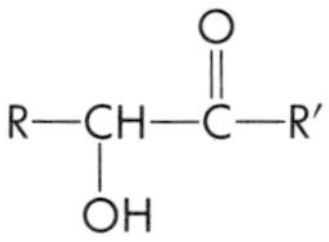

$$R-\underset{\underset{OH}{|}}{CH}-\underset{\overset{O}{\|}}{C}-R'$$

is readily oxidized. This system is found in fructose, an important sugar, which gives positive tests with Benedict's reagent.

important individual ketone

acetone. Acetone is an important organic solvent because it dissolves both water and nonpolar solvents. It is very volatile and therefore very flammable.

carboxylic acids

structural features

Organic compounds, we have learned, are aggregations of neutral, although usually polar molecules. Certain kinds of these molecules, although fully covalent in the free state, are hydrogen-ion producers in aqueous systems. It is proper, therefore, to call them acids. Most of the important organic acids contain the functional group:

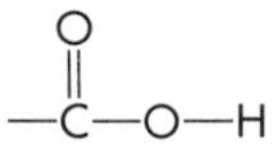

$$-\underset{\overset{O}{\|}}{C}-O-H \qquad -CO_2H \quad \text{or} \quad -COOH$$

Carboxyl group   common abbreviations
(carbonyl + hydroxyl)   for the carboxyl group

This *carboxylic acid group,* or *carboxyl group,* characterizes molecules of a class of organic compounds called the *carboxylic acids.* Some important members of this class are listed in Table 12.5.

As we learned earlier, one of the several ways of making carboxylic acids is by the oxidation of aldehydes. Weak oxidizing agents (e.g., Ag^+) will do. Since *carboxylic acids are exceptionally resistant to further chemical oxidation,* strong oxidizing agents (e.g., MnO_4^- and $Cr_2O_7^{2-}$) may also be used.

The carboxyl group is made of two functional groups, carbonyl and hydroxyl. Both are polar. Both can accept hydrogen bonds; one can donate a hydrogen bond. These facts explain the relatively high boiling points of the acids in comparison with members of the other functional groups we have studied. The data in Table 12.6 reflect a combination of increasing polarities and increasing opportunities for hydrogen-bonding.

The carboxyl group also helps carboxylic acids dissolve in water, and those containing from one to four carbon atoms are soluble. Long-chain carboxylic acids (caproic acid and higher), however, are not appreciably soluble. (Notice that they become increasingly hydrocarbon-like as the alkane-like chain lengthens.)

These considerations are directly relevant to the chemistry of health, for long-chain acids (C_{12}—C_{18}) are normal products of the digestion of fats and oils. The body has a mechanism for dissolving them in its aqueous fluids (e.g., blood and lymph). If and when this mechanism breaks down, fats in the diet present serious problems, especially when they tend to clog the circulatory system.

The low-formula-weight carboxylic acids with three to eight carbons have extremely nauseous odors.

acidity. In an aqueous medium, molecules of carboxylic acid interact with water molecules (if the collisions between the two are strong enough) to furnish a small percentage of hydronium ions ("hydrogen ions").

in general:

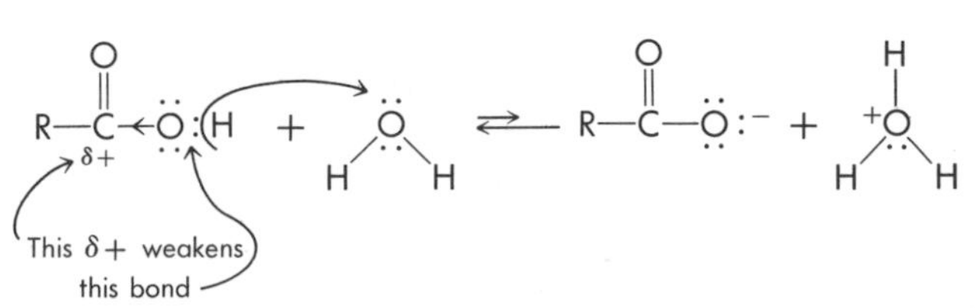

This δ+ weakens this bond

Table 12.5 Some Common Carboxylic Acids

Carbon Number	Common Name[a]	Structure	Boiling Point, in °C
C_1	Formic acid (ants)	$H-\overset{\overset{\text{O}}{\|}}{C}-OH$	100
C_2	Acetic acid (vinegar)	$CH_3\overset{\overset{\text{O}}{\|}}{C}-OH$	118
C_3	Propionic acid	$CH_3CH_2\overset{\overset{\text{O}}{\|}}{C}-OH$	141
C_4	Butyric acid (rancid butter)	$CH_3CH_2CH_2\overset{\overset{\text{O}}{\|}}{C}-OH$	163
C_5	Valeric acid (goats)	$CH_3(CH_2)_3\overset{\overset{\text{O}}{\|}}{C}-OH$	187
C_6	Caproic acid (goats)	$CH_3(CH_2)_4\overset{\overset{\text{O}}{\|}}{C}-OH$	205
C_8	Caprylic acid (goats)	$CH_3(CH_2)_6\overset{\overset{\text{O}}{\|}}{C}-OH$	237
C_{12}	Lauric acid (laurel family)	$CH_3(CH_2)_{10}\overset{\overset{\text{O}}{\|}}{C}-OH$	m.p. 44
C_{14}	Myristic acid (nutmeg seed fat)	$CH_3(CH_2)_{12}\overset{\overset{\text{O}}{\|}}{C}-OH$	m.p. 58
C_{16}	Palmitic acid (palm oil; all fats)	$CH_3(CH_2)_{14}\overset{\overset{\text{O}}{\|}}{C}-OH$	m.p. 63
C_{18}	Stearic acid (animal fats)	$CH_3(CH_2)_{16}\overset{\overset{\text{O}}{\|}}{C}-OH$	m.p. 70
—	Benzoic acid (balsams)	phenyl$-\overset{\overset{\text{O}}{\|}}{C}-OH$	m.p. 123
—	Salicylic acid (salicylates)	ortho-hydroxyphenyl$-\overset{\overset{\text{O}}{\|}}{C}-OH$	m.p. 159

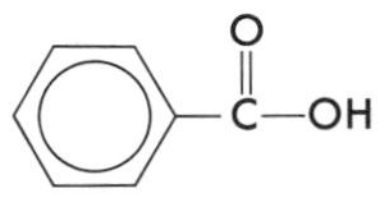

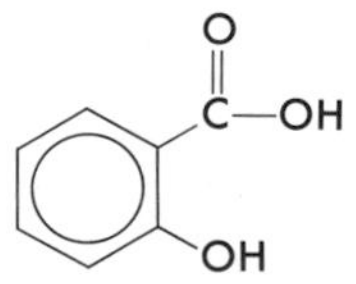

[a] In parentheses beneath each name is information about a source of the acid or about an association with an odor.

Table 12.6   Effect of Polarity and Hydrogen-bonding Ability on Boiling Point

Substance		Formula Weight	Boiling Point (°C)
Propane	$CH_3CH_2CH_3$	44	−42
Methyl chloride	CH_3—Cl	50	−24
Ethylamine	$CH_3CH_2NH_2$	45	17
Acetaldehyde	CH_3CH=O	44	21
Ethyl alcohol	CH_3CH_2OH	46	78
Formic acid	HCO_2H	46	101

specific example:

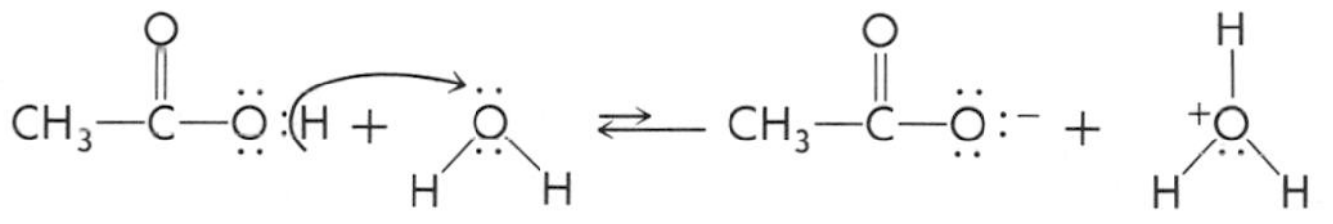

Acetic acid   Acetate ion   Hydronium ion

For this reason, carboxylic acids are weak acids. (A 1 molar solution of acetic acid is ionized to the extent of only about 0.5%.) Another way of saying

the same thing is that the carboxylate ion, R—$\overset{\overset{\displaystyle O}{\|}}{C}$—$O^-$, is a fairly good proton binder or proton acceptor. It binds protons in the form of un-ionized carboxylic acid.

When water is the solvent, the best proton-acceptor you can add to it is the hydroxide ion, OH^-. It will take a proton and hold it in the form of a molecule of water. It will take a proton from any particle that holds it less strongly than it can be held as part of a water molecule. That is why the carboxylic acids, although weak acids, react smoothly and quickly with strong bases, such as sodium or potassium hydroxide.

in general:

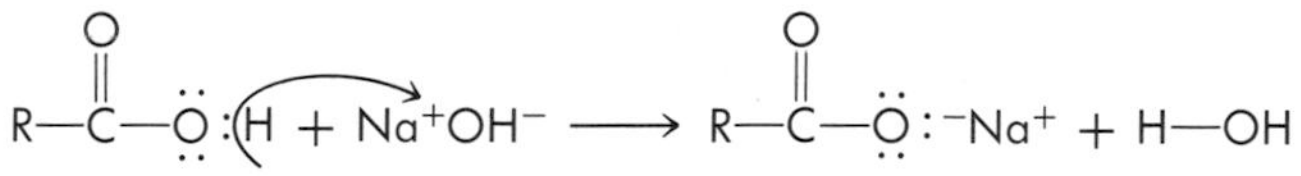

specific examples:

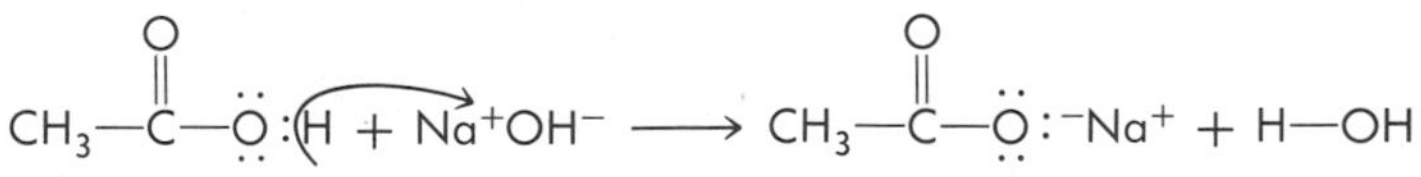

Acetic acid   Sodium   Sodium acetate
                     hydroxide

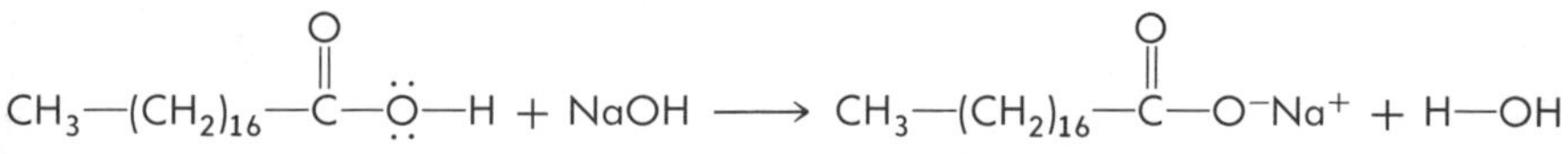

Stearic acid   Sodium stearate
                      (a "soap")

properties of salts of carboxylic acids. Sodium and potassium salts of carboxylic acids are *ionic substances*. They are usually soluble in water. The salts of even long-chain acids (e.g., sodium stearate) dissolve in water, and they serve as excellent soaps.

Solutions of the salts of carboxylic acids contain, among other things, negatively charged carboxylate ions. These are good proton acceptors or proton binders. Hence, if a strong acid (a strong proton donor) is added to the solution of the salt, its protons will become attached to the negative carboxylate ions, and the free carboxylic acid will form.

in general:

$$R-\overset{\displaystyle O}{\overset{\|}{C}}-O^- + Na^+ + H^+ + Cl^- \rightleftarrows R-\overset{\displaystyle O}{\overset{\|}{C}}-O-H + Na^+ + Cl^-$$

specific examples:

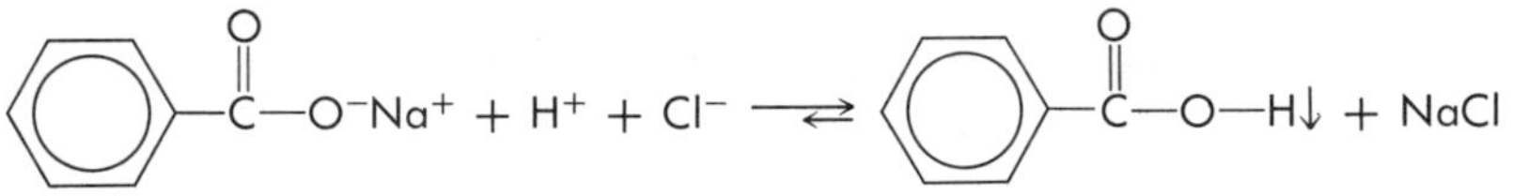

Sodium benzoate (soluble in water) + Hydrochloric acid $\rightleftarrows$ Benzoic acid (insoluble in water) + NaCl

$$CH_3-(CH_2)_{16}-\overset{\displaystyle O}{\overset{\|}{C}}-O^-Na^+ + HCl \rightleftarrows CH_3-(CH_2)_{16}-\overset{\displaystyle O}{\overset{\|}{C}}-O-H + NaCl$$

Sodium stearate   Stearic acid (insoluble in water)

We learn from these reactions that water-insoluble carboxylic acids can be solubilized by converting them into their sodium or potassium salts. They can be recovered from their salts by the action of any strong acid. The group

$$-\overset{\displaystyle O}{\overset{\|}{C}}-O^-$$

is an excellent water-solubilizing group in body chemicals, especially among proteins, and the fact that the solubilities of large molecules bearing this group can be drastically altered simply by changing the pH of the solution is a most important fact in the molecular basis of life.

reactions of carboxylic acids with alcohols; esterification. One of the most important reactions of both carboxylic acids and alcohols is their behavior toward each other. In general, a molecule of each can be expected to react together in such a way that the elements of water (H and —OH) are split out between them and an *ester* forms. This reaction is named *esterification,* and the acid is said to be *esterified* by the alcohol (or vice versa). The reaction is catalyzed by acids.

carbonyl compounds: aldehydes and ketones, carboxylic acids, esters and amides

in general:

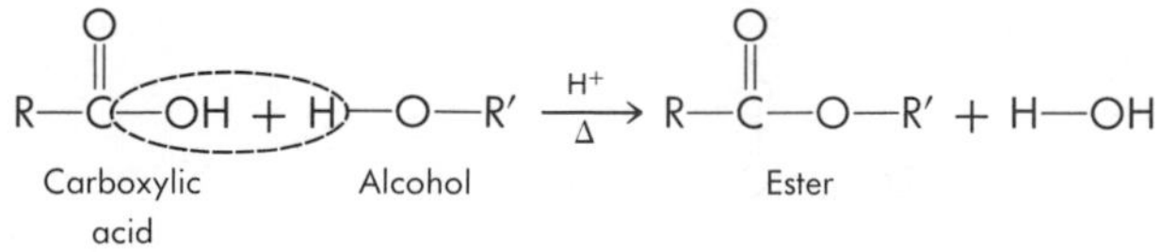

$$R-\overset{\overset{O}{\|}}{C}-OH + H-O-R' \xrightarrow[\Delta]{H^+} R-\overset{\overset{O}{\|}}{C}-O-R' + H-OH$$

Carboxylic   Alcohol   Ester
acid

specific examples:

$$CH_3-\overset{\overset{O}{\|}}{C}-O-H + H-O-CH_2CH_3 \xrightarrow[\Delta]{H^+} CH_3-\overset{\overset{O}{\|}}{C}-O-CH_2CH_3 + H_2O$$

Acetic   Ethyl   Ethyl acetate
acid   alcohol

Salicylic   Methyl   Methyl
acid   alcohol   salicylate
                          (oil of wintergreen)

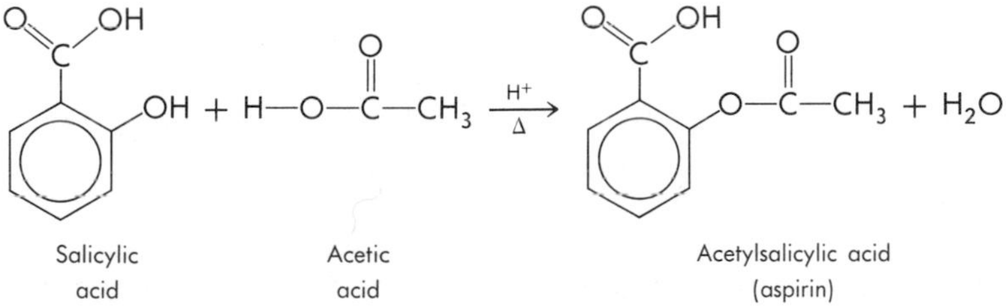

Salicylic   Acetic   Acetylsalicylic acid
acid   acid   (aspirin)

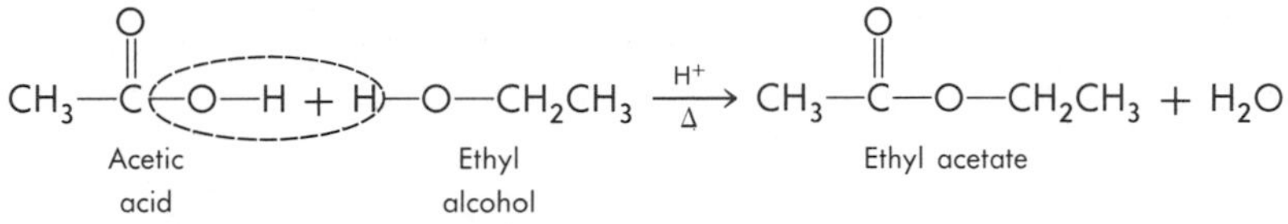

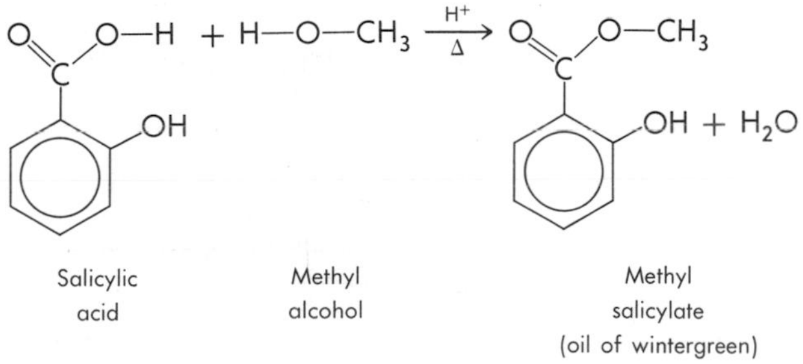

As an aid in studying the course of this reaction, note carefully that the elements of water originate as follows:

> H—O— from the carboxylic acid group, and
> H— from the alcohol.

In any new situation involving esterification, simply envision that the elements of water are "erased" from the structures of the reactants. Then join the remaining fragments by attaching the oxygen of the original alcohol to the carbonyl carbon of the original acid.

Problem 1. What ester would form between propionic acid and methyl alcohol?

Step 1. Set down the correct structures of the reactants first (you cannot do anything else until this is done correctly):

$$CH_3CH_2\overset{\overset{\displaystyle O}{\|}}{C}-O-H \ + \ CH_3-O-H$$

Propionic acid   Methyl alcohol

Step 2. Blacken or erase the hydrogen atom on the —OH function of the alcohol; do the same to the hydroxyl group on the acid:

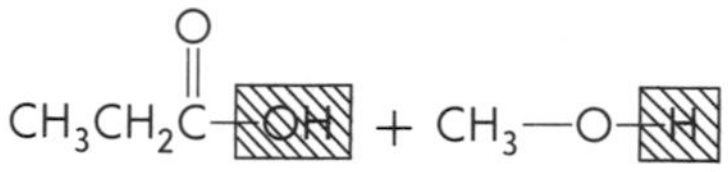

$$CH_3CH_2\overset{\overset{\displaystyle O}{\|}}{C}-\boxed{OH} \ + \ CH_3-O-\boxed{H}$$

Step 3. Link the remaining fragments—oxygen of the alcohol to carbonyl carbon of the acid:

$$CH_3CH_2\overset{\overset{\displaystyle O}{\|}}{C} \ + \ CH_3-O- \ \longrightarrow \ CH_3CH_2\overset{\overset{\displaystyle O}{\|}}{C}-O-CH_3$$

Step 4. Having determined the correct structure of the ester, write a neat and orderly equation for its formation:

$$CH_3CH_2\overset{\overset{\displaystyle O}{\|}}{C}-OH \ + \ CH_3O-H \ \overset{H^+}{\longrightarrow} \ CH_3CH_2\overset{\overset{\displaystyle O}{\|}}{C}-O-CH_3 \ + \ H_2O$$

Propionic acid   Methyl alcohol   Methyl propionate

    Esterification is very important in the chemistry of lipids (animal fats and vegetable oils). A mastery of the essential features of this reaction now will make our study of this class of foods much easier. To that purpose, a knowledge of the mechanism of esterification is helpful.

mechanism of esterification. One way to write the mechanism for this reaction is as follows.

Step 1. The transfer of a proton occurs from the oxygen on the hydronium ion to one of the oxygens of the acid.

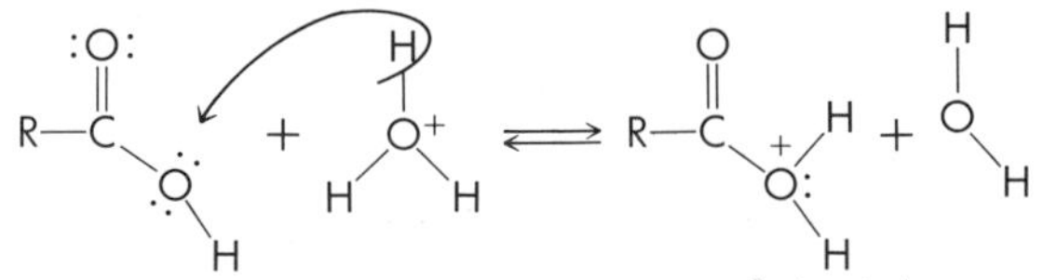

Protonated acid

carbonyl compounds: aldehydes and ketones, carboxylic acids, esters and amides

When a positive charge is acquired by an oxygen of the acid, the following changes can be expected.

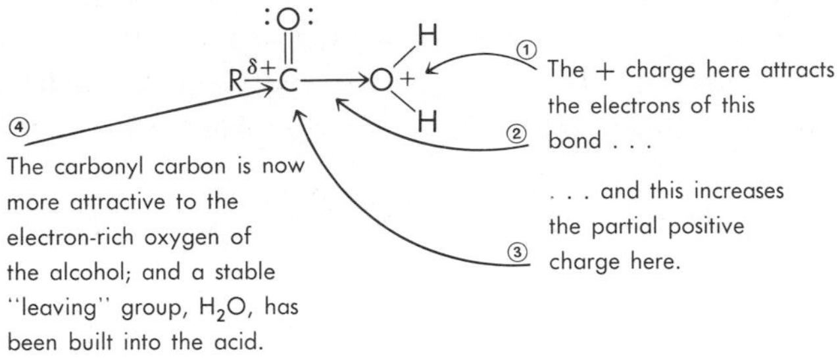

① The + charge here attracts the electrons of this bond . . .

② . . . and this increases the partial positive ③ charge here.

④ The carbonyl carbon is now more attractive to the electron-rich oxygen of the alcohol; and a stable "leaving" group, H_2O, has been built into the acid.

Step 2. The alcohol attacks the protonated acid and drives out a molecule of water.

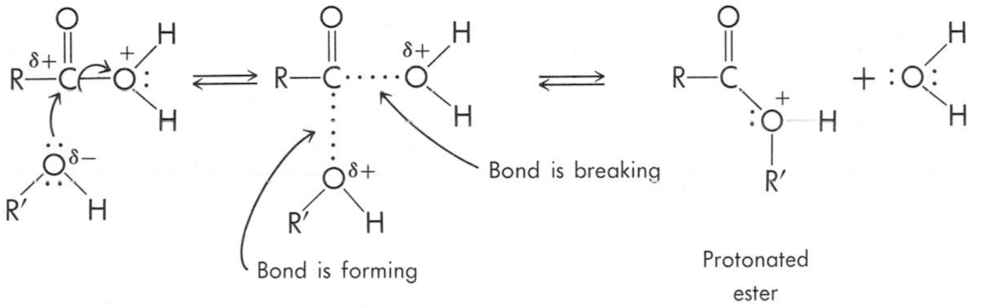

Bond is breaking

Bond is forming

Protonated ester

Step 3. The protonated ester gives up its "extra" proton to some acceptor; e.g., an unchanged molecule of acid or alcohol or even a water molecule (from the catalytic amount provided by the initial catalyst), in the rare event that one happens to be nearby.

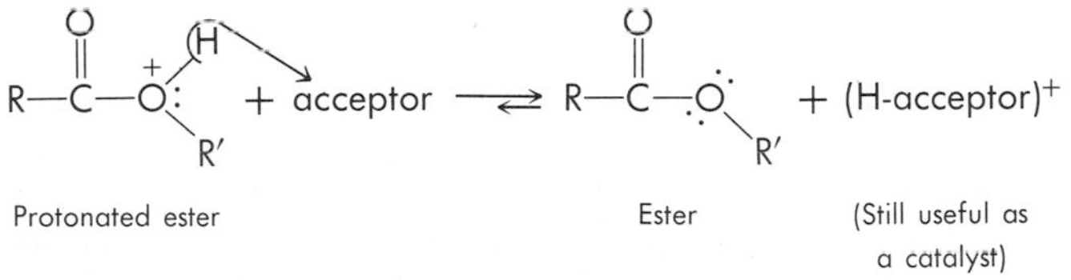

Protonated ester   Ester   (Still useful as a catalyst)

acetic acid. Vinegar is sour because it contains an acid, acetic acid. Pure acetic acid is a substance that melts at 16.6°C (63°F). At temperatures found in some laboratories, it solidifies in the bottle to a glass-like solid. That is why it is often called *glacial acetic acid*. It is one of the most important intermediates in the metabolism of all foodstuffs.

important individual acids

2,4-D. 2,4-dichlorophenoxyacetic acid.

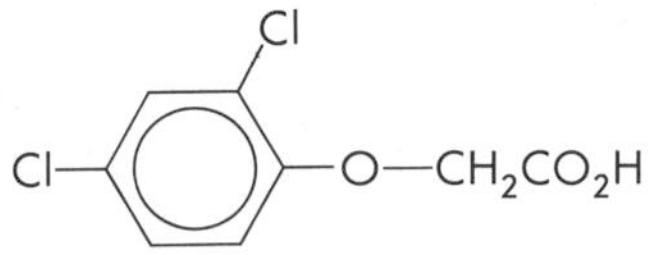

This compound and several of its acids and salts are plant growth hormones that serve as herbicides (weed killers). When a plant takes any of them into its system, its growing patterns are so upset that it dies. Throughout the period of deepening concern over the poisons we put into our environment, 2,4-D has remained acceptable at least for spot treatment. Both the Audubon Society and the Consumer's Union have rated it "acceptable" when carefully used.

2,4,5-T. 2,4,5-trichlorophenoxyacetic acid.

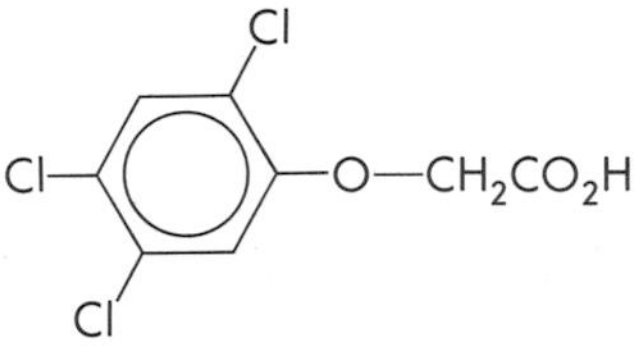

In the late sixties and on into the 1970s this herbicide was the center of great controversy. It was (together with 2,4-D and a herbicide known as picloram) heavily applied to kill trees and shrubs in Vietnam. There was evidence that it or one of its impurities (called "dioxin") was highly teratogenic (causer of birth defects). In 1970 the evidence seemed to be swinging toward associating this terrible property more with the impurity but tests were continuing. Because of the possible risks the Secretary of the U. S. Department of the Interior, Walter Hickel, in 1970 banned its use on all federal lands administered by his department. The Department of Agriculture in the same year suspended legal permission to use this herbicide around homes, on ponds, lakes, ditch banks, and all food crops, and the Department of Defense announced in April 1970 that it no longer would use it in its chemical warfare operations in Vietnam. (It continued to do so throughout the summer of 1970.)

esters
structural
features

Although carboxylic acids possess some of the most disagreeable odors encountered in organic compounds, esters have some of the most pleasant fragrances. Many are responsible for distinctive fruit flavors, and some are used in making perfumes. Exceptionally high-formula-weight esters (long chains in both acid and alcohol portions) are waxes. They are used as car polishes, shoe dressings, and the like. Table 12.7 lists several esters.

The basic skeleton of the ester function is:

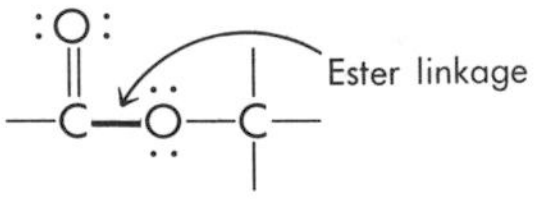

Ester function
(carbonyl-oxygen-carbon)

The heavily drawn bond, carbonyl-to-oxygen is the *ester linkage*.

carbonyl compounds: aldehydes and ketones, carboxylic acids, esters and amides

Table 12.7 **Important Individual Esters**

Common Name	Structure	B. Pt.	Source or Flavor
Isobutyl formate	$\underset{\displaystyle CH_3CHCH_2-O-\overset{\displaystyle O}{\overset{\displaystyle \|}{C}}-H}{\overset{\displaystyle CH_3}{\overset{\displaystyle \|}{}}}$	98°C	Raspberries
Ethyl acetate	$CH_3CH_2-O-\overset{\displaystyle O}{\overset{\displaystyle \|}{C}}CH_3$	77°C	—
Ethyl butyrate	$CH_3CH_2-O-\overset{\displaystyle O}{\overset{\displaystyle \|}{C}}CH_2CH_2CH_3$	120°C	Pineapples
Methyl benzoate	$C_6H_5-\overset{\displaystyle O}{\overset{\displaystyle \|}{C}}-O-CH_3$	199°C	—
Methyl salicylate	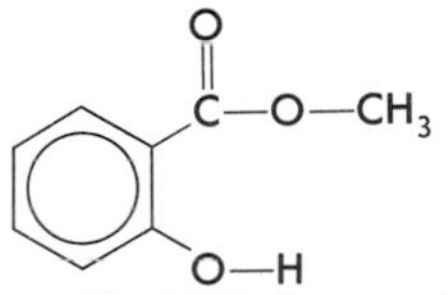 $\overset{\displaystyle C-O-CH_3}{}$, $O-H$	222°C	Oil of wintergreen
"Waxes"	$CH_3(CH_2)_n\overset{\displaystyle O}{\overset{\displaystyle \|}{C}}-O(CH_2)_nCH_3$	(solids)	n = 23 to 33: Carnauba wax = 25 to 27: Beeswax = 14 to 15: Spermaceti

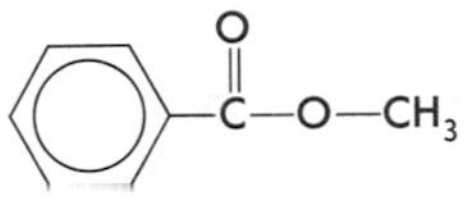

Although moderately polar, the ester function is not quite as good a water-solubilizing group as either the alcohol or the carboxyl functions. It cannot donate hydrogen bonds. But it can accept them, and esters of four or five carbons, or fewer, dissolve in water to some extent. **physical properties**

The two most important reactions of esters (hydrolysis and saponification) both involve attack by a reagent at the ester linkage. **chemical properties**

hydrolysis. The hydrolysis of an ester, both in terms of mechanism and products, is simply the reverse of its formation—the reverse of esterification.

in general:

$$R-\overset{\displaystyle O}{\overset{\displaystyle \|}{C}}-O-R' + H-OH \xrightarrow{H^+} R-\overset{\displaystyle O}{\overset{\displaystyle \|}{C}}-O-H + H-O-R'$$

specific examples:

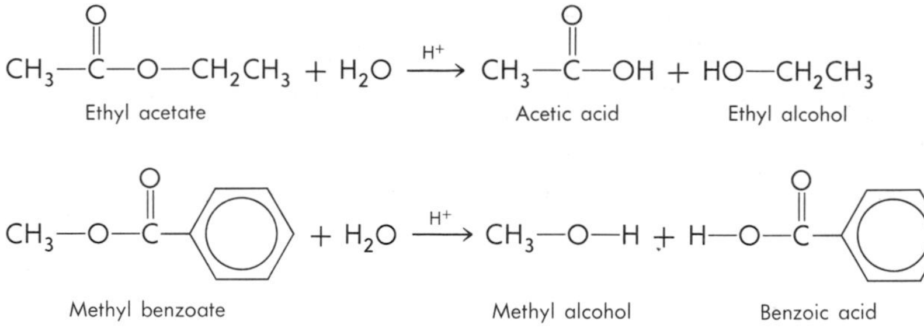

$$CH_3-\overset{\overset{\displaystyle O}{\|}}{C}-O-CH_2CH_3 + H_2O \xrightarrow{H^+} CH_3-\overset{\overset{\displaystyle O}{\|}}{C}-OH + HO-CH_2CH_3$$

Ethyl acetate   Acetic acid   Ethyl alcohol

$$CH_3-O-\overset{\overset{\displaystyle O}{\|}}{C}-\bigcirc + H_2O \xrightarrow{H^+} CH_3-O-H + H-O-\overset{\overset{\displaystyle O}{\|}}{C}-\bigcirc$$

Methyl benzoate   Methyl alcohol   Benzoic acid

 Note carefully, in the hydrolysis of an ester, that the carbonyl-to-oxygen bond is the *only* bond that breaks in the ester molecule.

Problem 2. Write the equation for the hydrolysis of *n*-propyl acetate.

Step 1. Set down the structure of the ester:

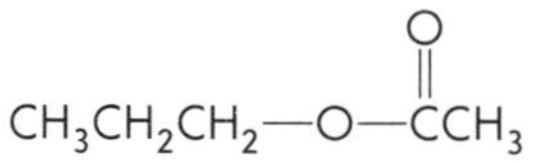

$$CH_3CH_2CH_2-O-\overset{\overset{\displaystyle O}{\|}}{C}CH_3$$

n-Propyl acetate

Step 2. Write out or mentally envision the fragments that would form if the *carbonyl-to-oxygen* bond were ruptured:

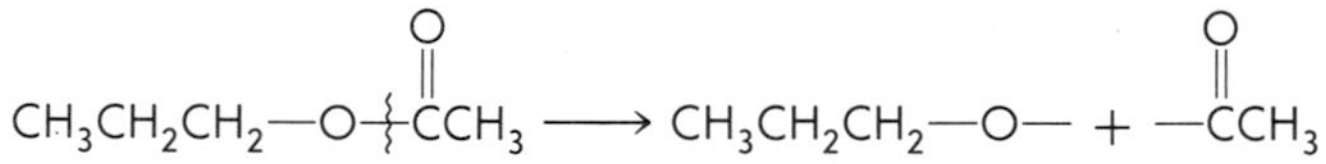

$$CH_3CH_2CH_2-O\{\overset{\overset{\displaystyle O}{\|}}{C}CH_3 \longrightarrow CH_3CH_2CH_2-O- + -\overset{\overset{\displaystyle O}{\|}}{C}CH_3$$

Step 3. Attach the elements of water to these fragments:

H— goes to the oxygen of the developing alcohol;
—OH goes to the carbonyl carbon:

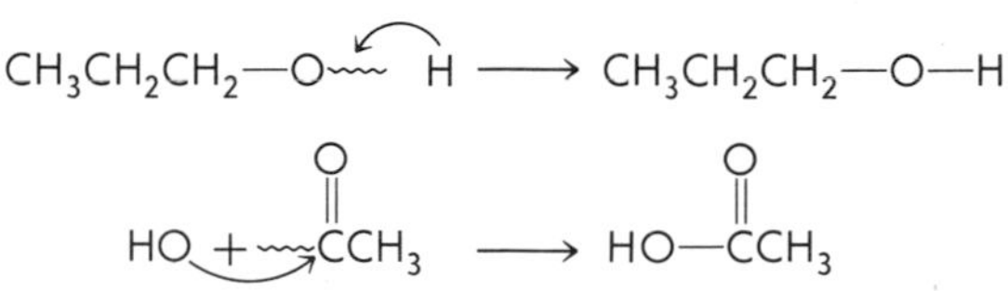

$$CH_3CH_2CH_2-O\!\!\sim\!\!\overset{\curvearrowleft}{H} \longrightarrow CH_3CH_2CH_2-O-H$$

$$HO+\sim\!\!\overset{\overset{\displaystyle O}{\|}}{C}CH_3 \longrightarrow HO-\overset{\overset{\displaystyle O}{\|}}{C}CH_3$$

 These operations enable you to write the correct structures for the products.

Step 4. Assemble this information into a conventional sequence:

carbonyl compounds: aldehydes and ketones, carboxylic acids, esters and amides

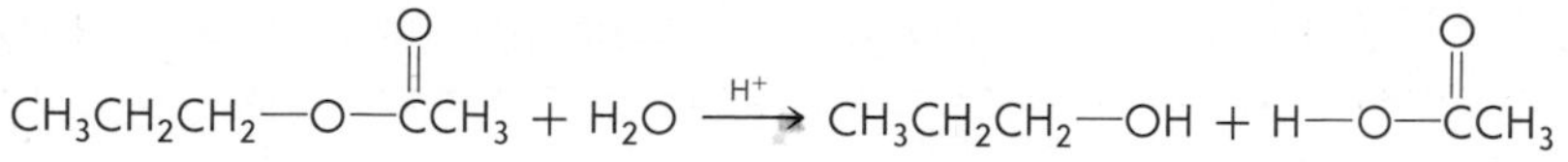

$$\text{CH}_3\text{CH}_2\text{CH}_2\text{—O—}\overset{\displaystyle\text{O}}{\overset{\|}{\text{C}}}\text{CH}_3 + \text{H}_2\text{O} \xrightarrow{\text{H}^+} \text{CH}_3\text{CH}_2\text{CH}_2\text{—OH} + \text{H—O—}\overset{\displaystyle\text{O}}{\overset{\|}{\text{C}}}\text{CH}_3$$

n-Propyl acetate   n-Propyl alcohol   Acetic acid

With a little practice, you should be able to use the *name* of the ester alone to set down the structures of its hydrolysis products.

Animal fats and vegetable oils are special kinds of esters, and during the process of their digestion hydrolysis of their ester linkages occurs.

saponification. This reaction of esters is a slight variation of ester hydrolysis. Ester hydrolysis occurs in the presence of an acid catalyst or an enzyme. Saponification occurs in aqueous sodium or potassium hydroxide. Essentially the same products form; the difference is that the carboxylic acid appears not as a free acid, but as its sodium or potassium salt. The alcohol, however, emerges as the free alcohol in both hydrolysis and saponification.

in general:

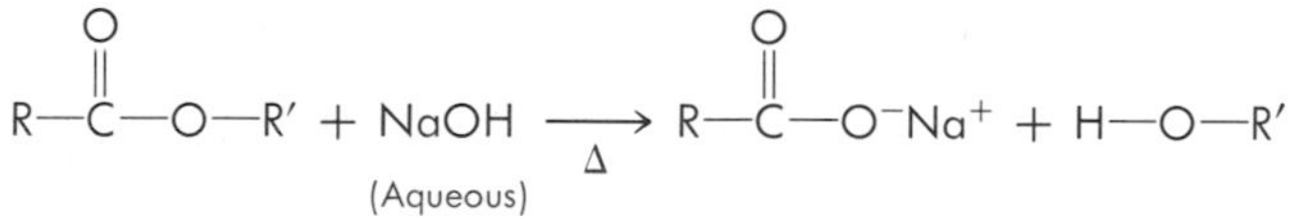

$$\text{R—}\overset{\displaystyle\text{O}}{\overset{\|}{\text{C}}}\text{—O—R}' + \text{NaOH} \xrightarrow{\Delta} \text{R—}\overset{\displaystyle\text{O}}{\overset{\|}{\text{C}}}\text{—O}^-\text{Na}^+ + \text{H—O—R}'$$

(Aqueous)

specific examples (wherein the same esters used to illustrate ester hydrolysis are used):

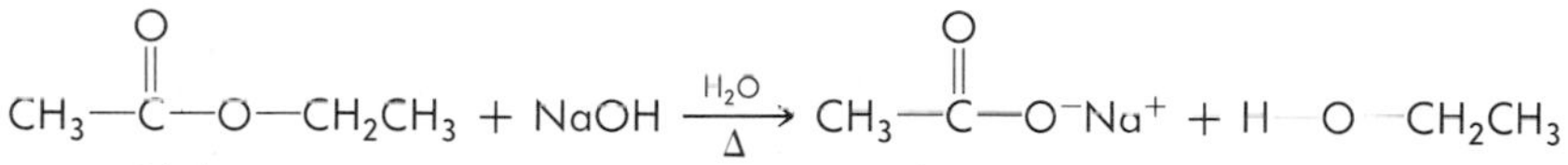

$$\text{CH}_3\text{—}\overset{\displaystyle\text{O}}{\overset{\|}{\text{C}}}\text{—O—CH}_2\text{CH}_3 + \text{NaOH} \xrightarrow[\Delta]{\text{H}_2\text{O}} \text{CH}_3\text{—}\overset{\displaystyle\text{O}}{\overset{\|}{\text{C}}}\text{—O}^-\text{Na}^+ + \text{H—O—CH}_2\text{CH}_3$$

Ethyl acetate   Sodium acetate   Ethyl alcohol

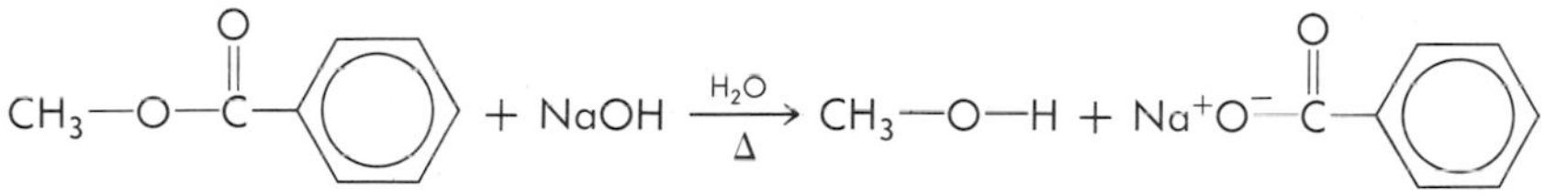

$$\text{CH}_3\text{—O—}\overset{\displaystyle\text{O}}{\overset{\|}{\text{C}}}\text{—}\bigcirc + \text{NaOH} \xrightarrow[\Delta]{\text{H}_2\text{O}} \text{CH}_3\text{—O—H} + \text{Na}^+\text{O}^-\text{—}\overset{\displaystyle\text{O}}{\overset{\|}{\text{C}}}\text{—}\bigcirc$$

Methyl benzoate   Methyl alcohol   Sodium benzoate

The mechanism for saponification may be written as follows in which the key event is collision between a hydroxide ion, OH⁻, and the carbonyl carbon with its partial positive charge.

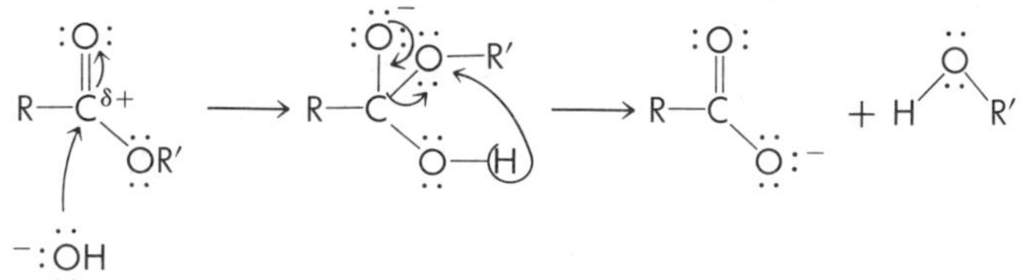

The term *saponification* comes from the Latin *sapo, onis,* or "soap + fy": that is, to make soap. Ordinary soap is a mixture of sodium salts of long-chain carboxylic acids.

important individual esters

the salicylates. Salicyclic acid can function either as an acid or as an alcohol (more correctly, a phenol), since it possesses both functional groups.

Salicylic acid, its esters, and its salts, taken internally, have both an analgesic effect (depressing sensitivity to pain) and an antipyretic action (reducing fever). As analgesics, they act to raise the threshold of pain by depressing pain centers in the thalamus region of the brain. Salicyclic acid, itself, is too irritating to be used internally, but sodium salicylate and acetylsalicylic acid (aspirin) are widely used, especially aspirin.

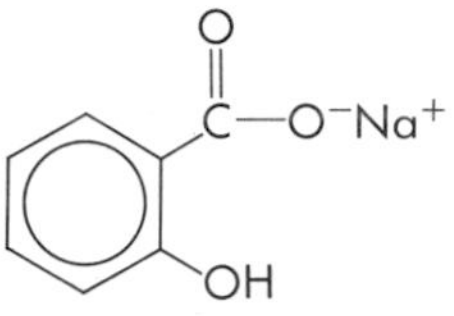

Sodium salicylate

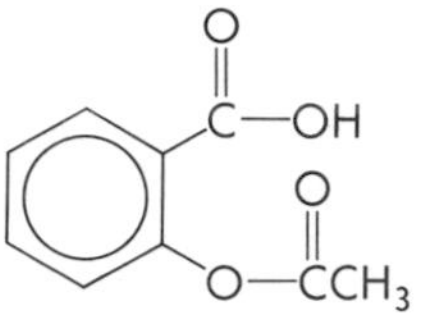

Acetylsalicylic acid
(aspirin)

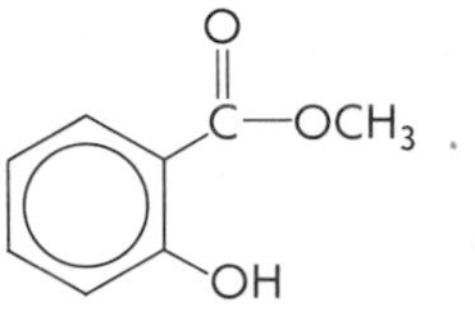

Methyl salicylate
(oil of wintergreen)

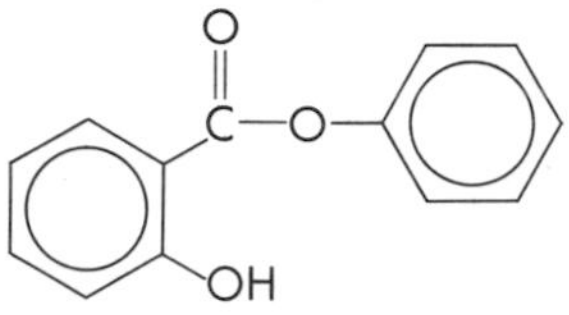

Phenyl salicylate
(salol)

Methyl salicylate is used in liniments. Phenyl salicylate has been used in ointments that protect the skin against ultraviolet rays.

Dacron. Dacron shares most of the desirable properties of nylon. Most distinctive is its ability to be set into permanent creases and pleats. It does not tend to become grayish or yellowish with long usage, as does some white nylon. Chemically, Dacron is a polyester. It is made by the copolymerization of ethylene glycol with terephthalic acid.

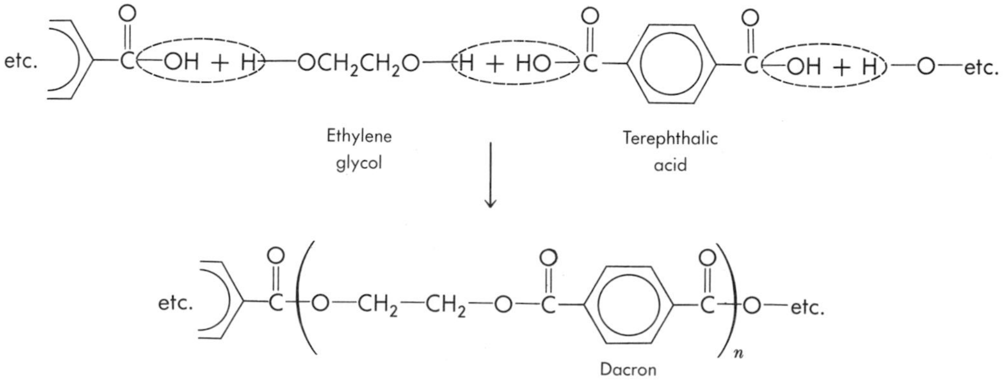

Ethylene
glycol

Terephthalic
acid

Dacron

carbonyl compounds: aldehydes and ketones, carboxylic acids, esters and amides

As is characteristic of all chemicals that can be formed into useful fibers, molecules of Dacron are extremely long and very narrow and symmetrical, properties that resemble those of a fiber itself.

esters of inorganic oxyacids. Inorganic oxyacids such as nitric acid, nitrous acid, sulfuric acid, and phosphoric acid all possess hydroxyl groups in their structures. In this respect, they resemble carboxylic acids, and they can be esterified by alcohols. Three examples are:

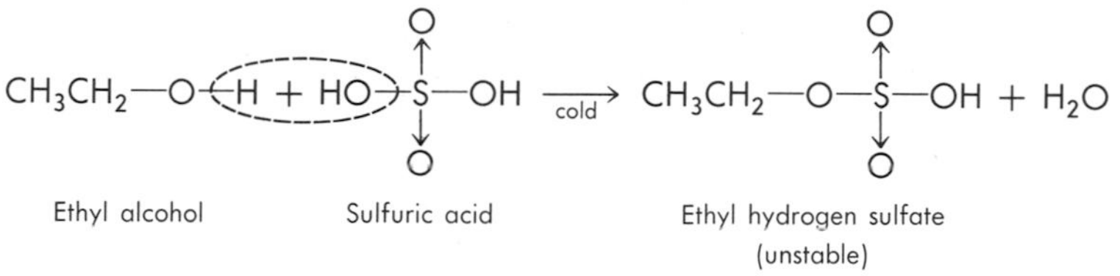

$$CH_3CH_2-O-H + HO-\overset{\displaystyle O}{\underset{\displaystyle O}{\overset{\uparrow}{\underset{\downarrow}{S}}}}-OH \xrightarrow{cold} CH_3CH_2-O-\overset{\displaystyle O}{\underset{\displaystyle O}{\overset{\uparrow}{\underset{\downarrow}{S}}}}-OH + H_2O$$

Ethyl alcohol   Sulfuric acid   Ethyl hydrogen sulfate (unstable)

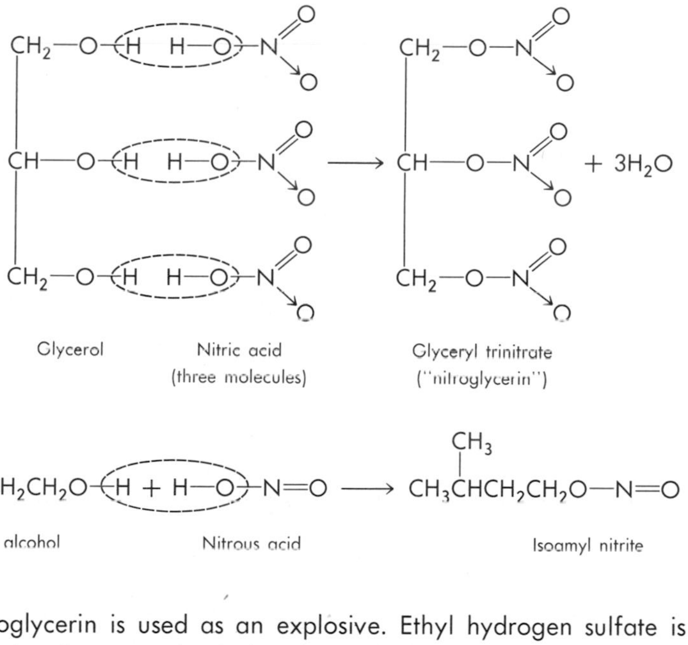

Glycerol   Nitric acid (three molecules)   Glyceryl trinitrate ("nitroglycerin")

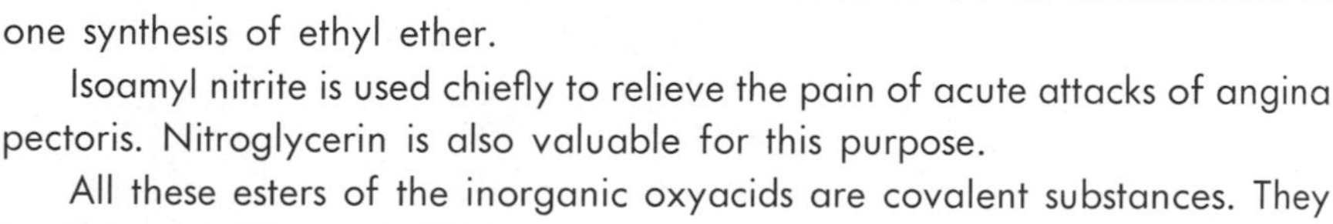

$$\overset{\displaystyle CH_3}{\underset{}{|}}$$
$$CH_3CHCH_2CH_2O-H + H-O-N=O \longrightarrow CH_3CHCH_2CH_2O-N=O + H_2O$$

Isoamyl alcohol   Nitrous acid   Isoamyl nitrite

Nitroglycerin is used as an explosive. Ethyl hydrogen sulfate is known to form, but it cannot be isolated. It is believed to be an intermediate in one synthesis of ethyl ether.

Isoamyl nitrite is used chiefly to relieve the pain of acute attacks of angina pectoris. Nitroglycerin is also valuable for this purpose.

All these esters of the inorganic oxyacids are covalent substances. They have no salt-like properties.

The esters of phosphoric acid and some of its "relatives" deserve special mention, for they are encountered in virtually every important reaction sequence in the human body. The structure of phosphoric acid may be written as:

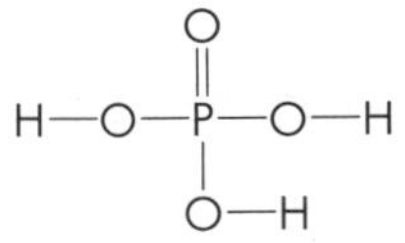

$$H-O-\overset{\overset{\displaystyle O}{\|}}{\underset{\underset{\displaystyle O-H}{|}}{P}}-O-H$$

Phosphoric acid

An ester of this acid would have the general structure:

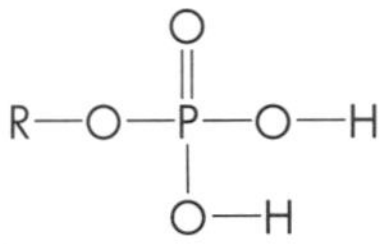

$$R-O-\overset{\overset{\displaystyle O}{\|}}{\underset{\underset{\displaystyle O-H}{|}}{P}}-O-H$$

Alkyl phosphate

Although an alkyl phosphate is an ester, it still has properties of an acid and is capable of forming the following negative ions:

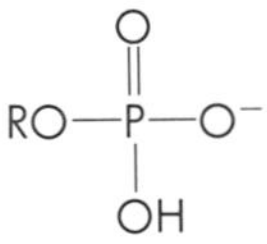

$$RO-\overset{\overset{\displaystyle O}{\|}}{\underset{\underset{\displaystyle OH}{|}}{P}}-O^- \quad \text{and} \quad RO-\overset{\overset{\displaystyle O}{\|}}{\underset{\underset{\displaystyle O^-}{|}}{P}}-O^-$$

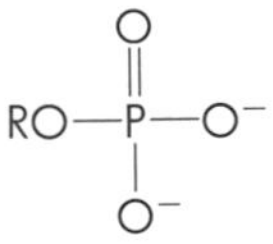

In the body, esters of polyphosphoric acids are also known. They may be represented as:

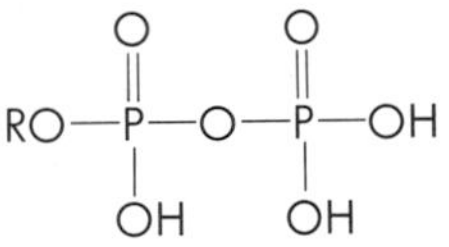

$$RO-\overset{\overset{\displaystyle O}{\|}}{\underset{\underset{\displaystyle OH}{|}}{P}}-O-\overset{\overset{\displaystyle O}{\|}}{\underset{\underset{\displaystyle OH}{|}}{P}}-OH \qquad RO-\overset{\overset{\displaystyle O}{\|}}{\underset{\underset{\displaystyle OH}{|}}{P}}-O-\overset{\overset{\displaystyle O}{\|}}{\underset{\underset{\displaystyle OH}{|}}{P}}-O-\overset{\overset{\displaystyle O}{\|}}{\underset{\underset{\displaystyle OH}{|}}{P}}-OH$$

A diphosphate ester 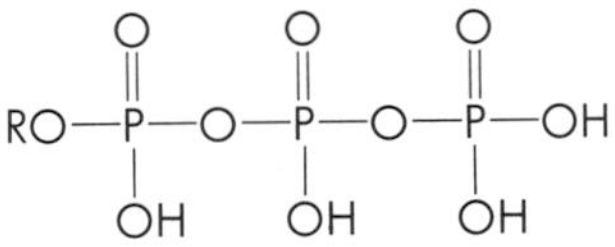   A triphosphate ester

These polyphosphate esters are very energy-rich molecules. Their internal energy provides much of the chemical energy that the body uses for muscular work and other energy-demanding processes. We shall encounter them again when we study the metabolism of carbohydrates.

organophosphate insecticides. A few of the commercially more important members are shown in Table 12.8. These compounds were among those developed to replace as much as possible the organochlorine pesticides (e.g., DDT, dieldrin, etc.). Many insects became resistant to the organochlorines;

carbonyl compounds: aldehydes and ketones, carboxylic acids, esters and amides

Table 12.8 Some Organophosphate Pesticides

Common Name	Structure	Acute Oral Toxicity to Rats LD$_{50}$ (mg/kg)[a]
Organophosphates		
Dichlorvos (DDVP, Vapona^R, Shell "No Pest Strip"^{R})	$Cl_2C{=}CH{-}O{-}\overset{\displaystyle O}{\underset{\displaystyle \|}{P}}(OCH_3)_2$	70
Naled (Dibrom^R)	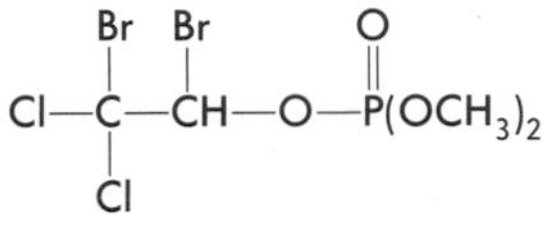 $Cl{-}\underset{\displaystyle Cl}{\overset{\displaystyle Br}{\underset{\|}{\overset{\|}{C}}}}{-}\overset{\displaystyle Br}{\underset{\|}{CH}}{-}O{-}\overset{\displaystyle O}{\underset{\|}{P}}(OCH_3)_2$	430
TEPP (tetraethylpyrophosphate)	$(CH_3CH_2O)_2\overset{\displaystyle O}{\underset{\|}{P}}{-}O{-}\overset{\displaystyle O}{\underset{\|}{P}}(OCH_2CH_3)_2$	1.1
Thiophosphates		
Abate^R	$(CH_3O)_2\overset{\displaystyle S}{\underset{\|}{P}}{-}O{-}\bigcirc{-}S{-}\bigcirc{-}O{-}\overset{\displaystyle S}{\underset{\|}{P}}(OCH_3)_2$	2000
Guthion^R (Azinphosmethyl)	$(CH_3O)_2\overset{\displaystyle S}{\underset{\|}{P}}{-}SCH_2{-}N{<}\,\text{(benzotriazinone ring)}$	20
Diazinon	$(CH_3CH_2O)_2\overset{\displaystyle S}{\underset{\|}{P}}{-}O{-}\,\text{(pyrimidine ring with }CH(CH_3)_2\text{ and }CH_3)$	150–220
Methyl parathion	$(CH_3O)_2\overset{\displaystyle S}{\underset{\|}{P}}{-}O{-}\bigcirc{-}NO_2$	9–25
Parathion	$(CH_3CH_2O)_2\overset{\displaystyle S}{\underset{\|}{P}}{-}O{-}\bigcirc{-}NO_2$	5
Malathion	$(CH_3O)_2\overset{\displaystyle S}{\underset{\|}{P}}{-}S{-}\underset{\displaystyle CH_2\overset{\|}{\underset{O}{C}}OCH_2CH_3}{CH\overset{\displaystyle O}{\underset{\|}{C}}OCH_2CH_3}$	4000

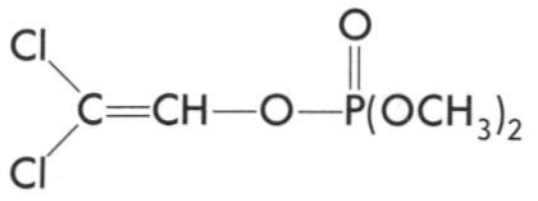

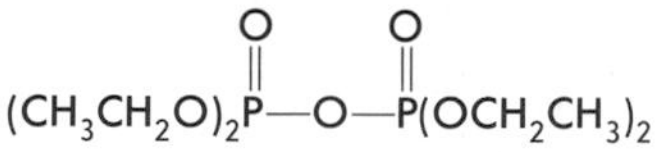

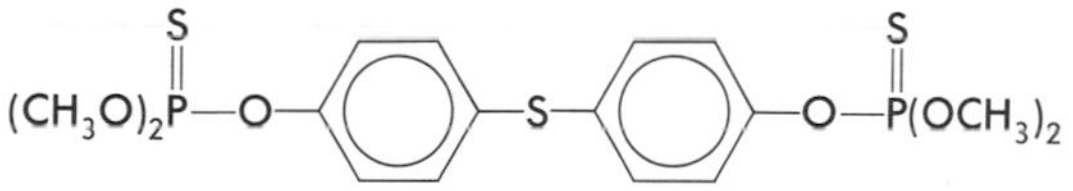

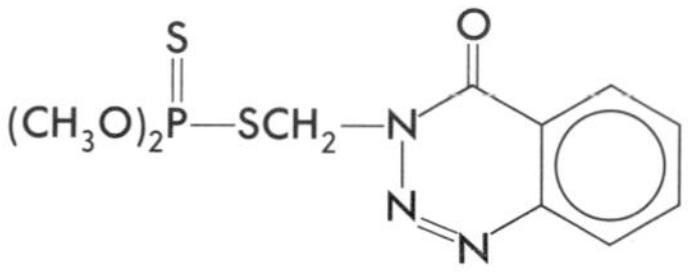

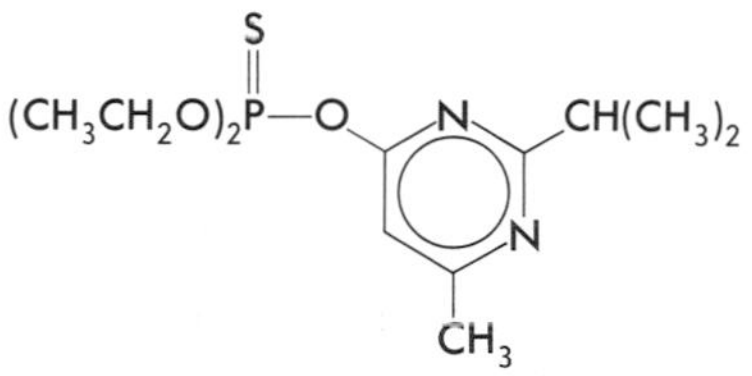

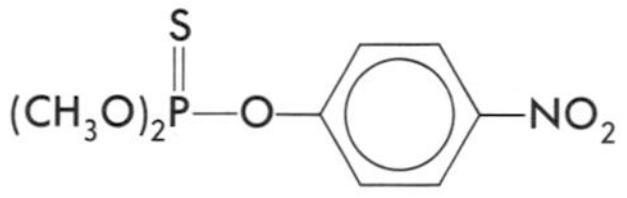

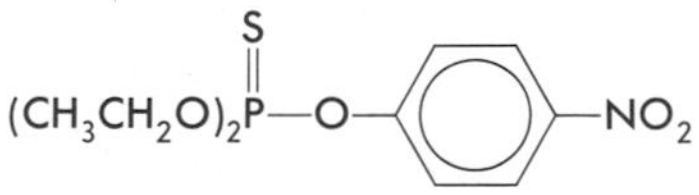

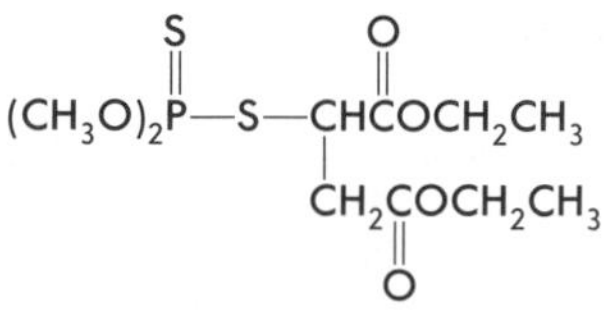

[a]See footnote to Table 10.10.

moreover, these poisons cause grave damage to nontarget organisms such as birds. The organophosphates are far less persitent in the environment than the organochlorines. They break down to less toxic substances more quickly because they are esters that can be hydrolyzed. At the same time, many of the organophosphates are highly toxic to humans and must be handled very carefully. Nerve gases, for example, are certain organophosphate compounds. It has to be said, though, that slight changes in structure may cause great changes in physiological effects. The organophosphates also include some of the relatively most safe insecticides to say nothing of the many organophosphate compounds essential to all forms of life.

In this family of pesticides are many members in whose molecules oxygens have been replaced by sulfurs. Some examples of these thiophosphates are in Table 12.8. One compound, parathion, has been responsible for more accidental human poisonings and deaths than all other pesticides combined. Children have died simply from using a parathion-contaminated bag as a swing, or bathing in a tub sprayed days earlier with 10% parathion. Parathion contaminated flour, sugar, or wheat has poisoned hundreds of people in Egypt, Columbia, Mexico, and India with a total of over 200 deaths.

amides
structural
features
and names

The *amide function* has the characteristic features shown in the following ''skeleton'':

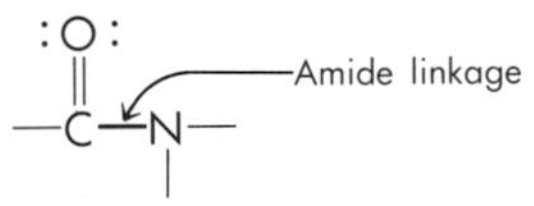

Amide function
(carbonyl-to-nitrogen)

The heavily drawn bond, carbonyl-to-nitrogen, is the amide linkage. A few representative amides are listed in Table 12.9. The word parts for making common names of ''simple'' amides, those derived from ammonia rather than from an amine, are in Table 12.2. No alkyl groups are attached to the nitrogen in simple amides. If alkyl groups are on nitrogen, the name for the corresponding simple amide is preceded by the name of the alkyl group attached to nitrogen. To show unequivocally that the named alkyl group is on nitrogen rather than on the carbon chain, the designation N is used. For example:

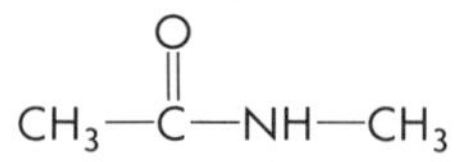

N-Methylacetamide

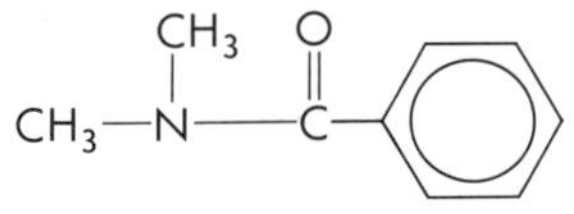

N,N-Dimethylbenzamide

carbonyl compounds: aldehydes and ketones, carboxylic acids, esters and amides

Table 12.9   Some Simple Amides

Common Name	Structure	Melting Point in °C	Solubility in Water
Formamide	H—C(=O)—NH$_2$	2	Soluble
Acetamide	CH$_3$C(=O)—NH$_2$	82	Soluble
Propionamide	CH$_3$CH$_2$C(=O)—NH$_2$	79	Soluble
Benzamide	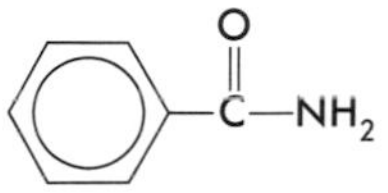 (phenyl)—C(=O)—NH$_2$	130	1.5 grams/ 100 grams H$_2$O

At elevated temperatures, ammonia reacts with carboxylic acids in a way that resembles esterification. The elements of water split out between the acid and ammonia, and the remaining fragments combine. The product is called an *amide*.

synthesis of amides

in general:

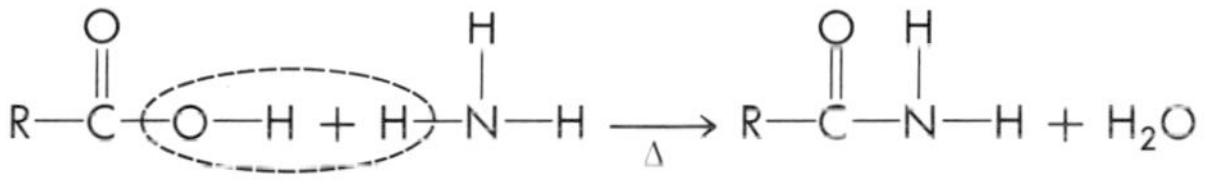

$$R-C(=O){-}(O{-}H) + (H){-}N(H){-}H \xrightarrow{\Delta} R-C(=O)-N(H)-H + H_2O$$

specific examples:

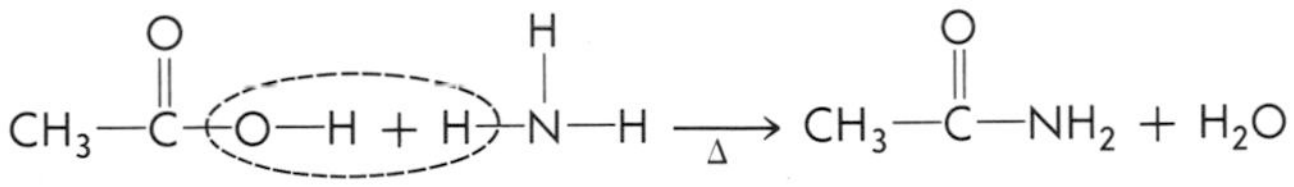

$$CH_3-C(=O){-}(O{-}H) + (H){-}N(H){-}H \xrightarrow{\Delta} CH_3-C(=O)-NH_2 + H_2O$$

Acetic acid   Acetamide

$$H-N(H){-}(H + H{-}O){-}C(=O)-(phenyl) \xrightarrow{\Delta} H-N(H)-C(=O)-(phenyl) + H_2O$$

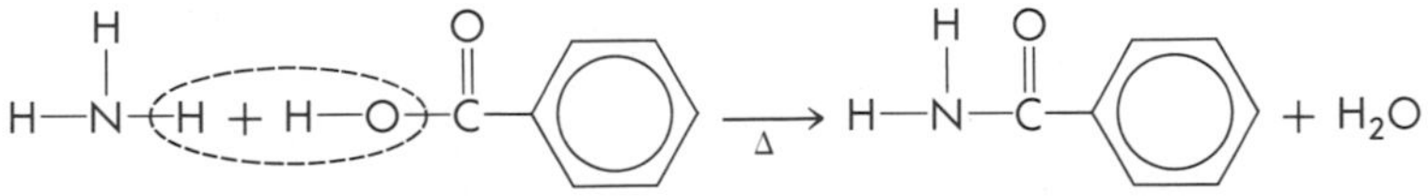

Benzoic acid   Benzamide

Amide formation involves one of the N—H bonds in ammonia. Substituted ammonias, that is, amines, that have at least one such bond also form amides.

287

specific examples:

$$CH_3-\overset{\overset{\textstyle O}{\|}}{C}-O-H + H-\overset{\overset{\textstyle H}{|}}{N}-CH_3 \xrightarrow{\Delta} CH_3-\overset{\overset{\textstyle O}{\|}}{C}-\overset{\overset{\textstyle H}{|}}{N}-CH_3 + H_2O$$

Acetic acid   Methylamine   N-Methylacetamide

$$CH_3-\overset{\overset{\textstyle CH_3}{|}}{N}-H + H-O-\overset{\overset{\textstyle O}{\|}}{C}-\bigcirc \xrightarrow{\Delta} CH_3-\overset{\overset{\textstyle CH_3}{|}}{N}-\overset{\overset{\textstyle O}{\|}}{C}-\bigcirc + H_2O$$

Dimethylamine   Benzoic acid   N,N-Dimethylbenzamide

Trisubstituted amines (e.g., trimethylamine) obviously cannot enter into amide formation. They possess no N—H bond.

The interaction of an amine with a carboxylic acid is the essential feature of protein synthesis. Proteins, as we shall see in Chapter 15, are huge molecules whose "backbones" involve amide linkages.

physical properties of amides

Amide molecules are very polar because of the amide group. The fact that nearly all amides are solids at room temperature attests to an electrical condition in their molecules that gives rise to strong intermolecular forces. Because amide molecules are polar, they are soluble in water, provided that the alkane-like chain is not too long. The amide group is a water-solubilizing group.

Simple amides and others that have a hydrogen attached to nitrogen can participate in hydrogen bonding. Proteins consist of huge molecules in which a great many amide linkages are found. In such large molecules, often an overall *shape* or surface contour is an important feature. Hydrogen bonds involving hydrogen on nitrogen in amide linkages stabilize these shapes. For example:

$$R-\overset{\overset{\textstyle \cdots O}{\|}}{C}-\overset{\overset{\textstyle H}{|}}{N}-\overset{\delta+}{H}\cdots\overset{\delta-}{\underset{\underset{\textstyle R-\overset{\overset{\textstyle O}{\|}}{C}-N-H\cdots}{|}}{O}}\ H$$

Hydrogen bonding between amide molecules

In contrast to both carboxylic acids and amines, amides are, for the most part, odorless.

chemical properties

basicity. In the amide group, we have another example of how one functional group can modify the properties of another. We encountered this first among hemiacetals; the ether linkage in a hemiacetal is very unstable in

carbonyl compounds: aldehydes and ketones, carboxylic acids, esters and amides

contrast to an ordinary ether linkage. We also saw among carboxylic acids how a carbonyl group, attached to a hydroxyl group changed the properties of the —OH group to make it slightly acidic. Among the amides, we find that the presence of the carbonyl group on nitrogen essentially destroys the basicity of the former amino group. Amides are neutral compounds in spite of the structural fact that the nitrogens in their molecules carry an unshared pair of electrons. The carbonyl group exerts a tightening influence on this pair in the sense that the pair is not available for sharing with a proton. Amides, therefore, are not proton acceptors; they are not basic.

hydrolysis of amides. Just as hydrolysis is the most important reaction of an ester, so it is with amides. And just as ester hydrolysis is actually the reverse of esterification, so amide hydrolysis is the exact reverse of amide formation.

in general:

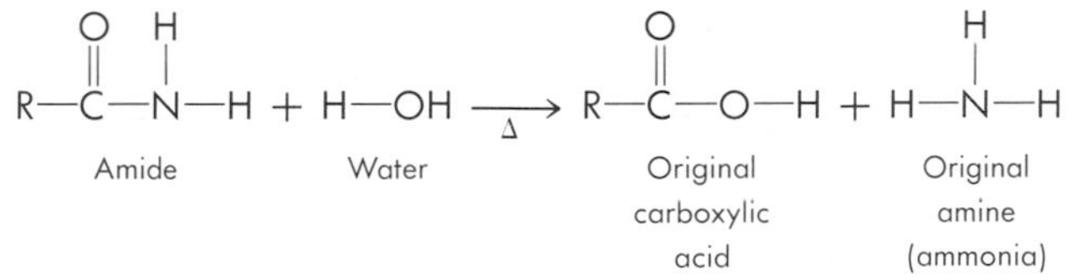

$$
\underset{\text{Amide}}{R-\overset{\overset{\text{O}}{\|}}{C}-\overset{\overset{\text{H}}{|}}{N}-H} + \underset{\text{Water}}{H-OH} \xrightarrow{\Delta} \underset{\substack{\text{Original}\\\text{carboxylic}\\\text{acid}}}{R-\overset{\overset{\text{O}}{\|}}{C}-O-H} + \underset{\substack{\text{Original}\\\text{amine}\\\text{(ammonia)}}}{H-\overset{\overset{\text{H}}{|}}{N}-H}
$$

or

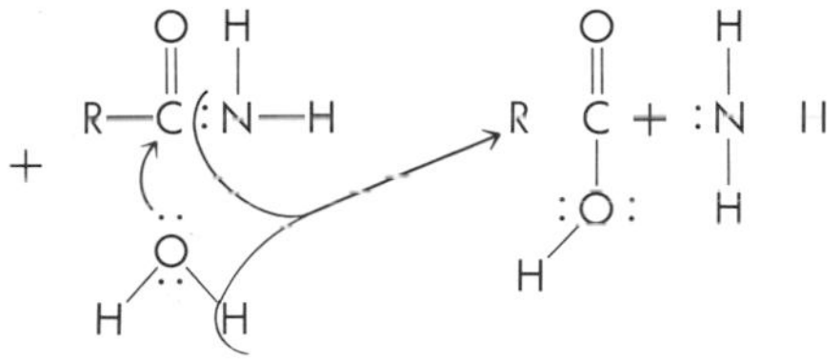

Note carefully what has happened, structurally. First, the carbonyl-to-nitrogen bond (and only this bond) has ruptured:

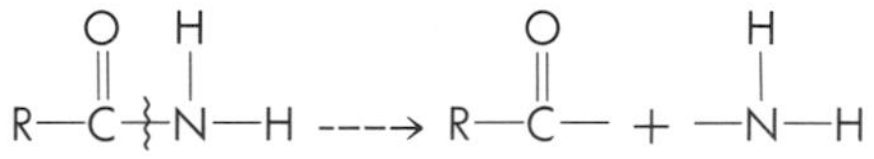

Second, a hydroxyl group from water has become attached to the carbonyl carbon. The hydrogen left over from water has become attached to nitrogen:

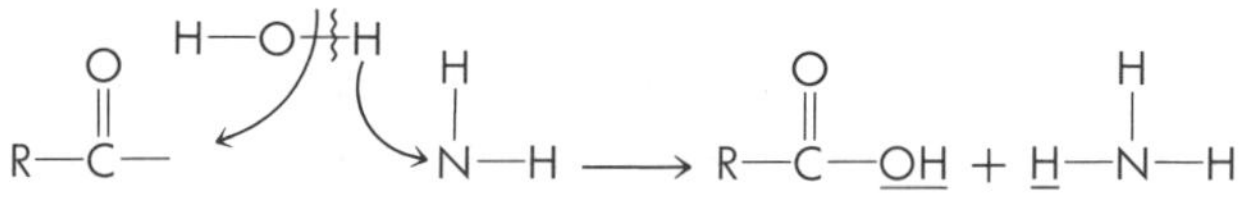

specific examples:

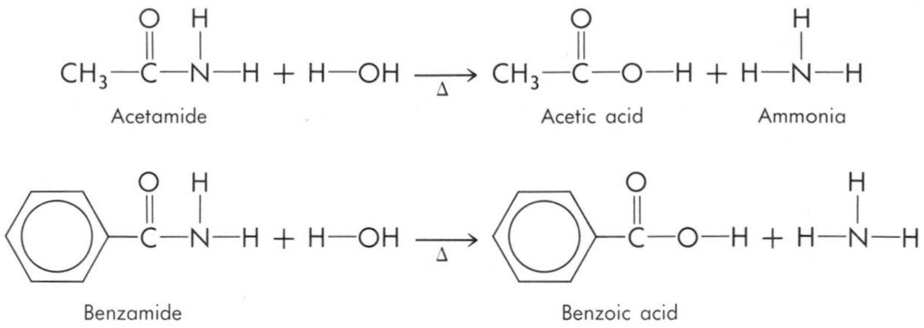

For all practical purposes, the only significant reaction that occurs to proteins when they are digested is just this one—amide hydrolysis. That is why mastery of this reaction now is important.

As with ester hydrolysis, acids catalyze amide hydrolysis. Alkalies also can be used as catalysts.

important individual amides

nicotinamide (niacinamide).

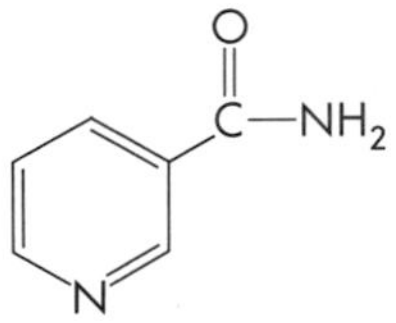

Nicotinamide, the amide of nicotinic acid (niacin), has the physiological properties of niacin and is the usual form in which niacin is administered. It bears some structural resemblance to the deadly poison, nicotine.

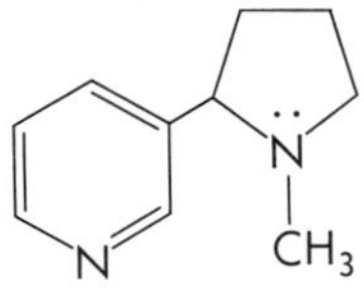

Nicotine

Nicotine, in sufficient dosage, is lethal; niacin is essential to every cell in the human body. Niacin is a vitamin; how vitamins function in body chemistry is discussed in Chapter 16.

nylon. The term *nylon* is a coined name that applies to any synthetic, long-chain, fiber-forming polymer with repeating amide linkages. One of the

carbonyl compounds: aldehydes and ketones, carboxylic acids, esters and amides

most common members of the nylon family is so-called nylon-66. It is made from hexamethylene diamine and adipic acid according to the following reaction:

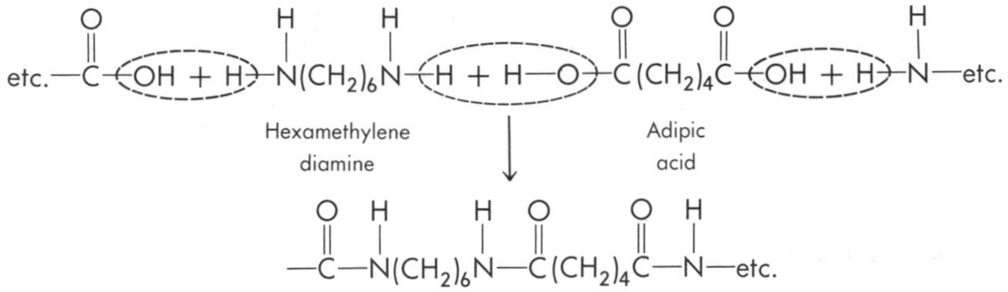

Hexamethylene
diamine

Adipic
acid

Nylon-66

(The "66" comes from the fact that each monomer contains six carbons.) To be useful as a fiber-forming polymer, each nylon-66 molecule should contain from 50 to 90 of each of the monomer units. Shorter nylon molecules form weak or brittle fibers.

carbamate insecticides. Like the organophosphates, the carbamate insecticides were developed to be substitutes for the troublesome organochlorines. The essential structural feature of carbamates is:

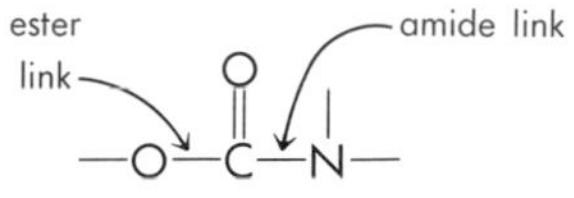

carbamate system

The most important example, commercially, is carbaryl (Sevin[R]). Two others are Baygon[R] and BuxTen[T].

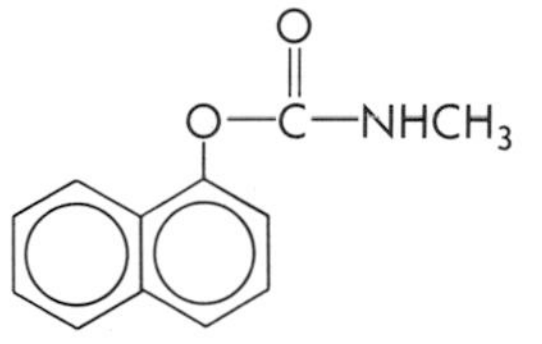

Carbaryl

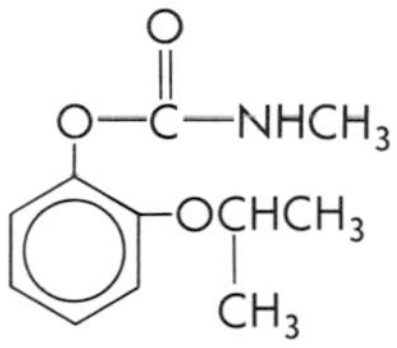

Baygon[R]

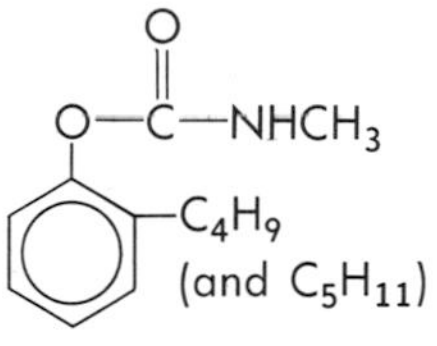

Buxten[R]

Since the carbamate system is both an ester and an amide, it is subject to hydrolysis. Hence carbamates do not persist indefinitely in the environment.

To illustrate but one pitfall in pesticide work, namely that the toxicity of a compound can vary widely from species to species, carbaryl is unusually toxic to bees. Farmers using this insecticide on crops find themselves subject to angry complaints from those nearby who raise bees commercially, as happened in 1970, for example, in the "valley of the Jolly Green Giant" in Minnesota. In April, 1971, two billion honeybees were airlifted from northern California to the fruit-growing regions of Washington and Oregon to save the spring fruit crop. Corn growers, using Sevin[R] (carbaryl) had decimated the local pollinators.

Selected Reading List

Any text in organic chemistry is obviously a reference for more information about carbonyl compounds. The following are some references to additional information about pesticides and the pros and cons in the controversy over these substances.

Books

1. J. R. Holum and R. Boolootian, Coeditors. *The Environmental Sciences—An Introduction to Their Topics and Terms.* Little, Brown & Co., Boston, to be published in 1972. Definitions of environmentally relevant terms from all the sciences with special expanded discussions for many entries.

2. The "Mrak Report." *Report of the Secretary's Commission on Pesticides and Their Relationship to Environmental Health.* Parts I and II. U. S. Government Printing Office, 1969. This report is particularly detailed on what was known as of 1969 about pesticides as causers of mutations, birth defects, tumors, and cancer.

3. G. S. Hartley and T. F. West. *Chemicals for Pest Control.* Pergamon, Oxford, 1969.

4. J. H. Stapely and F. C. H. Gayner. *Pests and Diseases.* (Vol. 1 of *World Crop Protection.*) Chemical Rubber Company, Cleveland, 1969.

5. K. A. Hassall. *Pesticides.* (Vol. II of *World Crop Protection;* see above.)

6. D. E. H. Frear, editor. *Pesticide Index,* 4th edition. College Science Publishers, State College, Penn., 1969. A compilation of about 1500 chemicals cross-indexed to over 4300 synonyms and trade names.

7. Thomas Whiteside. *Defoliation.* Ballantine/Friends of the Earth, New York, 1970. A detailed study of the use of chemicals to destroy trees and crops in Vietnam.

8. Rachel Carson. *Silent Spring.* Houghton, Mifflin, Boston, 1962. Although some of the critic's charges were true, Rachel Carson was basically right. Someone had to blow the whistle into the ears of a planet blissfully going deaf (and sightless) to many of the dangers of pesticides.

9. Frank Graham, Jr. *Since Silent Spring.* Houghton, Mifflin, Boston, 1970. One of the editors of *Audubon* magazine recounts the reactions to Rachel Carson's book and reports on what has and has not been accomplished in the meanwhile.

carbonyl compounds: aldehydes and ketones, carboxylic acids, esters and amides

Articles

1. J. van Overbock. "The Control of Plant Growth," *Scientific American*, July 1968, page 75.

2. C. A. Edwards. "Soil Pollutants and Soil Animals." *Scientific American*, April 1969, page 88.

3. M. S. Meselson. "Chemical and Biological Weapons." *Scientific American*, May 1970. Page 15.

4. G. M. Woodwell. "Effects of Pollution on the Structure and Physiology of Ecosystems." *Science*, April 24, 1970, page 168.

5. R. C. Clement. "An *Audubon* Guide to Pesticide Dos and Don'ts." *Audubon*, March 1970, page 50.

6. "Weed Killers." *Consumer Reports,* June 1970. Page 359.

7. T. Aaronson. "A Tour of Vietnam." *Environment*, March 1971, page 34. A survey of the nine-year United States defoliation program in Vietnam.

8. Julian McCaull. "Questions for an Old Friend." *Environment*, July/August 1971, page 2. How safe is DDT to man? Read this.

9. I. C. T. Nisbet and D. Miner. "DDT Substitute." *Environment*, July/August 1971, page 10. How safe is carbaryl? Read this, also.

Brief Summary

Aldehydes, $(H)R{-}\overset{\displaystyle O}{\overset{\|}{C}}{-}H$

1. The aldehyde group is moderately polar and confers moderate water solubility to a molecule.

2. The aldehyde group may be oxidized to a carboxylic acid:

$$RCHO + (O) \longrightarrow RCO_2H$$

3. The aldehyde group may add an alcohol to form a (usually unstable) hemiacetal:

$$RCHO + HOR' \rightleftarrows RCH\Big\langle\begin{matrix}OH\\[2pt]OR'\end{matrix}$$

4. With respect to oxidation the aldehyde group is very susceptible to this change. Mild reagents such as Tollens' reagent, Benedict's solution and Fehling's solution work well.
   (a) In the Tollens' test, a silver mirror forms.
   (b) In Benedict's or Fehling's test, a blue colored solution gives way to a red precipitate of Cu_2O.

Hemiacetals, (H)RCH
$\begin{array}{c} \diagup \text{OH} \\ \diagdown \text{OR}' \end{array}$

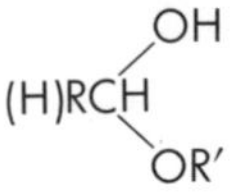

1. These revert easily to their precursors, the original aldehyde and alcohol. (See 3, above, the reverse reaction.)

2. Hemiacetals may split out water with an alcohol to form acetals

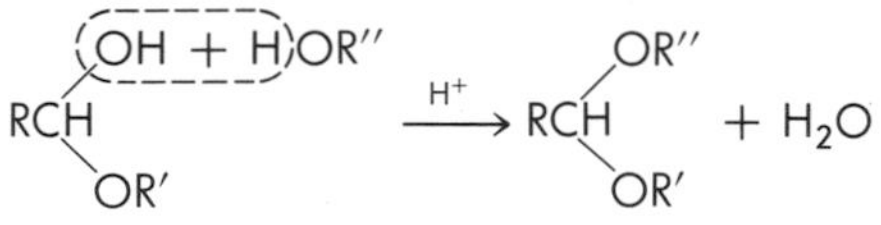

$$\underset{\text{OR}'}{\overset{\widetilde{\text{OH + H}}\text{OR}''}{\text{RCH}}} \xrightarrow{\text{H}^+} \underset{\text{OR}'}{\overset{\text{OR}''}{\text{RCH}}} + \text{H}_2\text{O}$$

(R' and R'' are often identical)

Acetals, (H)RCH
$\begin{array}{c} \diagup \text{OR}'' \\ \diagdown \text{OR}' \end{array}$

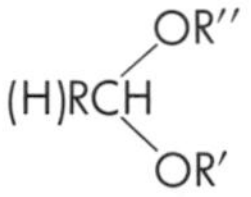

1. Acetals are hydrolyzed to their original alcohols and carbonyl compound

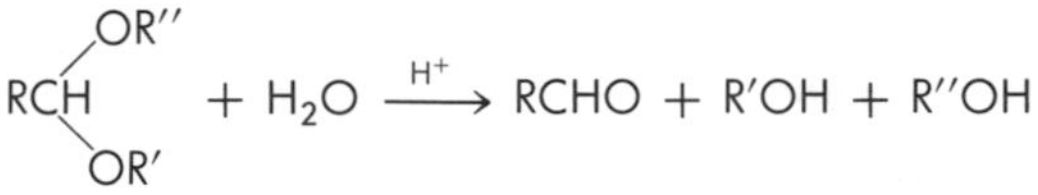

$$\underset{\text{OR}'}{\overset{\text{OR}''}{\text{RCH}}} + \text{H}_2\text{O} \xrightarrow{\text{H}^+} \text{RCHO} + \text{R}'\text{OH} + \text{R}''\text{OH}$$

Ketones, $\underset{|}{\overset{|}{-\text{C}}}-\overset{\overset{\text{O}}{\|}}{\text{C}}-\underset{|}{\overset{|}{\text{C}}}-$

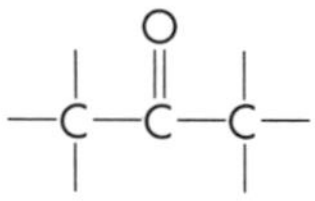

1. The ketone group is very stable toward mild and strong oxidizing agents. Like an aldehyde group, it is the cause of moderate polarity in molecules. There are no reactions of this group that we shall need for our future study, except that we note that a ketone group sometimes may enter into hemiacetal and acetal formation. It does this in certain sugars. (Strictly speaking, the products should be called hemiketals and ketals.)

Carboxylic Acids, (H)R$-\overset{\overset{\text{O}}{\|}}{\text{C}}-$OH, *and Their Salts*

1. The carboxyl group, $-\text{CO}_2\text{H}$, is a polar group and confers moderate water solubility to a molecule. At the same time, monocarboxylic acids are soluble in hydrocarbon solvents.

2. It is very resistant to attack by oxidizing agents.

3. The bond between O and H in the $-\overset{\overset{\text{O}}{\|}}{\text{C}}-O-$H group is much weaker than in alcohols. Hence, in aqueous medium carboxylic acids are proton donors (acids), whereas alcohols are not. However, the bond is strong enough to render carboxylic acids weak acids. Carboxylate ions, $-\overset{\overset{\text{O}}{\|}}{\text{C}}-O^-$, are actually proton acceptors.

carbonyl compounds: aldehydes and ketones, carboxylic acids, esters and amides

4. Salts of carboxylic acids are ionic substances with high melting points. Sodium and potassium salts are usually soluble in water.

5. The carboxyl group can split out water with alcohols (under acid or enzyme catalysis) to form esters; the reaction is called "esterification:"

$$RCO_2H + R'OH \longrightarrow \overset{\overset{\displaystyle O}{\|}}{R}COR' + H_2O$$

6. The carboxyl group can split out water with ammonia or amines to form amides:

$$RCO_2H + H-N\diagup^{}_{\diagdown} \longrightarrow \overset{\overset{\displaystyle O}{\|}}{R}CN- + H_2O$$

Esters, $(H)R-\overset{\overset{\displaystyle O}{\|}}{C}-O-R'$

1. Esters are hydrolyzed in an acidic medium to liberate an alcohol and a carboxylic acid:

$$R\overset{\overset{\displaystyle O}{\|}}{C}-OR' + H_2O \xrightarrow{H^+} R\overset{\overset{\displaystyle O}{\|}}{C}OH + HOR'$$

2. Alkalies saponify esters:

$$R\overset{\overset{\displaystyle O}{\|}}{C}-OR' + NaOH \longrightarrow R\overset{\overset{\displaystyle O}{\|}}{C}O^-Na^+ + HOR'$$

Amides, $H(R)-\overset{\overset{\displaystyle O}{\|}}{C}-N-$ (Rs or Hs attached to N)

1. Amides, unlike amines, are neither acidic nor basic.
2. Amides are hydrolyzed to acids and amines:

$$R\overset{\overset{\displaystyle O}{\|}}{C}-\overset{\overset{\displaystyle |}{}}{N}- + H_2O \longrightarrow R\overset{\overset{\displaystyle O}{\|}}{C}OH + H-\overset{\overset{\displaystyle |}{}}{N}-$$

Brief Survey of What Functional Groups Are Attacked By Specific Reagents[2]

1. Groups Affected by Oxidizing Agents, (O).

   Alcohol groups are converted to carbonyl groups.

$$-\overset{\overset{\displaystyle |}{}}{\underset{\underset{\displaystyle H}{|}}{C}}-O\diagdown_H + (O) \longrightarrow \diagup^{}_{\diagdown}C=O + H_2O$$

[2] We summarize here only those reactions that we have studied. In terms of the whole field of organic chemistry the list, of course, is very incomplete.

Mercaptans are changed to disulfides.

$$2R\text{—}S\text{—}H + (O) \longrightarrow R\text{—}S\text{—}S\text{—}R$$

Aldehydes are converted to carboxyl groups.

$$RCHO + (O) \longrightarrow RCO_2H$$

2. Groups Affected by Reducing Agents (hydrogen donors), (H).

Carbon-carbon double bonds become saturated.

$$\overset{\diagdown}{\underset{\diagup}{}}C{=}C\overset{\diagup}{\underset{\diagdown}{}} + H_2 \xrightarrow[\Delta,P]{Ni} H\text{—}\overset{|}{\underset{|}{C}}\text{—}\overset{|}{\underset{|}{C}}\text{—}H$$

Disulfides are changed to mercaptans.

$$R\text{—}S\text{—}S\text{—}R + 2(H) \longrightarrow 2RSH$$

3. Groups Split Apart by Water (Hydrolysis).

Acetals are hydrolyzed to aldehydes and alcohols.

$$RC\overset{\diagup OR'}{\underset{\diagdown OR'}{H}} + H_2O \xrightarrow{H^+} RCHO + 2HOR'$$

Esters are hydrolyzed to acids and alcohols.

$$R\overset{O}{\overset{||}{C}}\text{—}OR' + H_2O \xrightarrow{H^+} RCO_2H + HOR'$$

Amides are hydrolyzed to acids and amines (or ammonia).

$$R\overset{O}{\overset{||}{C}}\text{—}\overset{|}{N}\text{—} + H_2O \xrightarrow{H^+} RCO_2H + H\text{—}\overset{|}{N}\text{—}$$

4. Groups that can neutralize strong acids at room temperature.

Amines: e.g. $R\overset{..}{N}H_2 + H_3O^+ \rightleftharpoons R\overset{+}{N}H_3 + H_2O$

Acid Salts: $R\overset{O}{\overset{||}{C}}O^- + H_3O^+ \rightleftharpoons R\overset{O}{\overset{||}{C}}OH + H_2O$

5. Groups that can neutralize strong bases at room temperature.

Amine Salts: e.g. $R\overset{+}{N}H_3 + {}^-OH \rightleftharpoons RNH_2 + H_2O$.
Acids: $RCO_2H + {}^-OH \rightleftharpoons RCO_2^- + H_2O$

6. Other Reactions Involving Water.
   Water is a Reactant:
      Carbon-carbon double bonds can add water to form alcohols.
   Water Is a Product When:
      carbon-carbon double bonds are introduced by the dehydration of an
      alcohol;

carbonyl compounds: aldehydes and ketones, carboxylic acids, esters and amides

acetals are formed from hemiacetals and alcohols;

esters are formed from acids and alcohols;

amides are formed from acids and amines.

Problems and Exercises

The first ten exercises provide for drill in handling certain reactions while providing for the study of common names.

1. Write the structure and the common name of the carboxylic acid that would form by the oxidation of each of the following.

   (a) acetaldehyde (c) formaldehyde
   (b) butyraldehyde (d) propionaldehyde

   Ans: (a) CH_3CO_2H
   acetic acid

2. Write the structures of the *hemiacetal* and *acetal* that would be preparable from:

   (a) acetaldehyde and ethyl alcohol
   (b) propionaldehyde and methyl alcohol
   (c) butyraldehyde and n-propyl alcohol
   (d) acetaldehyde and methyl alcohol
   (e) formaldehyde and n-butyl alcohol

   $$\overset{OH}{\underset{|}{Ans: (a)\ CH_3CH}}—OCH_2CH_3;\ \overset{OCH_2CH_3}{\underset{|}{CH_3CHOCH_2CH_3}}$$

3. Write the structures of the original aldehyde and the alcohol(s) to which the following acetals and hemiacetals could be made to revert.

   (a) CH_3CH_2—O—$\underset{\underset{CH_3}{|}}{CH}$—O—$CH_2CH_3$

   (b) CH_3OCH_2OH

   (c) $CH_3CH_2OCH_2CH_2OCH_2OH$

   (d) $\begin{matrix} CH_2—O \\ CH_2 \qquad\quad CH—O—CH_2CH_3 \\ CH_2—CH_2 \end{matrix}$

   (e) CH_3—O—CH—O—CH_3
   $\underset{\underset{CH_2}{\overset{||}{CH}}}{|}$

   Ans: (a) $CH_3CHO + CH_3CH_2OH$

4. Write equations for the esterification of the following acids by ethyl alcohol. Beneath the structure of each ester that forms, write its common name.

   (a) propionic acid (e) benzoic acid
   (b) formic acid (f) stearic acid
   (c) butyric acid (g) oxalic acid (use 2 moles ethyl
   (d) acetic acid   alcohol)

   Ans: (a) $CH_3CH_2CO_2CH_2CH_3$
   (ethyl propionate)

5. Write equations for the esterification of acetic acid by each of the following alcohols. Beneath the structure of each ester that forms write its common name.
   (a) isopropyl alcohol
   (b) n-propyl alcohol
   (c) ethyl alcohol
   (d) isobutyl alcohol
   (e) n-decyl alcohol
   (f) sec-butyl alcohol
   (g) phenol
   (h) ethylene glycol (use 2 moles of acetic acid; you may omit the name)

   Ans: (a) (CH₃)₂CHOCCH₃ (isopropyl acetate)

   $$\text{Ans: (a) } (CH_3)_2CHO\overset{\overset{\displaystyle O}{\|}}{C}CH_3 \text{ (isopropyl acetate)}$$

6. Write equations for the hydrolysis of each of the following esters:
   (a) ethyl formate
   (b) methyl acetate
   (c) n-propyl butyrate
   (d) isopropyl propionate
   (e) sec-butyl propionate
   (f) t-butyl acetate
   (g)

   $$CH_3\overset{\overset{\displaystyle O}{\|}}{C}-O-CH_2CH_2-O-\overset{\overset{\displaystyle O}{\|}}{C}CH_3$$

   $$\text{Ans: (a) } H\overset{\overset{\displaystyle O}{\|}}{C}OCH_2CH_3 + H_2O \longrightarrow HCO_2H + CH_3CH_2OH$$

7. Write equations for the saponification by NaOH$_{aq}$ of each of the following esters:
   (a) methyl formate
   (b) ethyl acetate
   (c) isopropyl propionate
   (d) n-propyl butyrate

   $$\text{(e) } CH_2-O-\overset{\overset{\displaystyle O}{\|}}{C}-CH_3$$
   $$CH-O-\overset{\overset{\displaystyle O}{\|}}{C}-CH_3$$
   $$CH_2-O-\overset{\overset{\displaystyle O}{\|}}{C}-CH_3$$

   $$\text{Ans: (a) } H\overset{\overset{\displaystyle O}{\|}}{C}OCH_3 + NaOH_{aq} \xrightarrow{H^+} HCO_2^-Na^+ + CH_3OH$$

8. Write the structure and common name of the amide that could be prepared from ammonia and each of the following carboxylic acids.
   (a) acetic acid
   (b) formic acid
   (c) butyric acid
   (d) propionic acid
   (e) benzoic acid
   (f) oxalic acid (use 2 moles ammonia; do not name)

   $$\text{Ans: (a) } CH_3\overset{\overset{\displaystyle O}{\|}}{C}NH_2 \text{ (acetamide)}$$

9. Repeat Exercise 8 using methylamine instead of ammonia.

   $$\text{Ans: (a) } CH_3\overset{\overset{\displaystyle O}{\|}}{C}NHCH_3 \text{ (N-methylacetamide)}$$

10. Write the structures of the products of the hydrolysis of the following amides.

carbonyl compounds: aldehydes and ketones, carboxylic acids, esters and amides

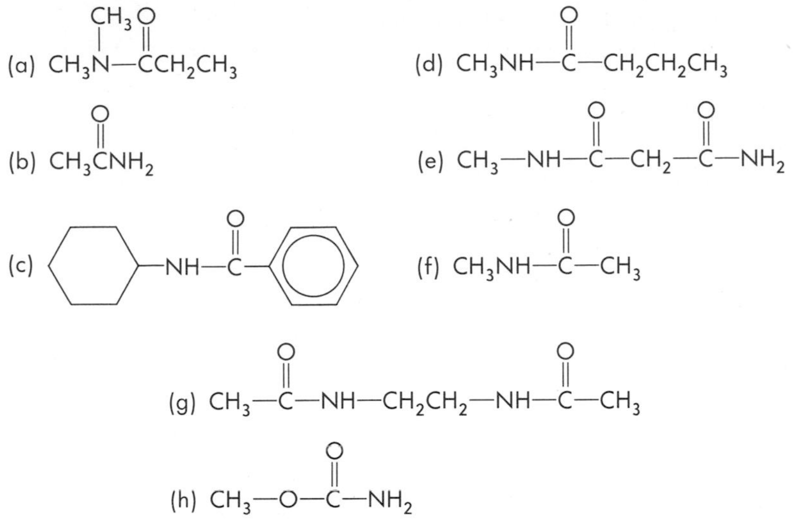

(a) CH$_3$N(CH$_3$)—CCH$_2$CH$_3$ (with CH$_3$ and O above)

(b) CH$_3$CNH$_2$ (with O above)

(c) (cyclohexyl)—NH—C(=O)—(phenyl)

(d) CH$_3$NH—C(=O)—CH$_2$CH$_2$CH$_3$

(e) CH$_3$—NH—C(=O)—CH$_2$—C(=O)—NH$_2$

(f) CH$_3$NH—C(=O)—CH$_3$

(g) CH$_3$—C(=O)—NH—CH$_2$CH$_2$—NH—C(=O)—CH$_3$

(h) CH$_3$—O—C(=O)—NH$_2$

Ans: (a) $(CH_3)_2NH + CH_3CH_2CO_2H$

11. How might the compound $\ddot{N}H_2CH_2COH$ (with O double bonded to C) act, alone, as a buffer in an aqueous solution? Show equations. (In other words, what is the service a buffer performs? What reactions will this compound undergo that would constitute performance of this service?)

12. Methylamine (formula weight 31) boils at $-7°C$; methyl alcohol (formula weight 32) boils at $65°C$. Explain *how* these data support the statement that hydrogen bonding is weaker in amines than in alcohols.

13. When hydrochloric acid is added to a solution of the salt, sodium benzoate, a precipitate forms. Write its structure (it is not sodium chloride), and write an equation for its formation.

14. A solution that is one molar in sodium acetate and one molar in acetic acid has a pH of about 4, and this pH remains quite constant even when small amounts of strong acids or bases are added. Write equations that explain this behavior.

15. Oxalic acid is fairly soluble in water but insoluble in ether. Its diethyl ester,

$$CH_3CH_2—O—C(=O)—C(=O)—O—CH_2CH_3$$

is only slightly soluble in water but completely soluble in all proportions in ether. How might these facts be understood and explained?

16. Consider the following boiling points: methyl alcohol, $65°C$; acetic acid, $118°C$; methyl acetate, $57°C$. How might the relatively low boiling point of methyl acetate, the ester of the first two, be explained?

17. Write the structure(s) of the principal organic product(s) that would be expected to form in each of the following situations. (Count ammonia as an organic compound for purposes of this question.) You are expected to provide answers

only on the basis of the material presented in this text. If we have not studied a reaction for two specific reactants, then you will have to assume that no reaction occurs.

(a) $\overset{\overset{\displaystyle O}{\|}}{H}CCH_2CH_3 + (O) \xrightarrow{\Delta}$

(b) 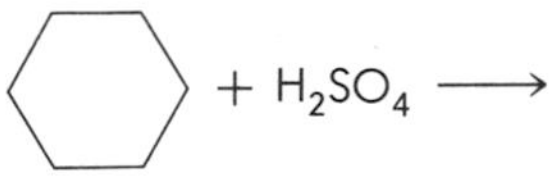 ⬡ $+ H_2SO_4 \longrightarrow$

(c) $CH_3\overset{\overset{\displaystyle O}{\|}}{C}H + 2CH_3OH \xrightarrow{H^+}$

(d) 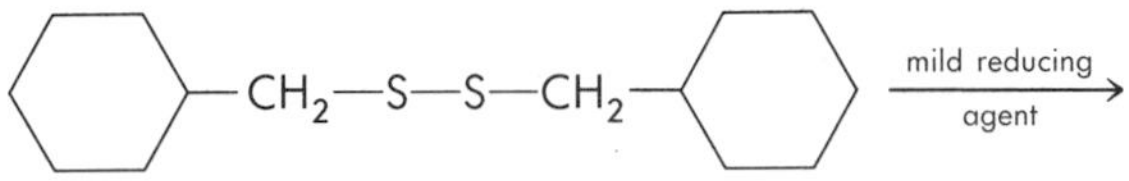 ⬡$-CH_2-S-S-CH_2-$⬡ $\xrightarrow[\text{agent}]{\text{mild reducing}}$

(e) $CH_3CH_2CH_2\overset{\overset{\displaystyle O}{\|}}{C}H + (O) \longrightarrow$

(f) $CH_3CH_2\overset{\overset{\displaystyle OCH_3}{|}}{\underset{\underset{\displaystyle OCH_3}{|}}{C}}H + H_2O \xrightarrow{H^+}$

(g) 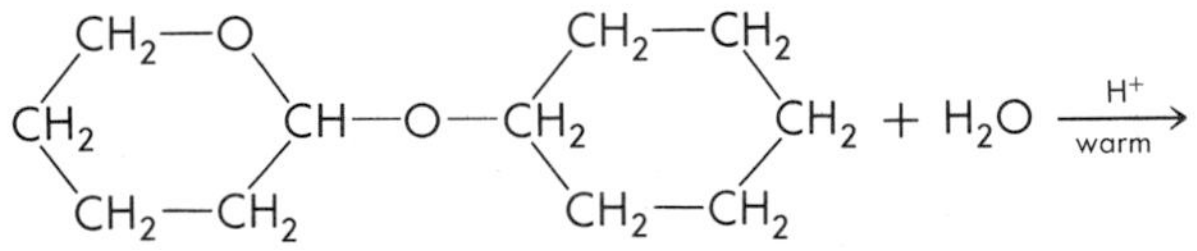 (cyclic structures) $CH_2 \cdot CH-O-CH_2 \cdot CH_2 + H_2O \xrightarrow[\text{warm}]{H^+}$

(h) $CH_3CH_2CH_2CH_2CH_3 + Na \longrightarrow$

(i) $CH_3CH_2\overset{\overset{\displaystyle O}{\|}}{C}OH + NaOH_{aq} \longrightarrow$

(j) $CH_3OH + CH_3\overset{\overset{\displaystyle O}{\|}}{C}H \rightleftharpoons$

(k) $CH_3CH_2OH + CH_3CH_2\overset{\overset{\displaystyle O}{\|}}{C}OH \xrightarrow[\Delta]{H^+}$

(l) $CH_3-O-\overset{\overset{\displaystyle O}{\|}}{C}-CH_3 + H_2O \xrightarrow[\Delta]{H^+}$

(m) $CH_3CH_2OCH_2CH_3 + H_2O \xrightarrow{\Delta}$

(n) $CH_3CH=CHCH_3 + H_2O \xrightarrow[\Delta]{H^+}$

carbonyl compounds: aldehydes and ketones, carboxylic acids, esters and amides

(o) $Na^{+-}\overset{\displaystyle O}{\overset{\|}{O}}CCH_2CH_3 + HCl_{aq} \longrightarrow$

(p) $CH_3CH{=}CHCH_2CH_3 + H_2 \xrightarrow[\text{pressure}]{\text{Ni, heat}}$

(q) $CH_3\underset{\displaystyle \underset{CH_3}{|}}{C}HOH + (O) \longrightarrow$

(r) $CH_3O\overset{\displaystyle O}{\overset{\|}{C}}CH_2CH_3 + H_2O \xrightarrow[\Delta]{H^+}$

(s) $CH_3CH_2CH_2OH \xrightarrow[\Delta]{H_2SO_4}$

(t) $CH_3CH_2\overset{\displaystyle O}{\overset{\|}{C}}OH + CH_3CH_2CH_2OH \xrightarrow[\Delta]{H^+}$

(u) $CH_3CH_2NH_3{}^+Cl^- + NaOH_{aq} \longrightarrow$

(v) 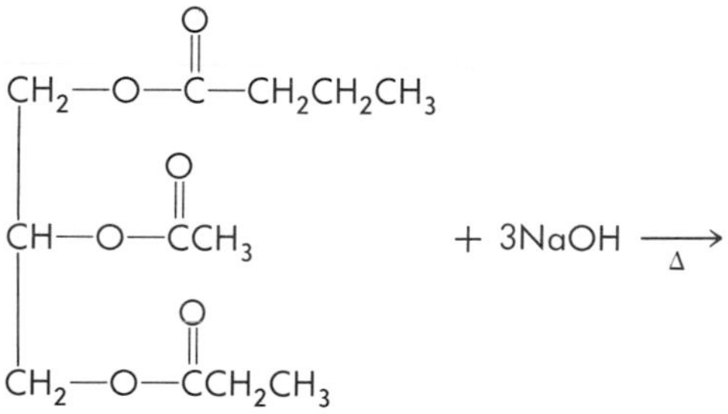
$$CH_2{-}O{-}\overset{\displaystyle O}{\overset{\|}{C}}{-}CH_2CH_2CH_3$$
$$|$$
$$CH{-}O{-}\overset{\displaystyle O}{\overset{\|}{C}}CH_3 \qquad + 3NaOH \xrightarrow{\Delta}$$
$$|$$
$$CH_2{-}O{-}\overset{\displaystyle O}{\overset{\|}{C}}CH_2CH_3$$

(w) $CH_3\underset{\displaystyle \underset{CH_3}{|}}{C}HSH + (O) \longrightarrow$

(x) 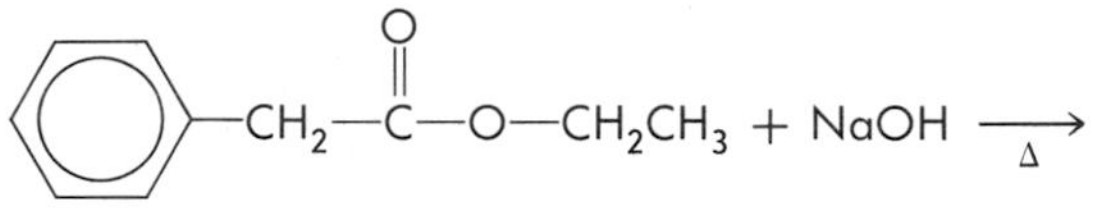 $\langle\!\!\langle \bigcirc \rangle\!\!\rangle{-}CH_2{-}\overset{\displaystyle O}{\overset{\|}{C}}{-}O{-}CH_2CH_3 + NaOH \xrightarrow{\Delta}$

(y) $NH_3 + CH_3\overset{\displaystyle O}{\overset{\|}{C}}OH \xrightarrow{\Delta}$

(z) $NH_2\overset{\displaystyle O}{\overset{\|}{C}}CH_2CH_3 + H_2O \xrightarrow{\Delta}$

chapter 13 carbohydrates

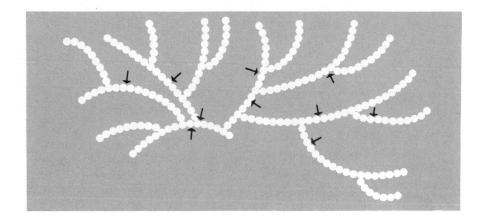

The three great classes of foods are carbohydrates, lipids, and proteins. In this chapter and the next two we shall inquire into the structures of the molecules in these foods, and then we shall be able to concentrate almost entirely on topics relating to the theme of this study, the molecular basis of life. We get our foods from plants or from animals that feed on plants. While we can do a great deal of molecular engineering, while we enjoy the sun and its brightness and warmth, we cannot ourselves start with simple molecules and sunlight and get either materials or energy for living.

Solar energy that pours into our planet free of charge is about 5.3×10^{21} kilocalories per year. The clouds reflect approximately a third of the solar energy back to space. Just about all of the rest is also eventually radiated back; otherwise the planet would become hotter and hotter. But we use some of it first. Its warmth keeps most of the planet inhabitable, and about 0.04% of the received solar energy enters into metabolism in the biosphere—the thin layer of our planet within which any form of life operates. Green plants from microscopic, marine phytoplankton to towering forest giants accept that energy and make the molecules on which all animals depend for both their materials and chemical energy.

We had our first look at photosynthesis in Chapter 5 where we described the overall result by the equation:

$$CO_2 + H_2O + \text{solar energy} \xrightarrow[\text{several steps}]{\substack{\text{chlorophyll} \\ \text{plant enzymes}}} \underset{\substack{\text{basic unit in} \\ \text{carbohydrates}}}{(CH_2O)} + O_2$$

Certain amino acids are also produced and these, together with carbohydrates and oxygen, are the primary products of photosynthesis. Plants use some of each for their own needs. Many plants put into their seeds proteins and starches of use to man and animals. Plants also make oils (lipids) of nutritional use, oils such as peanut oil, olive oil, cottonseed oil, corn oil, and others. With great variations from species to species some plants specialize in making different kinds of secondary products. These include other oils and terpenes, waxes, steroids, alkaloids, pigments, cellulose, gums and pectins, resins and rubber, to say nothing of wood for lumber.

Swedish meteorologist Bert Bolin estimates that between 20 and 30 billion tons of carbon dioxide are fixed via photosynthesis each year by land plants and about 40 billion tons (probably more) by microscopic organisms, such as the phytoplankton, in the oceans. The earth's forests make about 15 billion tons of wood each year. The death and decay of plants and animals, as well as their normal respiration while living, converts photosynthetically fixed carbon and atmospheric oxygen back to carbon dioxide and water—an outline of these relations is in Fig. 13.1—but before that happens to us we use some of the plants' materials. We are a part of the cycles of nature. The first type of plant material we shall study is the carbohydrates.

classes of carbohydrates Molecules that comprise the carbohydrates have the properties of polyhydroxy aldehydes, polyhydroxy ketones, or substances that, by simple hydrolysis, yield these. Carbohydrates that cannot be hydrolyzed to simpler molecules are called monosaccharides; and they are classified according to the following criteria.

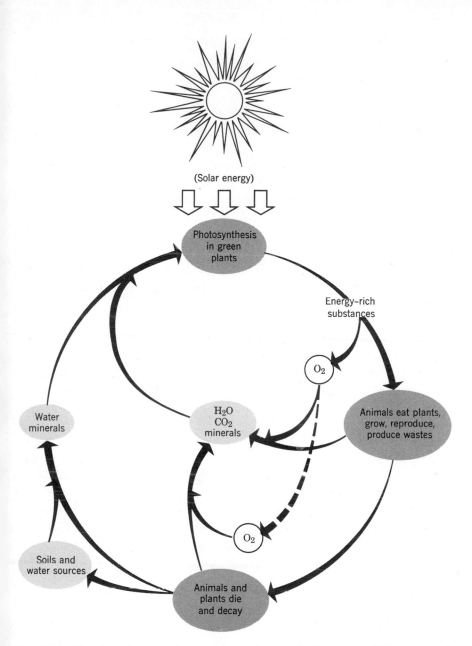

Fig. 13.1 The flux of energy from sun to earth is rendered most useful by means of photosynthesis. Shown here are the principal cycles necessary to life and powered by solar energy—the carbon dioxide, oxygen, and mineral cycles.

1. How many carbon atoms there are in one molecule:

If the carbon number is	the monosaccharide is a
3	triose
4	tetrose
5	pentose
6	hexose

2. Whether there is an aldehyde or a keto group present:

> If an aldehyde, the monosaccharide is an aldose.
> If a keto group, the monosaccharide is a ketose.

These terms may be combined. For example, a hexose that possesses an aldehyde group is called an *aldohexose*. A *ketohexose* possesses a keto group and a total of six carbon atoms.

Carbohydrates that can be hydrolyzed to two monosaccharide units are called *disaccharides*. Sucrose is a common disaccharide. Starch and cellulose are common *polysaccharides;* their molecules yield many monosaccharide units when they are hydrolyzed.

aldohexoses   Sixteen aldohexoses are known. They are all isomers; they have the common molecular formula, $C_6H_{12}O_6$. Only two are of great importance in the chemistry of health: glucose and galactose.

glucose (dextrose, grape sugar, blood sugar). Glucose, the most important hexose, is found in most sweet fruits, especially in ripe grapes. Glucose is also found normally in the bloodstream and in tissue fluids. Its energy-rich molecules constitute one of the body's chief "reservoirs" of energy for the operation of muscles and glands and for the transmission of signals along the nervous system.

Glucose is the building block for several carbohydrates: maltose, starch, glycogen, the dextrins, and cellulose. It is also a structural unit in lactose (milk sugar) and sucrose. The chemistry of glucose is basic, therefore, to all carbohydrate chemistry.

The structure of a glucose molecule is complicated by the fact that it can exist in three readily interconvertible forms. These are shown in Fig. 13.2. In aqueous solution, all three forms are present in dynamic equilibrium.

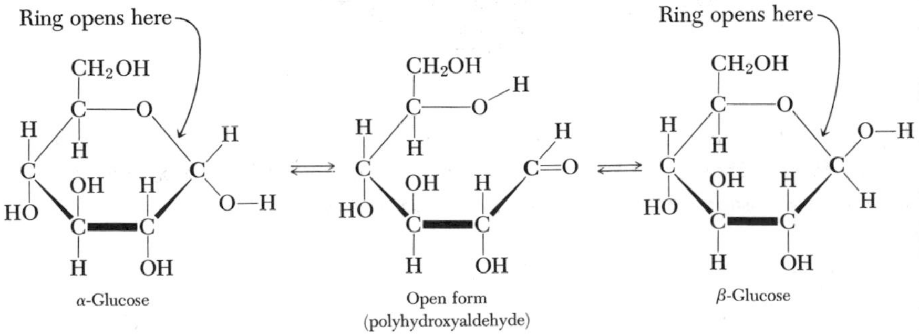

Fig. 13.2   Glucose. In aqueous solutions of glucose these three molecular species coexist in dynamic equilibrium. The open form is present to an extent of less than 0.5%.

The only structural difference between α-glucose and β-glucose is the upward or downward projection of the —OH group attached to the bold-faced carbon atom. This may seem a trivial difference now, but as we probe deeper into the chemistry of health such subtle matters will become of dominating importance. In this instance, for example, the direction of projection makes the difference between amylose (in starch) and cellulose; that is, between a digestible and an indigestible carbohydrate.

The ordinary form of crystalline glucose is the α-form. However, the molecule of glucose possesses a hemiacetal linkage, a carbon (boldface) to which an ether linkage and an —OH group are attached. When α-glucose is dissolved in water, the ring opens and closes at this point.

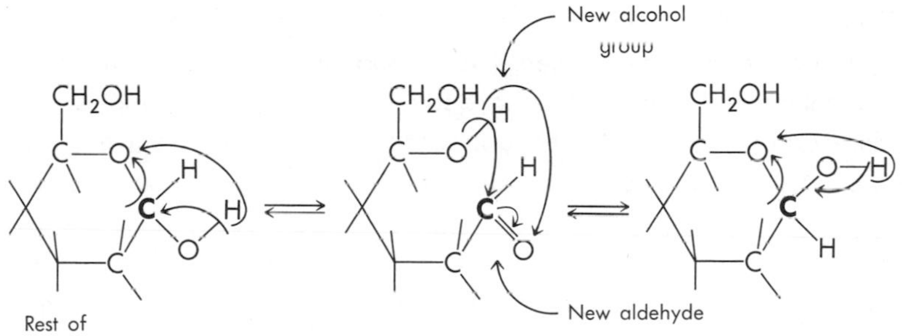

New alcohol group

New aldehyde group

Rest of molecule unchanged

| α-Glucose (a cyclic hemi-acetal) | Open form of glucose (a polyhydroxy aldehyde) | β-Glucose (a cyclic hemiacetal) |

A dynamic equilibrium is established between the open and the cyclic forms. Ring closure, however, can occur in such a way that the —OH at the hemiacetal carbon may project either downward relative to the —CH$_2$OH group (α-glucose) or upward (β-glucose). That is how three forms of glucose can exist together in dynamic equilibrium in solution; the proportions are approximately 36% α-glucose, 0.02% open form, 64% β-glucose.

Convenient condensed structures for α- and β-glucose are:

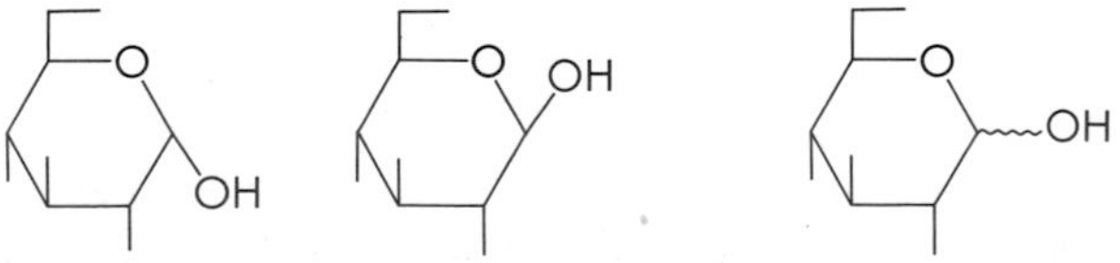

α-Glucose β-Glucose   May be used when the α and β designations are not needed.

physical properties. With five hydroxyl groups present in one molecule, glucose is certain to be very soluble in water and insoluble in nonpolar solvents.

chemical properties. The important reactions that glucose undergoes in the body are the subject of another chapter. What we can most profitably consider here are chemical ways to detect the presence of glucose.

Since glucose is a (cyclic) hemiacetal, it is a "potential aldehyde." The fact that only a trace amount (0.02%) of the open-chain aldehyde form is present at equilibrium in an aqueous solution of glucose does not reduce the *availability* of the aldehyde group to any reagent that is capable of oxidizing it,[1] because the hemiacetal linkage opens very easily. Of the three principal foods, only carbohydrates possess compounds whose molecules have such an easily available, oxidizable group as the aldehyde system. Glucose, therefore, gives positive tests with Benedict's, Fehling's, and Tollens' reagents. It is said to be a *reducing sugar* because of this behavior.

Glucose does not normally appear in the urine of healthy people for sustained periods of time. When it does appear, and persists in appearing, it is indicative of a malfunction in body chemistry (e.g., diabetes mellitus). The detection of glucose in the urine, therefore, is important in diagnosis. Benedict's test is most commonly used.

galactose. Galactose does not occur as such in nature. It is important because the hydrolysis of the disaccharide lactose (milk sugar) yields one molecule of galactose and one of glucose. Structurally, galactose and glucose are isomers; they differ only in the orientation of one hydroxyl group, as the comparisons below reveal. Like glucose, galactose can exist in three forms. It is a reducing sugar, for one of these forms is an open-chain aldehyde.

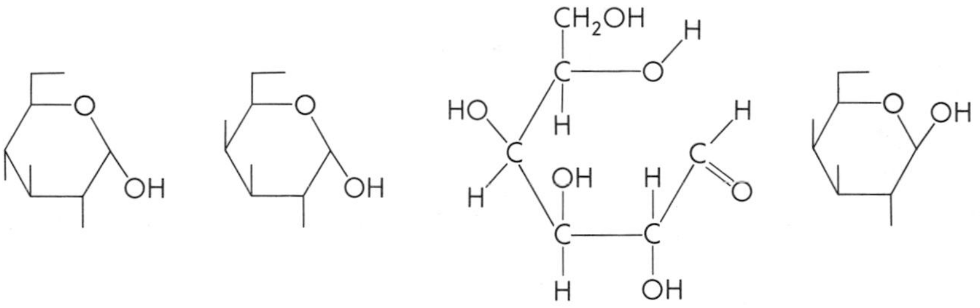

α-Glucose   α-Galactose   Galactose (open-   β-Galactose
                            chain form)

ketohexoses **fructose (levulose).** Fructose, the only important ketohexose, is found together with glucose and sucrose in honey and fruit juices. It is the sweetest of all sugars. Like glucose and galactose, it can exist in more than one form:

[1] It is for this reason that monosaccharides were defined as polyhydroxy *aldehydes* (or ketones) rather than as polyhydroxy cyclic hemiacetals. The "aldehyde" term in the definition more correctly conveys an idea of many of the chemical properties to be expected of these substances.

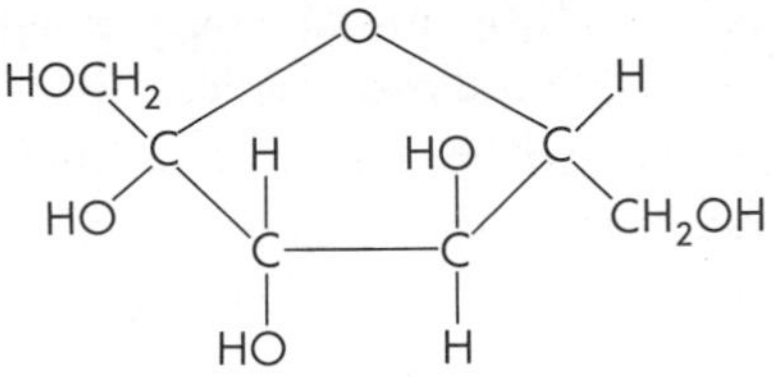

Fructose (one of
its cyclic
forms)

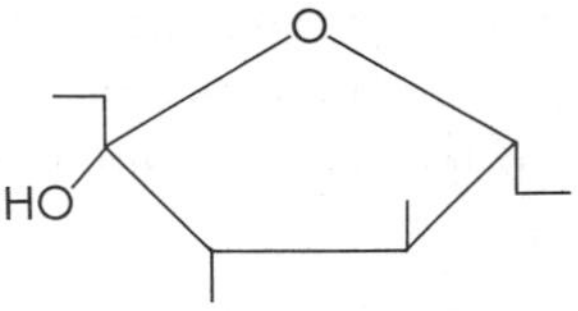

Fructose (condensed symbol)

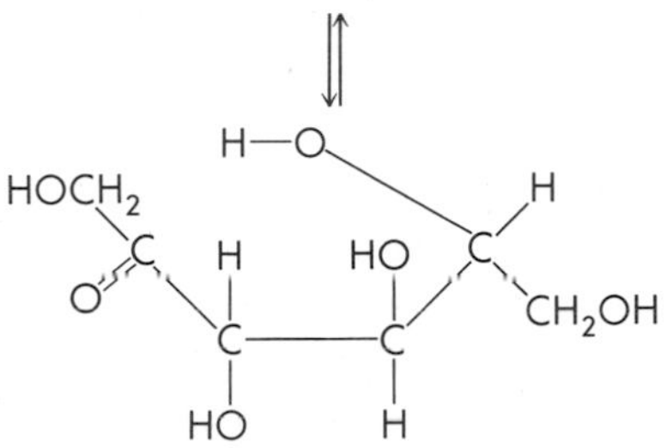

Fructose (open chain
form; note where
—OH group can add
across the keto
group to close the
ring)

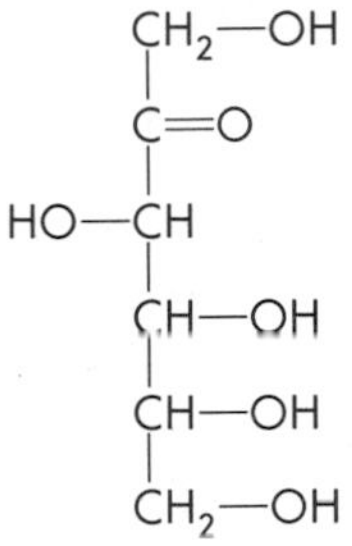

Fructose (another way of
writing the structure of
its open-chain form)

In the keto form of fructose each of the carbon atoms that flank the carbonyl group bears a hydroxyl group. These hydroxyls are sufficiently activated by the keto group to be oxidized by such mild oxidizing agents as Benedict's and Fehling's reagents. Fructose, therefore, is also a reducing sugar.

These are the three important monosaccharides: glucose, galactose, and fructose. All three are reducing sugars. All three occur in key foodstuffs, and all three can be metabolized by the human body.

Nutritionally, there are three important disaccharides: maltose, lactose, and **disaccharides** sucrose. The relationships these bear to the monosaccharides just discussed may be seen by these "word equations":

$$Maltose + H_2O \rightleftharpoons glucose + glucose$$
$$Lactose + H_2O \rightleftharpoons glucose + galactose$$
$$Sucrose + H_2O \rightleftharpoons glucose + fructose$$

maltose (malt sugar). Maltose, although present in germinating grain, does not occur abundantly in the free state in nature. It can be prepared from starch by the action of enzymes. Along with glucose and dextrins, it is present in corn syrup.

Maltose consists of two glucose units linked by means of an acetal linkage, an acetal oxygen bridge. The structural relationship of maltose to glucose may be seen from the following equation, which illustrates its formation (forward reaction) or hydrolysis (reverse reaction):

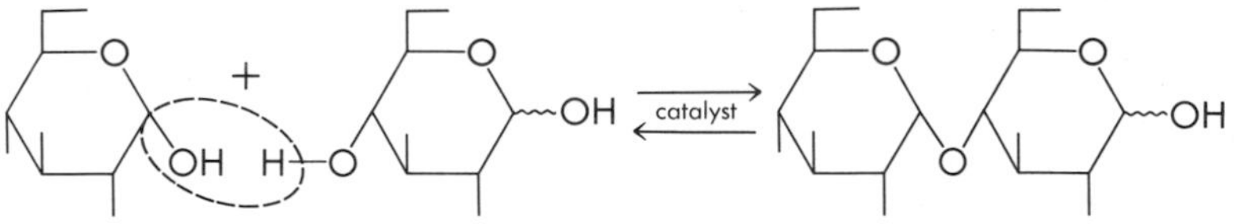

α-Glucose   Glucose   Maltose

This reaction is essentially the formation of an acetal from a hemiacetal (first glucose unit) and an alcohol (second glucose unit):

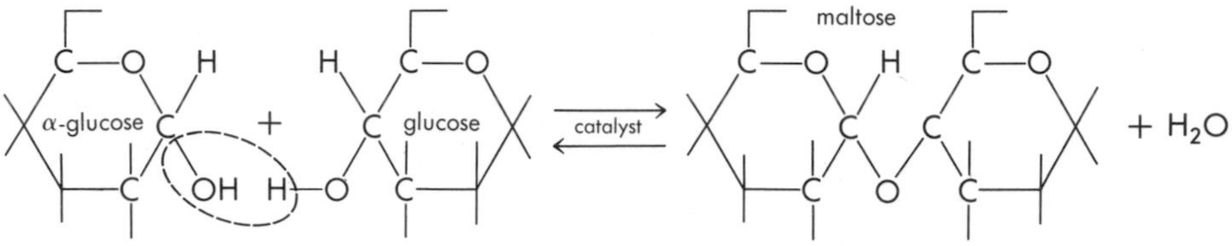

Hemiacetal   +   Alcohol   ⇌   Acetal   + H₂O

Or:

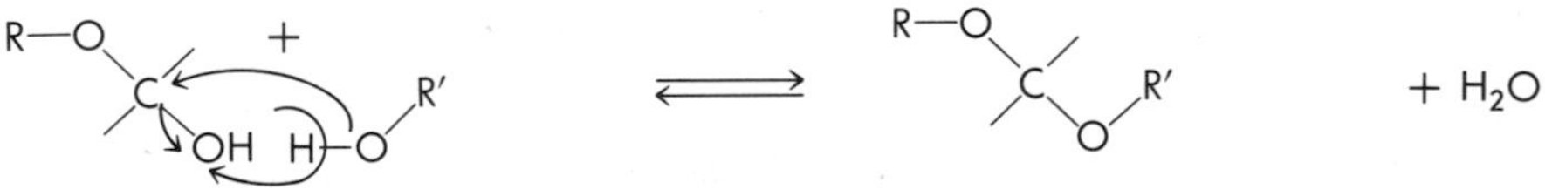

Hemiacetal + Alcohol   ⇌   Acetal   + H₂O

An acetal linkage is more stable than a hemiacetal linkage. Acid catalysis is required to hydrolyze it. (In the body, enzymes act as catalysts.) The linkage is stable to bases. None of the oxidizing agents that attack a hemiacetal linkage (potential aldehyde group)—Fehling's, Tollens' or Benedict's reagents—has any effect on an acetal oxygen bridge because all these reagents involve strongly basic solutions.

Maltose, however, retains a hemiacetal linkage in one of the glucose units. (It is the farthest to the right in the structure as it is written.) This isolated portion of the molecule can open and close in the manner of glucose and can make available an aldehyde group. Therefore, maltose is a reducing sugar.

lactose (milk sugar). Lactose occurs in the milk of mammals. Cow's milk contains 4 to 6% lactose; human milk has 5 to 8%. Commercially, it is obtained as a by-product in the manufacture of cheese. Its galactose unit is linked to its glucose unit by means of an acetal oxygen bridge, as in maltose.

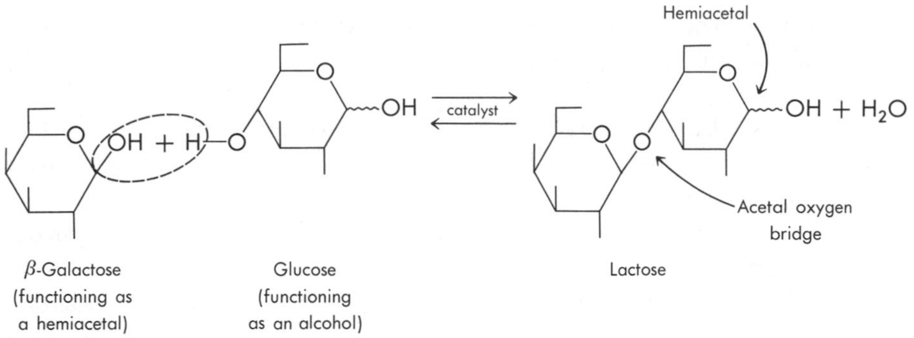

| β-Galactose (functioning as a hemiacetal) | Glucose (functioning as an alcohol) | Lactose |

Since lactose possesses a hemiacetal linkage (potential aldehyde group), it is a reducing sugar.

sucrose (cane sugar, beet sugar, table sugar). The juice of sugar cane contains about 14% sucrose. Sugar beets have about 10 to 16% sucrose. Much of our supply of sucrose now comes from sugar beets, and so-called beet sugar and cane sugar are indistinguishable. White sucrose is probably the purest single organic compound known that is so widely and inexpensively sold.

Structurally, a molecule of sucrose is derived from one glucose unit and one fructose unit:

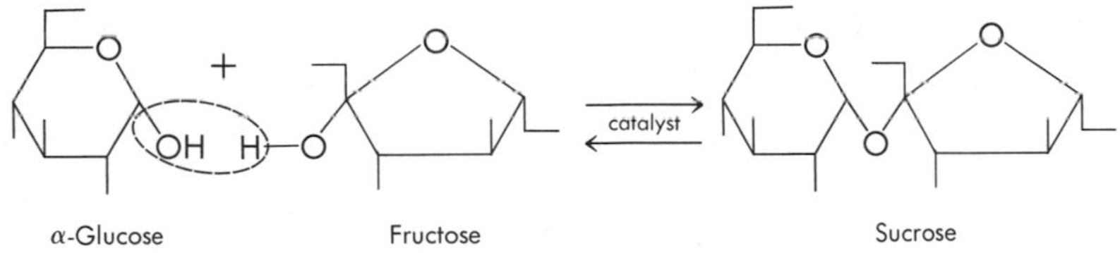

| α-Glucose | Fructose | Sucrose |

An acetal oxygen bridge links the two units. No hemiacetal linkage is present in a molecule of sucrose. With no potential aldehyde group, sucrose is a nonreducing sugar.

The 50:50 mixture of glucose and fructose that forms when sucrose is hydrolyzed is often called *invert sugar*. Honey, for example, is largely invert sugar.

Polysaccharides are polymers of monosaccharides with the polymers of glucose, starch and cellulose, being the most important.

Much of the glucose produced in a plant by photosynthesis is used to erect the plant's living quarters (its cell walls) and its rigid fibers. Much is

polysaccharides

also stored, not as glucose, which is too soluble, but as insoluble starch. Starch is particularly abundant in plant seeds. Man uses these two glucose polymers in about the same way that plants do. Cellulose and its "woody" relatives are utilized to build a variety of things from shirts and blouses to frame houses, and starch is used for food.

starch. The skeletal outline of what is believed to constitute the basic structure of starch, as proposed by K. H. Meyer, is shown in Fig. 13.3. As this figure reveals, it is not correct to consider naturally occurring starch as consisting of only one kind of molecule. Natural starches are mixtures of polyglucose molecules. Basically, however, there are two general types: the *amylose* type, which is believed to be a long, unbranched polymer of α-glucose units; and the *amylopectin* type, which is believed to involve all the features of amylose but with considerable branching. Natural starches consist of approximately 10 to 20% of amylose and 80 to 90% of amylopectins.

physical properties. Judging from the enormous number of "waterlike" hydroxyl groups that must be present on a typical starch molecule, we might conclude that starch must be very soluble in water. However, the sheer size of a starch molecule tends to make it only slightly soluble in cold water. Amylose is more soluble than amylopectin. Starch "solutions" that can be prepared by grinding starch in water are really colloidal dispersions.

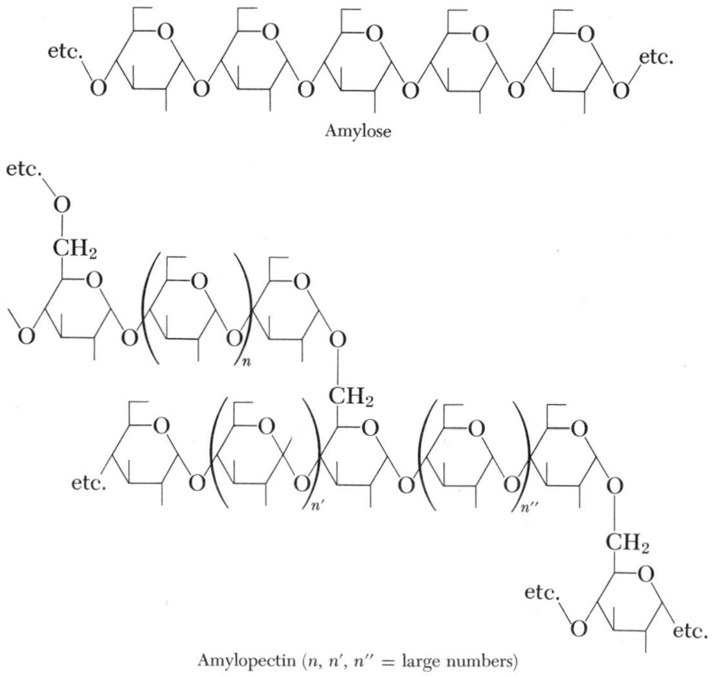

Fig. 13.3 Basic structural features of the types of glucose polymers found in starches.

chemical properties. Glucose units in starch molecules are linked to each other by oxygen bridges that involve acetal functions. Water, therefore, will act on starch to hydrolyze it, ultimately to glucose. Acids and certain enzymes catalyze this reaction. The hydrolysis of starch, therefore, is very similar to that of maltose.

Amylopectin, under controlled conditions, yields partial breakdown products that are collectively called *dextrins*. Dextrins are used in mucilages, pastes, and fabric sizes. P. Bernfeld depicts the step-by-step hydrolysis of amylopectin to glucose through the dextrins as shown in Fig. 13.4.

Starch is not a reducing carbohydrate, for it has too small a percentage of terminal glucose units, where potential aldehyde groups would be found, to be detectable by Benedict's reagent. Starch, however, gives an intense, brilliant, blue-black color with iodine. This *iodine test* can detect extremely minute traces of starch in solution. The chemistry of the test is not definitely known, but it is believed that iodine molecules become trapped within the vast network of starch molecules. Should this network disintegrate, as it does during the hydrolysis of starch, the test fails. In fact, the course of the hydrolysis of starch can be followed by this test, for as the reaction proceeds a gradual change in the color produced by iodine occurs: blue-black to purple to red to none.

Step-by-step hydrolysis to maltose and finally to glucose is the fate of starch in the digestive tract.

glycogen. As starch is the reserve or storage form of glucose in plants, glycogen is the reserve carbohydrate in animals. During periods of fasting, animals draw from their stores of glycogen for the glucose they need to maintain normal body functions.

Structurally, glycogen, which is a polymer of α-glucose, and amylopectin are nearly identical. However, glycogen has considerably more branching than does amylopectin. It does not give the iodine test.

cellulose. Like starch and glycogen, cellulose is a high-formula-weight polymer of glucose. Starch and glycogen, however, are polymers of the α-form of glucose, whereas cellulose is a polymer of the β-form. Like amylose, cellulose involves no branching in the polyglucose chain. A portion of the structure of cellulose is depicted in Fig. 13.5.

The structural difference between amylose and cellulose is one of the "tremendous trifles" in nature. Amylose is digestible; cellulose is not. Yet the only difference between them, structurally, is the orientation of the oxygen bridges. The problem of digestibility, however, reduces itself to a matter of adequate enzymes. Enzymes, protein-like catalysts in the living organism, are extremely sensitive to the gross shapes of molecules. Human beings and carnivorous animals simply do not have enzymes that can catalyze the hydrolysis (that is, the digestion) of cellulose. However, many microorganisms,

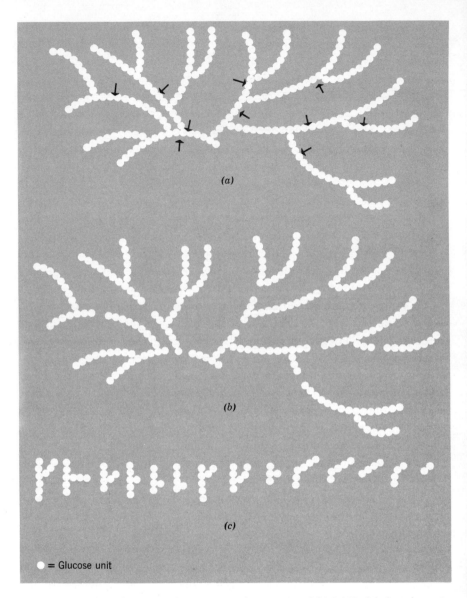

Fig. 13.4 The hydrolysis of amylopectin according to P. Bernfeld. (a) Model of amylopectin. (b) Dextrins of medium molecular weight that give purple to red colors with iodine. These dextrins result from random hydrolysis of about 4% of the oxygen bridges of amylopectin. See arrows in (a). (c) Low-formula-weight dextrins (limit dextrins) that actually are hepta-, hexa-, and pentasaccharides. These give a brown color in iodine. (From *Advances in Enzymology*, Vol. 12, 390, (1951).)

snails, and ruminants (cud-chewing animals) can digest cellulose. The ruminants do so because they have suitable microorganisms in their alimentary tracts whose own enzyme systems catalyze the conversion of cellulose into small molecules that the ruminant can use.

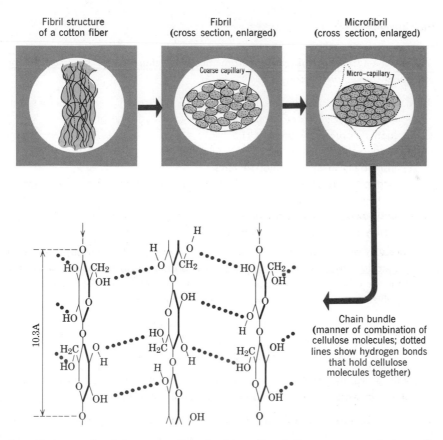

Fig. 13.5   Cellulose, a linear polymer of β-glucose. (Note that, in order to indicate the linearity of the structure, every other glucose unit is "flipped over" from the normal way of writing it, as we have done in this book.)

It is fortunate that *some* systems contain enzymes capable of catalyzing the hydrolysis of cellulose. Otherwise the land would soon be covered by the dead debris of grasses, leaves, annual plants, and fallen trees. But soil organisms go to work on these remains and break them down.

Cellulose makes up the cell membranes of the higher plants and gives them their rigidity. Cotton fiber (Fig. 13.6) is almost 98% cellulose, wherein each molecule has from 2000 to 9000 β-glucose units.

Fibril structure
of a cotton fiber

Fibril
(cross section, enlarged)

Microfibril
(cross section, enlarged)

Coarse capillary

Micro–capillary

10.3A

Chain bundle
(manner of combination of
cellulose molecules; dotted
lines show hydrogen bonds
that hold cellulose
molecules together)

Fig. 13.6   Details of the cotton fiber. In this series of diagrams, successively smaller portions of a cotton fiber are enlarged and depicted. (Adapted from illustrations appearing in H. R. Mauersberger, editor, *Matthews' Textile Fibers*, sixth edition, pages 73 and 77; John Wiley & Sons, New York, 1954.)

Selected Reading List

Articles

1. R. P. Levine. "The Mechanism of Photosynthesis." *Scientific American*, December 1969, page 58. It is not our intent to go into the chemical reactions of photosynthesis. Those who are interested may consult this article or any recent text in biochemistry.
2. P. Cloud and A. Gibor. "The Oxygen Cycle." *Scientific American*, September 1970. (Also listed at the end of Chapter 5.)
3. B. Bolin. "The Carbon Cycle." *Scientific American*, September 1970, page 125. (Also listed at the end of Chapter 5.)

Brief Summary

The salient features of carbohydrate molecules that should be retained for subsequent studies are these:

1. Molecules of aldohexoses (e.g., glucose and galactose) have properties that would be expected from the presence of several hydroxyl groups:
   (a) high polarity (they are solids),
   (b) ready solubility in water,
   (c) insolubility in all nonpolar solvents;
   and from the presence of an aldehyde group (or a potential aldehyde group, i.e., a hemiacetal linkage):
   (a) easy oxidation by mild oxidizing agents (e.g., Benedict's reagent),
   (b) ability to enter into hemiacetal and acetal formation.
2. Molecules of disaccharides owe their ready hydrolysis to monosaccharides to their acetal linkages which furnish oxygen bridges from one monosaccharide unit to the other. Although relatively stable in basic media, acetal linkages easily hydrolyze in acid media or under enzymic conditions.

> Maltose yields two glucose units.
> Lactose yields glucose and galactose.
> Sucrose yields glucose and fructose.

   With several hydroxyl groups per molecule, disaccharides are very polar, very soluble in water, and insoluble in all nonpolar solvents.

> Lactose and maltose are reducing sugars. Sucrose is not.

3. Starch, glycogen, and cellulose are all high-formula-weight polymers of glucose. Glucose units in all three are linked through acetal oxygen bridges that can be hydrolyzed by the action of acids or appropriate enzymes. Complete hydrolysis of all three yields glucose.

Starch is a mixture of polyglucose molecules derived from α-glucose. Some are unbranched (amylose); some are branched (amylopectin). Partial hydrolysis of amylopectin furnishes dextrins. Starch is readily detected by the starch-iodine test.

Glycogen resembles amylopectin in that it is a polymer of α-glucose but has much more branching than occurs in amylopectin.

Cellulose is an unbranched polymer of β-glucose.

Problems and Exercises

1. Explain how β-glucose and α-galactose, which have no aldehyde group, can give positive Tollens' tests.

2. Glucose can be made to react with ethyl alcohol in the presence of a trace of acid to form a compound having the molecular formula $C_8H_{16}O_6$. This substance does not give a Benedict's test. Write its structure.

3. Either α- or β-glucose can be made to react with a mild oxidizing agent to form the *same* monocarboxylic acid, $C_6H_{12}O_7$. What would be its most likely structure?

4. Would you expect similar behavior from galactose? Why? If "yes," write the structure of the product.

5. Would you expect similar behavior from fructose (i.e., form a monocarboxylic acid, without loss of any carbons, by action of a *mild* oxidizing agent)? Why?

6. Write equations that illustrate the hydrolysis of
   (a) maltose   (b) lactose   (c) sucrose

7. Write equations illustrating how maltose and lactose form from their monosaccharide units.

8. Maltose contains a potential aldehyde group. Show how a maltose molecule can undergo opening of one ring to free an aldehyde linkage. Repeat for lactose.

9. Acetic acid can be made to form an ester with each of the hydroxyl groups of cellulose. Write enough of the structure of this substance to show all essential structural features. The product is much more soluble in some nonaqueous solvents than is cellulose. How can this be explained?

10. Examine the following structure and answer the questions about it. (It is a sugar called trehalose found in young mushrooms.)

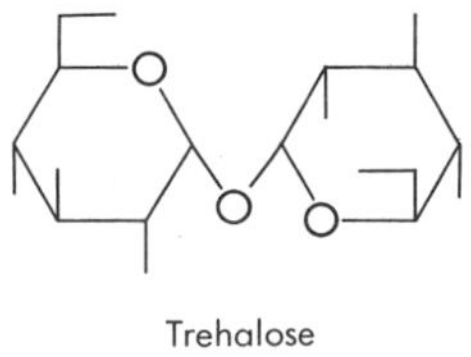

Trehalose

(a) Does it have a hemiacetal system? Where? (Draw an arrow to it or circle it.)

(b) Does it have an acetal system? Where? (Circle it.)

(c) Write the equation for its acid-catalyzed hydrolysis and name the product(s) that form.

(d) Would this substance give a positive Benedict's test? Why?

11. If galactose were present in urine to be tested by Benedict's reagent, how might an analyst erroneously report the presence of glucose instead?

12. For use in experiments on carbohydrates, a 2% sucrose solution was prepared with distilled water into which carbon dioxide (from the air) had dissolved. When freshly made, the sucrose solution gave the expected negative Benedict's test. After remaining for one week at room temperature, the solution gave a positive Benedict's test. What probably occurred, chemically, in the intervening time to cause the different behavior?

chapter 14 lipids

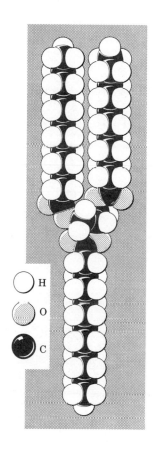

○ H

◐ O

● C

Greases, oils, and fats do not enjoy the widespread popularity of, for instance, sugar (a carbohydrate) or roast beef (largely protein). Indeed, they seem to be best known for the trouble they create in problems ranging from garbage disposal to excess weight. Yet we cannot live without them, for they are important substances in the chemistry of health.

Table 14.1 Lipid Classes

General Class	Subclasses	Generic Class Structure	Nature of Hydrolysis Products	Examples and Occurrences
Simple Esters	Waxes	$R-O-\overset{\displaystyle O}{\overset{\|}{C}}-R'$	Long-chain carboxylic acids Long-chain alcohols	Beeswax, cuticle waxes (on flower petals and fruit skins)
	Glycerides	$CH_2-O-\overset{O}{\overset{\|}{C}}-R$ $CH-O-\overset{O}{\overset{\|}{C}}-R'$ $CH_2-O-\overset{O}{\overset{\|}{C}}-R''$	Mixture of long-chain acids Glycerol	Animal fats (solids): lard, tallow Vegetable oils (liquids): olive oil, peanut oil, corn oil, cottonseed oil, linseed oil
	Lecithins	$CH_2-O-\overset{O}{\overset{\|}{C}}-R$ $CH-O-\overset{O}{\overset{\|}{C}}-R'$ $CH_2-O-\overset{O}{\overset{\|}{P}}-O-CH_2-CH_2-\overset{+}{N}(CH_3)(CH_3)(CH_3)$ with O^-	Mixture of long-chain acids Glycerol Phosphoric acid Choline (an amino alcohol)	Found in nerve tissue

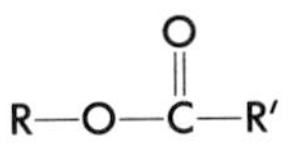

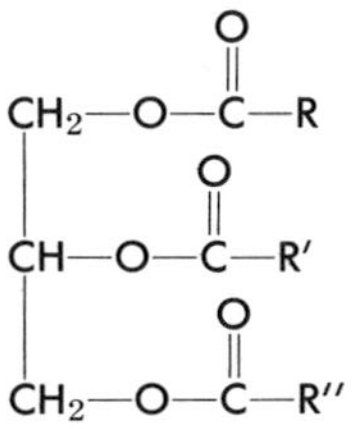

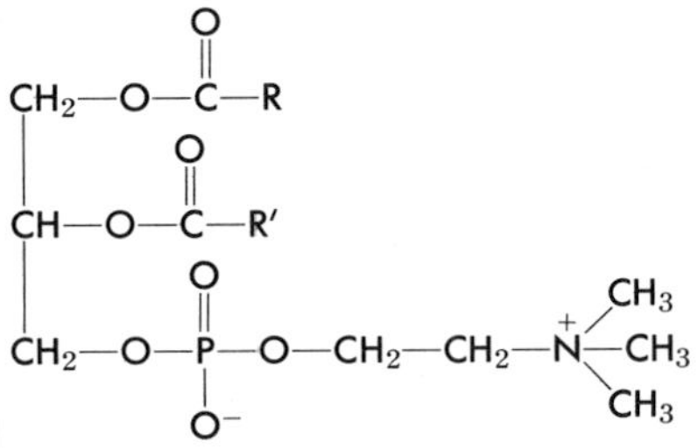

Table 14.1 Lipid Classes (continued)

Class	Name	Structure	Components	Occurrence
Phospholipids (Phosphoglycerides)	Cephalins	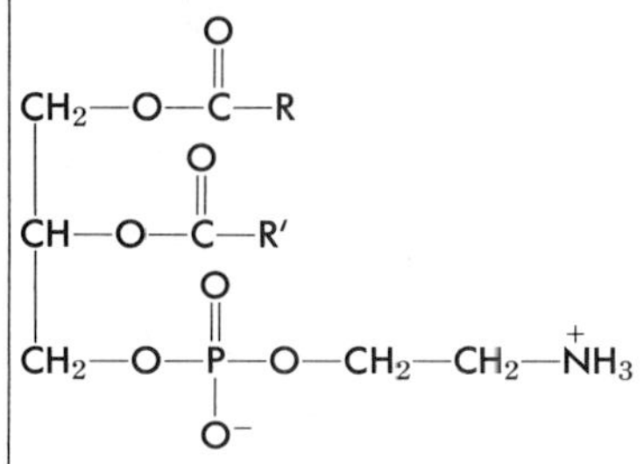 $CH_2-O-C(=O)-R$ $CH-O-C(=O)-R'$ $CH_2-O-P(=O)(O^-)-O-CH_2-CH_2-\overset{+}{N}H_3$	Mixture of long-chain acids Glycerol Phosphoric acid Aminoethanol	Found in nerve tissue
	Phosphatidylserines	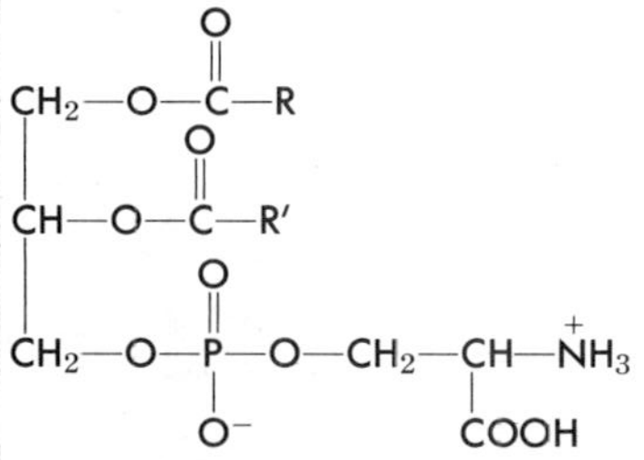 $CH_2-O-C(=O)-R$ $CH-O-C(=O)-R'$ $CH_2-O-P(=O)(O^-)-O-CH_2-\underset{COOH}{CH}-\overset{+}{N}H_3$	Mixture of long-chain acids Glycerol Phosphoric acid Serine	Found in nerve tissue
Sphingolipids	Sphingomyelins	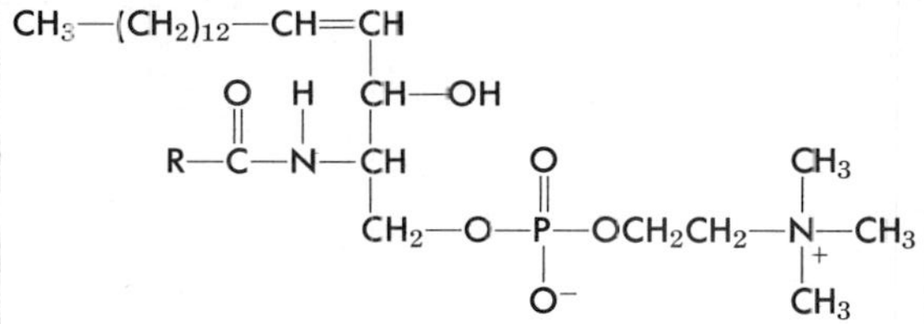 $CH_3-(CH_2)_{12}-CH=CH$ $CH-OH$ $CH-N(H)-C(=O)-R$ $CH_2-O-P(=O)(O^-)-O-CH_2CH_2-\overset{+}{N}(CH_3)_3$	Sphingosine (an unsaturated amino alcohol) A long-chain acid Phosphoric acid Choline	Found in brain tissue
	Cerebrosides	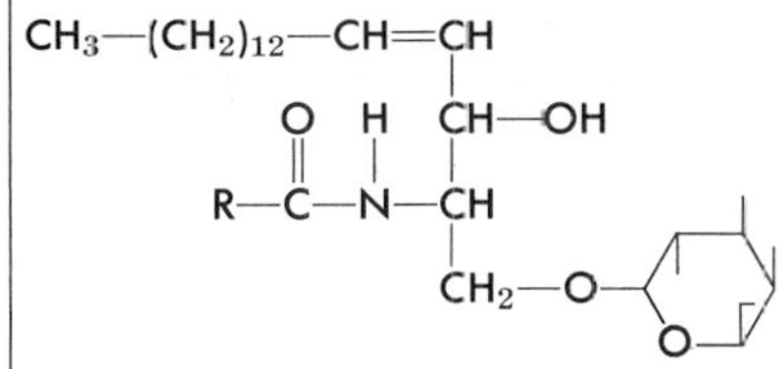 $CH_3-(CH_2)_{12}-CH=CH$ $CH-OH$ $CH-N(H)-C(=O)-R$ CH_2-O- (galactose)	Sphingosine A long-chain acid Galactose	Found in brain tissue (e.g., kerasin, phrenosin, nervon, and oxynervon)

types of lipids Lipids are plant and animal products that are soluble in ether or similar nonpolar solvents. Although there are many different types, all lipid molecules are substantially hydrocarbon-like. One major class consists of those that can be saponified; i.e., their molecules have one or more ester linkages, and the chief subclasses of the saponifiable lipids are shown in Table 14.1. The principal nonsaponifiable lipids are the steroids, described at the end of the chapter.

The simplest lipids of nutritional importance are listed in Table 14.1 as the glycerides (or, technically, the triglycerides). Other types are certainly essential; any constituents of nerve and brain tissue would be. But the glycerides are the most extensively studied; they are relatively simple and they provide the richest source of chemical energy in the body, the fatty acids. We shall confine our study of lipids almost exclusively to members of this subclass.

fatty acids All the lipids classified in Table 14.1 are in one way or another esters of long-chain carboxylic acids. For this reason, these acids are often called *fatty acids* and the following generalizations may be made about them.

1. They are usually monocarboxylic acids (one $-\overset{\overset{\text{O}}{\|}}{\text{C}}-\text{O}-\text{H}$ per molecule).
2. The alkyl group in the acid is usually a straight, unbranched carbon chain.
3. Nearly all fatty acids contain an even number of carbons.
4. The hydrocarbon portion of the fatty acid molecule may contain one, two, three, or four carbon-to-carbon double bonds.

The important saturated fatty acids (those containing no carbon-to-carbon double bonds) were listed in Table 12.5. Four important unsaturated fatty acids are listed in Table 14.2 of this chapter.

The most important saturated fatty acids are lauric (C_{12}), myristic (C_{14}), palmitic (C_{16}), and stearic (C_{18}). The basic skeleton of stearic acid is duplicated in oleic, linoleic, and linolenic acid. These acids differ from each other only in the degree of unsaturation; that is, in the number of alkene double bonds present. Notice how the melting points of these acids drop as we go from the saturated acid, stearic acid (m.p. 70°C), to the C_{18} acids that have progressively more double bonds. *The greater the degree of unsaturation, the lower the melting point.* This generalization helps to explain how it is that animal fats are solids and vegetable oils are liquids at room temperature. Both, structurally, are glycerides. However, the fatty acids bound up as esters in the vegetable oils have far more unsaturation than do those found in animal fats. The data in Table 14.3, discussed below, support this explanation.

Chemically speaking, all the fatty acids released when the ester linkages in the glycerides are hydrolyzed behave as ordinary carboxylic acids. They can be esterified and they can form salts. Being largely hydrocarbon-like, they are insoluble in water. Their sodium and potassium salts are soluble, however, and function as soaps (to be discussed later).

The unsaturated fatty acids show, in addition to the properties just given, the normal reactions of alkenes. Their carbon-to-carbon double bonds will add hydrogen and bromine, for example.

Structurally, the fats and oils obtained from nature are largely *mixed glycerides;* that is, their individual molecules yield different fatty acids when hydrolyzed. The structure of a typical mixed glyceride is shown in Fig. 14.1. It is not possible to write the structure of *the* representative molecule of, say, cottonseed oil or lard. Fats and oils from whatever source are mixtures of different glyceride molecules. All that can be concluded from careful analysis of any particular fat or oil is that certain of the fatty acids tend to predominate, and that certain others either are absent or are present in trace amounts.

The exact composition of lard, for example, varies with the diet of the hog. Corn-fed hogs produce a lard having less unsaturation than that from peanut-fed hogs. Weather conditions also seem to influence the composition of a fat or oil produced by nature. In one experiment, a supply of flax seed was divided into two portions. One portion was shipped to Switzerland, where it was planted in a relatively cold climate. The other portion was grown in a greenhouse in Berlin at or above room temperature. The linseed oil from the Swiss flax was about twice as unsaturated as that obtained from the flax in Berlin.

Table 14.3 shows average compositions of a variety of common fats and oils. The degree of unsaturation is indicated by the iodine number. *The iodine number is the number of grams of iodine that will add to the double bonds present in 100 grams of the fat or oil.*[1] The higher the iodine number, the greater the degree of unsaturation. In Table 14.3, note the change in iodine number with the percentage of unsaturated fatty acid present. Note also the predominance of oleic acid in all the glycerides. The considerable rise in iodine number (degree of unsaturation) in going from animal fats to vegetable oils, which accompanies the rise in percentages of unsaturated fatty acids, is attended by a change in physical state from solid to liquid. This is the same trend observed earlier with the free fatty acids.

glycerides: the neutral fats and oils

[1] Chlorine and bromine readily add to a carbon-carbon double bond:

$$\ce{>C=C< + X-X -> -C-C-} \quad (X = Cl \text{ or } Br)$$

The reaction resembles the addition of hydrogen, H—H (Chapter 10). Iodine is much less reactive than bromine and chlorine, and the determination of an iodine number is made using iodine chloride, ICl, or iodine bromide, IBr, or something similar to these. But the results are computed on the basis of iodine, I_2, itself.

Table 14.2 Important Unsaturated Fatty Acids

Number of Double Bonds	Total Number of Carbons	Name	Structure	Melting Point, in °C
One	18	Oleic acid	$CH_3(CH_2)_7CH=CH(CH_2)_7\overset{\displaystyle O}{\overset{\|}{C}}-OH$	4
Two	18	Linoleic acid	$CH_3(CH_2)_4CH=CHCH_2CH=CH(CH_2)_7\overset{\displaystyle O}{\overset{\|}{C}}-OH$	−5
Three	18	Linolenic acid	$CH_3CH_2CH=CHCH_2CH=CHCH_2CH=CH(CH_2)_7\overset{\displaystyle O}{\overset{\|}{C}}-OH$	−11
Four	20	Arachidonic acid	$CH_3(CH_2)_4CH=CHCH_2CH=CHCH_2CH=CHCH_2CH=CH(CH_2)_3\overset{\displaystyle O}{\overset{\|}{C}}-OH$	−49.5

Fat or Oil	Average Composition of Fatty Acids, in Percent						
	Iodine Number	Myristic Acid	Palmitic Acid	Stearic Acid	Oleic Acid	Linoleic Acid	Others
Animal Fats							
Butter	25–40	8–15	25–29	9–12	18–33	2–4	a
Lard	45–70	1–2	25–30	12–18	48–60	6–12	b
Beef tallow	30–45	2–5	24–34	15–30	35–45	1–3	b
Vegetable Oils							
Olive	75–95	0–1	5–15	1–4	67–84	8–12	
Peanut	85–100	—	7–12	2–6	30–60	20–38	
Corn	115–130	1–2	7–11	3–4	25–35	50–60	
Cottonseed	100–117	1–2	18–25	1–2	17–38	45–55	
Soybean	125–140	1–2	6–10	2–4	20–30	50–58	c
Linseed	175–205	—	4–7	2–4	14–30	14–25	d
Marine Oils							
Whale	110–150	5–10	10–20	2–5	33–40		e
Fish	120–180	6–8	10–25	1–3			e

[a] 3–4% butyric acid, 1–2% caprylic acid, 2–3% cupric acid, 2–5% lauric acid.
[b] 1% linolenic acid.
[c] 5–10% linolenic acid.
[d] 45–60% linolenic acid.
[e] Large amounts of other, highly unsaturated fatty acids.

The iodine number of the mixed glyceride of Fig. 14.1 is calculated to be approximately 89. This is in the range of olive oil or peanut oil.

hydrolysis in the presence of enzymes. Enzymes in the digestive tracts of human beings and animals act as efficient catalysts for the hydrolysis of glycerides. Glycerides are simply large molecules with ester groups. When

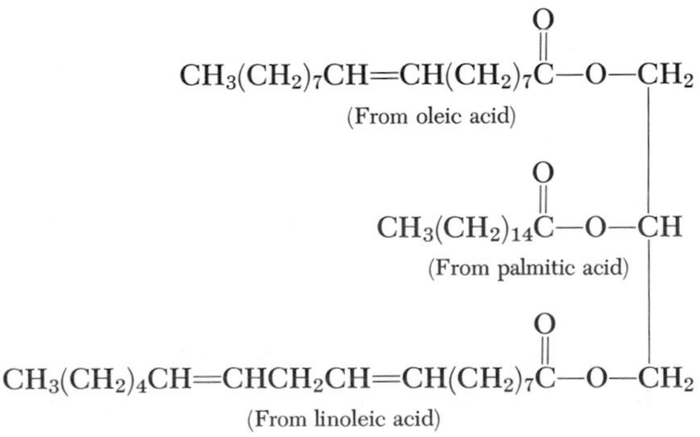

$$CH_3(CH_2)_7CH{=}CH(CH_2)_7\overset{\displaystyle O}{\overset{\|}{C}}{-}O{-}CH_2$$
(From oleic acid)

$$CH_3(CH_2)_{14}\overset{\displaystyle O}{\overset{\|}{C}}{-}O{-}CH$$
(From palmitic acid)

$$CH_3(CH_2)_4CH{=}CHCH_2CH{=}CH(CH_2)_7\overset{\displaystyle O}{\overset{\|}{C}}{-}O{-}CH_2$$
(From linoleic acid)

Fig. 14.1 A typical mixed glyceride (showing oleic acid, palmitic acid, and linoleic acid bound via ester linkages to one molecule of glycerol).

chemical properties of neutral fats and oils

hydrolyzed, the ester linkages (carbonyl-to-oxygen bonds) break and the elements of water combine with the fragments. (This is not *how* the reaction happens; it is merely the overall effect.)

in general:

$$
\begin{array}{l}
R\!-\!\overset{\displaystyle O}{\overset{\|}{C}}\!-\!O\!-\!CH_2 \\[1em]
R'\!-\!\overset{\displaystyle O}{\overset{\|}{C}}\!-\!O\!-\!CH \quad +\ 3H_2O \xrightarrow{\text{(Enzymes)}} \\[1em]
R''\!-\!\overset{\displaystyle O}{\overset{\|}{C}}\!-\!O\!-\!CH_2
\end{array}
\qquad
\begin{array}{l}
R\!-\!\overset{\displaystyle O}{\overset{\|}{C}}\!-\!OH \quad HO\!-\!CH_2 \\[0.6em]
\qquad\qquad + \\[0.6em]
R'\!-\!\overset{\displaystyle O}{\overset{\|}{C}}\!-\!OH + HO\!-\!CH \\[0.6em]
\qquad\qquad + \\[0.6em]
R''\!-\!\overset{\displaystyle O}{\overset{\|}{C}}\!-\!OH \quad HO\!-\!CH_2
\end{array}
$$

Three different   Glycerol
fatty acids

example (using the triglyceride of Fig. 14.1):

$$
\begin{array}{l}
CH_3(CH_2)_7CH\!=\!CH(CH_2)_7\!-\!\overset{\displaystyle O}{\overset{\|}{C}}\!-\!O\!-\!CH_2 \\[1em]
CH_3(CH_2)_{14}\!-\!\overset{\displaystyle O}{\overset{\|}{C}}\!-\!O\!-\!CH \quad +\ 3H_2O \xrightarrow{\text{(enzymes)}} \\[1em]
CH_3(CH_2)_4CH\!=\!CHCH_2CH\!=\!CH(CH_2)_7\overset{\displaystyle O}{\overset{\|}{C}}\!-\!O\!-\!CH_2
\end{array}
$$

$$
CH_3(CH_2)_7CH\!=\!CH(CH_2)_7\!-\!\overset{\displaystyle O}{\overset{\|}{C}}\!-\!OH \quad HO\!-\!CH_2
$$
Oleic acid

$$
+ \\
CH_3(CH_2)_{14}\!-\!\overset{\displaystyle O}{\overset{\|}{C}}\!-\!OH + HO\!-\!CH
$$
Palmitic acid

$$
+ \\
CH_3(CH_2)_4CH\!=\!CHCH_2CH\!=\!CH(CH_2)_7\overset{\displaystyle O}{\overset{\|}{C}}\!-\!OH \quad HO\!-\!CH_2
$$
Linoleic acid   Glycerol

Acids also catalyze the hydrolysis of glycerides, but they are seldom used because of the difficulty of dissolving glycerides in an acid medium. The same problem of solubility is present in the digestive tract. However, certain compounds in bile emulsify fats and oils and thereby make enzymic action possible.

Hydrolysis is the only important reaction that lipids undergo during the process of digestion.

saponification. The saponification of the ester linkages in glycerides yields sodium (or potassium) salts of the fatty acids, in addition to glycerol. These salts are soaps, and how they function will be discussed later in this chapter.

in general:

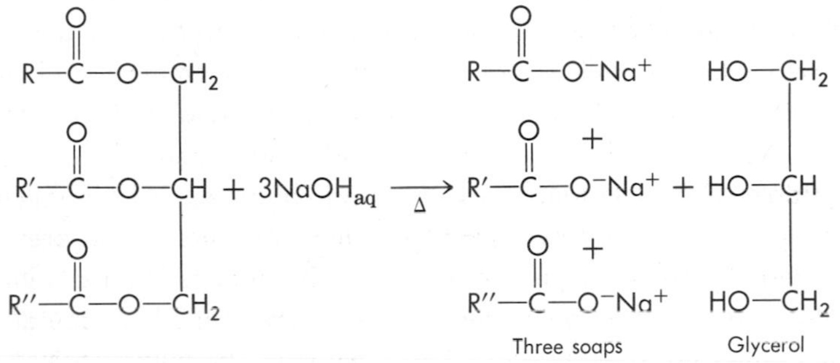

$$R-\overset{\overset{\displaystyle O}{\|}}{C}-O-CH_2$$
$$R'-\overset{\overset{\displaystyle O}{\|}}{C}-O-CH \;+\; 3NaOH_{aq} \xrightarrow{\Delta}$$
$$R''-\overset{\overset{\displaystyle O}{\|}}{C}-O-CH_2$$

$$R-\overset{\overset{\displaystyle O}{\|}}{C}-O^-Na^+ \quad HO-CH_2$$
$$+$$
$$R'-\overset{\overset{\displaystyle O}{\|}}{C}-O^-Na^+ \;+\; HO-CH$$
$$+$$
$$R''-\overset{\overset{\displaystyle O}{\|}}{C}-O^-Na^+ \quad HO-CH_2$$

Three soaps   Glycerol

example (using the triglyceride of Fig. 14.1):

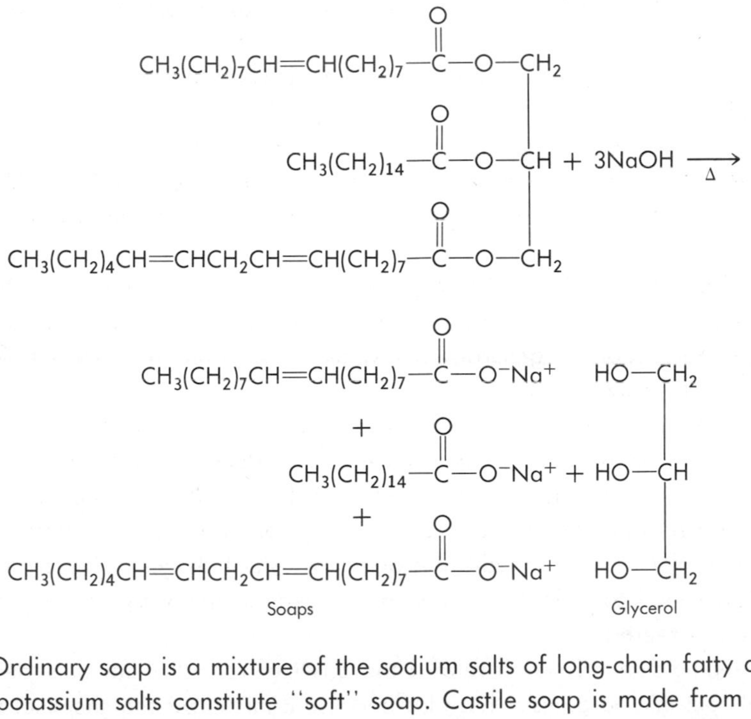

$$CH_3(CH_2)_7CH=CH(CH_2)_7-\overset{\overset{\displaystyle O}{\|}}{C}-O-CH_2$$

$$CH_3(CH_2)_{14}-\overset{\overset{\displaystyle O}{\|}}{C}-O-CH \;+\; 3NaOH \xrightarrow{\Delta}$$

$$CH_3(CH_2)_4CH=CHCH_2CH=CH(CH_2)_7-\overset{\overset{\displaystyle O}{\|}}{C}-O-CH_2$$

$$CH_3(CH_2)_7CH=CH(CH_2)_7-\overset{\overset{\displaystyle O}{\|}}{C}-O^-Na^+ \quad HO-CH_2$$
$$+$$
$$CH_3(CH_2)_{14}-\overset{\overset{\displaystyle O}{\|}}{C}-O^-Na^+ \;+\; HO-CH$$
$$+$$
$$CH_3(CH_2)_4CH=CHCH_2CH=CH(CH_2)_7-\overset{\overset{\displaystyle O}{\|}}{C}-O^-Na^+ \quad HO-CH_2$$

Soaps   Glycerol

Ordinary soap is a mixture of the sodium salts of long-chain fatty acids. The potassium salts constitute "soft" soap. Castile soap is made from olive oil; soaps that float have simply had air whipped into them. Perfumes and germicides are usually added. Whatever the method of processing or the composition, all soaps do their work in or about the same way.

hydrogenation. The facts that vegetable oils are liquids and that animal fats are solids at room temperature appear to be associated with the greater degree of saturation of the animal fats. Should double bonds in molecules of vegetable oils be hydrogenated, they would become more like those found in animal fats, and therefore "hydrogenated vegetable oils" would be solids at room temperature. A completely hydrogenated vegetable oil would be as brittle as tallow. Therefore, manufacturers of commercial products, such as Crisco, Fluffo, Mixo, and Spry, limit the degree of hydrogenation. Some double bonds are left; it does not matter very much exactly which ones. The product has a lowered iodine value (say, around 50 to 60), a higher degree of saturation, and a melting point such that it is a creamy solid at room temperature, similar to lard. Most of these commercial products are now blends of hydrogenated oils (i.e., solids) and unsaturated oils.

Vegetable oils, for instance, soybean and cottonseed oil, are cheap and very abundant. These are hydrogenated under pressure in the presence of a nickel catalyst until the degree of unsaturation is reduced to the point where the substance is a solid at room temperature. The peanut oil in popular brands of peanut butter has been partially hydrogenated. The lipid becomes a solid and does not separate.

If just one molecule of hydrogen were added to the molecule of the mixed glyceride of Fig. 14.1, its iodine number would drop from 89 to about 59, to the range of lard.

Oleomargarine is made by hydrogenating carefully selected and highly refined oils and fats and blending the solid products with unsaturated vegetable oils. The product is then emulsified with about 17% (by weight) of milk that has been cultured with a suitable microorganism to add flavor. Usually vitamins A and D, a yellow vegetable dye, and flavoring agents are added.

rancidity. When butter is left exposed to warm, moist air for any length of time, it turns "rancid"; that is, it loses its flavor and acquires a most disagreeable odor. In general, two kinds of reactions are responsible for rancidity: hydrolysis and oxidation.

The data in Table 14.3, footnote a, reveal that a variety of relatively volatile and odorous fatty acids would be produced if butterfat were hydrolyzed. Water for hydrolysis is present in butter. Microorganisms present in air can furnish catalysts for the reaction. Warmth accelerates virtually all reactions. Hence, simple hydrolysis of a few ester linkages in butterfat must inevitably lead to rancidity. It can be prevented simply by keeping butter cool and covered.

Keeping butter covered retards the onset of rancidity not only because it shuts out microorganisms but also because it minimizes the chemical effect of oxygen present in the air. Oxidation is the second type of chemical reaction that leads to rancidity. Atmospheric oxygen can attack unsaturated side chains on mixed glycerides. Some of these attacks may split off short-chain carboxylic acids or aldehydes. Both kinds of compounds are extremely disagreeable to the nose. (The C_6, C_8, and C_{10} acids, caproic, caprylic, and capric acids, are all named from the Latin *caper*, the goat.) People who exercise much and bathe little develop surface films containing, among many things, glycerides. If these are not washed away, they turn rancid; hence the "essence of stale locker room."

how detergents work. Glycerides and other types of "greases" (e.g., hydrocarbon oils) are the "glues" that bind dirt to surfaces. The problem of cleansing reduces itself to finding a way to loosen or to dissolve this glue. If the glue no longer sticks to the surface, neither can dirt particles, and they are easily washed away.

Water alone is a poor cleansing agent. Its molecules are so polar that they stick to each other (hydrogen bonds) rather than penetrate into a nonpolar region such as a surface film of grease.

When molecules of a soap or a synthetic detergent are present in water, they act to loosen greasy surface films. Molecules of a typical soap and a typical synthetic detergent are shown in Fig. 14.2. In both, there are a long, nonpolar, hydrocarbon-like "tail" and a very polar, water-soluble "head." Using the rule of thumb that "likes dissolve likes," we should expect the tail to be quite soluble in hydrocarbon-like compounds such as glycerides and other oils and greases. Indeed, the tail enters into solution in water only because the head, being so polar, in a sense "drags" it into solution. Figures 14.3 and 14.4 illustrate how this works.

Calcium and magnesium salts of long chain fatty acids are insoluble in

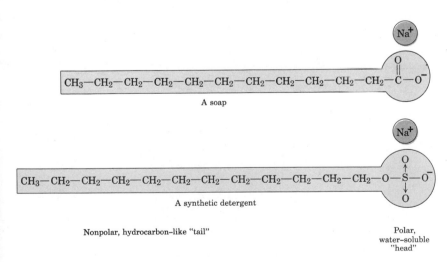

A soap

A synthetic detergent

Nonpolar, hydrocarbon–like "tail"

Polar, water–soluble "head"

Fig. 14.2 Two organic salts that have detergent properties.

chemical properties of neutral fats and oils

Surface   Surface

(a)   (b)

Fig. 14.3 Detergent action. (a) Nonpolar "tails" of detergent molecules become embedded in the grease layer. (b) Polar "heads" of detergent molecules tend to urge the grease layer away from the surface.

water. If ordinary soap is added to "hard water," water that contains calcium or magnesium ions, the following kind of reaction occurs:

$$2CH_3(CH_2)_{10}\overset{\overset{\displaystyle O}{\|}}{C}\!-\!O^-Na^+ + Ca^{2+} \longrightarrow \left[CH_3(CH_2)_{10}\overset{\overset{\displaystyle O}{\|}}{C}\!-\!O^-\right]_2 Ca^{2+} + 2Na^+$$

Sodium salt (soap)   Calcium salt ("scum")

Synthetic detergents are not affected by the ions present in hard water. Many are sodium salts of long-chain alkyl sulfuric acids, as illustrated by the structure in Fig. 14.2. Syndets such as these have largely supplanted soaps in industrial and home use. In the 1970 detergent market soaps accounted for only 15% (by weight) of the products (and 25% by value).

biodegradability. Ordinary soaps may have their disadvantages in hard water, but they cause virtually no lasting problems when waste water containing them is discharged into sewage disposal systems and eventually into the ground. This is because they are biodegradable. Microorganisms in sewage disposal plants and in the soil metabolize them. The search for economical detergents that would not precipitate in hard water led several companies to a variety of syndets that could be patented. Some of the types

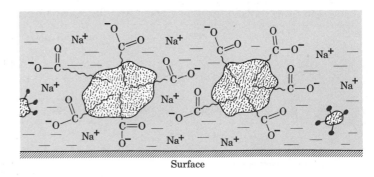

Surface

Fig. 14.4 These two grease globules, "pin cushioned" by negatively charged groups, cannot coalesce. Both carry negative charges, and like charges repel. They are now solubilized and are easily washed away.

are listed in Table 14.4. They worked in hard water, but in the sewage disposal systems of major metropolitan areas they did not "work" at all. Foams and suds which could not be degraded caused major breakdowns. Home owners with private wells complained that their tap water foamed. By 1966, however, the major syndet makers had found new syndets that were much more biodegradable, and the problem has been reduced to manageable proportions, at least in a technical sense. In the late 1960s, however, the major detergent manufacturers began to include enzymes in their products, an action that generated another controversy. In Chapter 16, where we shall study enzymes, we shall return to this topic. (Phosphates in laundry products were discussed in Chapter 7. They are a source of a different problem and have no bearing on biodegradability.)

In the simple triglycerides just discussed, all three hydroxyl groups of glycerol are esterified with various fatty acids. In the molecules of the glycerol-based phospholipids, one of these hydroxyl groups is esterified with phosphoric acid which, in turn, is further esterified with a particular amino alcohol. The nature of the groups attached at the remaining two —OHs of glycerol determines the subclass. (See Table 14.1.)

complex lipids
glycerol-based
phospholipids

phosphatides. In the phosphatides these two —OHs have become esterified with fatty acids. They may be regarded as derivatives of phosphatidic acid. Specific phosphatides are formed by esterifying the phosphate unit with choline, ethanolamine, or serine.

Table 14.4 **Biodegradability of Representative Types of Synthetic Detergents**

Types of Synthetic Detergents	Examples to Illustrate Structural Features	Biodegradable?
Sodium alkyl sulfate	$CH_3(CH_2)_{10}CH_2OSO_2O^-Na^+$	yes
Sodium alkylbenzene sulfonate, tetrapropylene-based	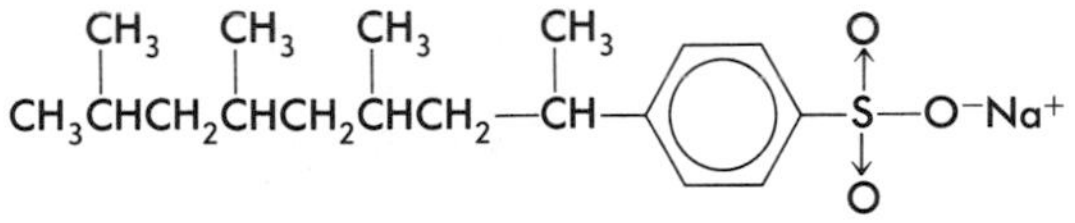	no
Sodium alkylbenzene sulfonate, n-paraffin or α-olefin-based	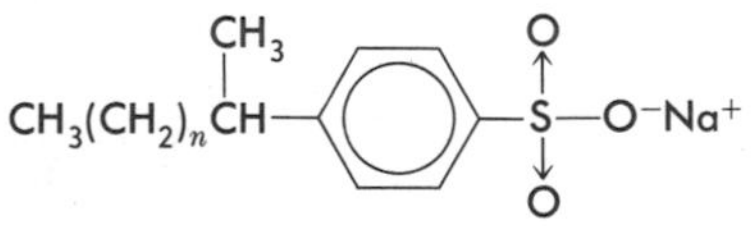 $(n = 7 - 11)$	largely so
Sodium alkane sulfonate	$C_nH_{2n+1}SO_3^-Na^+$ (chain is largely straight, n is 15 to 18)	almost completely

The phosphatides, and not all types are shown in Table 14.1 are often associated with membranes. They apparently have an essential role in the structure of cell walls and of the membranes enclosing cell nuclei, cytoplasmic organelles (e.g., mitochondria), and the endoplasmic reticulum. Serving this function, they appear to be metabolically more stable than ordinary triglycerides. Thus in animals that are starving the reserves of triglycerides (fats) become depleted as they are withdrawn for energy, but a certain amount of phosphatide materials remains, as it must since it is important to holding cells together.

The phosphatides also appear to be essential components of enzyme systems in mitochondria, which are small bodies located in the cytoplasm. Often referred to as the "powerhouse of the cell," a mitochondrion is involved in key energy-producing reactions for which complex systems of enzymes working in coordinated teams are necessary. The functional units of such systems consist of a group of enzymes embedded in a network of lipids (phosphatides) and proteins making up the walls of the mitochondria.

Phosphatides have also been implicated as essential for the formation of one of the factors needed to bring about the clotting of blood when injury occurs.

plasmalogens. The plasmalogens, another type of glycerol-based phospholipid, are widely distributed in animal tissue, particularly in the myelin sheaths of nerves and in heart and skeletal muscle.

The oxygen link to glycerol's middle carbon in most phospholipids is selectively hydrolyzed by the action of the enzyme *phospholipase A* (or "lecithinase A"), found in snake venom. Since the phosphatides are so intimately associated with the nervous system and with important cell parts, we readily understand why snake poisoning is so serious.

$$
\begin{array}{l}
\overset{\displaystyle O}{\underset{\displaystyle \|}{} } \\
CH_2OCR \\
| \\
CHOCH{=}CHR' \\
|\quad\ \ O \\
\quad\ \ \| \\
CH_2OPOCH_2CH_2{-}\overset{+}{N}(CH_3)_3 \\
|\ \ \\
O_-\quad or\quad {-}\overset{+}{N}H_3
\end{array}
$$

Plasmalogens

sphingosine-based lipids. sphingolipids Brain and nerve tissue as well as the lungs and spleen contain a lipid based not on glycerol but on an unsaturated amino alcohol, sphingosine. Table 14.1 shows the structures of two types of sphingolipids, the sphingomyelins and the cerebrosides. The cerebrosides are interesting lipids in that they contain a sugar unit, usually galactose. Their presence in brain and nerve tissue indicates their importance, but their exact function is not yet fully understood.

the myelin membrane. Structures called *axons* form the signal-bearing cores of nerve cells. Very long in relation to their diameters, they require protective insulation much like an electrical wire. The material serving this function for axons, called *myelin,* consists of lipids, proteins, polysaccharides, salts, and water, and is the most stable membrane known. Once formed about an axon, it endures for the lifetime of the individual. When the formation of myelin is faulty, the outlook is not bright. Niemann-Pick disease, multiple sclerosis, forms of leukodystrophy, and infantile Gaucher's disease are all related to unstable myelin membranes.

The stability of myelin is related, at least in part, to its lipid components. Compared to the proportion of sphingolipid in other membranes, that in myelin is much higher. The sphingolipids contain much longer fatty acid units than the triglycerides, units with from 19 to 26 carbons. Electron microscopy and X-ray diffraction analyses indicate that these long fatty acid side chains probably intertwine to give the molecular equivalent of steel mesh reinforcing concrete. When these side chains are much shorter (18 or fewer carbons) or highly unsaturated, studies have shown their intertwining to be less effective. The myelin is less stable, meaning a more vulnerable nervous system. Analysis of the myelin of individuals suffering from the diseases named has shown that for some reason the individuals have not succeeded in incorporating enough of the long-chain fatty acids in their myelin membranes, a significant example of the molecular basis of a disease.

steroids

The operation of extracting with solvents, which brings out triglycerides and complex lipids from plant and animal material, also brings out a group of nonsaponifiable compounds, the *steroids.* Their structures are generally characterized by a polycyclic carbon skeleton (Fig. 14.5). The alcohol group, the keto group, and the double bond are common. Since the ester linkage is seldom present, steroids are not saponifiable.

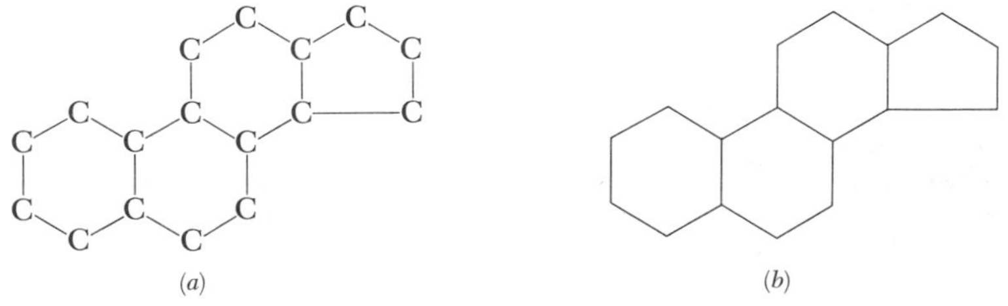

Fig. 14.5   (a) Basic carbon skeleton found in steroid molecules. (b) Most common condensation of the steroid "nucleus."

The physiological effects of the steroids vary greatly from compound to compound, ranging from vitamin activity to the action of sex hormones. Some steroids are fat emulsifiers found in bile; others are important hormones; one stimulates the heart; another has been implicated in hardening of the arteries; still another ruptures red blood cells. The structures, names, and chief physiological properties of a few important steroids are given in the following list.

Important Individual Steroids

Sex hormones

This is one human estrogenic hormone.

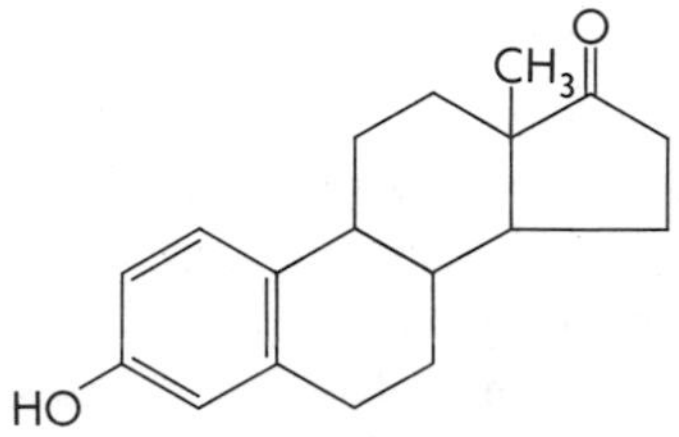

Estrone

This human pregnancy hormone is secreted by the corpus luteum.

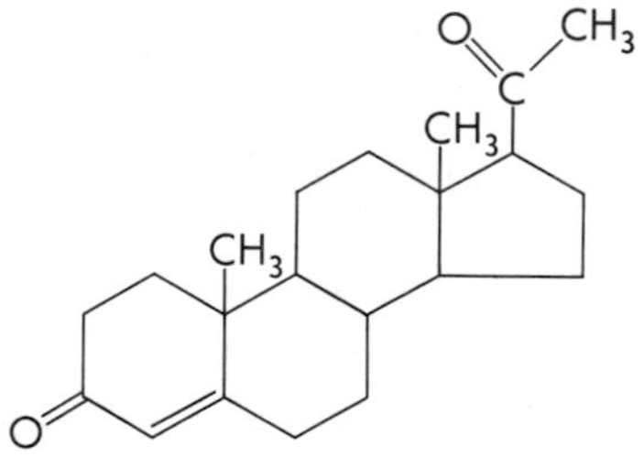

Progesterone

This male sex hormone regulates the development of reproductive organs and secondary sex characteristics.

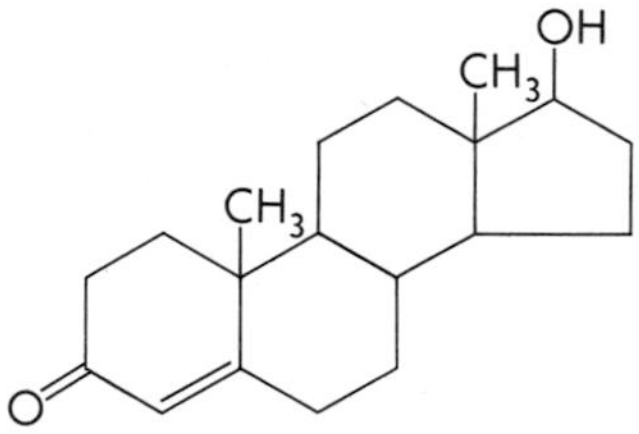

Testosterone

Androsterone, a second male sex hormone, is less potent than testosterone

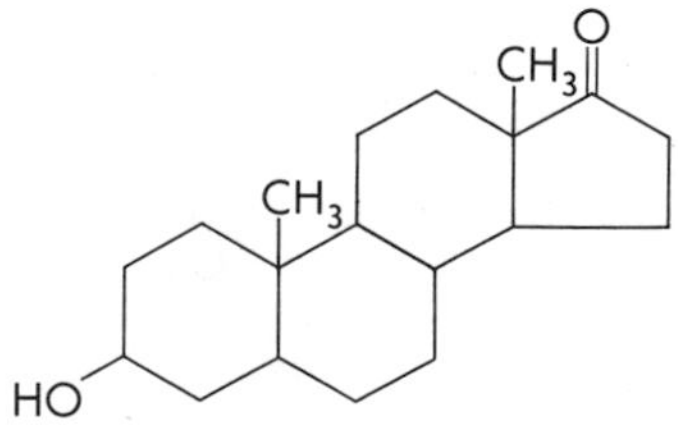

Androsterone

Synthetic Hormones in Fertility Control

Oral contraceptive pills contain (1971) two hormone-like compounds—an estrogen (0.05 mg or more) and a progestin (0.5 mg or more). If they are taken daily for 20–21 days, beginning on the fifth day of the menstrual cycle, they appear to affect the pituitary gland to induce a pregnancy-like state as far as the ovaries are concerned. Ovulation is therefore prevented making conception impossible. Probably the most widely sold pills contained (1971) mestranol and norethynodrel (as in Enovid) or mestranol and norethindrone (as in Ovulen). (Provest and C-Quens were taken off the market in October 1970 because they incorporated a progestin, not shown here, that in tests on beagle dogs gave cause for concern.) For reasons not at all clear, it is possible that the antifertility effect can be achieved by the progestin alone, and in the early 1970s many countries were investigating this development.

Synthetic Estrogens

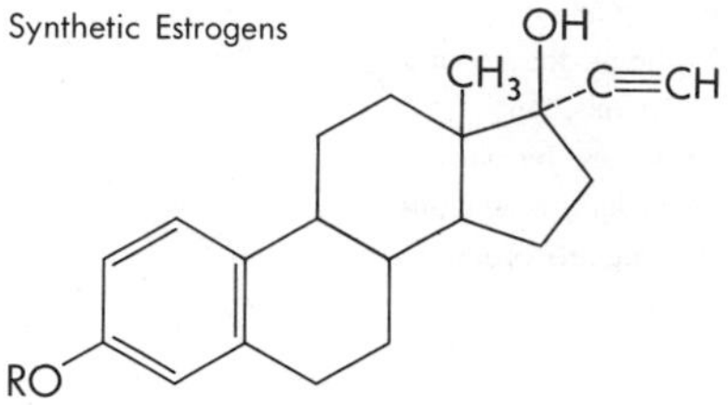

If R = H, Ethynylestradiol
R = CH_3, Mestranol

Synthetic Progestins

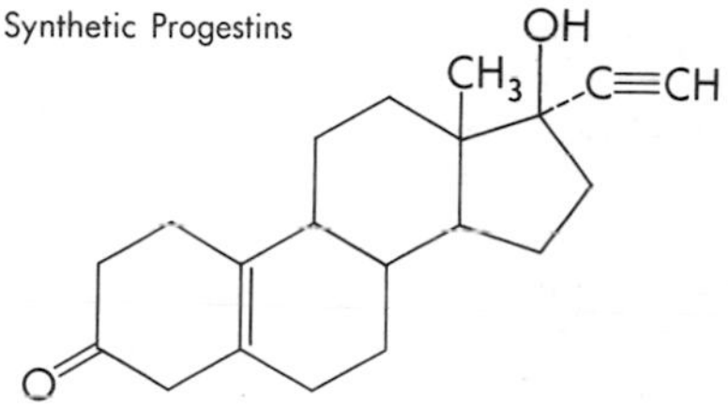

Norethynodrel

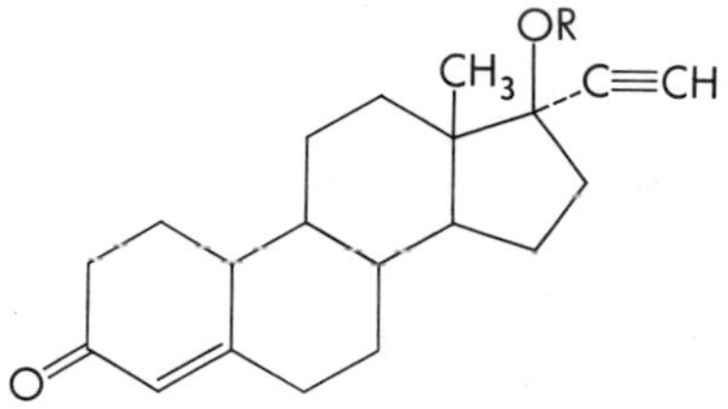

If R = H, Norethindrone

R = $\overset{\overset{\textstyle O}{\|}}{C}$—$CH_3$, Norethindrone acetate

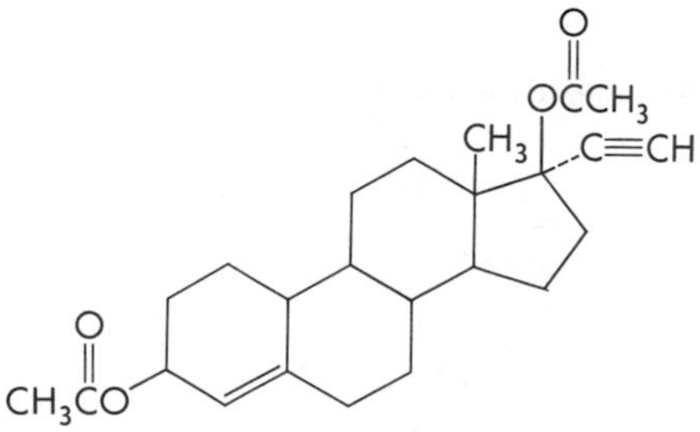

Ethynodiol diacetate

Vitamin D₂ precursor

Irradiation of this hormone, the commonest of all plant hormones, by ultraviolet light opens one of the rings to produce vitamin D₂.

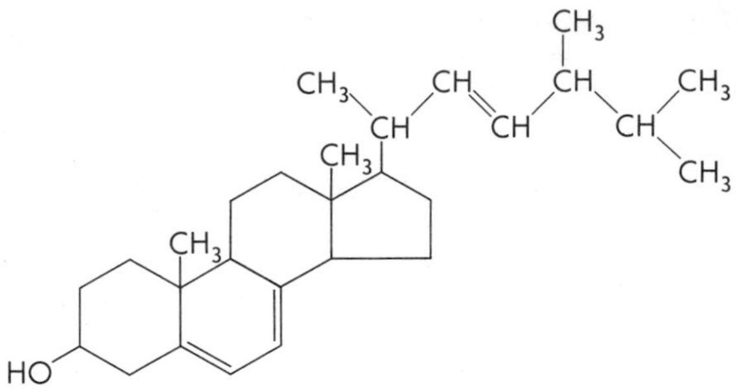

Ergosterol

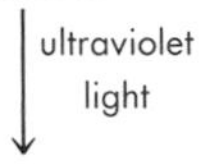

ultraviolet light

A deficiency of this antirachitic factor causes rickets, an infant and childhood disease characterized by faulty deposition of calcium phosphate and poor bone growth.

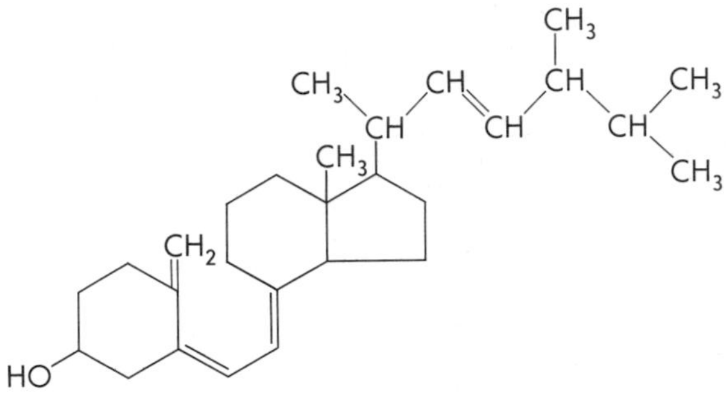

Vitamin D₂

Bile acid

Cholic acid is found in bile in the form of its sodium salt. This and closely related salts are the bile salts that act as powerful emulsifiers of lipid material awaiting digestion in the upper intestinal tract. The sodium salt of cholic acid is soaplike because it has a very polar head and a large hydrocarbon tail.

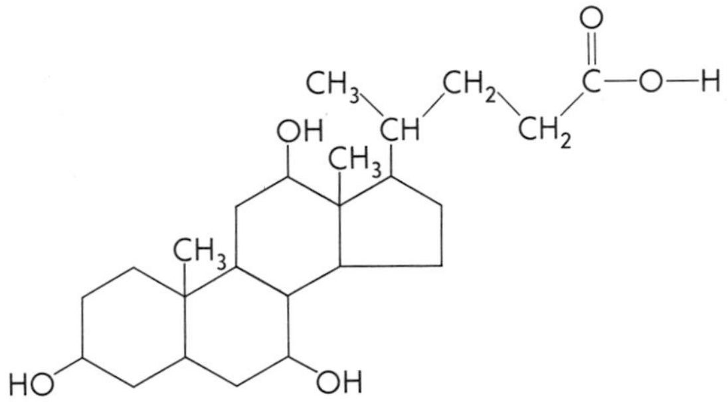

Cholic acid

Antiarthritic compound

One of the twenty-eight adrenal cortical hormones, cortisone is not only important in the control of carbohydrate metabolism but also effective in relieving the symptoms of rheumatoid arthritis.

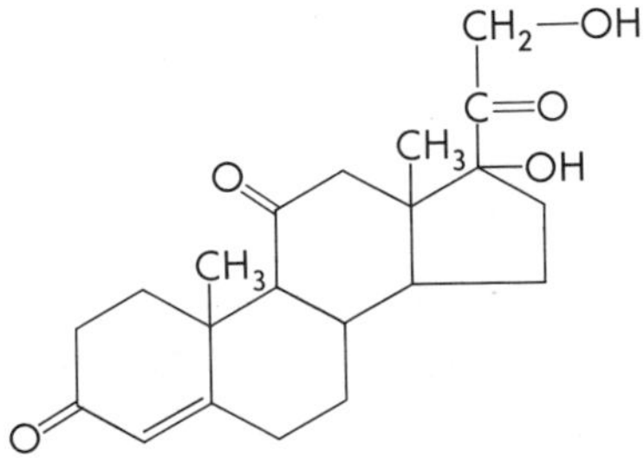

Cortisone

Digitoxigenin is found in many poisonous plants, notably digitalis, as a complex glycoside. In small doses it stimulates the vagus mechanism and increases heart tone. In larger doses it is a potent poison.

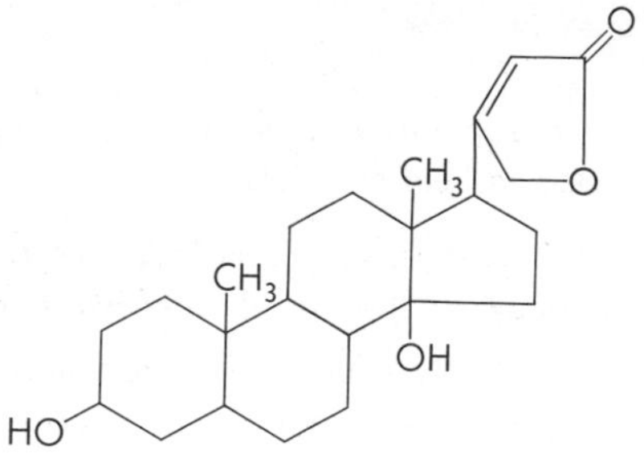

Digitoxigenin

cholesterol. Cholesterol is a steroid alcohol or *sterol*. It is found in nearly all tissues of vertebrates, particularly in the brain and spinal cord, and is the main constituent of gallstones. In recent years it has been associated with circulatory problems such as hardening of the arteries. Its physiological function is still not understood, but we generally assume that the body needs it as a raw material for building other usable steroids.

Human beings and the higher animals can synthesize cholesterol. Most recent evidence indicates that the body can make it from acetate units in about 36 steps and in a matter of seconds.

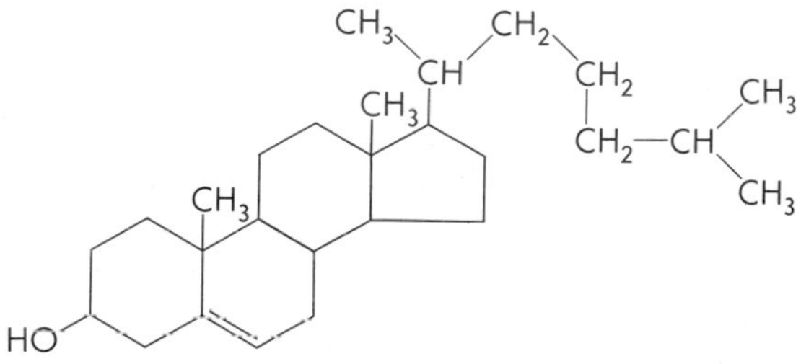

Cholesterol
(Greek: *chole,* bile; *stereos,* solid; plus "-ol," alcohol)

Selected Reading List

Any textbook on organic chemistry or biochemistry will contain additional information about lipids.

Pamphlet

1. *Food Fats and Oils.* Prepared by the Institute of Shortening and Edible Oils, Inc., Washington, D. C., 1968, for students and teachers, physicians and nutritionists to provide information at a relatively uncomplicated level about the main fats and oils and their food sources.

Brief Summary

The important aspects of lipid chemistry relate to the chief structural features found in lipid molecules.

1. Glycerides are mixed esters of glycerol and long-chain fatty acids. Therefore, they can be hydrolyzed (digestion) and saponified (soap making).

2. Since glyceride molecules are substantially hydrocarbon-like, they are only slightly polar; they are insoluble in water and soluble in the common organic solvents.

3. Glyceride molecules usually possess one or more alkene linkages. Hence they undergo typical alkene addition reactions (e.g., hydrogenation). A rise in saturation (i.e., a drop in iodine number) is accompanied by a rise in melting point, a fact important to manufacturers of "hydrogenated vegetable oils."

4. Detergents function primarily by emulsifying oils and greases. A successful detergent molecule must combine a portion that tends to be soluble in fats and oils with a section that tends to be very soluble in water.

5. Phospholipids are especially important in the nervous system.

6. Steroids are lipids that cannot be saponified but are largely hydrocarbon-like.

Problems and Exercises

1. Write the structure of a mixed glyceride between glycerol and the following three acids: linolenic, oleic, and myristic.
   (a) Write an equation illustrating the hydrogenation of this mixed glyceride to an iodine number of zero.
   (b) Calculate the iodine number of this mixed glyceride.
   (c) Would it most likely be found in a vegetable oil or an animal fat? Why?
   (d) What would be the iodine number of the glyceride resulting from the addition of hydrogen to just one of the double bonds in the mixed glyceride?

2. Write the structures of all the products that would form from the complete digestion of the following lipid.

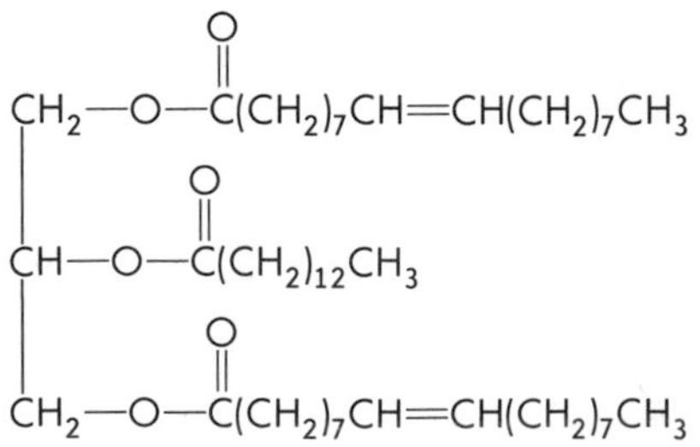

$$CH_2-O-\overset{\displaystyle O}{\overset{\|}{C}}(CH_2)_7CH=CH(CH_2)_7CH_3$$

$$CH-O-\overset{\displaystyle O}{\overset{\|}{C}}(CH_2)_{12}CH_3$$

$$CH_2-O-\overset{\displaystyle O}{\overset{\|}{C}}(CH_2)_7CH=CH(CH_2)_7CH_3$$

3. Write the structures of all the products that would form from the saponification of the lipid with the structure shown in Exercise 2.

4. Hydrolysis of a lipid produced glycerol, lauric acid, linoleic acid, and oleic acid. Write a structure of the lipid consistent with these results.

5. When hydrochloric acid is added to a solution of the soap:

$$CH_3(CH_2)_{12}\overset{\overset{\displaystyle O}{\|}}{C}-O^-Na^+$$

a precipitate forms that is soluble in ether. What is its structure and common name?

6. Some low-sudsing detergents for automatic washers consist of molecules of the following type:

$$R-\overset{\overset{\displaystyle O}{\|}}{C}-O-(CH_2-CH_2-O)_n-CH_2-CH_2-O-H$$

(R is long)   (n = 6–12)

Note that the structure is not ionic; yet it has detergent properties. Explain. (See Brief Summary, Part 4.)

chapter 15 proteins

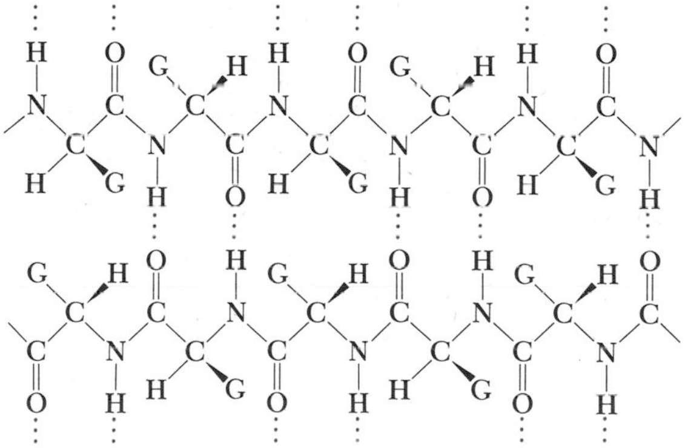

Structure determines property. This is true of organic compounds. It is also true of biological life. Among the most important problems of modern biology are the shapes and sizes of molecules and how their structures make possible their functions. In the chemical inventory of a living organism are a family of organic polymers called the proteins. They are jacks of all trades and masters of every one of them. Proteins hold a living organism together and run it. They give it a shell (skin); they provide levers (muscles and tendons); they establish a communications network (nerves); they are policemen and long-distance haulers (buffers, antibodies, hemoglobin); and they direct and control all forms of body repair and construction (enzymes and hormones). They are truly deserving of the name *protein*, taken from the Greek *proteios*, meaning first. They are the substance if not the essence of biological life.

primary structural features of proteins

Proteins are found in all cells and in all parts of cells. About 15% of human body weight is protein.

In addition to carbon, hydrogen, and oxygen, proteins contain nitrogen and sulfur. Trace amounts of other elements, including metal ions, are occasionally found.

Protein molecules are enormous in size and complexity. They have formula weights ranging from 10,000 to over a million. Analysis of one sample of hemoglobin, the protein that transports oxygen in the bloodstream, revealed a molecular formula of

$$(C_{738}H_{1166}O_{208}N_{203}S_2Fe)_4$$

amino acids; monomers of proteins. Complex though proteins are, they have one simplifying feature. All proteins, however complicated or large, are formed from a relatively small number of organic building blocks. These units, the *amino acids,* share a common structural feature:

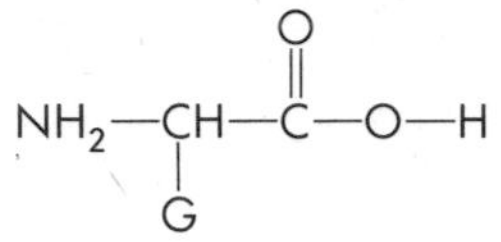

Generic structure of an amino acid, where G is an organic group

The primary difference between various amino acids is the nature of the group G—. Table 15.1 lists the 26 amino acids that are accepted as being the most important.

With thousands and thousands of different proteins in existence, it is some relief (for both students and practicing chemists) that they are constructed of as few as 26 building blocks. But then the entire English language, all the works of Shakespeare, Shaw, Tolstoi, the Bible, all the English language books and periodicals (or English language translations of other works) housed in the homes, schools, and libraries of the world are structured from exactly the same number of building units, the letters of our alphabet.

the peptide bond; the key to protein structure. Each amino acid can function either as an amine or as an acid, or as both. *In proteins, amino acid units are joined together by amide linkages.* Suppose that we have one molecule of glycine and one of alanine. Suppose that glycine acts as a carboxylic acid, and alanine acts as an amine in amide formation:

Glycine (acid) Alanine (amine) Glycylalanine (a dipeptide)

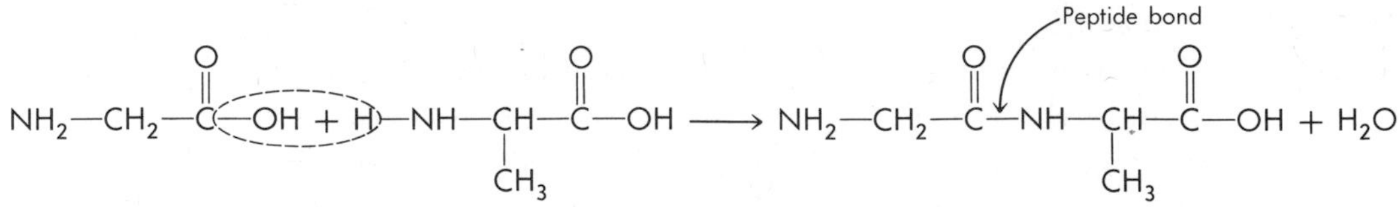

In another experiment, imagine that alanine acts as the carboxylic acid and glycine acts as the amine:

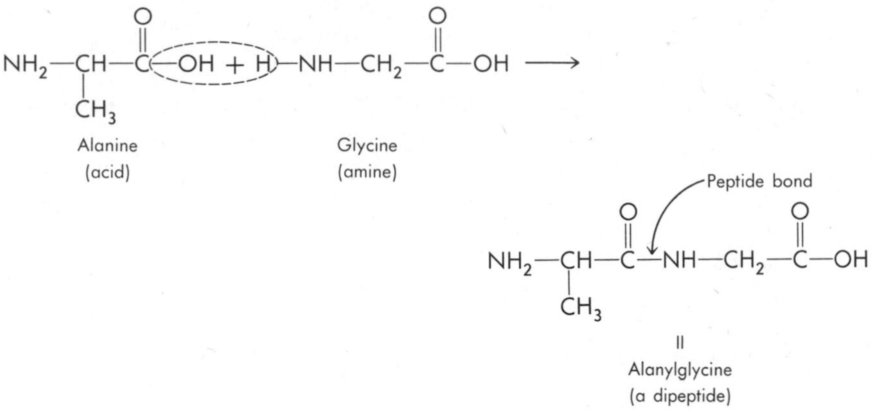

$$NH_2-CH-C \underset{\cdots}{(}OH + H)-NH-CH_2-C-OH \longrightarrow$$

(with CH_3 on the alanine carbon, and O double bonds on the carbonyls)

Alanine   Glycine
(acid)   (amine)

Peptide bond

$$NH_2-CH-C-NH-CH_2-C-OH$$

(with CH_3 on the alanine carbon, and O double bonds on the carbonyls)

II
Alanylglycine
(a dipeptide)

Amide linkages that occur in proteins are commonly called *peptide bonds*. When two or more amino acid units are joined by means of peptide linkages, the products, generically, are called *peptides*. The union of two amino acids results in a *dipeptide;* three amino acid units form a *tripeptide;* several units yield a *polypeptide*.

Structures I and II represent two different dipeptides. From two *different* amino acids, two dipeptides are possible (just as from two letters you can make two words: e.g., ON and NO). From three different amino acids, six isomeric tripeptides could possibly form, depending on the exact order in which the amino acids were combined. Using, for example, glycine, alanine, and cysteine, one of the possibilities is:

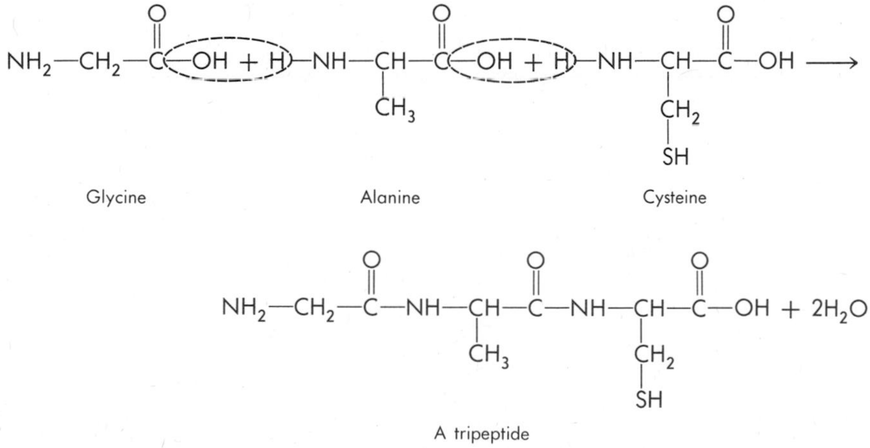

$$NH_2-CH_2-C(OH + H)-NH-CH-C(OH + H)-NH-CH-C-OH \longrightarrow$$

(with CH_3 and CH_2—SH side chains, and O double bonds on the carbonyls)

Glycine   Alanine   Cysteine

$$NH_2-CH_2-C-NH-CH-C-NH-CH-C-OH + 2H_2O$$

(with CH_3 and CH_2—SH side chains, and O double bonds on the carbonyls)

A tripeptide

In addition to the above glycine-alanine-cysteine sequence, the other five possible sequences (or isomers) are these (where the first amino acid in the

Table 15.1   Common Amino Acids

Structure	Name	Structure	Name
HO—C(=O)—CH—H, NH₂	Glycine	HO—C(=O)—CH(—NH₂)—CH₂CH₂CH₂N(H)—C(=NH)—NH₂	Arginine
—CH₃	Alanine	—CH₂—C=CH, HN, N, CH (imidazole)	Histidine
—CH—CH₃, CH₃	Valine		
—CH₂CHCH₃, CH₃	Leucine	—CH₂— (benzene ring)	Phenylalanine
—CHCH₂CH₃, CH₃	Isoleucine		
—CH₂OH	Serine	—CH₂—(benzene ring)—OH	Tyrosine
—CHCH₃, OH	Threonine		
—CH₂SH	Cysteine	—CH₂—(benzene ring with I, I)—OH	Diiodotyrosine
—CH₂—S, —CH₂—S	Cystine		
—CH₂CH₂SCH₃	Methionine	—CH₂—(benzene ring with Br, Br)—OH	Dibromotyrosine
—CH₂C(=O)—OH	Aspartic acid	—CH₂—(ring I, I)—O—(ring I, I)—OH	Thyroxine
—CH₂C(=O)—NH₂	Asparagine		
—CH₂CH₂C(=O)—OH	Glutamic acid	—CH₂—(indole ring), N—H	Tryptophan
—CH₂CH₂C(=O)—NH₂	Glutamine		
—CH₂CH₂CH₂CH₂NH₂	Lysine	HO—C(=O)—CH—CH₂, H—N—CH₂, CH₂ (proline ring)	Proline
—CH₂CH₂CHCH₂NH₂, OH	Hydroxylysine	HO—C(=O)—CH—CH₂, H—N—CH—OH, CH₂ (hydroxyproline ring)	Hydroxyproline

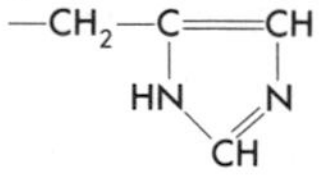

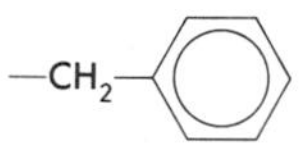

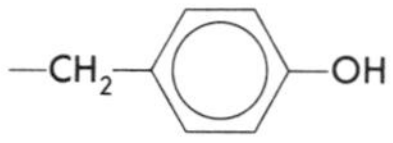

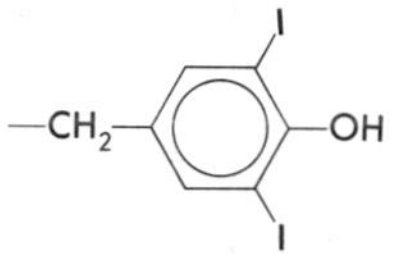

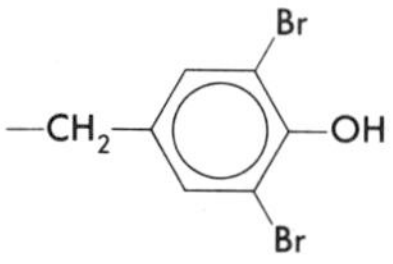

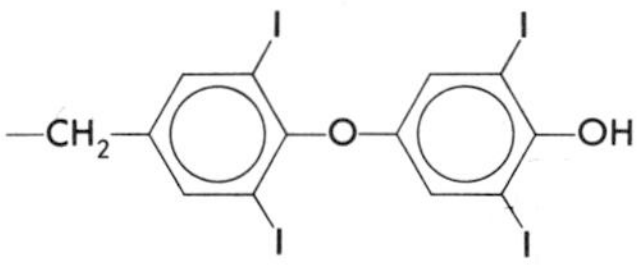

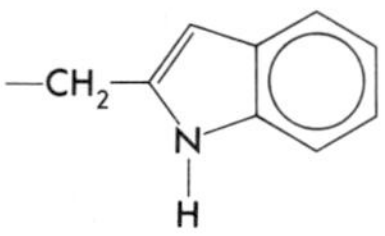

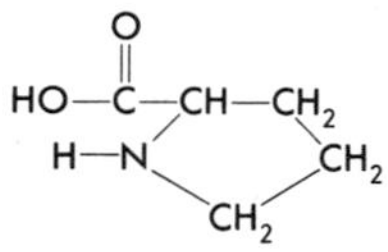

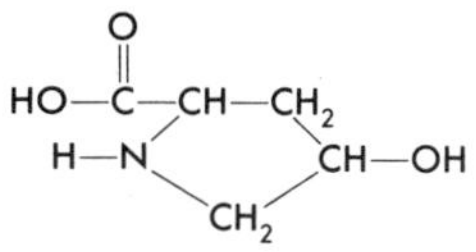

sequence is understood to have functioned as a carboxylic acid in peptide-bond formation):

Glycine-cysteine-alanine   Cysteine-glycine-alanine
Alanine-glycine-cysteine   Cysteine-alanine-glycine
Alanine-cysteine-glycine

(By analogy, if we worked with three letters, A, E, and T, the following six words would be possible:

AET   EAT   TAE
ATE   ETA   TEA

Not all are words in the English language, but then not all possible amino acid combinations would be found in one particular species, either.)

The more different amino acids that are used, the more polypeptides are possible. For example, if 17 different amino acids were used, a total of 3.56×10^{14} uniquely different but isomeric sequences would be possible! In many proteins, that many and more amino acid units appear many times. In one typical protein, which had a formula weight of about 34,000, 12 different amino acids were isolated. Analysis revealed that there were 288 peptide bonds; thus, it is obvious that many of the 12 amino acid units were used several times.

The "demand" for an almost infinite variety of proteins is seen in the estimate that the human body alone, as only one of thousands of animal organisms, contains upwards of 100,000 different kinds of protein molecules. Yet this "demand" is met far more than adequately by the possibilities offered by over 20 different amino acids. (For example, the protein above, with 12 different amino acids and 288 possible peptide bonds, is capable of existing in an estimated 10^{300} isomers—a number beyond the scope of the imagination. If the planet earth consisted of nothing more than a collection of one *molecule* of each of these isomers, each molecule weighing only about 10^{-20} gram, the earth would weigh about 10^{280} grams. However, the actual weight of the earth is only an estimated 6×10^{27} grams. Clearly, far fewer proteins exist than are theoretically possible.)

In summary, the primary structural feature of a protein, as illustrated in Fig. 15.1, is the "backbone" of a series of peptide linkages and the groupings

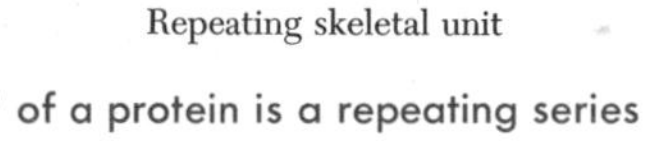

$$
\begin{array}{cccccc}
& & O & & & O & \\
& | & \| & | & | & \| & | \\
-N & -C & -C & -N & -C & -C & -N- \\
& | & & | & | & & | \\
\end{array}
$$

Repeating skeletal unit

Fig. 15.1   The "backbone" of a protein is a repeating series of nitrogen-carbon-carbonyl units contributed by amino acids.

of nitrogen-carbon-carbonyl. All proteins are identical in this respect. They differ in the lengths of "backbones" and in the kind, the number, and especially the sequence in which side chains occur.

secondary
structural
features If proteins were little more than very long molecules, they would be capable of existing in as many different and random shapes as are present in a tangle of thousands of long cotton threads. Just simply from the image of a long, stringy molecule, capable of utterly disordered twistings, it is difficult to see how the orderliness in certain protein systems would be possible. At least some, perhaps most, proteins exist in definite gross conformations or shapes. The secondary structural features are the factors that tend to restrict protein molecules to such unique shapes.

salt bridges. Salt bridges are ionic bonds existing between oppositely charged groups that project away from peptide backbones of protein molecules. Opposite charges can originate as follows. Molecules of two amino acids, aspartic acid and glutamic acid, possess carboxyl groups on their side chains. Molecules of several amino acids, such as lysine, have "extra" amino groups.

$$NH_2-CH-\overset{\displaystyle O}{\overset{\|}{C}}-OH \qquad NH_2-CH-\overset{\displaystyle O}{\overset{\|}{C}}-OH \qquad NH_2-CH-\overset{\displaystyle O}{\overset{\|}{C}}-OH$$

$$\begin{array}{ccc}
\underset{\displaystyle \overset{|}{C}-OH}{\overset{|}{CH_2}} & \underset{\displaystyle \overset{|}{CH_2}}{\overset{|}{CH_2}} & \underset{\displaystyle NH_2}{\overset{|}{(CH_2)_4}} \\
O & C-OH & \\
& O &
\end{array}$$

Aspartic acid   Glutamic acid   Lysine

Proton transfers between these two kinds of groups would leave oppositely charged ions. These would experience an attraction that would help keep one protein chain held to another. If the oppositely charged groups were on the same chain, then one portion of the chain would be folded back and held to another portion. These possibilities are illustrated in Fig. 15.2.

disulfide link. One of the amino acids, cysteine, carries a free mercaptan group (—S—H). Mercaptans are easily oxidized to disulfides (—S—S—). (See Chapter 11.) Mild oxidation of two molecules of cysteine yields one molecule of another amino acid, cystine. If the mercaptan-bearing side chain of cysteine appears on two neighboring protein molecules, mild oxidation will link the two molecules through a disulfide bond, as illustrated in Fig. 15.3. The cross linking may occur between segments of the same protein strand, in which case a closed loop results.

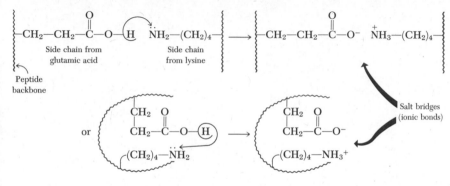

Fig. 15.2 By acid-base interactions, two peptide strands could acquire opposite charges that would act to hold them together.

The structure of what is regarded as a relatively simple protein, the hormone insulin, is reproduced in Fig. 15.4. Three disulfide bonds are important to its structure.

hydrogen bonds. The type of hydrogen bonding most common in proteins is illustrated in Fig. 15.5. A hydrogen attached to nitrogen at an amide link

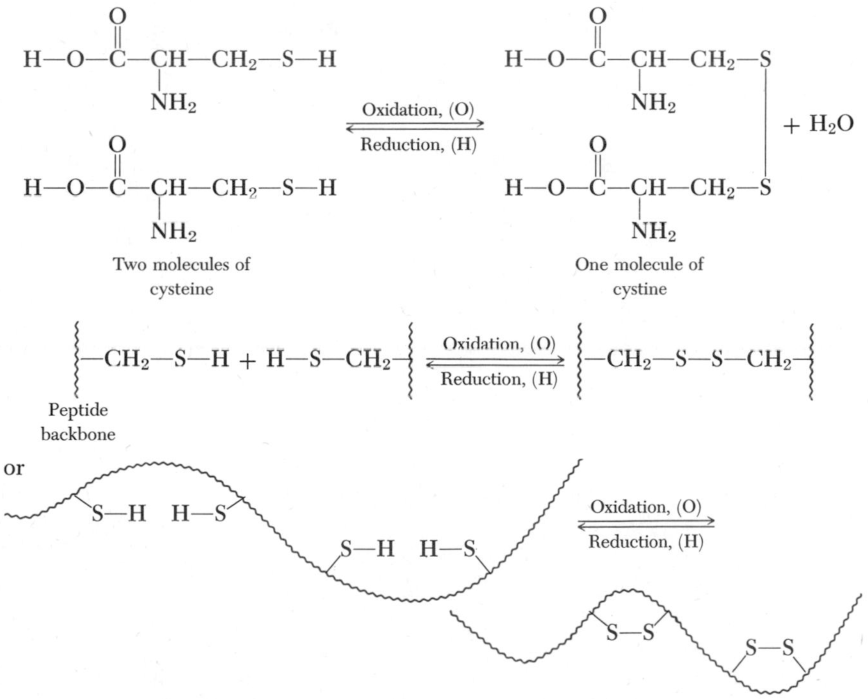

$$H-O-\overset{\overset{\displaystyle O}{\|}}{C}-CH-CH_2-S-H$$
$$NH_2$$

$$H-O-\overset{\overset{\displaystyle O}{\|}}{C}-CH-CH_2-S-H$$
$$NH_2$$

Two molecules of cysteine

Oxidation, (O) / Reduction, (H)

$$H-O-\overset{\overset{\displaystyle O}{\|}}{C}-CH-CH_2-S$$
$$NH_2$$
$$|$$
$$H-O-\overset{\overset{\displaystyle O}{\|}}{C}-CH-CH_2-S$$
$$NH_2$$

$+ H_2O$

One molecule of cystine

$$-CH_2-S-H + H-S-CH_2-$$

Peptide backbone

Oxidation, (O) / Reduction, (H)

$$-CH_2-S-S-CH_2-$$

or

S—H H—S

S—H H—S

Oxidation, (O) / Reduction, (H)

S—S

S—S

Fig. 15.3 The presence of cysteine units in peptide strands provides the occasion for the formation of disulfide links. These contribute to stabilizing a protein in a particular conformation.

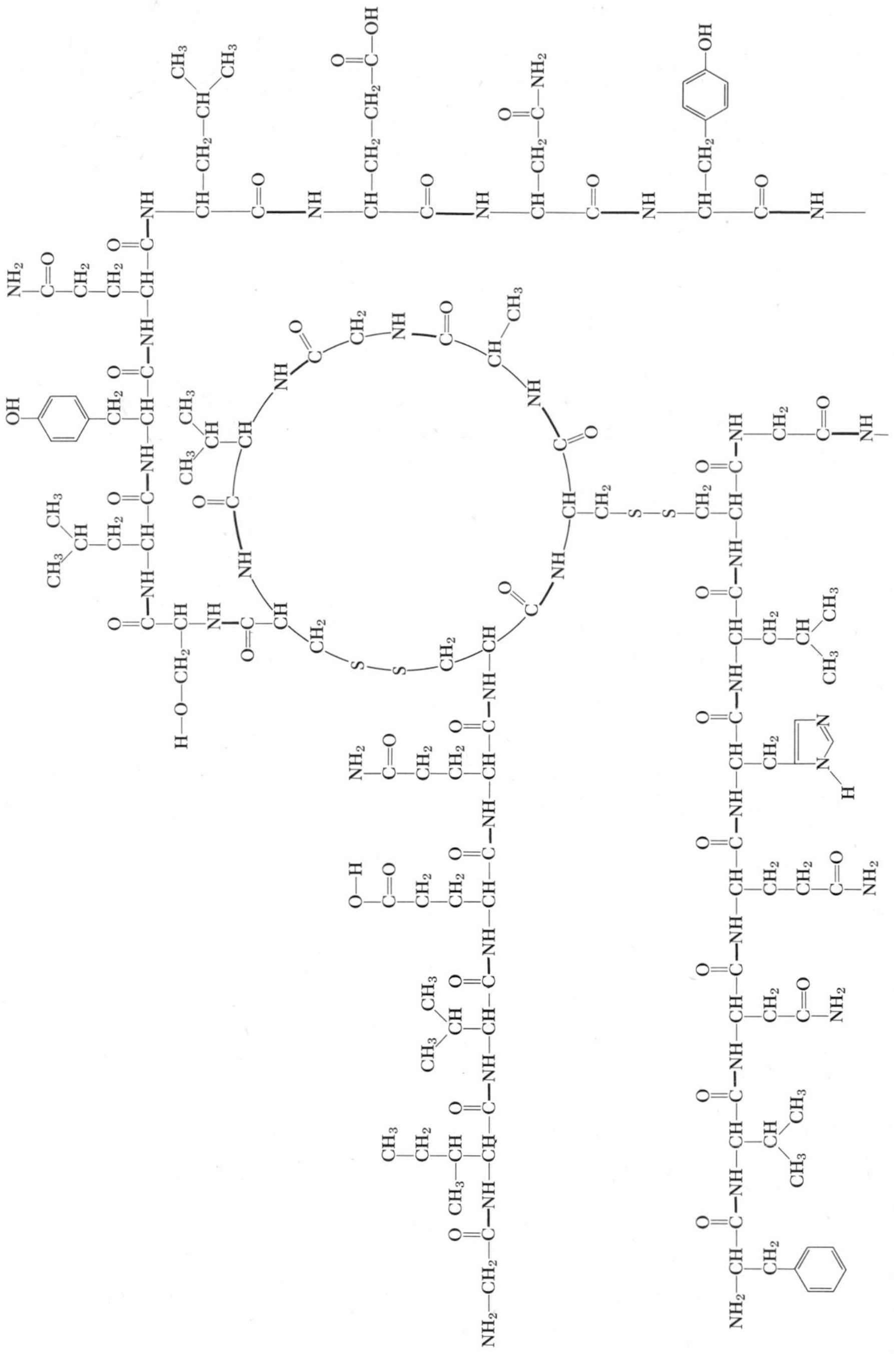

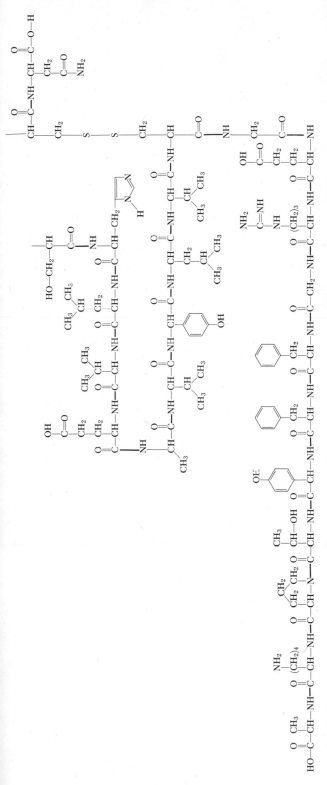

Fig. 15.4 Sheep insulin. Most proteins are vastly more complex than insulin, which is regarded by scientists as a relatively simple protein. Insulin molecules from other sources differ by one side chain. Cells that manufacture this protein must routinely, day in and day out, assemble the appropriate amino acids in the right sequence. The mechanism for accomplishing such a chemical task is discussed in Chapter 21. The bold-face lines in this structure are the peptide bonds.

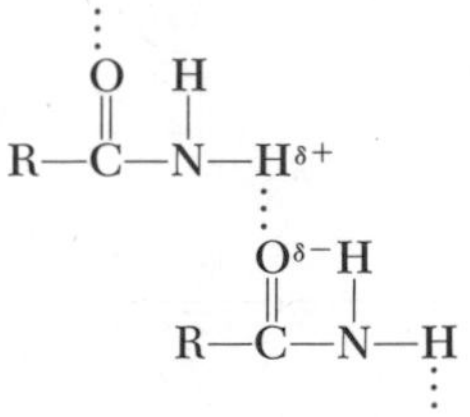

$$R{-}\overset{\overset{\displaystyle O}{\|}}{C}{-}\overset{\overset{\displaystyle H}{|}}{N}{-}H^{\delta+}$$

$$R{-}\overset{\overset{\displaystyle O^{\delta-}{-}H}{\|}}{C}{-}\overset{}{N}{-}H$$

Fig. 15.5 Hydrogen bonding between amide molecules. Hydrogen on nitrogen acts as a bridge to a carbonyl oxygen.

acts as a bridge (hydrogen bond) to an oxygen of a carbonyl group located elsewhere.

Hundreds of peptide (amide) links and carbonyl groups in protein molecules make possible hundreds of hydrogen bonds. Although a single hydrogen bond is quite weak, compared with a covalent bond, the accumulation of several creates great overall strength. The analogy with a zipper is so striking that hydrogen bonds are sometimes called the "zippers" of proteins. Figure 15.6 illustrates hydrogen bonding between two extended polypeptide strands.

possible spatial configurations for proteins Linus Pauling (Nobel Prize, 1954) and R. B. Corey suggested two possible kinds of configurations for polypeptide chains. One involves a nearly planar, sheetlike network of polypeptide chains lying more or less side by side, as indicated in Fig. 15.6. In the better representation of Fig. 15.7, these "sheets" according to Pauling and Corey, possess a regular pleated or folded structure. This *pleated-sheet* configuration appears to fit nearly all the known facts about the structure of the protein in silk.

A configuration that appears to occur more frequently than the pleated sheet, and one also suggested by Pauling and Corey, is the α-helix. In this arrangement the polypeptide backbone is coiled as one would coil a chain around a cylinder. The helix is stabilized internally by hydrogen bonds from one NH group to the carbonyl oxygen of the third amino acid unit down

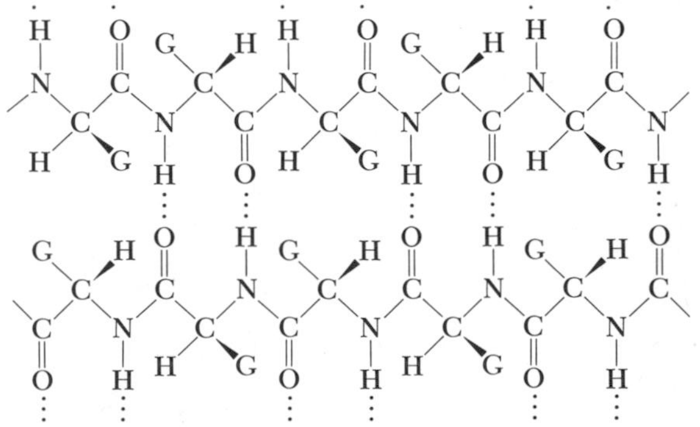

Fig. 15.6 Hydrogen bonding (···) between extended polypeptide chains.

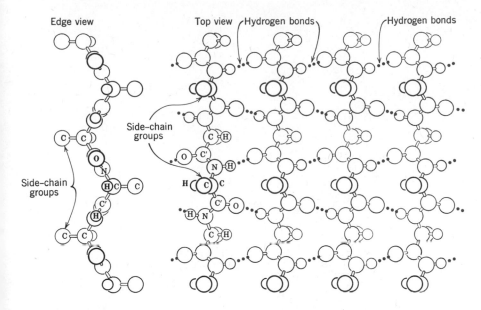

Edge view

Top view

Hydrogen bonds

Hydrogen bonds

Side-chain groups

Side-chain groups

Fig. 15.7 Pleated-sheet structure of extended polypeptide chains. Groups indicated by heavy lines are meant to project forward; those by light lines, backward. Dotted lines indicate hydrogen bonds that hold parallel polypeptide chains to each other and stabilize the configuration. (By permission of L. Pauling and R. B. Corey.)

the coiled chain. The α-helix, illustrated in Fig. 15.8, not only appears in many fibrous proteins but also occurs in some globular proteins. The helix arrangement plays its most dramatic role in the chemistry of heredity, the subject of Chapter 21.

The helix picture does not tell the whole story. Helices, in turn, may fold or twist into more complicated shapes. If you look back to Table 15.1, you will note that the first several amino acids have hydrocarbon side chains. These amino acids are commonly found in proteins. Seldom do they account for less than 40% of a protein structure. But these groups certainly do not contribute to any enhancement of a protein's water solubility. Yet, even the water-soluble proteins are rich in these alkane-like side chains. To minimize contact between these groups and water, many proteins are found to exist in helices that have become further folded and twisted in such a way that their hydrocarbon-like side chains are folded inside, away from the water, and their more polar side chains are left exposed. This phenomenon is particularly common among one class of proteins—the globular proteins—which in organisms are usually in an aqueous environment.

Whatever coiling and folding takes place is, in a sense, demanded by the primary structure of any given protein—its sequence of amino acids. If these are assembled correctly (and *how* this happens will be studied under the chemistry of heredity, Chapter 21), then the coiling and folding follows

(a)

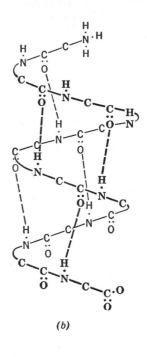

(b)

Fig. 15.8 Polypeptide chain in a helix configuration. (a) A ball and stick model. (b) The bare skeleton of the helix. Dashed lines indicate hydrogen bonds. [(a) By permission of L. Pauling and R. B. Corey. (b) From J. L. Oncley, F. O. Schmitt, R. C. Williams, M. D. Rosenberg, and R. H. Bolt. *Biophysical Science: A Study Program*, page 101. John Wiley & Sons, New York, 1959.]

automatically. In addition to the primary structure, the medium itself—especially its pH—is equally important in determining the final shape of a protein. Some of the most interesting evidence for this has come from work with two synthetic proteins, polylysine and polyglutamic acid. Polylysine does not coil in an acidic medium where all of its side chains are in the protonated form: $—(CH_2)_4—NH_3^+$. Repulsions between such rather closely spaced,

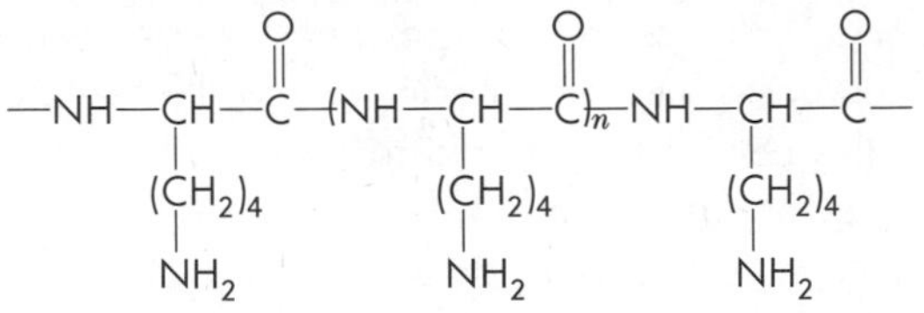

Polylysine

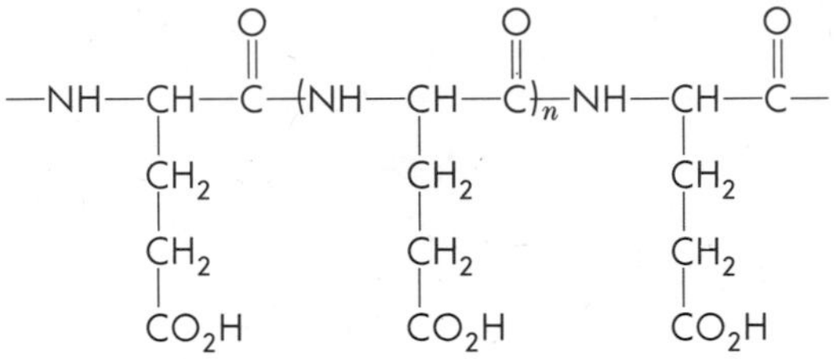

Polyglutamic acid

like-charged groups inhibits any tendency for an α-helix to form, and in acid this synthetic polypeptide is in a randomly flexing, "open" form. If the pH of the medium is changed such that the acid is neutralized, the side chains become uncharged: $-(CH_2)_4-NH_2$, and polylysine automatically takes up an α-helix configuration. In contrast, but illustrating the same principles, polyglutamic acid is coiled in acid but exists in a more random, open form in alkali. In this synthetic polypeptide, the side chains are:$-CH_2CH_2CO_2H$, and in an acidic medium, all such side chains would be in this electrically neutral form. In base, however, they would be in the form: $-CH_2CH_2CO_2^-$, and repulsions between such like-charged side chains prevents the polymer from coiling into an α-helix configuration.

With most proteins, particularly enzymes, the gross shape is critical. We shall find that each enzyme works best only within a narrow pH range, and it is evident that outside this range the enzyme does not have either the correct gross shape and (or) the correct pattern of electrically charged sites on the exposed side chains.

In addition to affecting the gross shape of a protein, the pH of the medium also influences its solubility. Proteins that are soluble in water at all are usually soluble only within narrow pH ranges, the range varying with each individual protein. To learn why this is so, we must explore the fuller truth about amino acid structures.

dipolar ionic character of amino acids; isoelectric points. In an aqueous medium, a molecule of an amino acid can act as both a proton donor and a proton acceptor. If both events occur, the net effect is self-neutralization:

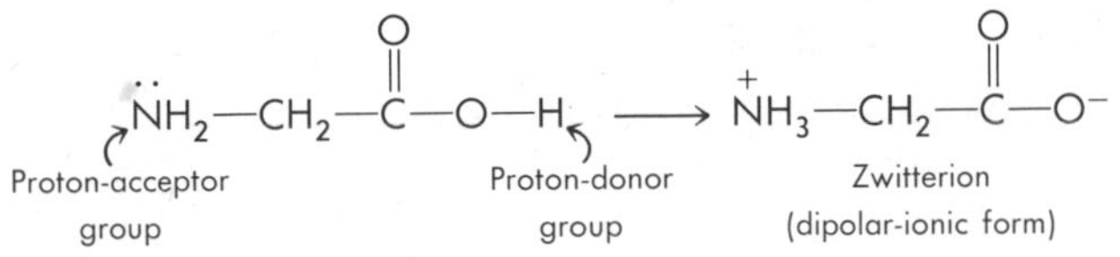

possible spatial configurations for proteins

This tendency for self-neutralization is so great among the amino acids that for all practical purposes they exist exclusively in the *zwitterion* form. When a molecule is in this condition it is said to be *isoelectric;* that is, it possesses the same number of opposite charges. In aqueous solution, not all molecules of an amino acid would be expected to be in an isoelectric condition unless their ability to act as proton donors were *exactly* matched by their ability to accept protons. By suitable adjustment of the pH of the solution, however, all the amino acid molecules present can be forced into the isoelectric form. Each amino acid has a distinctive pH at which all its molecules are isoelectric in solution. That pH is called the *isoelectric point* for the amino acid.

Any protein must have at least one free amino group (at one end) and at least one free carboxylic acid group (at the other end). Usually there are many more, for several of the amino acids have "extra" amino or carboxylic acid groups on their side chains. In one sense, then, protein molecules are simply huge amino acids. They too can exist in isoelectric forms, and they too have characteristic isoelectric points, pHs at which their molecules are in isoelectric conditions.

proteins are least soluble at their isoelectric points. When all molecules of a given protein are in an isoelectric condition, they tend to aggregate much as oppositely charged ions aggregate (Fig. 15.9). The effective result is a considerably larger and heavier "molecule." In our study of starch and cellulose, we learned that sheer size of a molecule can often overcome any solubilizing tendencies that may be present. Even though an isoelectric protein molecule possesses at least one each of the two best solubilizing groups an organic molecule can have ($-NH_3^+$ and $-\overset{\overset{\textstyle O}{\|}}{C}-O^-$), if these molecules aggregate, as in Fig. 15.9, their solubility in water is reduced.

The curdling of milk illustrates the effect of a change of pH on the solubility of a protein. The isoelectric point of casein, the principal protein of cow's milk, is 4.7, and it is only slightly soluble in water at this pH. Ordinarily, the pH of cow's milk is in the range 6.3 to 6.6. When bacterial

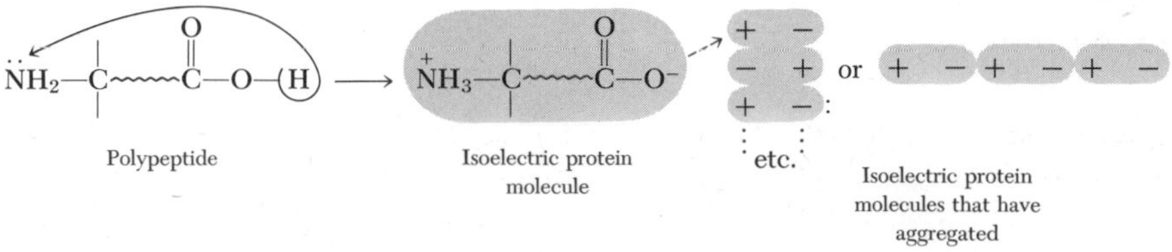

Polypeptide   Isoelectric protein molecule   etc.   Isoelectric protein molecules that have aggregated

Fig. 15.9   Isoelectric protein molecules can be expected to aggregate in a way reminiscent of the aggregation of oppositely charged ions that occurs in the formation of ionic crystals. The effect of this aggregation is to convert already large protein molecules into even larger ones whose solubility in water is reduced, compared with their unaggregated state.

action causes milk to sour, metabolic reactions of the growing bacteria produce lactic acid, which lowers the pH of the milk. As this happens, the molecules of casein become more and more isoelectronic, and eventually they coagulate and precipitate. The milk curdles. As long as the pH of milk is something other than the isoelectric pH, the casein remains dispersed in the medium. At or very near its isoelectric pH, it has its lowest solubility. Your grandmother used to make "sour milk" for certain of her recipes by adding lemon juice (containing citric acid) to milk. The change in pH caused coagulation of the casein.

A buffer system must neutralize small amounts of either acids or bases and thereby hold the pH of the medium constant. An amino acid in its zwitterionic form can perform this service, illustrated by the following equations:

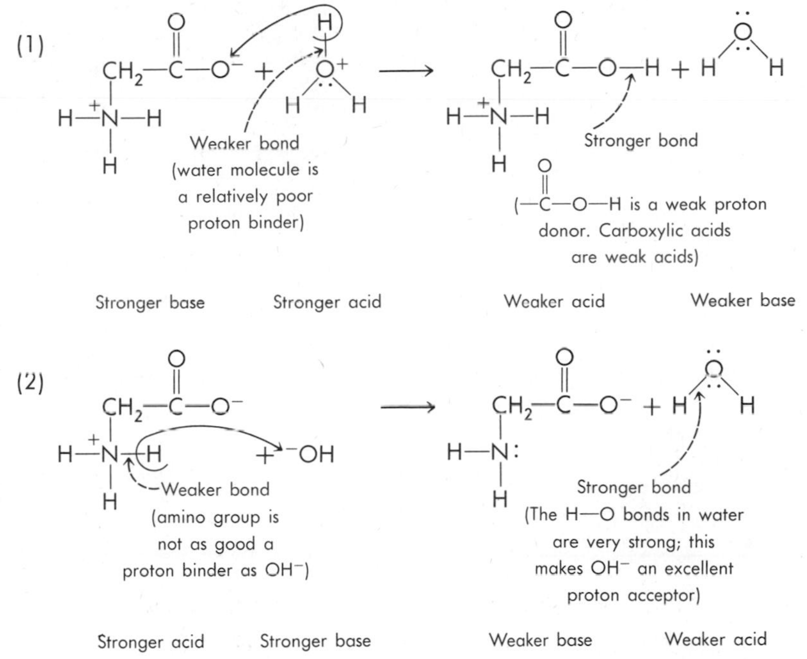

amino acids and proteins as buffers

(1)

Weaker bond
(water molecule is
a relatively poor
proton binder)

Stronger bond

$(-\overset{O}{\overset{\|}{C}}-O-H$ is a weak proton
donor. Carboxylic acids
are weak acids)

Stronger base   Stronger acid   Weaker acid   Weaker base

(2)

Weaker bond
(amino group is
not as good a
proton binder as OH⁻)

Stronger bond
(The H—O bonds in water
are very strong; this
makes OH⁻ an excellent
proton acceptor)

Stronger acid   Stronger base   Weaker base   Weaker acid

In Eq. 1 the isoelectric amino acid neutralizes hydronium ion; in Eq. 2 it neutralizes hydroxide ion. To the extent that protein molecules are simply huge amino acids, they too can perform the buffering service. Proteins constitute one of the important constituents of blood. Since the pH of blood must be kept well within the very narrow range of 7.00 to 7.90, the buffering action of blood proteins is one of their most important functions.

hydrolysis of proteins. The hydrolysis of proteins is nothing more than the hydrolysis of amide linkages, as illustrated in Fig. 15.10 with a hypothetic

355

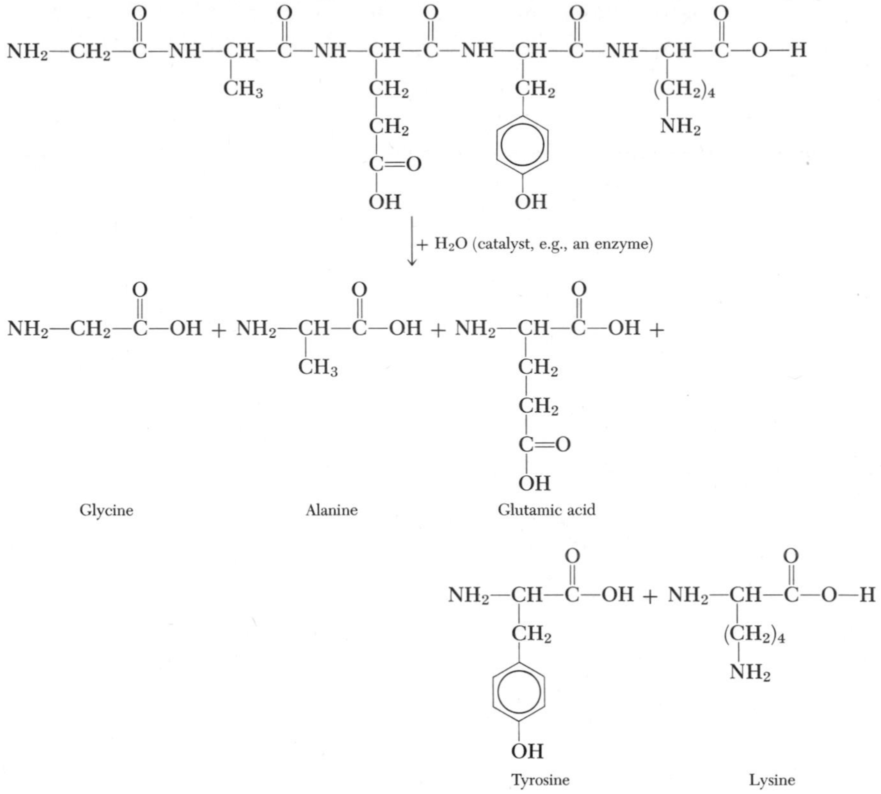

$$NH_2-CH_2-\overset{\overset{\displaystyle O}{\|}}{C}-NH-\underset{\underset{\displaystyle CH_3}{|}}{CH}-\overset{\overset{\displaystyle O}{\|}}{C}-NH-CH-\overset{\overset{\displaystyle O}{\|}}{C}-NH-CH-\overset{\overset{\displaystyle O}{\|}}{C}-NH-CH-\overset{\overset{\displaystyle O}{\|}}{C}-O-H$$

with side chains: CH_2–CH_2–$C{=}O$–OH (Glu); CH_2–(phenol ring)–OH (Tyr); $(CH_2)_4$–NH_2 (Lys)

$$\downarrow + H_2O \text{ (catalyst, e.g., an enzyme)}$$

$$NH_2-CH_2-\overset{\overset{\displaystyle O}{\|}}{C}-OH \; + \; NH_2-\underset{\underset{\displaystyle CH_3}{|}}{CH}-\overset{\overset{\displaystyle O}{\|}}{C}-OH \; + \; NH_2-CH-\overset{\overset{\displaystyle O}{\|}}{C}-OH \; +$$

with Glutamic acid side chain: CH_2–CH_2–$C{=}O$–OH

Glycine   Alanine   Glutamic acid

$$NH_2-CH-\overset{\overset{\displaystyle O}{\|}}{C}-OH \; + \; NH_2-CH-\overset{\overset{\displaystyle O}{\|}}{C}-O-H$$

Tyrosine side chain: CH_2–(phenol ring)–OH ; Lysine side chain: $(CH_2)_4$–NH_2

Tyrosine   Lysine

Fig. 15.10 Protein hydrolysis. In the complete hydrolysis of this hypothetical polypeptide, only carbonyl-to-nitrogen bonds are ruptured. A hydroxyl group (from water) becomes attached to each carbonyl carbon; a hydrogen (also from water) becomes attached to each nitrogen:

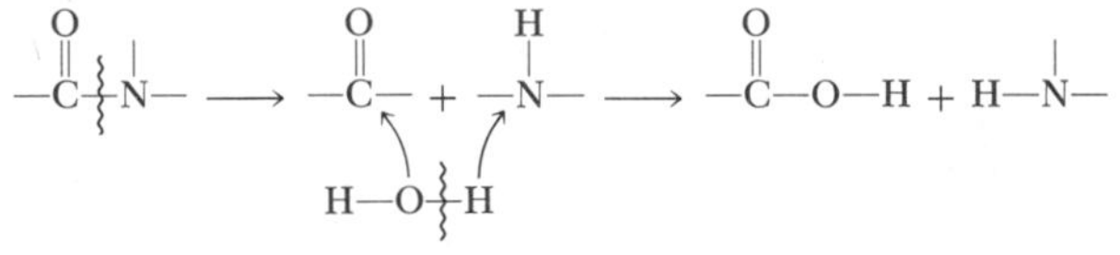

$$-\overset{\overset{\displaystyle O}{\|}}{C}\{N- \longrightarrow -\overset{\overset{\displaystyle O}{\|}}{C}- + -\overset{\overset{\displaystyle H}{|}}{N}- \longrightarrow -\overset{\overset{\displaystyle O}{\|}}{C}-O-H + H-\overset{\overset{\displaystyle |}{}}{N}-$$
$$H-O\{H$$

polypeptide. This is the chemistry of the digestion of proteins. Huge protein molecules are hydrolyzed during the digestive process to their several amino acid units. These, being very soluble in aqueous media, are rapidly absorbed into the bloodstream and transported to sites where they are needed.

denaturation. A wide variety of reagents and conditions do not hydrolyze peptide bonds, but still destroy the biological nature and activity of a protein. When this has happened, the protein is said to have been *denatured*. After denaturation, a separate process, coagulation, usually occurs. Several of the more common chemicals or conditions that denature a protein are listed in Table 15.2.

Structurally, denaturation is a disorganization of the molecular configu-

Table 15.2   Chemicals and Conditions that Cause Denaturation

Denaturing Agent	How the Agent May Operate
Heat	Disrupts hydrogen bonds and salt bridges by making molecules vibrate too violently. Produces coagulation as in the frying of an egg.
Solutions of urea $(NH_2-\overset{\overset{O}{\|\|}}{C}-NH_2)$	Disrupts hydrogen bonds. Being amidelike, urea can form hydrogen bonds of its own.
Ultraviolet radiation	Appears to operate the same way that heat operates. (Example: sunburning.)
Organic solvents (e.g., ethyl alcohol, isopropyl alcohol)	Being capable of hydrogen bonding themselves, alcohol molecules may interfere with hydrogen bonds in proteins. Bacteria are protein-rich. Ethyl alcohol (70% solution) quickly denatures their proteins, and they die (e.g., disinfectant action).
Strong acids or bases	Can disrupt hydrogen bonds and salt bridges.

$$2H^{\oplus} \quad \overset{\oplus}{} \;\; \overset{\oplus}{} \;\; S \;\; \overset{\ominus}{} \leftarrow \quad H^{\oplus} \;\longrightarrow\; \quad \overset{\oplus}{} \;\; \overset{\oplus}{} \;\; S \;\; H$$

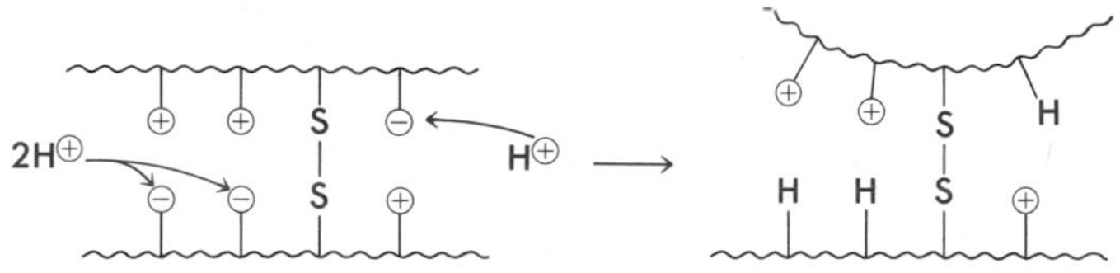

	Prolonged action of aqueous acids or bases leads to actual hydrolysis of proteins.
Detergents	May affect salt bridges (by forming new salt bridges of their own), or they may affect hydrogen bonds.
Salts of heavy metals (e.g., salts of the ions Hg^{2+}, Ag^+, Pb^{2+})	May disrupt salt bridges (by forming new salt bridges to themselves). These ions usually precipitate proteins (coagulation). Organomercury ions, e.g., methyl mercury (CH_3Hg^+), common in mercury pollution, act in this way.
Alkaloidal reagents (e.g., tannic acid, picric acid, phosphomolybdic acid)	May affect both salt bridges and hydrogen bonds. These reagents precipitate proteins.
Violent whipping	Surface films of denatured proteins are sometimes formed when protein solutions are whipped or shaken (e.g., beating egg white into meringue).

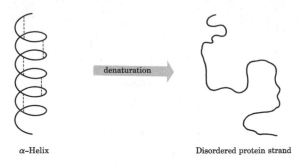

α–Helix   Disordered protein strand

Fig. 15.11   Denaturation as a disorganization of the molecular configuration of a protein. (Dashed lines represent secondary structural features, e.g., hydrogen bonds or salt bridges.)

ration of a protein. It can occur as an unfolding or uncoiling of a pleated or coiled structure or as the separation of the protein into smaller fragments, which may then unfold or uncoil (see Fig. 15.11).

Certain denaturation phenomena have positive medical advantages. The fact that certain heavy-metal salts denature and coagulate proteins is the basis of an important method of poison treatment. Mercuric, silver, and lead salts are poisons because their metallic ions wreak havoc among important body proteins, once they enter general circulation. However, they can be kept from general circulation if they are coagulated in the stomach. This can be accomplished by the administration of the handiest protein available, for example, raw egg albumin (egg white). Of course, if the coagulated poison-albumin mixture remains too long in the stomach, the process of digestion will eventually "dissolve" the protein and liberate the heavy-metal ions. That is the reason why an emetic must also be given, after the raw egg white. (Call a doctor at once, also!)

The so-called "alkaloidal reagents"—tannic acid, picric acid, and phosphomolybdic acid—have been used in studying structures of alkaloids, hence their group name. They also denature proteins, and this behavior has made them useful in the treatment of burns. Loss of body water through burned areas is very dangerous. To prevent it, solutions of alkaloidal reagents are often sprayed over the burned region. Surface proteins that are denatured and coagulated form a protective watertight crust. This treatment should, of course, be administered by a doctor.

Denaturing agents differ widely in their action, depending largely upon the protein. Some proteins (e.g., skin and hair) strongly resist most denaturing actions. It is noteworthy that proteins in hair, fur, feathers, nails, and hooves, and, to a lesser extent, in leather and skin are rich in the strongest of the secondary structural features, disulfide links.

Considerable emphasis has been placed in this chapter on the gross structure of proteins and on the factors that stabilize or denature them. This emphasis is necessary because a knowledge of the structures and stabilizing or denaturing factors for proteins is required for any understanding of how enzymes work. Furthermore, the whole concept of large-molecular shapes undergirds important aspects of the modern theory of the chemistry of heredity and the functions of genes. Lastly, it is important for anyone even remotely connected, professionally or otherwise, with the chemistry of health to learn how utterly dependent life is on seemingly small, weak things, such as the hydrogen bond and pH.

Having studied general principles related to protein structure and behavior, let us turn our attention to the myriad types of proteins. They may be classified in the various ways shown below.

how proteins are classified

I. According to Gross Structure and Solubility.
   A. *Fibrous proteins.* As the name implies, fibrous proteins consist of fibers. Both pleated-sheet and α-helix configurations are found. These proteins can be stretched, and they contract when the tension is released. They provide important structural, supporting, or protective functions. They are insoluble in aqueous media.
     1. Collagens. These are the proteins of connective tissue. About half the protein in a human body is collagen in nature. Action of boiling water converts collagens into soluble *gelatins*. Gelatins, in contrast to collagens, are readily digestible, that is, hydrolyzable. Perhaps action of boiling water on collagen merely unfolds and uncoils protein molecules, exposing their peptide links to hydrolytic action. The conversion of collagens to gelatins is one of the important processes that occurs during the cooking of food, especially of meat, where the breakdown of connective tissue (collagen) renders the meat more tender and more digestible.
     2. Elastins. Elastic tissues such as tendons and arteries are elastins. They are quite similar to collagens, but they cannot be converted to gelatins.
     3. Keratins. These proteins make up such various substances as wool and hair, hoofs and nails, and porcupine quills. They are exceptionally rich in the sulfur-containing amino acid cystine, which contains a disulfide linkage.
     4. Myosins. Muscle tissue is rich in the myosins. They are directly involved in muscle extension and contraction.
     5. Fibrin. Constantly circulating in the bloodstream is a soluble protein, fibrinogen. When an artery or vein is broken, a sequence of events is triggered, leading to the conversion of this soluble protein into insoluble fibrin. Fibrin is the protein that forms when blood clots are produced.
   B. *Globular proteins.* Members of this broad class are soluble in aqueous media; some in pure water, others in solutions of certain electrolytes. In contrast to the fibrous proteins, the globular proteins are easily denatured. Examples include the following:
     1. Albumins. Egg albumin is the most familiar member of this class. Albumins are soluble in pure water (actually, colloidal dispersions are formed), and are easily coagulated by heat. Albumins also circulate in the bloodstream, where they serve as buffers.

2. Globulins. These are soluble in solutions of electrolytes, and they are also coagulated by heat. Blood-serum globulins are important elements in the body's defensive mechanism against infectious disease.

II. According to Function.

Another way of classifying proteins, including, of course, those discussed above, is according to the biological functions they serve.

A. *Structural proteins.* Fibrous proteins, for example.

B. *Enzymes.* The catalysts of a living organism without which it could not live.

C. *Hormones.* Many, but not all, hormones are proteins.

D. *Toxins.* Proteins produced by bacteria in the living organism, which act as poisons to that organism.

E. *Antibodies.* These are proteins the body produces to destroy foreign proteins that invade it during an attack by an infectious agent.

F. *Oxygen-transporting protein.* Hemoglobin carries oxygen from the lungs to areas where it is needed.

Many other special functions could be listed.

III. According to the Nature of the Nonprotein Constituent.

Not all proteins liberate only amino acids when they are hydrolyzed. Those that do are called *simple proteins.* Others consist of simple proteins bound to a nonprotein group—a *prosthetic group* (Greek *prosthesis,* an addition). The nature of the prosthetic group is the basis for this way of classifying proteins.

A. *Glycoproteins.* Simple proteins bound to *carbohydrates.* Mucin in saliva is an example.

B. *Phosphoproteins.* Simple proteins bound to *phosphorus-containing substances,* other than phosphoglycerides (lipids) or nucleic acids. Casein in milk is an example.

C. *Chromoproteins.* Simple proteins bound to a *pigment.* Hemoglobin in blood is a compound of heme (the red pigment) and globin (a simple protein).

D. *Lipoproteins.* Simple proteins bound to a *lipid.* These are poorly understood complex proteins. They occur in the blood, in egg yolk, and in cell nuclei. They may play a role in transporting generally water-insoluble lipids and fatty acids from one part of the body to another.

E. *Nucleoproteins.* Simple proteins bound to a *nucleic acid.* Nucleic acids are the molecules of genes and will be discussed in Chapter 21.

Selected Reading List

Articles

1. J. C. Kendrew. "The Three-Dimensional Structure of a Protein Molecule." *Scientific American,* December 1961, page 96. Myoglobin is considered to be a small protein—only 150 amino acid units in one polypeptide chain plus a heme group.

Kendrew reports on its three-dimensional structure. A striking model of myoglobin, in color, is pictured.

2. J. Gross. "Collagen." *Scientific American,* May 1961, page 121. Magnificent electron photomicrographs of collagen fibrils illustrate this article about the principal component of connective tissue.

3. E. Zuckerkandl. "The Evolution of Hemoglobin." *Scientific American,* May 1965, page 110. The evolution of the specific chemical, human hemoglobin, is reconstructed by comparing its amino acid sequences with those in hemoglobin from other animals. An interesting discussion of how evolution might have proceeded at the molecular level.

4. R. D. B. Fraser. "Keratins." *Scientific American,* August 1969, page 87. The details of the molecular structure of keratins are described.

Brief Summary

1. The primary structural feature of a protein is the repeating skeletal unit:

$$-\left(N-\underset{|}{\overset{|}{C}}-\overset{O}{\overset{\|}{C}}\right)_{\!m}-, \text{ nitrogen-carbon-carbonyl.}$$

2. Approximately 26 different amino acids can furnish this skeletal unit. They differ in the nature of the substituents on the carbon to which both the carbonyl group and the nitrogen are attached.

3. The basic chemistry of protein synthesis is simply amide formation between amino acids.

4. The biological properties and functions of a protein appear to be directly related to:
   (a) the exact amino acid sequence present,
   (b) the molecular configuration of the whole protein molecule.

5. Secondary structural features—salt bridges, disulfide linkages, and hydrogen bonds—stabilize protein configurations. Important among these are the pleated-sheet and the α-helix arrangement and their folded or twisted variations.

6. The secondary structural features are relatively easily disrupted by denaturing agents, leading to disorganization of the protein configuration. Such disorganization nearly always is accompanied by loss of the protein's ability to function biologically. In this condition, the protein is denatured.

7. Protein molecules, like amino acids, can carry positively or negatively charged groups: $-NH_3^+$ or $-\overset{O}{\overset{\|}{C}}-O^-$. These ordinarily help bring these molecules into aqueous solution by the process of solvation. At certain pHs (isoelectric points), an equal number of each kind of charge will be present in each molecule, and for proteins this isoelectric condition is accompanied by reduced solubility.

8. Since amino acids and proteins carry proton-accepting and proton-donating groups, they can act as buffers.

9. The digestion of proteins is nothing more than the hydrolysis of their peptide (or amide) linkages.

Problems and Exercises

1. Draw the structure of the polypeptide that would form from the following amino acids if they became joined in the following sequence. (Let the first one function as a carboxylic acid, leaving its amino group intact. Refer to Table 15.1 for structures of amino acids.)

Glycine-valine-phenylalanine-isoleucine-alanine

2. Repeat Problem 1 with the sequence:

Glutamic acid-lysine-aspartic acid-tyrosine-threonine

3. Study the two structures you have written for Problems 1 and 2.
   (a) Which one is the more hydrocarbon-like?
   (b) Which one would tend to be more soluble in a nonaqueous, fat-like medium? Why?
   (c) Which one would tend to be more soluble in water? Why?
   (d) Which one would be more capable of participating in salt bridges? Why?

4. All amino acids are fairly high-melting solids. How is this fact consistent with their structures? Which structural form, the dipolar ionic or the nonionic, fits this fact better? Explain.

5. Write equations to show how alanine, in its dipolar ionic form, can function as a buffer.

6. What would be the products of the digestion of the polypeptide:

7. If the polypeptide of Problem 6 were subjected to mild reducing conditions, what products would form? (Show their structures.)

8. Discuss the role of hydrogen bonding in protein structure.

9. Why is a protein least soluble in a medium at its isoelectric point?

10. What is the difference between *digestion* and *denaturation* of a protein?

11. What is the relation between collagen and gelatin?

12. How are collagens and elastins alike? How are they different?

13. What services are performed by serum albumins? by serum globulins?

14. Explain how raw egg may be used as first aid in the case of poisoning by a copper insecticide or a lead-based paint? Why must "second aid" be given, and of what should this consist?

chapter 16 enzymes, vitamins, hormones, poisons, and drugs

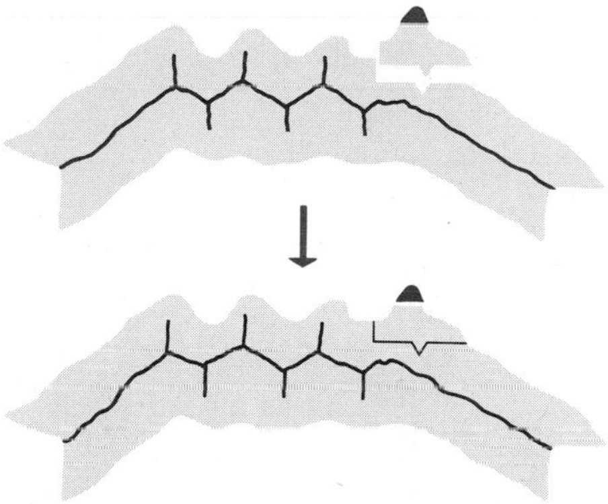

Life and health are most vulnerable to hostile assaults from the environment or to acts of carelessness on our part when the attacks are against either one of two kinds of cellular chemicals—nucleic acids and enzymes. Nucleic acids are the chemicals of genes. How they work and how chemicals and radiations can cause cancer or mutations will be discussed in Chapter 21. In the present chapter we shall study what enzymes are, what they do, how they work, and what happens if they are hit by chemicals classified as poisons.

Enzymes are catalysts absolutely essential to the chemical reactions of a living organism. Life as we know it would not be possible without the presence of hundreds of different enzymes to catalyze a myriad of chemical reactions in the body. Without these catalysts, body reactions would go too slowly to be of any use.

Vitamins are organic substances the body needs but cannot itself manufacture from carbohydrates, lipids, or proteins.

Minerals are metallic and nonmetallic ions necessary to growth and a variety of functions and which must be provided by the diet. They include Ca^{2+}, Mg^{2+}, Na^+, Fe^{2+}/Fe^{3+}, $H_2PO_4^-/HPO_4^{2-}$, and Cl^- besides sulfur (mostly as cysteine) and the trace elements of Table 16.1. (There may be others, but we are not sure.)

Hormones, which the body can and does make from its dietary raw materials, are "chemical messengers" secreted by various glands and sent to "target organs" where they trigger reactions corresponding to the "message." The overabundance or absence of various hormones has been related to such dramatic developments as cretinism, goiter, diabetes, dwarfism, and gigantism. The gap, however, between perceiving gross effects in the whole person and knowing the chemistry of hormonal action at the molecular level is still wide.

Table 16.1   Trace Elements of Nutritional Significance to Man[a]

Element	Approximate Amount in a 154 lb (70 kg) man, in mg	Some Uses
Chromium	<6	Probably an essential cofactor to insulin (glucose metabolism)
Cobalt	up to 3	Cofactor for Vitamin B_{12}
Copper	100	Cofactor for respiratory enzyme and other enzymes; in all body tissue
Iodine	30	Needed to make the hormone thyroxine; if deficient—goiter
Manganese	20	In several enzymes; peptidases, decarboxylases, kinases
Molybdenum	up to 5	Enzymes for metabolizing nucleic acids; enzymes for oxidizing aldehydes
Zinc	1600	Many dehydrogenating enzymes; carbonic anhydrase

[a] In addition to the minerals on this list there are several others that may be important to man but for which the picture is incomplete. These include aluminum, arsenic, barium, boron, selenium, strontium and vanadium. (Data from R. L. Pike and M. L. Brown. *Nutrition: An Integrated Approach*. John Wiley & Sons, Inc., New York, 1967, page 98.)

We are able to deduce much that is needed to understand how enzymes work from the fact that their molecules are almost entirely protein. They are sensitive, for example, to any or all of the denaturing agents. Excessive temperature or a change in the pH of the medium can alter the shape of an enzyme, denature it, and thereby alter its capacity to act as a catalyst. At its isoelectric pH, an enzyme will have its minimum solubility and perhaps its minimum activity as well, if the reaction it catalyzes must take place in solution.

cofactors: coenzymes; activators. Although enzymes are substantially protein in nature, they usually are not entirely so. Most enzymes possess a nonprotein group, a *cofactor*. Where these occur, neither the protein portion alone nor the cofactor alone has enzymic activity. The two must combine before an active enzyme is available. To distinguish the two portions, the purely protein part is called the *apoenzyme*. The cofactor is called a *coenzyme* if it is an organic substance, and an *activator* if it is a metal ion. As "word equations," then, we can write the following:

Coenzyme + apoenzyme $\longrightarrow$ enzyme (sometimes called the holoenzyme)

or

Metal-ion-activator + apoenzyme $\longrightarrow$ enzyme

Metal ions known to function as activators in enzyme systems in the human body and believed to be essential to man are included in Table 16.1.

coenzymes and vitamins. The importance of vitamins in daily living cannot be exaggerated. Not all diseases are caused by germs. If the diet is lacking in one or more vitamins, or if the body cannot use the vitamins it gets, the result could be scurvy, beriberi, pellegra, pernicious anemia, or some other disorder.

The term "vitamin" is applied to a compound if it meets these standards:

1. The compound is organic and cannot be synthesized at all (or at least made in sufficient amounts) by the metabolic reactions within the "host" and must be provided by the diet.
2. Its absence results in a specific "vitamin deficiency disease."
3. Its presence is required for normal growth and health.
4. The compound is present in foods in small concentrations and is not a carbohydrate, a lipid, or a protein. The vitamins or vitamin-like compounds of importance to man are given in Table 16.2.

For some vitamins, e.g. Vitamin A, there are in foods certain substances called *provitamins* which we can change into the required vitamins after

Table 16.2 Vitamins Important in Man

Vitamin	Structure[a]	Some Good Dietary Sources[b]	Recommended Daily Intake by an Adult	Results of Deficiency of the Vitamin
FAT SOLUBLE VITAMINS				
A_1	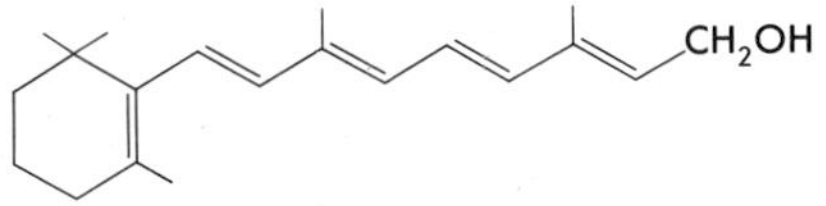 CH$_2$OH retinol	All green and yellow vegetables; cod liver oil	5000 I.U. (avoid overdose) (1 I.U. = 0.3 microgram retinol)	Eye disease (xerophthalmia)
A_2	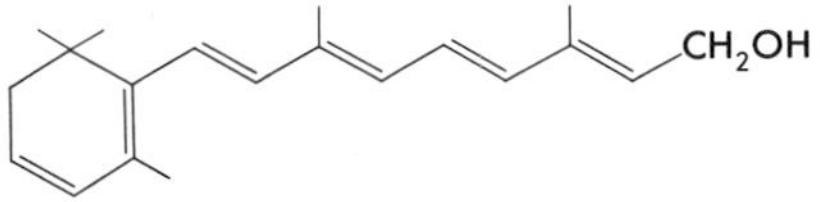 CH$_2$OH dehydroretinol			Night blindness (nyctalopia)
D_2	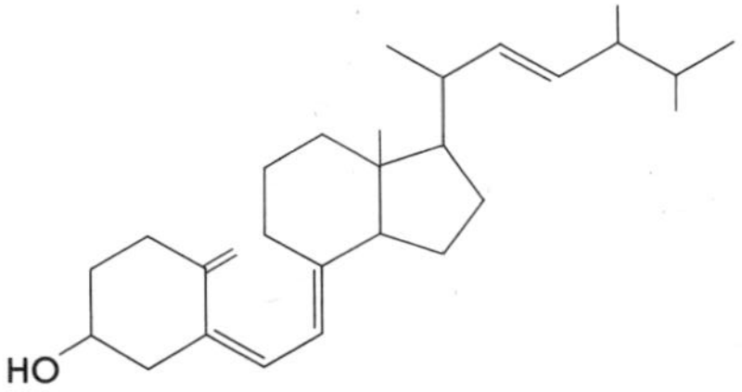 HO calciferol	Provitamins are in our skin and are activated by sunlight; Fish liver oils	400 I.U. (avoid overdoses; infant's growth retarded at >2000 I.U./day (I.U. = 0.025 microgram cholecalciferol)	Poor use of calcium; poor bone formations—rickets. Rickets apparently comes from a deficiency of sunlight not a deficiency in the diet although treatment of rickets by calciferol is successful. More and more scientists hold that it would be more proper to classify the D vitamins as hormones. (W. F. Loomis. *Scientific American*, December 1970.)
D_3	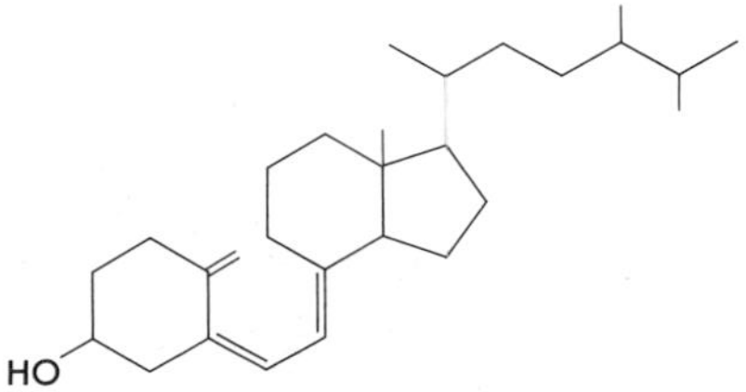 HO cholecalciferol	Fish liver oils		

[a] The name beneath the structure is the name recommended in 1966 by the Joint Commission on Biochemical Nomenclature of the International Union of Pure and Applied Chemistry and the International Union of Biochemistry.

[b] These sources are only partial lists and they provide either the vitamin itself, or the group of compounds, or provitamins for other compounds from which the body can make the needed vitamin activity.

Table 16.2 Vitamins Important in Man (continued)

	Structure	Sources	Est'd	Significance in human metabolism
E	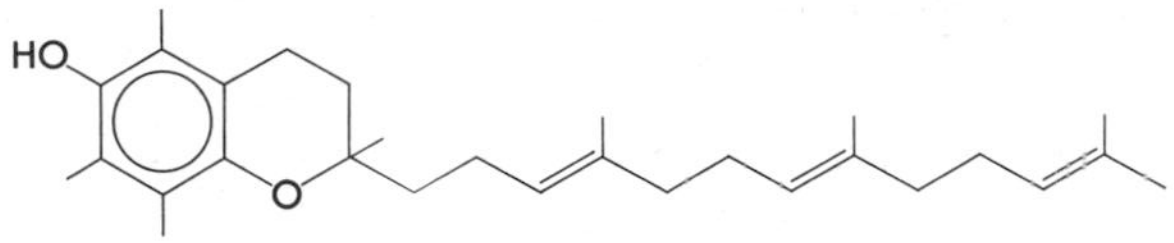 tocopherol (several other related compounds have Vitamin E activity)	Wheat germ oil; Cottonseed oil; Green, leafy vegetables	1C–30 mg/day	Significance in human metabolism is unclear
K	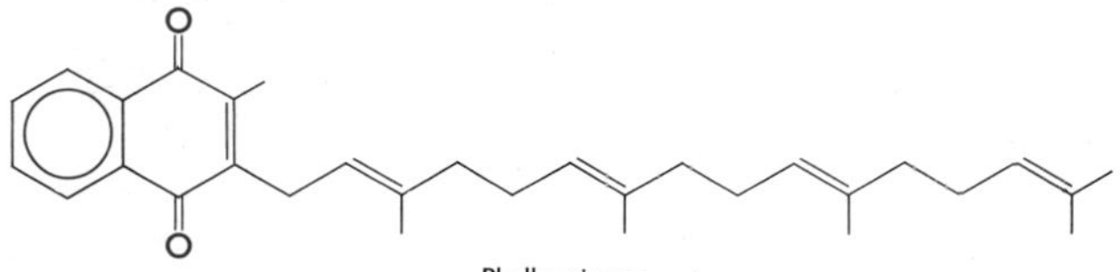 Phylloquinone (Vitamin K₂)	Bacterial reactions that occur in man's intestines make what he needs K₁—In plant materials (e.g., spinach, cabbage) K₂—In microorganisms	Unknown; normal diets seem adequate	Blood will not clot as well

WATER SOLUBLE VITAMINS

	Structure	Sources	Est'd	Significance
B₁	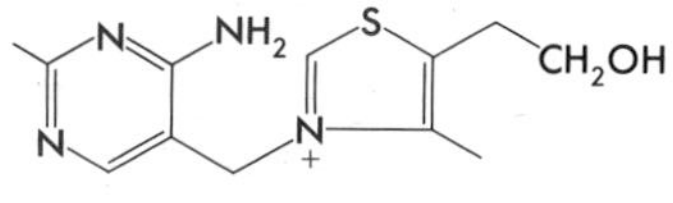 Thiamine	Cereal grains and nuts; Liver, heart, kidney; Legumes	1–2 mg	Beriberi; Loss of appetite (anorexia)
B₂	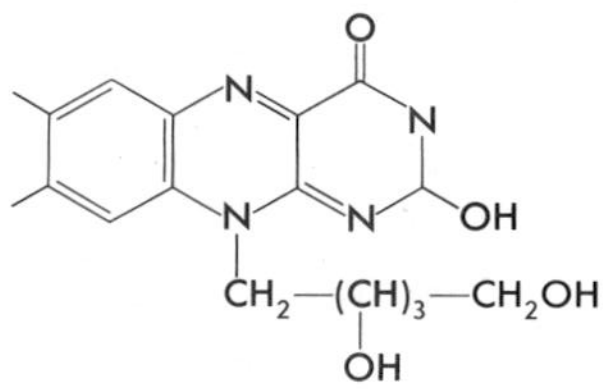 Riboflavin	Milk, meat products, liver; Cheese, eggs, yeast; Peas, lima beans, and many other vegetables; Wheat germ	1–2 mg	Reddening of tongue; Fissures at corners of mouth; Waxy deposits on skin

Table 16.2 Vitamins Important in Man (continued)

Vitamin	Structure[a]	Some Good Dietary Sources[b]	Recommended Daily Intake by an Adult	Results of Deficiency of the Vitamin
B₆	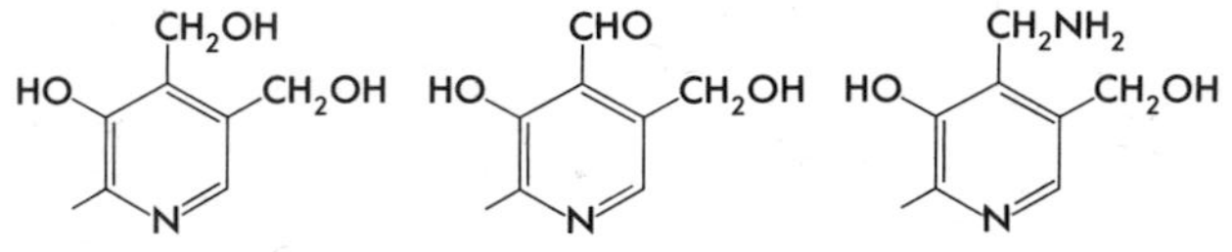 pyroxidine (pyroxidol) pyridoxal pyridoxamine	Cereals, legumes, liver, yeast, bananas	est'd 675–750 micrograms/day (adult)	In infants: convulsions; In adults: skin problems
Nicotinic acid and amide (Vitamin PP)	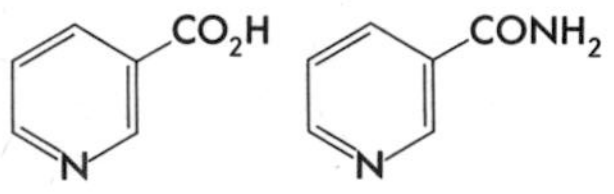 Nicotonic acid (niacin) Nicotinamide (Niacinamide)	Meats; yeast; wheat germ	est'd 15–20 mg	Pellagra (dermatitis, then diarrhea, then dementia, then death)
B₁₂	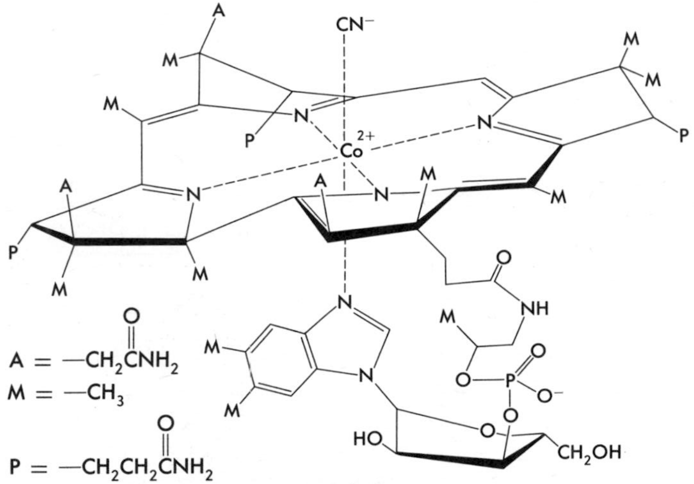 cyanocobalamin	Vitamin activity in eggs, meat, liver.	3–5 micrograms	Pernicious anemia

$$A = -CH_2CNH_2 \quad (O)$$
$$M = -CH_3$$
$$P = -CH_2CH_2CNH_2 \quad (O)$$

Table 16.2 Vitamins Important in Man (continued)

	Structure	Sources	Amount needed daily	Deficiency symptoms
C	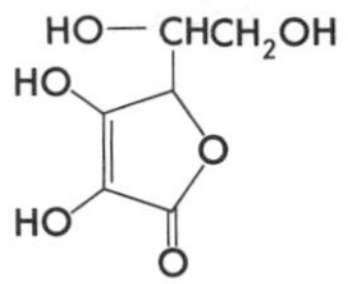 Ascorbic acid	Citrus fruits; berries; Green vegetables	75 mg	Scurvy (weight loss, painful joints and muscles, bleeding at gums)
Biotin	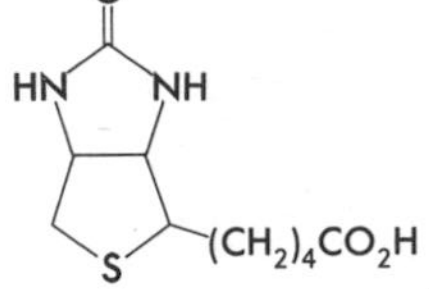 Biotin	Liver; dried peas and lima beans; chocolate (made by bacteria in intestinal tract)	est'd 150–300 micrograms	Skin disorders
Folic acid	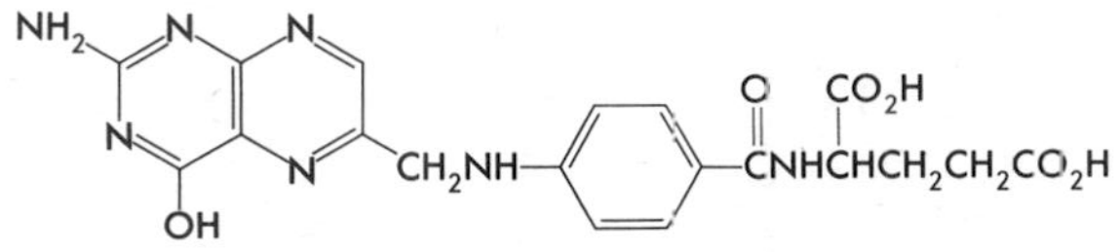 Pteroylglutamic acid	Animal organs; yeast; wheat germ; chicken; oysters	0.15 mg	Gastrointestinal disorders Inhibition of mitosis
Pantothenic acid	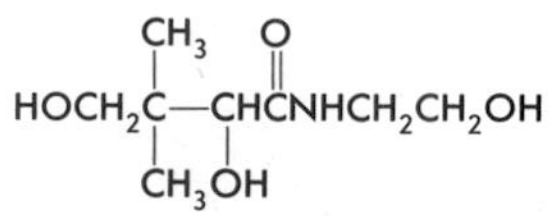 Pantothenic acid	Liver, kidneys; yeast, egg yolk	10 mg	Not known for man
Inositol	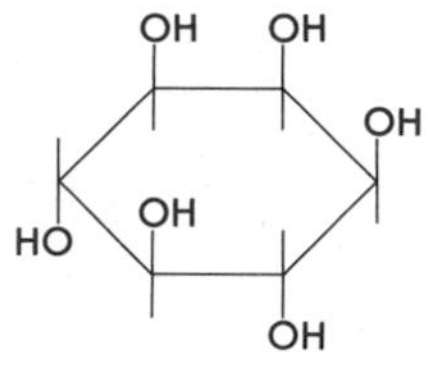 meso-inositol	Widely distributed in vegetables and fruits	?	Probably poor phospholipid utilization, but effects of inositol deficiency in man not known.
Choline	$HOCH_2CH_2\overset{+}{N}(CH_3)_3$	Egg yolk; asparagus, peas, spinach; wheat germ	Not strictly a vitamin but an essential metabolite that can be made from adequate protein	Not known for man

ingesting them. Carotene, for example, is a provitamin for Vitamin A.

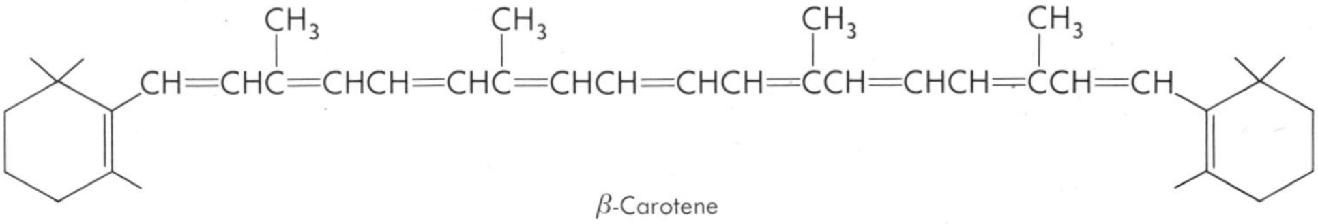

$$CH_3 \quad CH_3 \quad CH_3 \quad CH_3$$

CH=CHC=CHCH=CHC=CHCH=CHCH=CCH=CHCH=CCH=CH

β-Carotene

Science is a long way from a complete knowledge of how vitamins are involved in health. It might even be possible that not all the vitamins have been discovered. But one fact is known. Certain of the vitamins participate as part of enzyme systems. *A large number of coenzymes either are identical with certain of the vitamins or are simple derivatives of them.* Many coenzymes are simply monophosphate or diphosphate esters of the B-vitamins. Examples include thiamine pyrophosphate, riboflavin phosphate (FMN), pyridoxal phosphate, and the pyridine nucleotides, NAD and NADP.[1] (Shaded portions of the structures shown highlight the vitamin portions of the coenzymes.)

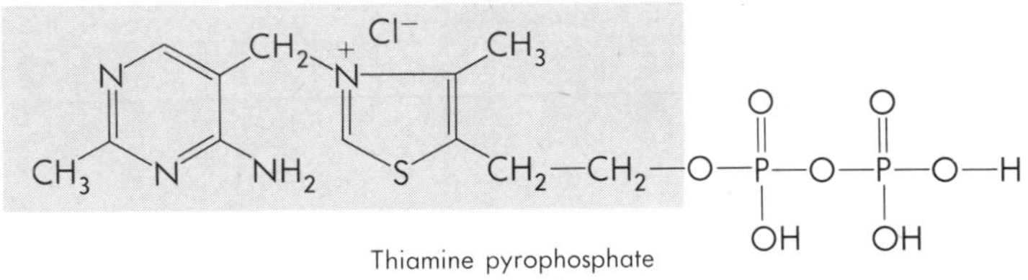

Thiamine pyrophosphate
(cocarboxylase)

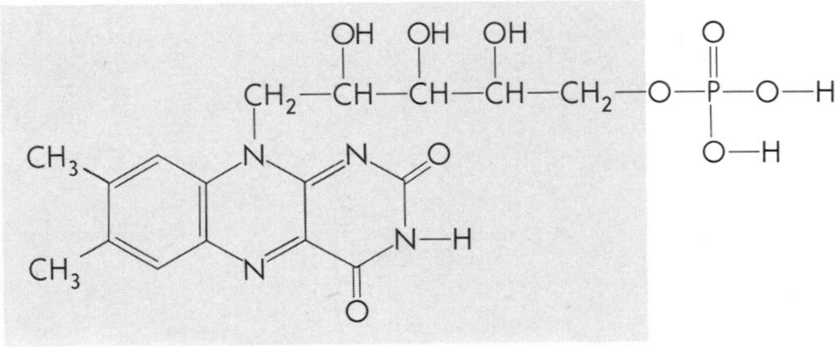

Riboflavin phosphate
(flavin mononucleotide;
FMN)

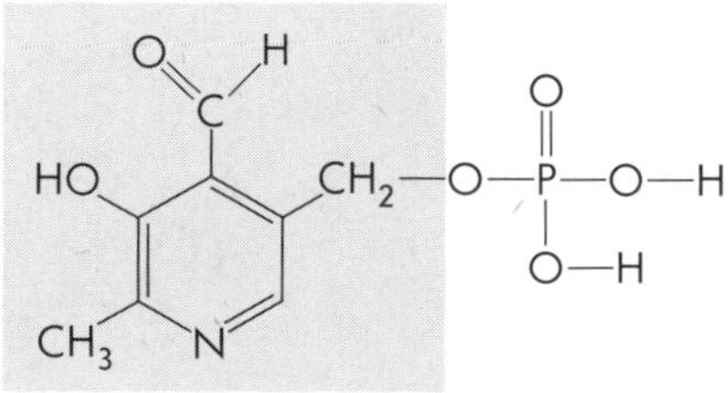

Pyridoxal phosphate

[1] In older usage, still frequently seen, the pyridine nucleotides, NAD and NADP, are respectively designated DPN (for diphosphopyridine nucleotide) and TPN (for triphosphopyridine nucleotide).

enzymes, vitamins, hormones, poisons, and drugs

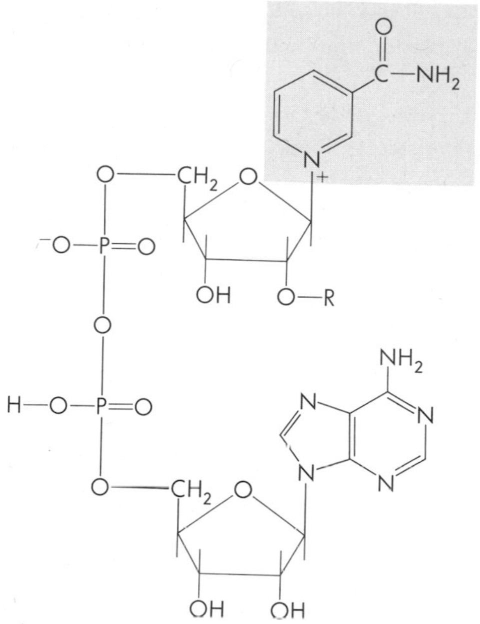

NAD. R = H (nicotinamide adenine dinucleotide; DPN)

NADP. R = PO₃H₂ (nicotinamide adenine dinucleotide phosphate; TPN)

FMN, NAD, and NADP are all important as acceptors of hydrogen during biological oxidation (see Chapter 18). Since these coenzymes require certain of the B-vitamins, and since virtually all cells have to carry on oxidations, the B-vitamins are needed by every cell of the body. Since the B-vitamins are water-soluble they are easily eliminated from the body. Hence these vitamins are needed every day. If these vitamins are missing, key enzymes are missing (or are present in reduced concentrations), important reactions do not occur as rapidly as needed, and eventually the body exhibits serious physiological disorders. The vitamins provide some of our most dramatic examples of the great dependence of life on trace amounts of not-too-complicated chemicals.

how enzymes are named. The compound acted on by an enzyme is called the *substrate*. The names of most enzymes have the ending "-ase" attached either to the name of the substrate or the kind of reaction performed. Maltase, for example, is an enzyme that acts on maltose. An oxidase is an enzyme that catalyzes biological oxidations. Esterases act on esters; peptidases, on peptides. A transferase is an enzyme that assists the transfer of a group or radical from one substrate to another. The names of some very common enzymes of the digestive system—pepsin, trypsin, for example—stand as exceptions to these rules.

types of enzymes

classes of enzymes. The following classification of enzymes includes most of the important types together with specific examples.

    I. Hydrolytic Enzymes; Hydrolases.
        A. *Esterases and lipases.* These act on esters, for example, glycerides or lipids:

$$\underset{\|}{\overset{O}{\underset{RC}{}}}-OR' + H_2O \longrightarrow \underset{\|}{\overset{O}{\underset{RC}{}}}-OH + HOR'$$

The name *aliesterase* is given to an enzyme that affects rates of hydrolysis of aliphatic esters.
        B. *Carbohydrases.* These catalyze the hydrolysis of di- and polysaccharides ultimately to their monosaccharide units. Examples are maltase, lactase, sucrase, and amylase (acts on amylose and starch):

$$H_2O + Sugar'-O-Sugar'' \longrightarrow Sugar' + Sugar''$$

        C. *Proteolytic enzymes and peptidases.* These assist hydrolysis of peptide linkages in proteins:

$$\underset{\|}{\overset{O}{\underset{RC}{}}}-NHR' + H_2O \longrightarrow \underset{\|}{\overset{O}{\underset{RC}{}}}-OH + R'NH_2$$

Examples include pepsin, trypsin, and chymotrypsin, which act on huge protein molecules in the digestive tract. Other proteolytic enzymes are dipeptidase, carboxypeptidase, and aminopeptidase, which are effective with polypeptide fragments produced by partial hydrolysis of larger proteins.
        D. *Phosphatases.* These catalyze the hydrolysis of phosphate esters.
    II. Oxidizing Enzymes.
        A. *Oxidases.* These are essential to the body's utilization of molecular oxygen. Examples include:
            Catalase (converts hydrogen peroxide to water and oxygen):

$$2H_2O_2 \longrightarrow 2H_2O + O_2$$

            Peroxidase (permits the body to use hydrogen peroxide as an oxidizing agent).
            Cytochrome oxidases (essential to respiration in cells).
        B. *Dehydrogenases.* These enzymes bring about oxidations through the removal of the elements of hydrogen. The coenzymes riboflavin and the pyridine nucleotides, NAD and NADP, are important to several dehydrogenases.
    III. Transferases.
        A. *Transmethylase:* Transfer of CH_3-.

        B. *Transacylases:* Transfer of $R-\overset{O}{\overset{\|}{C}}-$ (e.g. $CH_3-\overset{O}{\overset{\|}{C}}-$).

enzymes, vitamins, hormones, poisons, and drugs

C. *Transglycosylase:* Transfer of a monosaccharide unit.

D. *Transphosphatase:* Transfer of a phosphate unit. (Often these are called kinases.)

E. *Transthiolase:* Transfer of a sulfur-containing group.

F. *Transaminase:* Transfer of an amino group.

IV. *Lyases.* These catalyze additions to double bonds: $\diagdown C{=}C\diagdown$, $\diagdown C{=}O$, or $\diagdown C{=}N{-}$.

V. *Isomerases.* These catalyze isomerizations.

VI. *Ligases.* Ligases act together with ATP to form new bonds.

specificity. One of the many striking properties of enzymes is their specificity. Some will catalyze only one reaction and will not affect the same kind of reaction with slightly different reactants. Urease has this absolute specificity. It will catalyze the hydrolysis of urea but not of the closely related compound biuret and not of any other amides.

$$NH_2{-}\overset{\overset{\displaystyle O}{\|}}{C}{-}NH_2 \qquad NH_2{-}\overset{\overset{\displaystyle O}{\|}}{C}{-}NH{-}\overset{\overset{\displaystyle O}{\|}}{C}{-}NH_2 \qquad R{-}\overset{\overset{\displaystyle O}{\|}}{C}{-}NH_2$$

     Urea   Biuret   Amides
                                          (general
                                          formula)

Many of the enzymes that catalyze hydrolytic reactions are less specific, but yet those that act to hydrolyze, say, esters, are usually far less efficient (or entirely ineffective) with amides. The digestive enzyme, trypsin, acts predominately on peptide bonds, but it will also catalyze the hydrolysis of some esters.

efficiency. The rates of reaction promoted by enzymes have to be described as simply astounding. It is not uncommon for an enzyme to promote a rate several hundred thousand or a million times faster than the rate under ordinary catalysis. β-Amylase, an enzyme that catalyzes the hydrolysis of amylose, provides a way for the equivalent of 4000 acetal oxygen "bridges" to be hydrolyzed per anylase molecule per second.

Each enzyme works best within a narrow temperature range (body temperature) and a narrow pH range; and (up to a point) overall enzymic efficiency is improved by having a concentration of enzyme higher than that suggested by "trace."

The first step in enzymic action is the formation of more or less loose bonds between the enzyme and the compound on which it acts, the substrate. This combination is called the *enzyme-substrate complex*. In equation form, this and subsequent events may be written as follows:

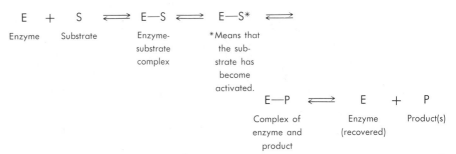

$$E \;+\; S \;\rightleftharpoons\; E{-}S \;\rightleftharpoons\; E{-}S^* \;\rightleftharpoons$$

Enzyme Substrate Enzyme-   *Means that
       substrate   the sub-
       complex   strate has
               become
               activated.

$$E{-}P \;\rightleftharpoons\; E \;+\; P$$

Complex of   Enzyme Product(s)
enzyme and (recovered)
product

During the very brief existence of the enzyme-substrate complex, the substrate is activated—often by the coenzyme portion—and on the surface of the enzyme the product molecule(s) forms. When the product leaves, the enzyme is ready for further work. Note that double arrows were used in the equations. Most enzyme-catalyzed reactions are reversible, and the enzyme only affects how rapidly equilibrium will be established between the forward and the reverse reactions. Whether a particular equilibrium is shifted from left to right (or in the other direction) depends on several other factors including the availability of reactants (substrates) or the occurrence of chemical events that use up the products as rapidly as they form.

"lock-and-key theory." It is in the formation of the enzyme-substrate complex where we can focus all we have learned about the importance of the gross shapes of proteins. Both enzymes and substrates have intricate, detailed molecular configurations. An enzyme-substrate complex of reasonable stability cannot be expected to form unless the substrate can find some cluster of sites—active binding sites—onto or into which this molecule may fit. A left foot can be forced into a right shoe; a right hand can be put into a left-hand glove. The results, however, are uncomfortable and are not long endured; indeed, the situations are highly unlikely in the first place. Similarly, with enzymes, the surface shapes of the enzyme and the substrate must fit together, almost as a key fits into a tumbler lock; in fact, this theory is often called the *lock and key theory*. Just as one key fits into and turns only one lock, so a particular enzyme is constructed to fit with and act on only one substrate or one kind of substrate linkage. The specificity that an enzyme shows toward a substrate is comparable to that which a tumbler lock has for its key.

When molecules of substrate and enzyme approach each other, electrical forces of attraction between the enzyme's active binding sites and the substrate are believed to assist the speedy formation of the complex. These forces are quite likely the result of electrically polar regions, partially charged groupings, or ionic sections (e.g., as in $R{-}\overset{\displaystyle O}{\overset{\|}{C}}{-}O^-$ or in $R{-}NH_3{}^+$) on both

enzymes, vitamins, hormones, poisons, and drugs

enzyme and substrate. This is illustrated schematically in Fig. 16.1. The reaction that occurs to the substrate may then introduce new functional groups with radically changed polarities. After the reaction, the enzyme and the chemically changed substrate, which still adheres momentarily to the enzyme's surface, may repel each other. Therefore, the enzyme "peels" away quite naturally and is freed for further action.

It is not the enzyme as a whole that is the catalyst; it is a distinct functional group on the enzyme, an *active catalytic site* as it is called, that acts. The shape and the electrical characteristics of the binding sites determine whether the enzyme accepts or rejects candidate substrates. Once accepted, the substrate finds, let us say, one of its alcohol groups right over an active catalytic site, and a reaction, such as dehydrogenation of the alcohol, occurs, with transfer of the pieces of the element hydrogen to the enzyme. The chances of the alcohol group finding that active site by random collisions

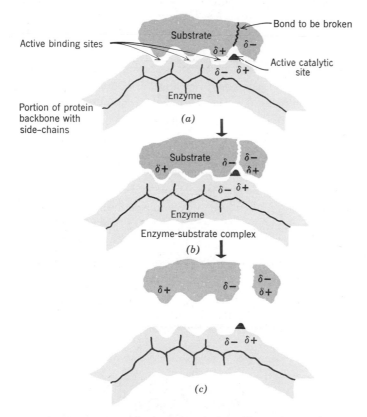

Fig. 16.1 A schematic representation of the "lock and key" theory of enzymic action. (a) Enzyme and substrate have complementary shapes, and electrical forces assist their association. (b) While locked together in the enzyme-substrate complex, the reaction proceeds. (c) A change in relative polarities that might accompany the reaction causes the pieces of the substrate to leave the enzyme.

theory of enzyme action

are extremely remote. If the substrate, attracted by electrical forces, fits neatly to the enzyme, then the reaction need not rely on random collisions. The active catalytic site and the reactive bond on the substrate suddenly appear together. It is in terms of the foregoing theory that both the efficiency and the specificity of enzymic catalysis are understood.

Temperatures and pHs are important in enzymic reactions because enzymes are largely protein in nature. Both factors influence geometries of large protein molecules.

In cases where coenzymes are needed, it appears that either the distinctive molecular configuration required for enzymic action or the active site is not provided without prior attachment of the coenzyme to the apoenzyme. A schematic illustration is depicted in Fig. 16.2, which shows the active site on the coenzyme portion. This is sometimes the case, but it is not necessarily so. (The digestive enzymes, for example, are wholly proteins.)

In some cases where metal-ion activators are required, it is believed that the metal ion acts as a "bridge" to link the substrate to the enzyme, as illustrated in Fig. 16.3.

regulation of enzymic activity

The normal growth and development of an organism as well as its day-to-day biochemical activities are subject to positive or negative control in a number of ways. There are fairly obvious and drastic methods of negative control—denial of materials (and chemical energy) and denial of information. Those who lack a balanced diet or who eat too little will not grow, develop, and function as well as others. Information needed for life comes to us genetically and environmentally. Disorders in either systems affect health, both physical and mental. (A 12-year-old girl was found in 1970 to have been locked up since infancy in a single, small room. Denied essentially all love, all education, all humane contacts, given only food, shelter, and clothing for 12 years,

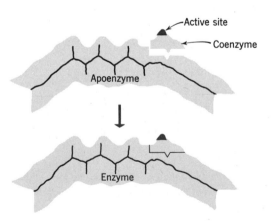

Fig. 16.2 Schematic representation of the formation of an enzyme by the union of an apoenzyme and coenzyme.

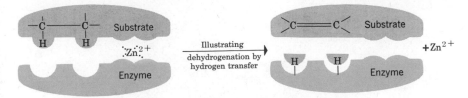

Fig. 16.3 Metal-ion activator in enzyme-substrate complex.

she was unable to speak much better than a 2-year old. Genetically, she was all right; environmentally, she had been crippled.)

At the cellular and much more subtle level of life we need both activating and deactivating mechanisms. At times certain reactions should be inhibited; when enough of one compound has been made, its synthesis should be switched off. When a compound is in short supply, its synthesis should be started. In a sudden emergency, when (for example) a compound such as glucose is needed at once for energy, there should be a way to get it out of storage immediately. When poisons, viruses, or bacteria invade, or when the circulatory system is breached by a cut, defensive reactions should swing into action at once, and then subside when they are no longer needed.

Two of the most important natural methods that control biochemical events are the molecular managements of enzyme *concentration* and of enzyme *reactivity*. At the enzyme level control by either means can be sensitive because enzymes are not needed in huge concentrations and because switching one enzyme on or off will frequently switch on or off a whole series of reactions, one following the other and depending upon the product of one reaction being the reactant for the next reaction in the series.

regulatory enzymes. Sometimes the enzymes for an entire sequence of reactions coexist together in one multienzyme complex. In a tight complex the product of one reaction need not go far to be the substrate for the next enzyme and the next reaction. Sometimes the end-product of the sequence is the control agent or *modulator*. Suppose, to keep the discussion very general, the sequence is as follows:

$$A \underset{E_1}{\rightleftharpoons} B \underset{E_2}{\rightleftharpoons} C \underset{E_3}{\rightleftharpoons} D \underset{E_4}{\rightleftharpoons} F$$

To make compound F from compound A suppose several steps are needed, that each step has its own enzyme (E_1, E_2, E_3, E_4), and that the enzymes happen to be organized as a multienzyme complex. Figure 16.4 is a schematic way of representing this. Suppose, however, that molecules of the final product, F, can temporarily react with the enzyme, E_1, for the first step—react in a loose, reversible manner but yet in a way that changes the shape of E_1 and E_1 no longer can accept its substrate:

$$E_1 + F \rightleftharpoons E_1-F \text{ (inactive as an enzyme)}$$

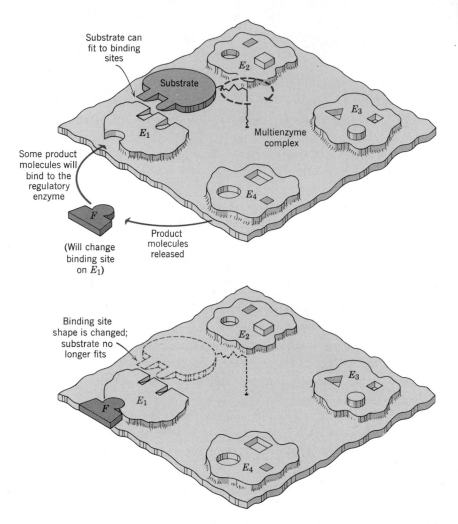

Fig. 16.4 Regulatory enzyme (E_1) in a multienzyme complex subject to control by molecules of the final product (F) which act as the modulators. When product molecules form they can bind reversibly with the regulatory enzyme, alter its shape, and make it less able to bind substrate. This, in effect, shuts down the whole complex. If molecules of F get in short supply elsewhere, those bound to the regulatory enzyme are then taken. The complex can now make more final product, F. In some reactions the substrate is temporarily bound to the complex, as illustrated here, and it moves as a "swinging arm" from one enzyme to the other.

The more concentrated is F the more to the right will this equilibrium lie and less will be the concentration of the active enzyme, E_1. Molecules of E_1 are "taken out" as more and more molecules of F are made, and the rate of the whole sequence slows down. In this manner an enzyme system can regulate itself. One example of this type of control occurs in the five-step conversion of the amino acid threonine to another amino acid, isoleucine.

enzymes, vitamins, hormones, poisons, and drugs

Isoleucine, the product, is an inhibitor of this series of reactions (intermediate products are not shown):

$$\underset{\text{threonine}}{\underset{\overset{|}{OH}}{\overset{\overset{NH_2}{|}}{CH_3CHCHCO_2H}}} \xrightarrow{E_1} \xrightarrow{E_2} \xrightarrow{E_3} \xrightarrow{E_4} \xrightarrow{E_5} \underset{\text{isoleucine}}{\underset{\overset{|}{CH_3}}{\overset{\overset{NH_2}{|}}{CH_3CH_2CHCHCO_2H}}}$$

If and when isoleucine is used up, inhibition of the enzyme, E_1, is removed and the sequence can replenish the supply of isoleucine. As long as there is enough isoleucine, the sequence need not go and it remains shut down as it should. In a situation such as this the affected enzyme is called a *regulatory enzyme* or an *allosteric enzyme*; the chemical that inhibits it is called the *modulator* or the *effector*.[2]

regulatory genes. In Chapter 21 we shall study the chemistry of heredity[3] where we shall see how one of the most important functions of a gene in the life of a cell is to direct the synthesis of an apoenzyme. There are methods for switching genes on and off, and these mechanisms therefore control enzymic activity simply by controlling the *concentrations* of enzymes. Apoenzyme proteins are not as long-lasting as proteins with a structural role; they break down and their supply has to be replenished as needed. How this control over replenishment is accomplished will be a topic in Chapter 21.

The concentrations and (or) the activities of some enzymes are controlled by hormones, and to these compounds we next turn our attention.

The higher organisms are as complex as a modern, industrialized society. Both have groups of specialists, each group intent on doing its job well and relying on other groups to do the same. But the groups are not independent. Both an organism and a society become disordered, both may collapse, if specialists fail to communicate with each other. The performance of the brain, for example, depends altogether on the kidney's control of the blood's pH. There are basically two ways by which tissues and organs in the body communicate with each other and thereby work together harmoniously—the networks of neural and humoral communication.

hormones

[2] The phenomenon of effecting a change in an enzyme when a modulator binds at some site other than the catalytic site is called the *allosteric effect*. ("Allosteric" means "other space" or "other location.")

[3] Except for the fact that Chapter 21 assumes information about adenosine triphosphate and similar triphosphates presented in Chapter 18, there is no reason why Chapter 21 could not be taken up next. The topic of the triphosphates is not any great hurdle, and we did briefly look at them in Chapter 12.

Neural communication has to do with the nervous system and the signals sent back and forth through it. It provides the basic route of communication between the interior of the body and signals from the environment received by sight, smell, taste, touch, and hearing.

Humoral communication (L. *humor,* fluid) takes place via the circulating fluids of the body, principally the bloodstream. Certain organs in the body have become specialized in the task of synthesizing and sending "chemical signals" via humoral circulation, organs which are called the *endocrine glands* or the glands of internal secretion. ("Endocrine" comes from the Greek: *endon,* within; *krinein,* to separate, i.e., to secrete.) The compounds which they specialize in making and secreting are called *hormones* (Greek *hormon,* arousing, exciting). The locations of the principal endocrine glands are shown in Fig. 16.5 and the general functions of the hormones they secrete are given in Table 16.3. The control of the secretion of an individual hormone into circulation varies from hormone to hormone. With some it depends on the concentration of one or more substances in the blood. (In Chapter 17, for example, we shall see how vasopressin's release is related to the osmotic pressure of the blood.) With others the nervous system plays a significant role.

Because the question of how hormones work is still the subject of intense research, only a very general answer will be attempted here. (In succeeding

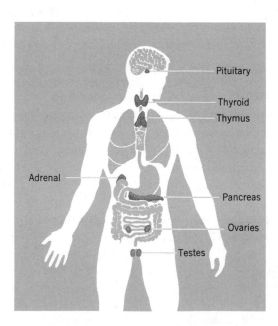

Fig. 16.5   The endocrine glands. (From G. E. Nelson, G. G. Robinson, and R. A. Boolootian. *Fundamental Concepts of Biology,* 2nd edition, 1970. John Wiley & Sons, New York, Page 115. Used by permission.)

enzymes, vitamins, hormones, poisons, and drugs

Table 16.3 The Principal Endocrine Glands and Tissues of Man and Their Hormones

Gland or Tissue	Hormone	Major Function of Hormone
Thyroid	Thyroxine	Stimulates rate of oxidative metabolism and regulates general growth and development.
	Thyrocalcitonin	Lowers the level of calcium in the blood.
Parathyroid	Parathormone	Regulates the levels of calcium and phosphorus in the blood.
Pancreas (Islets of Langerhans)	Insulin	Decreases blood glucose level.
	Glucagon	Elevates blood glucose level.
Adrenal medulla	Epinephrine (adrenalin)	Various "emergency" effects on blood, muscle, temperature.
Adrenal cortex	Cortisone and related hormones	Control carbohydrate, protein, mineral, salt, and water metabolism.
Anterior pituitary	1. Thyrotropic	1. Stimulates thyroid gland functions.
	2. Adenocorticotropic	2. Stimulates development and secretion of adrenal cortex.
	3. Growth hormone	3. Stimulates body weight and rate of growth of skeleton.
	4. Gonadotropic (2 hormones)	4. Stimulate gonads.
	5. Prolactin	5. Stimulates lactation.
Posterior pituitary	1. Oxytocin	1. Causes contraction of some smooth muscle.
	2. Vasopressin	2. Inhibits excretion of water from the body by way of urine.
Ovary (follicle)	Estrogen	Influences development of sex organs and female characteristics.
Ovary (corpus luteum)	Progesterone	Influences menstrual cycle, prepares uterus for pregnancy; maintains pregnancy.
Uterus (placenta)	Estrogen and progesterone	Function in maintenance of pregnancy.
Testis	Androgens (testosterone)	Responsible for development and maintenance of sex organs and secondary male characteristics.
Digestive system	Several gastrointestinal	Integration of digestive processes.

From G. E. Nelson, G. G. Robinson, and R. A. Boolootian. *Fundamental Concepts of Biology*, 2nd edition, 1970. John Wiley & Sons, New York, page 114. Used by permission.

chapters, the action of a few specific hormones will be discussed in more detail.)

hormonal control. For each hormone there is a certain organ or a certain kind of cell whose biochemical reactions are most affected by it—the target organ or the target cell. The exquisite selectivity of a hormone for just its "own" target cells probably is related to some "lock-and-key" interaction at the cell walls.

Suppose that within a particular target cell compound A is supposed to react with compound B to produce compound C. A specific enzyme, E, is required. The reaction may be symbolized as follows:

$$A + B \overset{E}{\rightleftharpoons} C$$

The rate at which more of C can be made will depend on the following factors: the availability of A and (or) B, the concentration of E, the activity of E and the concentration of C already present.

Research during the last several years increasingly points to at least three major routes by which different hormones control chemical events in cells of target organisms—by gene activation, by enzyme activation and by changing cell walls.

Some hormones, by activating genes, manage to induce the synthesis of enzymes in the target cells, and the topic of enzyme induction will be studied in Chapter 21 as part of the chemistry of heredity. Estrogen and testosterone, two important sex hormones, probably work as gene activators.

Another major route of hormonal control is through the regulation of the availability of a reactant *within* the cell (and not just in circulation outside the cell). Some hormones act on the walls of target cells to change the ability of the wall to admit chemicals the cell needs. If the cell is denied important reactants the corresponding products obviously cannot be made and the functions of the involved tissue are impaired or stopped. This method of control makes it easy for us to understand how hormones whose molecules are very large (e.g., insulin) can work. Because of their size they could hardly be admitted through the wall of the cell, but by interacting with the surface of the wall they could still affect its permeability to other chemicals.

Human growth hormone appears to act by altering the permeability of cell walls to amino acids. In the absence of this hormone, cells become relatively starved for just those chemical building blocks they must have if they are to grow and divide. Thus, where human growth hormone is insufficiently available, poor growth and physical retardation result. (The laboratory synthesis of human growth hormone, a polypeptide with 188 amino acid units, by a team headed by Choh Hao Li, University of California Hormone Research Laboratory, was announced in early 1971.)

enzymes, vitamins, hormones, poisons, and drugs

The hormone, insulin, acts primarily by affecting the permeability of certain cells to glucose. (This hormone will be studied in much greater detail in subsequent chapters. It provides an elegant illustration of the molecular basis of a rather widespread, but fortunately controllable disease, diabetes mellitus.)

There are five main hormones involved in the regulation of the secretion of digestive juices, and all appear to exert their effects by modifying the transport properties of cellular membranes (see Chapter 17).

The hormones that regulate secretion and reabsorption in the tubules of the kidneys also appear to work by affecting permeabilities of cell walls (see Chapter 17).

The activation of an enzyme whose basic apoenzyme unit is already present but in an inactive geometry is another way by which some hormones work. Adrenaline is a well-studied example. How it works is described in Chapter 18 (Metabolism of Carbohydrates), but it appears to change to the active form an inactive enzyme incorporated into the wall of the target cell. This enzyme, still part of the cell wall, then catalyzes a reaction on the other side of the wall, on the cell's interior, which sets off a cascade of reactions to release glucose into circulation.

prostaglandins—hormone-like agents. First recognized in 1935 but not studied until about 1957, the prostaglandins are a family of hormone-like compounds that (unlike true hormones) occur in nearly all tissues and organs of the body. Fourteen have been identified thus far; two are shown here.

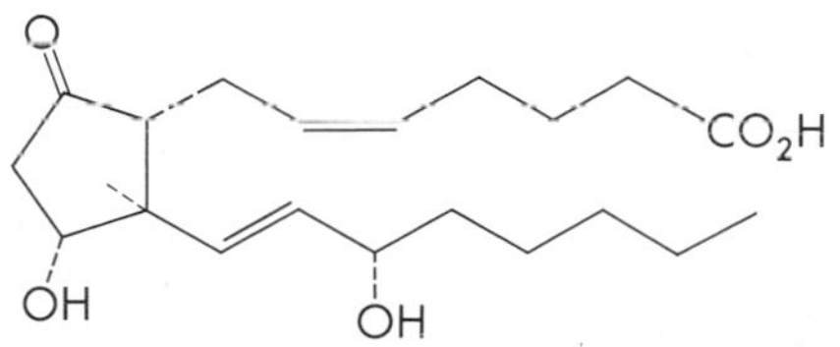

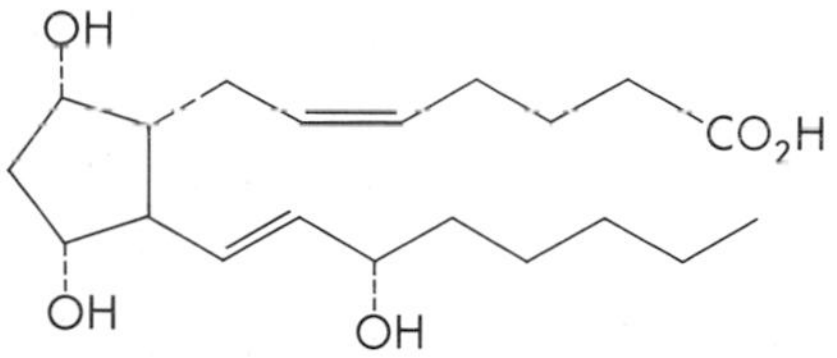

Two of the many prostaglandins

They work inside cells; if they leak out they quickly break down. How they work is not at all clear—the prostaglandins currently are objects of intensive research—but they seem to be regulators of hormone action. In a sense they translate "messages" cells receive from the primary chemical messengers, the hormones. Sometimes they may increase the urgency of the message; other times they may tell the system "to cool it." They are implicated in an astonishing variety of activities all of which suggest that prostaglandins may have an impact on the next generation of drugs. (They are surely affecting current drug research!) For example, prostaglandins can help to open up small passages in the lungs (emphysema treatment?), open stuffed nasal passages (cold treatment?), switch off the secretion of gastric juice (ulcer therapy?) and lower blood pressure (aid in treating cardiovascular disease?). Thus far the prostaglandins have been used in medicine to provide a simple and safe method to induce abortion in early pregnancy (before the eighth week) or to induce labor when the pregnancy is full-term. Evidence appeared in early 1971 that intrauterine devices may work by stimulating the uterus to release prostaglandins that prevent implantation of the ovum. Another development in 1971 was the startling discovery that aspirin and similar drugs inhibit the synthesis of certain prostaglandins in some tissues. The prostaglandins involved had earlier been found to be potent inducers of fever and inflammation. By inhibiting these prostaglandins, aspirin combats the symptoms.

inhibition of enzyme activity by poisons

Anything that prevents formation of an enzyme from its apoenzyme and coenzyme, or that binds a metal-ion activator, will clearly inhibit or prevent the reaction for which the enzyme is needed. Anything that will inhibit an enzyme and its substrate from forming their complex will give the same negative results. It is at this point that the connection between poisons and enzymes is seen. *The most powerful known poisons act simply by inhibiting key enzymes.* All are effective in very small doses, for only catalytic amounts of poisons, after all, are needed to inhibit catalytic amounts of enzymes.

cyanides. Hydrogen cyanide (hydrocyanic acid) and metal cyanides furnish the cyanide ion: $C\equiv N^-$. This ion reacts with many of the metal-ion activators to render them unavailable to an apoenzyme. Cells that consume oxygen require the presence of the enzyme cytochrome oxidase, which contains iron. Cyanide ion inhibits this enzyme causing cellular respiration to cease. This, ironically, stimulates the individual to breathe more deeply in an effort to rush oxygen to the cells.

ions of heavy metals. mercury and lead poisons and pollution. One of the amino acids is cysteine whose side-chain: $-CH_2-SH$, contains a mercaptan group. If an apoenzyme contains even one cysteine unit, it is vulnerable to the denaturing action of ions derived from several heavy metals, notably mercury, lead, and copper. Ions of these metals bind strongly to mercaptan units in enzymes.

Lead gets into the environment from leaded gasoline and it gets into small children if they eat flaking, lead-based paints. (We discussed lead poisoning in Chapter 10.)

Mercury enters the environment principally as mercury-based fungicides (chemicals that kill or inhibit the growth of fungi and molds), from carelessness in industrial operations (cf, e.g., Chapter 4, question 4), and from world-wide, large-scale combustion of coal. Because mercury will persist in the environment for decades, the accumulation of this pollutant in the waters of the planet is one of the most serious entries on the long list of chemical

enzymes, vitamins, hormones, poisons, and drugs

insults man has delivered to the biosphere, including himself and his children. Since 1900, 160 to 170 million pounds of mercury have been used in this country. Just during the decade of the 1960s U. S. consumption of mercury increased from 4 to 6 million pounds per year. About 20% went into making fungicides, which means that at least this much was scattered permanently into the environment, but actually much more disappeared—an estimated 4 million pounds in 1969 alone. Although coal contains only traces of mercury so much coal is burned each year that as much as 3,000 tons of mercury annually enter the earth's atmosphere from this source.

The principal mercury-based fungicides are compounds that can release the following positive ions:

$$CH_3Hg^+ \qquad CH_3CH_2Hg^+ \qquad C_6H_5Hg^+$$

methylmercury   ethylmercury   phenylmercury
fungicides   fungicides   fungicides

Various negative ions are also present, e.g. Cl^-, $CH_3CO_2^-$, CN^-. These compounds are used to treat batches of cereal grains set aside for seeds.

The methylmercury fungicides are the most dangerous, and in the biosphere the other types sooner or later are changed into methylmercury. They are also used as catalysts in the manufacture of acetaldehyde and polyvinylchloride plastics. Because Japanese plastics manufacturers upstream from the Bay of Minamata dumped mercury wastes into the streams, these poisons in the form of a methylmercury compound got into the high-fish diet of Japanese fishermen and their families living by the Bay. At least 121 adults and children were affected; 46 died in the period between 1953 and 1960. There were 23 children and infants, some even from mothers showing no symptoms of mercury poisoning during pregnancy, born with a strange type of cerebral palsy that came to be called Minamata disease.

Small repeated doses of mercury compounds accumulate in the liver and the kidneys. Methylmercury is especially devastating to the nervous system. The unwitting victim will begin to notice excessive salivation, sore gums, loose teeth, skin rashes, jerkiness, irritability, emotional disturbance, loss of vision and hearing, nephritis, and eventually death. As the Japanese found out, the poisons cross the placental barrier and the infants will have damaged brains. The infant brain is more susceptible to mercury poisoning than the adult.

No one yet knows what the lower limit is (if there is one) for exposure to mercury compounds over a long-range period. A level of 0.5 ppm mercury has been set by the U. S. Food and Drug Administration and by Canada to the limit of this pollutant in fish. Levels higher than 0.5 ppm have been found in fish and game birds in most of the states and Canada. It has become commonplace to warn sports fishermen not to eat catches more than once a week when they come from certain lakes and rivers. Tuna marketed in 1971 was found to have 0.1 to 0.8 ppm mercury and millions of tins were recalled. Samples of swordfish, another popular seafood, were found in 1971 with 0.18 to 2.4 ppm mercury.

Some of the mercury in the environment as a pollutant comes from natural sources, but most is probably from activities of man. During the decades of ignorance and carelessness, the first half of the century, users of mercury simply assumed that waste mercury would settle into and eventually disappear beneath the bottom muds of lakes and oceans. But the innumerable microorganisms in bottom muds, organisms that are at the bases of marine food chains, metabolize mercury compounds and change them mostly to the methylmercury form, a form much more soluble in fat tissue than Hg^{2+}. Mercury moves up food chains and then returns to the ever-active bottom muds when higher organisms die and decay.

arsenic compounds. Arsenic poisons (e.g., sodium arsenate, Na_3AsO_4) provide an ion, AsO_4^{3-}, that closely resembles the phosphate ion, PO_4^{3-}. (Arsenic and phosphorus are in the same chemical family.) If an enzyme uses arsenate when it should use phosphate, a whole series of reactions may be uncoupled.

nerve poisons. A variety of deadly poisons act by attacking enzymes of the nervous system. In certain parts of the system, the so-called cholinergic nerves, arrival of a nerve impulse at one nerve cell stimulates formation of a trace amount of acetylcholine all along its length. See Fig. 16.6. This small, ionic, and therefore water-soluble compound then reacts with a *receptor protein* on the next cell, making it possible for that cell to send the signal along. Once the signal has been sent, the acetylcholine must be hydrolyzed to leave the cell in readiness for the next signal. This hydrolysis must occur within a few millionths of a second after the acetylcholine appears. The equation for this reaction, an ordinary ester hydrolysis, is:

$$(CH_3)_3 \overset{+}{N}CH_2CH_2O-\overset{\overset{O}{\|}}{C}CH_3 \xrightarrow{\text{cholinesterase}} (CH_3)_3 \overset{+}{N}CH_2CH_2OH + CH_3CO_2H$$

acetylcholine   choline   acetic acid

Cholinesterase is the enzyme. Without it, the reaction is too sluggish; for all practical purposes it does not take place at all. The excess acetylcholine produces a prolonged, unwanted, and therefore dangerous stimulation of the nerves and the glands and muscles they control. Eyes, salivary glands, heart muscles, the digestive tract, and the adrenal glands, among other things, are affected.

Compounds that deactivate cholinesterase are called *anticholinesterases*. The most powerful of such compounds are the nerve gases. Less powerful, but still dangerous, are organophosphate and carbamate insecticides (Chapter

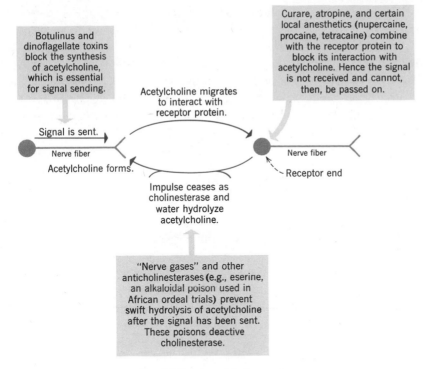

Curare, atropine, and certain local anesthetics (nupercaine, procaine, tetracaine) combine with the receptor protein to block its interaction with acetylcholine. Hence the signal is not received and cannot, then, be passed on.

Acetylcholine migrates to interact with receptor protein.

Signal is sent.

Nerve fiber

Acetylcholine forms.

Nerve fiber

Receptor end

Impulse ceases as cholinesterase and water hydrolyze acetylcholine.

"Nerve gases" and other anticholinesterases (e.g., eserine, an alkaloidal poison used in African ordeal trials) prevent swift hydrolysis of acetylcholine after the signal has been sent. These poisons deactive cholinesterase.

Fig. 16.6   Acetylcholine cycle.

12). Other substances that affect the operation of the nervous system are included in Fig. 16.6.

"food poisoning." This is sometimes caused by the secretion of toxic proteins by the botulinus bacillus, a microorganism that multiples in spoiled food. These food poisons are the most powerful yet discovered, surpassing even the nerve gases. As indicated in Fig. 16.6, they act to block the synthesis of acetylcholine. Failure of this compound to form means that signals are not sent, leading to paralysis of key organs, such as the pharyngeal muscles, and death is caused by respiratory failure. Symptoms appear from 12 to 36 hours after exposure.

dinoflagellate poisons. At various unpredictable periods, one of the microscopic marine organisms, the dinoflagellate *Gymnodinium,* multiplies almost explosively. Its secretions include a red pigment that kills fish by the millions in what people living along coastal areas know all too well as "red tides." Dinoflagellate poisons act in the same way as the botulinus toxins.

antimetabolites. *Chemotherapy* is the use of chemicals—drugs—that destroy infectious organisms without seriously harming human protoplasm. Chemotherapeutic agents include chemicals, called *antimetabolites,* that simply inhibit

enzyme inhibition and chemotherapy

the growth of microbes to prevent them from overwhelming the defensive mechanisms of the host. Some of the *antibiotics* ("against life") are believed to function as antimetabolites. Antibiotics are chemicals that are produced specifically by microorganisms, and in small concentrations they are able to inhibit the growth of or even destroy other microorganisms. Microbes that have been fruitful in producing antibiotics have been found chiefly in the soil, and tens of thousands of soil samples from all over the world have been examined for antibiotic-producing microbes. From these studies have come such famous antibiotics as Terramycin, Aureomycin, streptomycin, and chloramphenicol.

These and other antibiotics have been widely used among both people and food animals. From 20 to 25% of all antibiotics manufactured in the United States are given to animals either in their feed or to treat specific ailments. For unknown reasons, the antibiotics in feed stimulate growth in chickens, pigs, and beef cattle causing the development of fatter, tastier meat. The antibiotics also hold down diseases whose outbreaks would be especially threatening when food animals are raised cooped and penned in large numbers. The practice of giving food animals antibiotics may, however, be contributing to a potentially serious health problem among people.

The number of drug-resistant species of disease bacteria is increasing throughout the world. When an antibiotic fails to kill *all* of the target bacteria, the survivors are likely to include individuals that happen to be able to resist the antibiotic. The offspring of the survivors have a good chance to inherit this resistance, and in this way drug-resistant species develop. (The same kind of problem occurs as insects become resistant to various insecticides.) What is particularly serious is that the drug-resistant bacteria apparently manufacture a factor, called *R*, a *resistance-transfer factor*, which they can pass to bacteria never exposed to an antibiotic. The evidence is still incomplete, but critics of the antibiotic-feeding program of food animal raisers are concerned that drug-resistant bacteria of animals will pass this factor to human disease bacteria. British scientists who worried about this problem induced the British government to place controls on the kinds of antibiotics that could be used in animal feeds.

Drug-resistant germs are a problem in hospitals also, where both drugs and bacteria abound (and compete) in spite of stringent measures of control.

sulfa drugs as antimetabolites. The sulfa drugs are among the best understood of the antimetabolites, and, according to D. D. Woods, they function by interfering with an important enzyme system in several pathogenic microbes. These, unlike human beings, require *para*-aminobenzoic acid, a B vitamin, to complete the formation of folic acid, an important coenzyme. (Human beings must apparently obtain folic acid intact in the diet.) Structures of several important sulfa drugs are indicated in Fig. 16.7; apparently these molecules bear a close enough resemblance to *para*-aminobenzoic acid to

enzymes, vitamins, hormones, poisons, and drugs

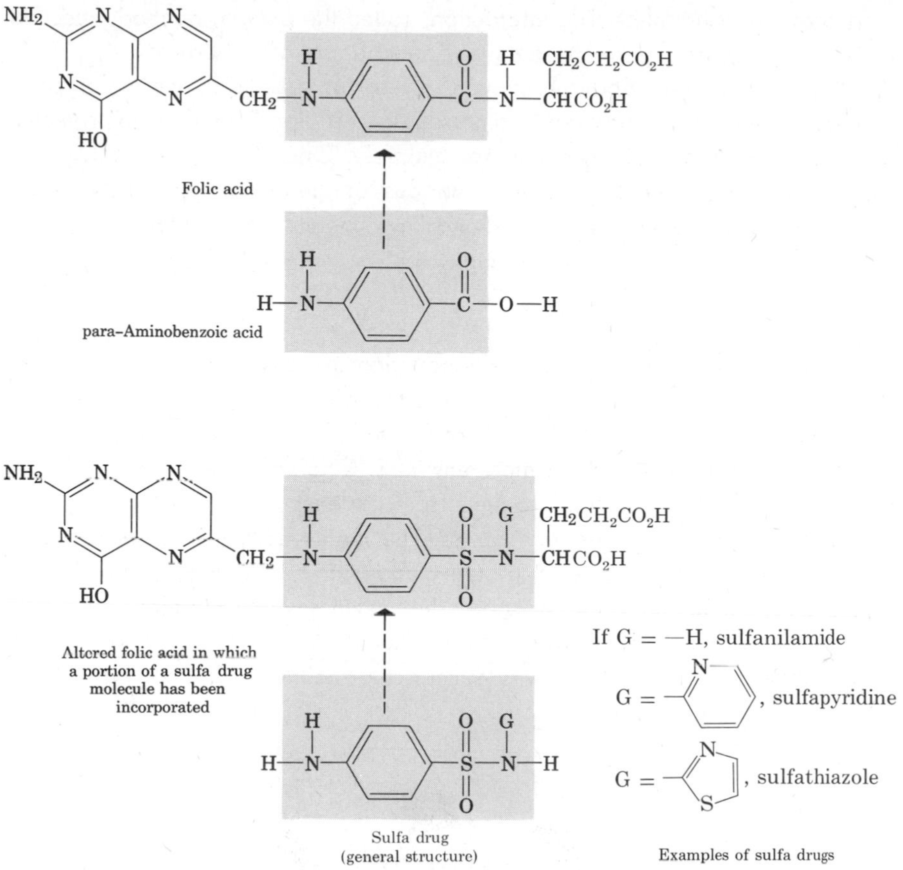

Fig. 16.7 Sulfa drugs as antimetabolites. When a microbe selects a sulfa drug to synthesize folic acid, it fashions an altered folic acid that is ineffective as a coenzyme. Reactions requiring it do not occur, and the growth of the microbe is inhibited. It suffers, in effect, from a vitamin-deficiency disease.

permit their incorporation into the coenzyme, as illustrated in Fig. 16.7. Once made, however, the altered coenzyme fails to function, and an important metabolic process in the microbe is inhibited.

the antigen-antibody reaction. If "bodies" foreign to the bloodstream enter it, specific, serum-soluble proteins called *antibodies* are usually generated. Any substance that can evoke the generation of an antibody is called an *antigen* (*antibody generator*), and all pathogenic microbes are in this category. *Toxins* are antigens that are poisonous products of the metabolism of certain bacteria. The purpose of an antibody is to combine with its antigen

lock-and-key
theory and
immunochemistry

and render it harmless. This interaction, called the *antigen-antibody reaction*, is an important part of the defensive mechanism of a body.

The antigen-antibody reaction is at least as specific as the action of an enzyme. Antibodies that protect a person against diphtheria give no protection against streptococcal infections, for example. Once formed, antibodies can "recognize" differences between various antigens. The specificity of this reaction is explained by a "lock and key" theory very similar to that used to explain enzyme activity (see Fig. 16.8).

enzymes in technology

the detergent industry. A major innovation in household detergents developed in the late 1960s with the introduction of enzymes as additives to detergents. By the end of 1970, three-fourths of the volume of home laundry detergents contained one or more enzymes. Originally a protease was used, a protein-digesting enzyme isolated from varieties of the bacterium *Bacillus subtilis*. Later an amylase was added. The idea was that these enzymes, by catalyzing the hydrolysis of proteins and starches in the soiled spots on clothing, would help clean the spots. The enzymes were reportedly compatible with the alkaline *p*H generated by the detergents in water, as well as with the other additives in detergents (except chlorine bleaches) and with the high

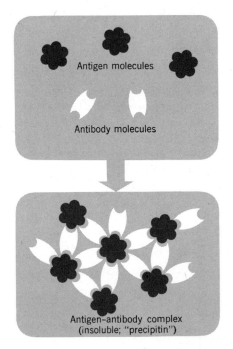

Fig. 16.8 If opportunities for "fitting" exist, antigen molecules (shown here as "multi-valent") will combine with antibody molecules to produce a huge molecular complex that leaves solution—the precipitin reaction.

enzymes, vitamins, hormones, poisons, and drugs

temperatures used. The optimum temperature for enzymic action is roughly 100 to 125°. If water hotter than that (or colder) is used in the presoak, the enzyme will do little good (except to sales). Whether or not dusts from enzyme-treated detergents, as they get into the soft, moist, warm, protein-rich, poorly protected tissues in the lungs, will damage the lungs became a subject of controversy. At the relatively very high concentrations of enzymes that detergent workers encountered in handling enzyme concentrates, many workers in the early period of this development experienced allergic respiratory conditions and skin reactions. Handling techniques have been improved, and the detergent industry claims that the consumer would be exposed to no more than 0.002% of the level now deemed safe for detergent workers. Some are not sure (e.g., Ralph Nader); they are concerned about long-term effects. Thus we had yet another cameo illustration of a major cause of our environmental malaise. We act first, or permit others to act on us, in effect offering ourselves as the experimental animals for the study of long-term effects; in this case, a study of an additive of no necessity whatsoever. By February 1971, according to the *New York Times,* the major detergent makers had quietly removed enzymes from some leading brands. By the mid 1970s detergent enzymes might be no more than a paragraph in advertising history; in mid-1971 René Dubos (Rockefeller University) reported that enzyme preparations used in detergents contain several potentially toxic substances. Among many effects of these substances was an enhancement of staphylococcus infection in experimental animals (*Science,* July 16, 1971, page 259).

the food industry. Flavor-producing enzymes extracted from unprocessed waste products such as apple cores, pineapple tops, or pea hulls may be added to canned, frozen, dehydrated or irradiated food to help restore flavors lost in processing.

The proteolytic enzyme, papain, is one component of popular meat tenderizers. It acts to catalyze the partial hydrolysis of meat proteins prior to eating them. The idea is that this action makes tough meat tender, and it will work, especially to the extent that collagens—connective proteins—are broken down.

Enzymes in the body normally are confined to intracellular fluids. Only minute traces of enzymes are present in such extracellular fluids as urine, plasma, cerebrospinal fluid, and bile. In certain diseases, however, the enzyme concentration of one or another of these extracellular fluids is known to increase greatly. Since samples of these fluids are easily withdrawn from a patient, and since enzymes are highly specific in the reactions they catalyze, analysis of a fluid for enzyme content is relatively easy. This amounts to a *biochemical biopsy,* in contrast with biopsy of tissue; and four examples that illustrate this approach follow.

**enzymes in
medical
diagnosis**

human infectious hepatitis. In this disease, the concentration of the enzyme glutamic pyruvic transaminase in blood serum increases ten-fold *even before the symptoms appear.* Assay of blood serum for the enzyme is a much simpler way of detecting the disease or its carriers than microscopic examination of a sample of liver tissue.

coronary occlusion with damage to heart muscle. An electrocardiograph is generally used to diagnose this condition and to measure the extent of damage. With patients suffering from a second attack, however, this method gives data that are very difficult to interpret. Coronary occlusions followed by injury to heart muscles are accompanied by a rise in the concentration of the enzyme glutamic oxaloacetic transaminase in blood serum. Serum analysis for this enzyme assists the physician not only in his diagnosis but also in his assessment of the possible degree of disability or recovery.

monocytic leukemia. The enzyme lysozyme, normally found in the fluid of human tears, saliva, and the white blood cells known as monocytes, appears in unusually high amounts in the blood and urine of people with monocytic leukemia. Recognition of this fact may provide a tool for identifying this form of leukemia in its early stages.

arteriosclerosis. It was found in 1970 that at least in experimental rabbits the level in the blood of the enzyme proline hydroxylase is high when plaque deposits are being formed in arteries. Such deposits are associated with hardening of the arteries.

Selected Reading List

Books

1. A. F. Wagner and K. Folkers. *Vitamins and Coenzymes.* Interscience Publishers (a division of John Wiley & Sons), New York, 1964. Before taking up the technical aspects of the chemistry and modes of action of vitamins and coenzymes, the authors provide a highly informative discussion of the evolution of the vitamin theory in their first chapter.

2. M. A. Benarde. *Our Precarious Habitat.* W. W. Norton & Co., New York, 1970. A public health scientist discusses in separate chapters each major type of pollution, including chapters on bacterial food poisoning and chemicals in food.

3. W. Marx. *The Frail Ocean.* Sierra Club—Ballantine, New York, 1967. Marx includes both the red tides and the mercury pollution at the Bay of Minamata in this survey of the ways we may ruin our oceans.

enzymes, vitamins, hormones, poisons, and drugs

4. N. N. Nelson, Study Group Chairman. *Hazards of Mercury.* Special Report to the Secretary's Pesticide Advisory Committee, U. S. Department of HEW, November 1970.

Articles

1. W. R. Loewenstein. "Intercellular Communication." *Scientific American,* May 1970, page 79. How signal molecules travel from inside one cell to the interior of a neighbor cell.

2. J. T. Bonner. "Hormones in Social Amoebae and Mammals." *Scientific American,* June 1969, page 78. Our kinship with all forms of life is again illustrated; ameobae and mammals employ the same secondary messenger, cyclic AMP.

3. N. Sharon. "The Bacterial Cell Wall." *Scientific American,* May 1969, page 92. In discussing the structure of the cell walls of bacteria the author explains how insulin attacks bacterial cells and not human cells.

4. J. Eccles. "The Synapse." *Scientific American,* June 1965, page 56. A discussion of how one nerve cell transmits a nerve impulse to the next.

5. G. M. Edelman. "The Structure and Function of Antibodies." *Scientific American,* August 1970, page 34. A discussion of the antigen-antibody reaction and the structure of immunoglobulin.

6. H. J. Sanders. "Allergy." *Chemical and Engineering News,* May 11, 1970, page 84. An extensive, but not highly technical discussion of all types of allergies and what causes them.

7. L. J. Goldwater. "Mercury in the Environment." *Scientific American,* May 1971, page 15. A discussion of the ways mercury exists in and moves through the environment.

8. Neville Grant. "Mercury in Man." *Environment,* May 1971, page 2. How mercury reaches us and what it does is surveyed.

9. Terri Aaronson. "Mercury in the Environment." *Environment,* May 1971, page 16. Sources of mercury pollution are discussed.

10. Staff. "Mercury in the Air." *Environment,* May 1971, page 28. Monitoring the air over St. Louis, Missouri, and nearby areas revealed that considerable quantities of mercury enter the environment via smokestacks.

Brief Summary

1. The molecules of some enzymes are entirely protein or clusters of protein.

2. Many enzymes require, besides the protein or apoenzyme unit, a cofactor—another molecule or ion—before the complete enzyme (or holoenzyme) is in

being. If the cofactor is an organic molecule it is called a coenzyme; if it is a metal ion, it is called an activator, and many of the "trace elements" or minerals of nutrition perform this service.

3. A number of coenzymes are phosphate or diphosphate esters of the B-vitamins.

4. The vitamins on man's "required list" are organic compounds we cannot make from molecules of carbohydrates, lipids, or proteins, and we must have them (or their provitamins where such occur) in our diets or we will develop a vitamin-deficiency disease.

5. Hormones are chemical messengers manufactured in various endocrine glands and sent as needed to target cells and organs to initiate reactions and changes corresponding to their messages.

6. A "lock-and-key" mechanism of enzyme-substrate interaction explains the specificity of enzymes as well as the specificity of the antigen-antibody reaction.

7. Enzymes operate best in specific ranges of temperature, pH, and concentration.

8. Enzyme action is otherwise affected by
   (a) rate of enzyme synthesis (genetic control)
   (b) modification of enzyme ability (control by modulators or effectors)
   (c) complete inhibition by molecules of poisons or certain drugs (antimetabolites).

Problems and Exercises

1. In general terms, what is the difference between an apoenzyme and a coenzyme?

2. What relation exists between B-vitamins and some coenzymes?

3. Vitamins A and D tend to accumulate in the body (in fatty tissue) but any unused amounts of the B-vitamins and vitamin C are excreted. What *physical* property would vitamins A and D have, but not vitamins B and C, that would help us to understand this.

4. Many vegetables contain B-vitamins but these vitamins are easily (and often) lost when the vegetables are cooked in water. Explain.

5. In general terms discuss three ways by which different hormones exert their effects.

6. Explain what is meant by these terms:
   (a) multienzyme complex,
   (b) regulatory enzyme,
   (c) effector (or modulator). (Explain how it works.)

7. In general terms, how do the following poisons act at the molecular level:
   (a) cyanides,
   (b) anticholinesterases.

8. In general terms, what is an antimetabolite?

9. Explain in general terms how sulfa drugs work. (You need not write any structures; use the names of substances.)

enzymes, vitamins, hormones, poisons, and drugs

10. What do ionic compounds derived from mercury do in the body at the molecular level?

11. Toxicologists have analyzed feathers of museum specimens of birds for their mercury content. In this way they could get data on mercury pollution from decades ago to compare with present-day figures. Why would keratin, the protein of feathers, tend to accumulate mercury?

12. Why will mercury remain in lakes a long time?

13. What are the principal sources of mercury in the environment?

14. What are some effects that seem to be caused by prostaglandins?

15. What is a possible danger of routinely giving food animals antibiotics in their food?

16. Define the following terms.
    (a) antibiotic
    (b) antigen
    (c) antibody
    (d) toxin
    (e) chemotherapy
    (f) peptidase
    (g) transaminase
    (h) active catalytic site
    (i) binding site
    (j) allosteric effect
    (k) fungicide

chapter 17 important fluids of the body

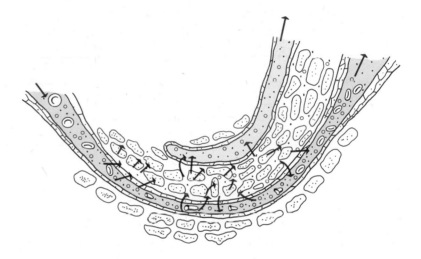

Claude Bernard, the great French physiologist of the nineteenth century, was the first to point out that all higher animals live not only in an external environment of wind and weather but also with an internal environment of fluids and solutions. Because it exerts nearly perfect control over this internal environment, an animal (or man) can handle a wide range of outside conditions. In this chapter, we shall study in a general way the chemistry of how this control is kept.

the internal environment	All the fluids in the body that are not inside cells comprise the internal environment. In man they amount to about 20% of body weight, with three-fourths constituting interstitial fluids—fluids within which most cells are continuously bathed—and almost all the rest, nearly one-fourth, is in the bloodstream. Other fluids include lymph,[1] cerebrospinal fluid, digestive juices, and synovial fluid. Our study will concentrate on the digestive juices and the blood. We shall examine diuresis (urine formation) and how it is intimately related to the chemistry of the blood. Fluid exchange at tissue cells and gas exchange at cells and lungs are other aspects of the internal environment that we shall study. Finally, we shall investigate the clotting mechanism, which stands guard over the tissues that enclose the bloodstream.

the digestive juices and digestion the digestive tract	The digestive tract is essentially a tube running through the body. Its principal parts and organs are located and named in Fig. 17.1. When a meal is eaten, ingested food is acted on by a series of chemical "baths" in which huge, largely water-insoluble food molecules are degraded to small, soluble molecules. These migrate out of the digestive tract through the walls of the intestines. They enter the bloodstream or the lymph system and are carried to regions of the body where they are needed.

The chemical "baths" are the various digestive juices: saliva, gastric juice, pancreatic juice, intestinal juice, and bile. With the exception of bile, they are fundamentally solutions of enzymes.

[1] Some authors lump interstitial fluid and lymph together. Others prefer to restrict the term *lymph* to the fluid obtainable directly from lymph ducts.

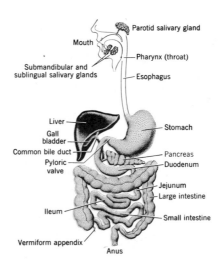

Fig. 17.1 Organs of the digestive tract. (Adapted from Eva D. Wilson, Katherine H. Fisher, and Mary E. Fuqua, *Principles of Nutrition*, second edition, John Wiley and Sons, New York, 1965. Used by permission.)

We shall study the digestive process by examining each digestive juice, its components, and its action on food molecules.

saliva. Ingested food encounters its first digestive juice in the mouth, where saliva is secreted. The most important components of saliva are summarized in Table 17.1.

We all know from experience that the flow of saliva is greater at certain times than at others. Secretory nerves, stimulated by the sight, smell, taste, or even the thought of food, activate and regulate this flow. The average person secretes about 1 to $1\frac{1}{2}$ liters of saliva per day.

Chewing action breaks food into smaller particles. This is important, for it permits a more rapid attack by digestive chemicals. As chewing proceeds, food particles become lubricated by water and mucin. Of greatest importance is the action of *ptyalin,* the salivary amylase, which catalyzes the partial hydrolysis of starch to various dextrins and to some maltose. Final hydrolysis of these breakdown products to glucose is completed farther along the tract, in the small intestine.

The partial hydrolysis of starch is the only digestive reaction that occurs in the mouth. Proteins and lipids pass through essentially unchanged.

gastric juice. The chief components of gastric juice, secreted into the stomach, are listed in Table 17.2.

Gastric juice is a mixture of more than one secretion originating in various glands or areas of the stomach wall. Its hydrochloric acid appears to come from one group of cells and the enzymes from another. A normal adult's stomach secretes about 2 to 3 liters of gastric juice per day. This flow is regulated by the nervous system and by the agency of a hormone, gastrin. When food enters the stomach, gastrin is secreted into the bloodstream. It circulates to the cells that produce gastric secretions and stimulates them to discharge their juices into the stomach.

Before secretion, *pepsin,* the proteolytic enzyme in gastric juice, is present in an inactive form known as *pepsinogen.* Its conversion to the active form,

Table 17.1 **Components of Saliva**

Nonenzymic substances:	1. Water (99.5%)
	2. Mucin, a glycoprotein that gives saliva its characteristic consistency
	3. Inorganic ions: Ca^{2+}, Na^+, K^+, Mg^{2+}, $H_2PO_4^-$, Cl^-, HCO_3^-
	4. Miscellaneous molecules found also in blood and urine: urea, ammonia, cholesterol, amino acids, uric acid
	Average pH of saliva, 6.8
Enzymes	α-Amylase ("ptyalin")

Table 17.2 Components of Gastric Juice

Nonenzymic substances:	1. Water (99%)
	2. Mucin
	3. Inorganic ions: Na^+, K^+, Cl^-, $H_2PO_4^-$
	4. HCl (0.5%); range of pH, 1.6–1.8
Enzymes:	1. Pepsin, a proteolytic enzyme
	2. Gastric lipase

pepsin, is accomplished by the acid that pours into the stomach from other cells. The change from pepsinogen to pepsin is believed to involve a slight degradation of the protein molecule of pepsinogen. Perhaps this exposes active sites previously folded in.

Pepsinogen is not classified as an apoenzyme, since it does not require a coenzyme for conversion to an enzyme. Together with other enzymes of its type, it is classified as a *zymogen*. Names of individual zymogens bear the suffix "-ogen." The prefix is, in each case, the name of the active enzyme to which the zymogen can be converted.

Pepsin catalyzes partial degradation of proteins to intermediate breakdown products of proteins given names as defined by the "word equation":

$$\text{Proteins} \longrightarrow \text{proteoses} \longrightarrow \text{peptones} \longrightarrow \text{"polypeptides"} \longrightarrow \text{amino acids}$$
$$\succ\!\!\text{------ Fragments become progressively smaller} \longrightarrow$$

Peptic hydrolysis converts proteins into a mixture of proteoses and peptones. The optimum pH for pepsin is about 2.

Gastric lipase catalyzes the hydrolysis of ester linkages in fats and oils. However, its optimum pH is close to neutrality, much too high for effective action in a medium of pH 1 to 2. Very little fat digestion occurs in the stomach, therefore. In fact, there is still some question whether this lipase is a true component of gastric juice or whether it makes its way into the stomach by regurgitation of contents of the upper intestinal tract *via* the pyloric valve.

Food material in the stomach assumes a liquid consistency as gastric digestion proceeds. This mixture, known as the *chyme*, is released in portions through the pyloric valve into the upper intestinal tract. Complete evacuation of the stomach takes from 2 to 5 hours, depending on the nature of the meal eaten.

intestinal juice (succus entericus). Mucosal glands of the duodenum secrete this digestive juice whenever chyme enters it from the stomach. The regulation of its flow is not well understood. It appears to be stimulated in more than one way, including hormonal action. The chief components of intestinal juice are listed in Table 17.3.

Table 17.3 Components of Intestinal Juice

Nonenzymic substances:	1. Water
	2. Inorganic ions: Na^+, K^+, Ca^{2+}, Cl^-, HCO_3^-, HPO_4^{2-}
Enzymes:	1. Aminopeptidase
	2. Dipeptidase
	3. Nucleases, nucleotidase, nucleosidase
	4. Maltase
	5. Sucrase
	6. Lactase
	7. Intestinal lipase
	8. Lecithinase
	9. Phosphatase
	10. Enterokinase

The enzyme-rich intestinal juice is important to the digestion of all the foodstuffs. Various peptidases complete the hydrolysis of proteins to amino acids. Sucrase, maltase, and lactase handle conversion of the important disaccharides, sucrose, maltose, and lactose to glucose, fructose, and galactose. Simple lipids are acted on by a lipase; more complex lipids are hydrolyzed by the catalytic action of lecithinase and phosphatase. Nucleic acids (cf. Chapter 21) respond to enzymes peculiar to their hydrolytic needs.

One of the most important enzymes found in intestinal juice is *enterokinase*. Its unique task is to convert the zymogen, *trypsinogen*, of pancreatic juice, into the very important proteolytic enzyme, *trypsin*. It does this by catalyzing the hydrolysis of one peptide bond in trypsinogen to clip off a short segment of the protein chain. The remaining unit then automatically undergoes a change in configuration and the active catalytic site is exposed.

Even though intestinal juice is rich in enzymes, it appears that much of its enzymic influence is exerted right within the cells of the duodenal mucosa, rather than in the duodenum itself. If nutrient molecules that are not completely hydrolyzed begin to dialyze through the intestinal walls, their hydrolysis is completed during the journey by action of the intestinal-juice enzymes.

pancreatic juice. The pancreas produces two secretions. The internal secretion, which contains insulin, is discharged into the bloodstream. The external secretion, pancreatic juice, is emptied into the duodenum. Its principal components are listed in Table 17.4.

The flow of pancreatic juice is regulated by an ingenious, although indirect, cooperation with the gastric juice. Gastric juice is acidic. When acidic chyme enters the duodenum, the acid acts to liberate a hormone, *secretin*, from the duodenal mucosa. Systemic circulation of this hormone brings it to the pancreas, where it stimulates the pancreas to discharge its digestive juice. Action of the hormone ceases when entry of acidic chyme into the duodenum

Table 17.4   Components of Pancreatic Juice

Nonenzymic substances:	1. Water
	2. Inorganic ions: Na^+, K^+, Ca^{2+}, Cl^-, HCO_3^-, HPO_4^{2-}
	Range of pH: 7–8
	Average daily volume: 500–800 cc
Enzymes:	1. Pancreatic lipase ("steapsin")
	2. α-Amylase
	3. Maltase
	4. Ribonuclease
Zymogens:	1. Trypsinogen (converted to trypsin)
	2. Chymotrypsinogen (converted to chymotrypsin)
	3. Procarboxypeptidase (converted to carboxypeptidase)

ceases. The average adult pancreas secretes from 500 to 800 cc of juice per day.

proteolytic enzymes. Enterokinase from intestinal juice converts the zymogen, trypsinogen, into the active, proteolytic enzyme, *trypsin.* One of the roles of trypsin is to convert chymotrypsinogen into its corresponding active enzyme, *chymotrypsin.* Trypsin also changes the third zymogen of pancreatic juice, procarboxypeptidase, into *carboxypeptidase.* The chief enzymic function of trypsin is to convert native proteins to proteoses, peptones, and polypeptides. Chymotrypsin acts in a similar way. Carboxypeptidase works on smaller polypeptides by hydrolyzing amino acids from the ends of the chain having the free carboxylic acid unit.

carbohydrases. α-Amylase in pancreatic juice acts on acetal links in amylose and amylopectin molecules that have escaped hydrolysis in the mouth. The end product of this action is maltose, which is acted on by maltase to yield glucose.

lipase. The pancreatic lipase, steapsin, is the body's most important fat-splitting enzyme. It acts to hydrolyze lipids to glycerol and fatty acids. The efficiency of its action depends a great deal on the presence of powerful fat emulsifiers secreted in bile. The chief problem in lipid digestion is that lipids are notoriously water insoluble. They tend to form large globules. Any digestive attack on them, which involves water-soluble enzymes and water, can occur only at the surface of such a globule. If large globules of lipid material are broken into numerous microscopic globules, the effective total surface area of the lipid is greatly increased, and digestion can occur more rapidly. The fat emulsifiers in bile are called *bile salts.* They are merely special kinds of soaps (see Chapter 14).

bile. Bile, the third juice that empties into the duodenum, contains no digestive enzymes. Nevertheless, it is vitally important to digestion, for it contains bile salts, whose fat-emulsifying action was described above. Bile is an alkaline fluid manufactured continuously in the liver and stored and concentrated in the gall bladder. The important constituents are the *bile salts,* *bile pigments,* and *cholesterol.*

When partially digested food enters the duodenum, a hormone, *cholecystokinen,* is elaborated. It circulates through the bloodstream until it reaches the gall bladder, where it stimulates that organ to contract. Bile is thus forced out of the gall bladder and into the duodenum. Secretin, the hormone discussed in connection with the regulation of the flow of pancreatic juice, stimulates the liver to produce more bile.

In addition to facilitating the digestive action of steapsin, bile salts emulsify the fatty acids that are produced by lipid digestion. This action assists the body in absorbing these fatty acids out of the digestive tract. Bile salts not only are needed for lipid digestion; they are also important in the digestion of other foods. Fats and oils in the diet tend to coat other food particles. This lipid coating inhibits the digestive action of other enzymes. Bile salts, however, acting as soaps, remove this coating, making it possible for the food particles to be attacked digestively.

Bile pigments are the result of the partial breakdown of hemoglobin, and they impart the characteristic yellowish brown or green color to bile.

Cholesterol is removed from the body through the bile. Occasionally, it precipitates in the gall bladder in the form of gallstones. The fact that bile contains two substances that the body excretes—cholesterol and bile pigments—makes bile an excretion as well as a secretion.

End products of digestion are absorbed by the body largely in the upper intestinal tract, about the first 25 feet of the intestines. Food that escapes digestion or absorption is subjected to chemical processes in the lower intestinal tract before evacuation as feces. **changes occurring in the lower digestive tract**

Feces are composed of undigested food, water, digestive enzymes, mucus, bile pigments (whence the characteristic color of feces), toxic amines, fatty acids, cholesterol, and dissolved gases. The gases, the fatty acids, and the toxic amines are produced by bacterial action on undigested food in the large intestines. Indeed, dried feces are almost 25% bacteria (largely nonpathogenic). Toxic amines and gases originate primarily from amino acids.

Starch and the three disaccharides—maltose, lactose, and sucrose—are the chief carbohydrates in nutrition. Digestion of cooked starch begins in the mouth, where amylase is active. It continues for a time in the stomach until the hydrochloric acid in the gastric juice inactivates the ptyalin that has **brief summary of the digestion of the** accompanied swallowed food. Ptyalin is not considered active toward uncooked starch. Dextrins and maltose are the end products of ptyalin's action.

The disaccharides probably undergo some nonenzymic hydrolysis in the stomach where the action of hydrochloric acid hydrolyzes acetal linkages in these molecules, but this is not of great importance.

The amylase in pancreatic juice completes the hydrolysis to maltose of both raw and cooked starch. The three carbohydrases—maltase, lactase, and sucrase—that appear in the duodenum complete the digestion of the disaccharides. *The end products of carbohydrate digestion, then, are fructose, galactose, and glucose.*

Cellulose in the diet (e.g., in leafy vegetables) passes through essentially unchanged. It furnishes much of the bulk needed for efficient operation of the excretory system in the lower intestinal tract.

lipids

For all practical purposes, no digestion occurs to lipids until they reach the duodenum, in spite of the presence of a lipase in the gastric juice. This lipase has an optimum pH too high for effective action in the stomach. It may begin to function after it is carried with chyme into the duodenum, for after chyme has been neutralized the pH is more favorable. Fats that are already highly emulsified (e.g., lipids occurring in milk and eggs) are most susceptible to the action of gastric lipase while they are in the stomach.

Rapid emulsification of lipids occurs by action of bile salts in the duodenum. Once emulsified, steapsin smoothly hydrolyzes lipids to *glycerol and fatty acids, the end products of the digestion of the neutral fats and oils.* (There is some evidence that all three ester linkages in lipid molecules are not hydrolyzed in every case.) The lipase of the intestinal juice acts on lipids that escape hydrolysis by action of steapsin.

proteins

Simple proteins are not acted on in the mouth. In the stomach, pepsin catalyzes conversion of proteins to proteoses and peptones.

Trypsin and chymotrypsin, in the duodenum, act rapidly on proteoses and peptones (and, to a certain extent, on native proteins), converting them to simple peptides and amino acids. Peptidases in intestinal juice and pancreatic juice complete digestion of proteins. *The end products of protein digestion are amino acids and, perhaps, some simple, soluble di- and tripeptides.*

blood
functions of blood and the circulatory system

A schematic diagram of the circulatory system is given in Fig. 17.2. This system is one of the main lines of communication between the external and the internal environment. Hormones released by various glands in response to signals triggered by our several senses; dismantled food molecules sent in from the digestive tract; oxygen picked up by red cells in the lungs; waste

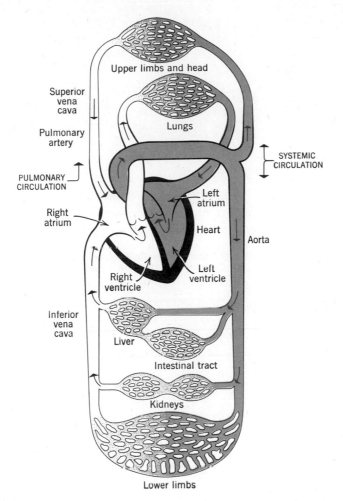

Fig. 17.2 The circulatory system in man. Shaded areas designate oxygenated blood. Blood received from the veins at the right atrium of the heart passes into the right ventricle, and from there it is forced through the spongy capillary networks of the lungs. In the capillaries carbon dioxide is removed and oxygen is taken up. The blood then goes to the left atrium for delivery to the left ventricle and on to the rest of the body.

products dumped by cells everywhere; traveling scavangers (the white blood cells or leukocytes) that engulf or bind invading bacteria; cruising healers that help to plug breaks in the tubes—the circulatory system carries them all. To handle these substances and get them around the blood contains a large number of specialized chemicals and cells. We shall study some features here, but a full treatment requires specialized texts and courses.

Blood *plasma* is the aqueous solution left after removal of the cellular bodies which are also called the *formed elements:* red cells (erythrocytes), white cells (leukocytes), and platelets. Blood *serum* is the fluid left with both

functions of blood and the circulatory system

the formed elements and the clotting protein (fibrinogen) removed. (Defibrinated blood is whole blood without fibrinogen.) There are about six quarts of blood in a normal, adult male, and about 55% of this is plasma. The rest is made up of the formed elements.

About 7 to 8% (by weight) of blood plasma is made up of various proteins. Of these the *albumins* account for roughly 55%. They appear to have principally two functions: to transport molecules otherwise insoluble in water (e.g., fatty acids) and to help maintain osmotic pressure relations.

Globulins constitute about 40% of the total protein. Three types are recognized: α-globulin, β-globulin, and γ-globulin. Each type consists of several kinds of proteins. The γ-globulins are important in the body's defense against infectious disease. The other globulins appear to be necessary for the transport of metal ions such as Fe^{2+} and Cu^{2+}, which otherwise would be insoluble in the slightly basic medium of blood.

Fibrinogen, the third major protein found in plasma, amounts to about 5 to 6% of the total protein. It is the immediate precursor of fibrin, a plasma-insoluble protein that precipitates as a tangled "brush heap" in a developing blood clot.

Electrolytes constitute another general type of plasma solute. Body fluids, in general, contain inorganic ions. They serve two principal ends: maintenance of suitable pHs and control of osmotic pressure relations.

Extracellular fluids (those of the internal environment) are solutions in which the ions Na^+, Cl^-, and HCO_3^- predominate. Within cells, that is, in intracellular fluids, the following ions: K^+, Mg^{2+}, SO_4^{2-}, HPO_4^{2-}, and $H_2PO_4^-$ are relatively abundant. The electrolyte compositions of the main body fluids are shown in Fig. 17.3. The electrolyte compositions of plasma and interstitial fluid are virtually identical because capillary walls are permeable both to water and to electrolyte ions. These fluids differ primarily in protein composition, a difference that has important implications to be discussed later in the chapter. In view of the purposes electrolytes have in body fluids, it is vital that their concentrations be carefully regulated. This problem is handled in large part by the kidneys.

diuresis The kidneys, in cooperation with certain hormones, exert control over the concentrations of electrolytes in general, and over the acid-base balance in particular. The first is handled largely by regulating the volume of water that will be excreted as urine and by policing movements of various ions across the renal thresholds. Control of the acid-base balance is accomplished by retaining or excreting hydrogen ions.

The kidneys are located behind the other organs on either side of the spinal column. Into each, a single large artery brings blood, and from each, blood leaves by a large vein. While in the kidneys, the blood undergoes a fantastic filtering process. It flows through the kidneys at a rate of about

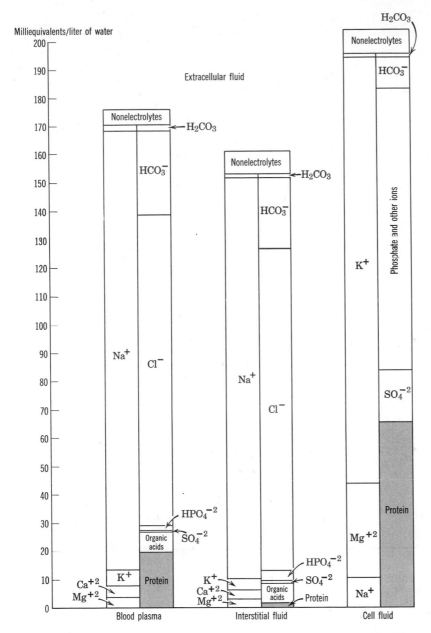

Fig. 17.3   Electrolyte composition of body fluids. (Adapted from J. L. Gamble. *Chemical Anatomy, Physiology and Pathology of Extracellular Fluid,* Sixth Edition. Harvard University Press, Cambridge, Mass., 1954. Used by permission.)

1700 quarts a day. Only about one-thousandth of this amount (1 to 2 quarts) is converted into urine. Nevertheless, approximately 180 quarts of fluid per day temporarily leave the circulatory system and filter into the tubules of the kidneys, but 178 quarts are reabsorbed. In this filtration-reabsorption process, more than 2 pounds of salt move out of the bloodstream, and all but a fraction of an ounce returns. The whole process of urine formation is called diuresis (Greek, ''to make water or urine'').

regulation of electrolyte concentration of blood. The sketches in Fig. 17.4 show successively enlarged views of the kidneys or parts of them. To accommodate the huge volumes involved in daily filtration-reabsorption, an enormous surface area is supplied by the approximately two million *nephrons* found in two kidneys. At each nephron, filtration occurs when blood water, together with dissolved electrolytes and small molecules (e.g., urea), is forced out of the capillaries of the *glomerulus* and into the *renal capsule*. Plasma proteins, lipids, and cellular elements remain behind in the bloodstream. About seven-eighths of this *glomerular filtrate* is reabsorbed from the first part of the tubule, the *proximal tubule*, that twists and turns among a network of fine capillaries. Reabsorption in this region returns to the circulatory system most of the electrolytes as well as most of the water and the blood sugar. Urea, uric acid, and creatinine tend to remain in the developing urine. The remaining

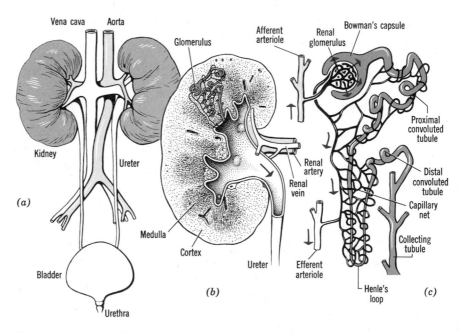

Fig. 17.4 The excretory system of the kidneys. (a) The principal parts. (b) Longitudinal section of a kidney indicating the location of the nephrons. (c) Details of the structure of a nephron and the blood capillary bed through which it twines. (Adapted with permission from G. E. Nelson, G. G. Robinson, and R. A. Boolootian, *Fundamental Concepts of Biology*, 2nd edition, 1970, page 152. John Wiley & Sons, Inc., New York, 1967.)

one-eighth of the glomerular filtrate may or may not be reabsorbed in the distal tubule. Distal reabsorption, which is optional, is regulated by an antidiuretic hormone called *vasopressin*. When the hormone is not secreted, optional reabsorption ceases, and relatively large amounts of urine form. When the hormone is secreted in significant amounts, there is nearly 100% reabsorption. In this case, urine formation almost ceases. Secretion of vaso- pressin is controlled by the hypophysis[2] via its sensitivity to changes in the osmotic pressure of the blood.

(Since the concept of osmotic pressure will be used frequently in this chapter, it would be well to take a few minutes to review it; see page 138. In general, a solution has a high osmotic pressure if it is concentrated, and a low osmotic pressure if it is dilute. The osmotic pressure of water is zero.)

Vasopressin is elaborated by cells of the posterior, or neural, region of the hypophysis. If the osmotic pressure of the blood varies as much as 2% up or down, secretion of vasopressin is increased or decreased, respectively. If, for example, blood has a relatively high osmotic pressure (a condition known as *hypertonicity*), the body acts to keep it from going higher. It does this by conserving its water. The hypophysis secretes vasopressin, which stimulates reabsorption of water in distal tubules, preventing its loss as urine, and keeping it in the blood. Accompanying this activity, the sensation of thirst is stimulated. Satisfaction of thirst, of course, brings in more water. Vasopressin secretion, in a sense, "holds the fort," while thirst satisfaction brings in water to cut the concentration of the blood and thereby lower its osmotic pressure.

Too much water intake dilutes the blood and causes its osmotic pressure to drop too far, a condition of *hypotonicity*. The hypophysis is thereby stimulated to reduce its secretion of vasopressin. Optional reabsorption decreases, and large amounts of water that left the plasma at the glomerulus remain in the developing urine. The concentration of solutes in the plasma, therefore, increases, thus raising its osmotic pressure back to the normal level.

When vasopressin secretion is blocked, as in *diabetes insipidus*, optional reabsorption ceases, and the volume of urine increases. Upwards of 5 to 12 liters of urine may be voided per day by people suffering from this rare disease, which illustrates the importance of optional reabsorption and the necessity for smooth operation of the hypophysis. In a normal person, the intake of fluids may vary enormously without upsetting a nearly perfect balance of internal water.

Loss of specific ions in urine is regulated by hormones of the adrenal cortex, especially the hormone aldosterone. Major portions of Na^+, Cl^-, K^+, and HCO_3^- are reabsorbed from the glomerular filtrate during its passage through the proximal tubules. Cells in the distal tubules, acting under hor- monal control, make final adjustments in the relative amounts of these ions that will remain in the urine.

[2] The hypophysis was initially called the *pituitary gland*.

regulation of the acid-base balance of blood. The pH of blood must remain within the extremely narrow range of 7.0 to 7.9 and is normally around 7.4, as measured at room temperature. A shift toward the acid side is termed *acidosis*, and toward the basic side, *alkalosis*. Acidosis is the more common tendency, for ordinary metabolism produces acids. Two agencies, blood buffers and the kidneys, stabilize the pH of the blood and, thereby, of the whole internal environment.

The most important buffer of the blood is the system HCO_3^-/H_2CO_3. In neutralizing acids, bicarbonate ions in blood combine with hydrogen ions:

$$H^+ \quad + \quad HCO_3^- \quad \rightleftharpoons \quad H_2CO_3$$

| Hydrogen ions of developing acidosis | Bicarbonate ions of the buffer system | Carbonic acid, a weak acid with a small tendency to ionize |

Too much carbonic acid can be handled by its decomposition to water and carbon dioxide:

$$H_2CO_3 \longrightarrow H_2O + CO_2$$

Excreted at
the lungs

Removal of the carbon dioxide at the lungs means a net replacement of a hydrogen ion by a water molecule at the expense of a bicarbonate ion. This, of course, depletes part of the buffer system, but the kidneys come to the rescue, for they are able to generate a fresh supply of bicarbonate ions for the bloodstream. At the same time, they produce a more acidic urine.

acidification of the urine. R. F. Pitts proposed the following mechanism to explain how cells of the distal tubules increase the supply of bicarbonate ion in blood, feed hydrogen ions to the urine, and thereby help to restore an acid-base balance in a developing acidosis. His scheme may best be studied by reference to Fig. 17.5. The encircled numbers in the following paragraph refer to this figure.

Catabolism of some nutrient molecule in a distal tubule cell produces carbon dioxide ①. Action of the enzyme, carbonic anhydrase, causes it to combine with water to form carbonic acid ②, which ionizes to produce bicarbonate ions and hydrogen ions ③. In a sense, the ionization is forced, for sodium ions from tubular urine are made to exchange for hydrogen ions ④. The hormone aldosterone appears to be essential to promote this exchange. The urine thereby becomes more acidic. Bicarbonate ions, together with the sodium ions that have just arrived by exchange, leave the distal cell and enter the bloodstream ⑤. In this way, bicarbonate ions used earlier to neutralize hydrogen ions are replaced, and the urine is made slightly acidic. Freshly voided urine has a pH of about 6, although in severe acidosis, as

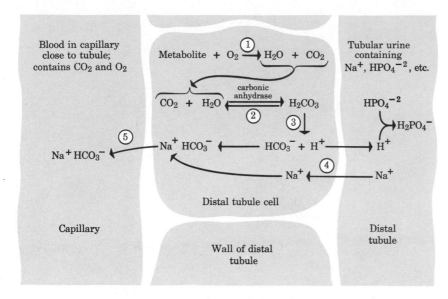

Fig. 17.5 The acidification of the urine, according to R. F. Pitts. (Circled numbers refer to textual discussion.) (*American Journal of Medicine*, Vol. 9, 356, (1950).)

the kidneys battle to control it, they may produce a urine with a *p*H as low as 4. Such urine has a hydrogen-ion concentration 1000 times that of normal blood.

the lymphatic system. The bloodstream and the lymphatic system are the two circulatory systems in the body. The lymphatics perform the following functions: (1) recirculation of interstitial fluid to the bloodstream, (2) transportation of some chemicals from where they were made to general circulation as well as conveyance of freshly absorbed, resynthesized lipid material from the intestinal tract to the bloodstream, and (3) service in the defensive mechanisms of the body.

As illustrated in Figs. 17.6 and 17.7, the lymphatic system is made up of successively more branched ducts that terminate in a spongy mesh of tiny, thin-walled capillaries, all with closed ends, that bed within most of the soft tissue of the body. The larger lymph vessels, which have valves, receive lymph fluid from the branches and convey it to large blood vessels near the neck. The *thoracic duct* drains the lower limbs and the tissues of all the organs except the lungs, the heart, and the upper part of the diaphragm. The *right lymphatic duct* takes care of these organs, and the *cervical ducts* take lymph from the head and neck. Spaced along the larger lymphatic vessels are *lymph nodes*. These are specialized capillary beds that filter out solid matter in lymph before it reaches the bloodstream. More importantly, these nodes contain white cells that destroy bacteria and other foreign substances, and they have

lymph

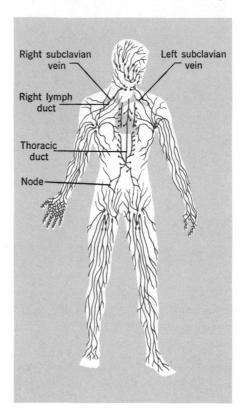

Fig. 17.6 The relations of the larger vessels of the lymphatic system to each other and to the bloodstream. (Courtesy of G. E. Nelson, G. G. Robinson, and R. A. Boolootian, *Fundamental Concepts of Biology*, page 126, John Wiley & Sons, Inc., New York, 1967. Used by permission.)

special cells that make antibodies. They are very important to the defenses of the body. At the same time, if cancer strikes, the lymph ducts are avenues for its spread from one tissue to another, a phenomenon known as metastasis.

Having learned something about the bloodstream and some of the ways its composition is controlled, and having looked briefly at the second circulatory system, the lymphatics, we are now in a position to discuss how these two systems participate in bringing nutrients to cells and carrying waste products away.

transport of chemicals
fluid exchange at tissue cells
Capillary walls may be treated as selectively permeable membranes or "filters." They allow for the passage of water with dissolved nutrient molecules in one direction and for the flow of water with dissolved waste products in the other. Of course, it is important that these flows not only go in the right direction but also that they occur evenly and smoothly. Fluids that leave the bloodstream must return in equal volume. There are two mechanisms that

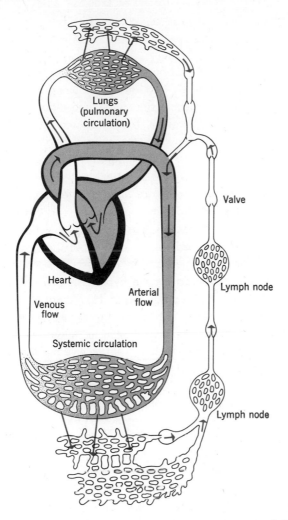

Fig. 17.7 General features of the relations between lymph flow and the bloodstream. Oxygenated blood is shown in dark. Water and other substances leave the bloodstream at its capillaries and they circulate and seep past cells. Fluids, unused nutrients, waste molecules, and the like return to circulation partly via the lymph system and largely by direct return through the wall of a blood capillary.

cooperate to ensure both conditions: first, the pumping action of the heart, which generates a simple, ordinary pressure and, second, osmotic-pressure relations that cause dialysis. Dialysis returns fluids and chemicals not only directly back to the bloodstream but also indirectly back through the lymph ducts.

exchange of chemicals at tissue cells. The pumping action of the heart creates a simple, ordinary pressure that is higher on the arterial side of a capillary than on the venous side. Since the fluids of the blood, the cells, and the interstitial spaces have dissolved materials, osmosis and dialysis also occur. The cooperation of these two factors plus the involvement of the lymph system are illustrated in Fig. 17.8.

Plasma differs from interstitial fluid primarily in being more concentrated in proteins. Therefore, from the standpoint of inducing osmosis and dialysis, plasma is effectively more concentrated than interstitial fluid. The natural, net direction for dialysis is, therefore, *from* the interstitial compartment *into* the bloodstream. This is true on *both* the arterial and the venous ends of the capillary constriction. But on the arterial end, the higher blood pressure reverses this tendency, making the net direction of fluid flow *from* the capillary *into* the interstitial space. Nutrients are brought into contact with the tissue cells that selectively abstract those they need and send out waste chemicals such as carbon dioxide and excess water and others. No *net* changes in total *concentrations* of dissolved solutes occur, but the kinds of the solutes change as nutrients are consumed and by-products are produced. What has been described in this paragraph is the hypothesis of E. H. Starling (1866 to 1927), one of the great British physiologists. He did not allow for "leakage" of proteins and lipids from the capillaries, but subsequent to his work, the use of radioactively labeled proteins and other techniques have demonstrated that these larger molecules do, in fact, routinely leave the bloodstream. It is very difficult for them to return to the bloodstream directly, and they return via the lymph.

Fluid diffusion in the various capillary beds of the body adds up to great proportions. It has been estimated that, in the entire capillary network of a 160-pound man, fluid diffusion occurs at a *rate* of about 400 gallons per minute. Delicate balances in fluid exchange exist at cells, and they may be upset in two clinically important problems, shock and edema.

traumatic shock. Leakage of proteins through capillaries appears to increase when an individual has been subjected to sudden, severe injury, extensive burns, or even major surgery. Loss of protein from the blood means an upsetting of osmotic-pressure relations. Fluids forced out on the arterial side of a capillary "loop" do not return as they should. The blood volume drops, and the circulatory system no longer brings enough oxygen and nutrients to cells. Those in the central nervous system are most seriously affected, and a condition known as shock ensues. Shock results also from extensive hemorrhage. Any failure of the circulatory system will cause shock. Restoration of blood volume is mandatory to control it.

edema. When fluids accumulate in the interstitial and cellular regions in abnormally large amounts, a condition of edema exists. It may have one of several causes, of which only a few can be mentioned here.

If proteins leak through the kidneys into the developing urine ("albumi-

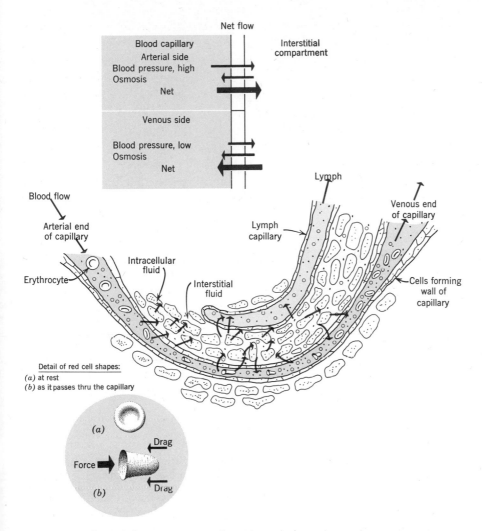

Fig. 17.8 Fluid exchange at capillaries. Dots represent proteins; circles are lipids. Erythrocytes (red cells) have the shape of a disk dented on opposite sides, but during their passage through the most constricted region of a capillary, their shapes are distorted as shown. This is believed to aid somehow in the release of oxygen. As much as half the total protein in blood each day leaves the bloodstream and returns via the lymph.

At the top, a schematic diagram summarizes Starling's hypothesis concerning how fluids leave the capillaries at their arterial sides and reenter at their venous sides. On the arterial side, blood pressure counterbalances osmosis and dialysis, and the net movement occurs from capillary to interstitial space. Blood pressure drops as it goes through the constricted capillary, and on the venous side it no longer overpowers osmosis and dialysis, and the net movement is reversed.

nuria''), osmotic-pressure relations may be upset to the point where enough fluid is retained in the interstitial compartment to produce noticeable swelling or edema in some tissues, notably the lower limbs. The swelling that usually accompanies malnutrition arises from similar causes. Prolonged malnutrition that amounts to starvation will eventually result in less concentrated blood fluid, with the same result, edema.

Localized edema or ''swelling'' occurs around an injured area. The injury may have damaged either blood vessels or lymph capillaries preventing normal drainage, and the fluid that accumulates produces the swelling. In a particularly ugly tropical disease, elephantiasis, small worms (filari) enter the body and live in the lymphatics, thereby reducing drainage through them. The swelling assumes grotesque proportions.

Obstructions in veins, as in certain cancers or in varicose veins, may cause a ''back pressure'' on the venous sides of the capillary loops that hinders dialysis of interstitial fluids into veins. Again, not quite as much fluid returns as enters the interstitial compartment, and swelling occurs.

respiratory functions of the blood

Moving oxygen from air to tissue cells is a task of enormous magnitude. If an adult generates 3000 kcal per day from his food, he requires 600 liters of oxygen, and he generates about 480 liters of carbon dioxide. The movement of these gases to and from air and cells may be studied by reference to Fig. 17.9. The rate of this movement requires large surface areas across which contact between the blood flow and the inhaled air can be rapidly made. To provide this surface, the trachea (''wind pipe'') undergoes a succession of branchings until the final, smallest functional unit, the individual *alveolus* is reached. Incoming air is distributed to about 300 million alveoli, each of which is little more than a bundle of fine capillaries suspended in air. An estimated 1500 miles of such exposed capillaries provide about 800 square feet of diffusing surface. Through these capillaries blood flows at a total blood flow rate of about 5 liters per minute during resting periods and from 20 to 30 liters per minute during severe exercise.

oxygen toxicity. If an individual breathes pure oxygen, enough oxygen is present in a simple, dissolved state in plasma to supply nearly all needs at tissues. Consequently, oxyhemoglobin has difficulty in dissociating at cells, ④ in Fig. 17.9. The isohydric shift ⑨, therefore, cannot be used, and the hydrogen ions produced at ⑧, instead of being buffered by a hemoglobin molecule, tend to force the pH of the blood down. The resulting acidosis may be severe enough to be very serious.

oxygen deficiency; anoxia. Up to an altitude of about 18,000 feet, there is enough oxygen in air to provide the pressure in the lungs needed to saturate erythrocytes with oxygen, provided little exercise is done. At higher altitudes

important fluids of the body

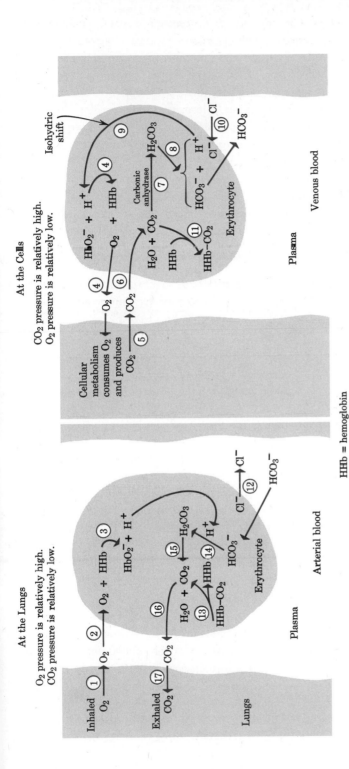

At the Lungs

O$_2$ pressure is relatively high.
CO$_2$ pressure is relatively low.

At the Cells

CO$_2$ pressure is relatively high.
O$_2$ pressure is relatively low.

Isohydric shift

HbO$_2^-$ + H$^+$ ④ O$_2$ + HHb

Carbonic anhydrase

H$_2$CO$_3$

⑨

⑦ HCO$_3^-$ + H$^+$ ⑧

Cl$^-$ Cl$^-$ ⑩

HCO$_3^-$

H$_2$O + CO$_2$ ⑪ HHb HHb-CO$_2$

Erythrocyte

Plasma

Venous blood

Cellular metabolism consumes O$_2$ and produces CO$_2$

④ O$_2$
⑥ CO$_2$
⑤

Inhaled ① O$_2$ ② O$_2$ + HHb ③ HbO$_2^-$ + H$^+$

H$_2$CO$_3$ ⑮ HCO$_3^-$ Cl$^-$ Cl$^-$ ⑫ HCO$_3^-$

H$_2$O + CO$_2$ ⑯ ⑬ HHb ⑭ H$^+$ HHb-CO$_2$

Exhaled ⑰ CO$_2$

Lungs

Erythrocyte

Plasma

Arterial blood

HHb = hemoglobin
HbO$_2^-$ = oxyhemoglobin

$$HHb + O_2 \rightleftharpoons HbO_2^- + H^+$$

Fig. 17.9 Oxygen-carbon dioxide transport by the blood. Starting at the lungs with oxygen transport, the mechanics of breathing make oxygen pressure relatively high in the lungs. Oxygen is forced to diffuse into the bloodstream ①. Although blood may carry some dissolved, gaseous oxygen, virtually all is drawn into erythrocytes ②, where it combines with hemoglobin, HHb, to form oxyhemoglobin, HbO$_2^-$, and H$^+$, ③.

Two factors help shift this equilibrium from left to right in the lungs. The oxygen pressure is relatively high; and the hydrogen ion is neutralized by bicarbonate ion ⑭, something which must happen anyway if CO$_2$ s to be released. Thus, arrival of bicarbonate ion helps draw oxygen into the cell. At cellular areas needing oxygen, two factors help in its release from HbO$_2^-$. Oxygen pressure is now relatively low; and the carbon dioxide is poised to enter, ⑤ and ⑥. To get oxygen released from HbO$_2^-$, ④, a hydrogen ion is needed ⑨, and it is just the influx of carbon dioxide that makes it available, ⑦ and ⑧. If carbon dioxide is not available, then the cell presumably does not need oxygen anyway. This shift of hydrogen ion, ⑨, is called the isohydric shift. Bicarbonate ions leave the red cell during transport, and to replace their charge chloride ions move in, ⑩. (This switch is called the chloride shift.) Most carbon dioxide is taken to the lungs as bicarbonate ion, but some combines with hemoglobin to be carried as carbamino hemoglobin ⑪, written as HHb-CO$_2$ for short. Very little moves simply as the gas dissolved in the plasma. When the erythrocyte returns to the lungs, a reversal of events ⑫ to ⑰, sends carbon dioxide out into exhaled air and the cyclical process repeats itself.

the oxygen pressure is not enough. Symptoms of oxygen deficiency set in—restlessness, confused thinking, then unconsciousness ("blackout"). Portable oxygen or air tanks and pressurized cabins are familiar solutions to this problem.

Oxygen deficiency occurs in pneumonia, when the alveoli fill with fluids that hinder rapid exchange of gases. *Fibrosis* in alveoli, that is, tissues hardening and becoming fibrous, will also interfere with this exchange. Miners breathing ore dusts, farmers breathing organic dusts, and builders using asbestos are taking risks that may eventually lead to lung failure. Certain organic substances in cigarette smoke have been implicated in lung cancer, for which the only present cure is surgical removal of the affected area. Only about 10% of such patients survive more than 5 years, unless the development is caught in its earliest stages. The lungs have some capacity for repair, and medical experts insist that a heavy smoker should cut down or quit, however long he has been smoking.

Carbon monoxide is a poison that affects oxygen transport by combining with hemoglobin about 200 times more firmly than oxygen. In this situation, the administration of nearly pure oxygen is called for to displace the molecules of carbon monoxide and to make up for oxygen deficiency.

blood clotting Blood must clot when it is shed. It must not clot when it is not shed. These simply stated rules are a matter of life and death, and a complicated apparatus controls what happens. Not all its details are understood, and we shall confine our study to a broader view.

When blood clots, the soluble protein, *fibrinogen,* is converted to an insoluble protein, *fibrin,* whose fibers aggregate in a matlike way to seal off the sites where the blood vessel has been broken or cut. The formation of a clot can be studied in vitro. In fact, special precautions have to be taken to prevent freshly drawn blood from clotting. To change fibrinogen to fibrin, an enzyme is needed, but it can hardly be expected to be present all the time in blood. The key to the control of blood clotting is the control of the formation of this enzyme only when it is needed.

The clotting enzyme is called *thrombin,* and it exists in the bloodstream in an inactive form called *prothrombin.* To convert prothrombin to the active enzyme requires at least ten factors—calcium ion, anti-hemophilic factors, a coenzyme, and a group of molecules collectively called thromboplastin. Some are present in blood. Others are released when tissues are cut. Thus, the clotting mechanism is not thrown into operation unless a cut or injury occurs. (And when blood is removed, it is not easy to prevent any and all contact with tissues slightly injured by the act of inserting a needle. Clotting under these circumstances can be prevented simply by tying up the calcium ions. Sodium oxalate or sodium citrate may be used. In the first case, calcium

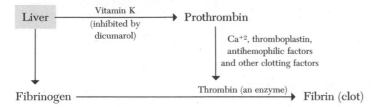

Fig. 17.10 Probable mechanism of blood clotting. Both fibrinogen and prothrombin are made in the liver. Clotting factors occur, some in platelets, and some in cells which release them when cut or injured.

precipitates as calcium oxalate. In the second, calcium ions complex with citrate ions and are effectively removed.)

Figure 17.10 illustrates the principal features of a probable mechanism for clot formation. Vitamin K deficiency (as in some hemorrhagic diseases) reduces the formation of the inactive form of the enzyme at the liver. The same effect can be achieved by dicumarol, a chemical formed in decaying sweet clover, which is sometimes given to prevent thrombosis—the unwanted formation of a clot within a blood vessel. Heparin, an extremely potent anticoagulant, is found in cells located near the walls of the tiniest capillaries. It acts by slowing the conversion of prothrombin to thrombin.

Selected Reading List

Articles

1. J. E. Wood. "The Venous System." *Scientific American,* January 1968, page 86. The veins actively cooperate in regulating the distribution of blood in the circulatory system. They are not just passive tubes for transporting blood.

2. H. S. Mayerson. "The Lymphatic System." *Scientific American.* June 1963, page 80. After discussing the anatomy of the lymphatic system and its general functions, Mayerson describes experiments he and others performed to prove that it is normal for capillaries to "leak" proteins and lipids.

3. J. H. Comroe, Jr. "The Lung." *Scientific American,* February 1966, page 57. The anatomy of the respiratory system is described and pulmonary circulation and the mechanics of breathing are discussed.

4. C. B. Chapman and J. H. Mitchell. "The Physiology of Exercise." *Scientific American,* May 1965, page 88. During periods of severe exercise the body mobilizes a vast array of mechanisms for meeting the demands of getting nutrients out of storage and circulated around and for removing waste products, notably carbon dioxide.

Brief Summary

(A summary of digestion appeared on pages 405–406.)

1. The "internal environment" consists primarily of a system of fluids that feed and surround tissue cells. Blood, lymph, and interstitial fluid are the most important components.

2. Electrolytes are found in all body fluids. They help to establish proper osmotic pressures, and some ions are important buffers. Albumins in blood make it effectively more concentrated than interstitial fluid, and the tendency is for interstitial fluid to dialyze into plasma. On venous sides of capillary loops this occurs, but on arterial sides the blood pressure is great enough to force fluids out of the plasma.

3. Some protein and lipid molecules that leak into the interstitial spaces return to general circulation by the lymph system.

4. Maintenance of the chemical integrity of the internal environment is necessary:
   (a) to keep osmotic pressure relations adjusted in order that fluids may move from the circulatory system to cells and back again, and
   (b) to preserve the blood's ability to transport oxygen and carbon dioxide.

5. Diuresis is one method of regulating the internal environment. It removes water, some waste products, and some inorganic ions. The distal cells in nephrons of the kidneys, acting under hormonal influence, exercise a very delicate control over the pH of the blood and the concentration of many other ions in blood. Optional reabsorption of water and several ions is possible by these cells.

6. By removing waste carbon dioxide, the process of breathing helps to police the internal environment.

7. The clotting mechanism helps to ensure that fluids of the internal environment will not be lost through cuts or ruptures.

Problems and Exercises

1. On a large sheet of paper draw a diagram of the digestive tract and label its parts. Next to each major region where digestion occurs, summarize by "word equations" all the important digestive reactions. Indicate the enzymes needed for each reaction.

2. In the section on organic chemistry, we studied three major hydrolysis reactions: the hydrolysis of acetals, of ester linkages, and of amide linkages. To what kinds of foods does each of these hydrolyses apply? Illustrate your answer with specific equations.

3. Selecting representative *structures* of your own choosing, write equations that illustrate the digestion of
   (a) a tripeptide   (b) a glyceride   (c) a disaccharide

4. Explain how the flow of each of the following digestive juices is controlled: (a) gastric juice   (b) pancreatic juice   (c) bile

5. In what ways would the absence of bile adversely affect digestion?

6. The hormone insulin is a protein. Explain why it cannot be administered orally to diabetics but must be given intravenously.

7. Alcohol in blood suppresses the secretion of vasopressin. How does this affect diuresis?

8. Referring to this chapter and previous ones, what are the three main buffers in blood? Show equations that illustrate *how* they work.

9. Explain *how* malnutrition upsets the osmotic pressure of blood.

10. Explain *how* the kidneys act to reduce developing acidosis.

11. Explain *how* fluid exchange occurs between plasma and cells. (How does arterial blood become venous blood?)

12. Describe three ways by which edema may originate.

13. *How* does acidosis inhibit oxygen transport?

14. Why is CO_2 pressure higher at cells than at lungs?

15. Describe in your own words how the blood transports oxygen and carbon dioxide, and does so in the right directions.

16. Explain how a blood clot forms.

17. Why is it dangerous to breathe pure oxygen if your respiratory organs are functioning smoothly?

18. How does the administration of vitamin K assist the clotting mechanism? Why is it sometimes administered to pregnant women just before delivery?

chapter 18 the metabolism of carbohydrates

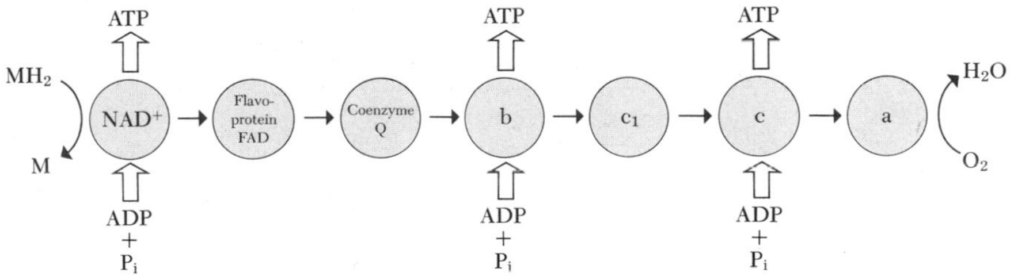

$$MH_2 \rightarrow NAD^+ \rightarrow \text{Flavo-protein FAD} \rightarrow \text{Coenzyme Q} \rightarrow b \rightarrow c_1 \rightarrow c \rightarrow a \rightarrow$$

ATP · MH$_2$ · M · ADP + P$_i$ · ATP · ADP + P$_i$ · ATP · ADP + P$_i$ · H$_2$O · O$_2$

We studied the molecules of foods partly because they supply chemicals that are oxidized in the body to furnish energy. We are now in a position to study how this is done.

There is an old saying, "Fire is man's most useful servant and his worst enemy." Since fire can function both ways, the problem of the successful use of fire, or any other form of readily available energy, is one of control.

Diet-conscious people are keenly aware of the amount of heat (calories) potentially available from foods. The complete combustion of 1 mole of glucose (180 grams), for example, liberates 673 kcal of heat:

$$C_6H_{12}O_6 + 6O_2 \longrightarrow 6CO_2 + 6H_2O + 673 \text{ kcal/mole}$$
Glucose

The heat available from the combustion of 1 mole (256 grams) of palmitic acid, a typical product from the digestion of fats and oils in your diet, is 2400 kcal.

$$CH_3(CH_2)_{14}CO_2H + 23O_2 \longrightarrow 16CO_2 + 16H_2O + 2400 \text{ kcal/mole}$$
Palmitic acid

Although the body needs a certain amount of steadily produced heat in order to maintain its proper working temperature, it also needs energy in many other forms. There are muscles to be moved (mechanical energy) and nerve messages to be sent (electrical energy). The body, therefore, must have a mechanism whereby some of the energy potentially available from glucose or fatty acids can be channeled into these other forms without its ever appearing as heat.

The only reason that energy can be said to be potentially available from glucose or a fatty acid is that these are "high-energy molecules," ones whose arrangements of electrons and atomic nuclei are not the most stable possible within their environment. We could liken a "high-energy molecule" to a wound-up mainspring in a stopwatch. A "low-energy molecule" (such as carbon dioxide or water) would be analogous to the unwound spring. To go from the high-energy to the low-energy state, all we need do is let the spontaneous process run its course.

An unwinding watch spring performs only one service. It does nothing more than move the hands of the watch. Conversion by *direct* combustion of high-energy glucose (or fatty acid) and oxygen into their low-energy products likewise accomplishes only one thing—production of heat.

The stopwatch could be made to provide other services, however. It is not hard to imagine, for example, that a little pulley arrangement could be fastened to a stopwatch and to the wheels of a small toy. Of course, if this were done, and if energy were used in this way to power a small toy, the hands of the watch would run more slowly. You would not receive as much of the intended service of a stopwatch. The total energy received (powering the toy plus moving the watch hands) would be the same, however. The controlled oxidation of foodstuffs *in the body* also has two functions. In

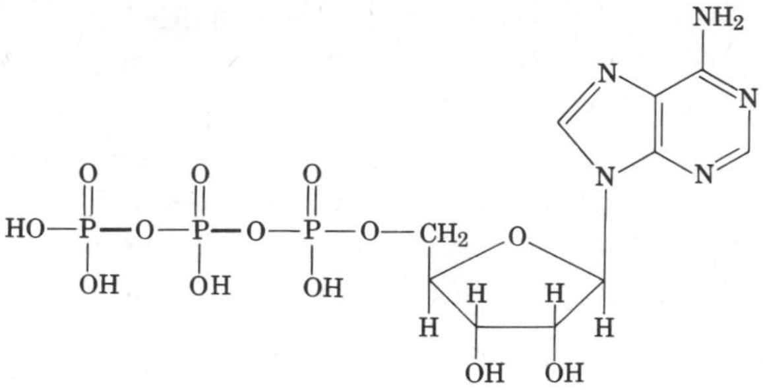

(a)

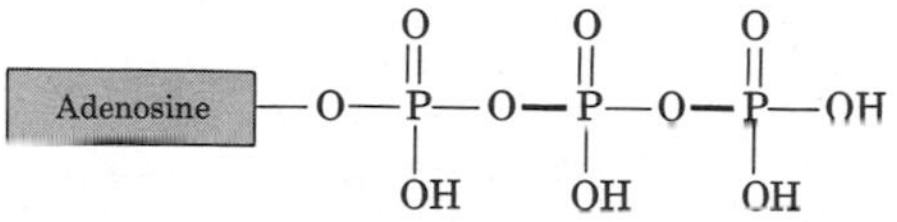

(b)

Fig. 18.1 (a) Adenosine triphosphate, ATP. (b) Abbreviated structure for adenosine triphosphate.

addition to furnishing some heat, it provides the "driving force" for the synthesis of another high-energy molecule, adenosine triphosphate, or ATP.

The structure of adenosine triphosphate is shown in Fig. 18.1. It is quite complicated, and we shall not be concerned with the details except for one part, the oxygen to phosphorus linkages indicated in Fig. 18.1 by boldface lines. Biochemists call these *high-energy phosphate bonds*. What is meant is that these bonds are the ones most likely to be broken in those reactions that furnish the energy, the "driving force," for a host of important events in the body.

adenosine triphosphate (ATP); the body's storehouse of energy

The energy needed for the contraction of a muscle comes from the breaking of one of these high-energy phosphate bonds. This might be expressed (in a grossly simplified way) by the following equation:

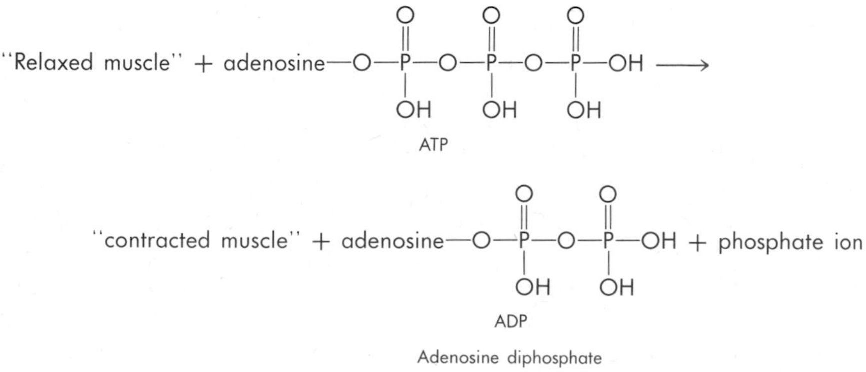

"Relaxed muscle" + ATP →

"contracted muscle" + ADP + phosphate ion

Adenosine diphosphate

adenosine triphosphate (ATP); the body's storehouse of energy

The "driving force" for muscle contraction is the great tendency for ATP to undergo a change to a more stable arrangement, in this case to the slightly less energy-rich substances, adenosine diphosphate (ADP) and phosphate ion. Muscular work consumes ATP. Obviously, if no way were available to replenish the supply, muscular work would soon become impossible, for the supply of ATP is by no means unlimited. *The major mechanism available in the body for the synthesis of fresh supplies of ATP is a series of reactions which is called the respiratory chain.*

cellular respiration and the respiratory chain

Cellular respiration means the use of oxygen in metabolic reactions in the cell. The enzymes involved are called the *respiratory enzymes,* and the term *respiratory chain* denotes the chain of chemical events leading to the reduction of oxygen to water in cells. The intent of this brief section is to describe the connection between the oxygen you breathe and the synthesis of ATP. We shall then proceed to the connection between the food you eat and the synthesis of ATP. The respiratory chain mediates the transfer of chemical energy from foods and oxygen to ATP without this energy leaking away as unneeded heat. (Some heat, of course, must be and is generated.)

converting oxygen to water. The reduction of oxygen to water requires that each oxygen atom be furnished with two electrons and two protons (i.e., hydrogen ions). The very barest statement of this event is the following hypothetical "equation:"

$$:\overset{..}{\underset{..}{O}} \quad + \quad : \quad + \quad 2H^+ \quad \longrightarrow \quad H:\overset{..}{\underset{..}{O}}:H \quad + \text{ energy}$$

| Oxygen atom | Pair of Electrons | Two protons | Water molecule |

The advantage of this stripped-down view is that it exposes the threefold nature of the problem:

1. Getting a pair of electrons out of an organic molecule and transported to oxygen.
2. Getting the protons.
3. Delivering the large energy associated with the reduction of oxygen to water at least partly into a new storage form, namely ATP.

The first two problems are at least partly solved whenever an organic intermediate in a cell suffers loss of the pieces of the element hydrogen $(H:^- + H^+)$, which could be rewritten as $(: + 2H^+)$, as in the above equation. *As sources of energy, this is primarily how organic intermediates serve—they provide the pieces of the element hydrogen for delivery to the respiratory chain and eventually to oxygen.* Some of these pieces, two electrons and one proton, usually come out of the organic intermediate from an attachment to a *carbon*. In other words, carbon-hydrogen covalent bonds, not oxygen-hydrogen or nitrogen-hydrogen covalent bonds, are the chief molecular sources of chemical energy for the synthesis of ATP. This explains why a fatty acid molecule is a much richer source of energy than a glucose molecule. In palmitic acid, there are 31 carbon-hydrogen covalent bonds per molecule; in glucose, only 7. Translated into ATP production, one molecule of palmitic acid will provide the chemical energy for the regeneration of 130 molecules of ATP. One glucose molecule, in contrast, will power the formation of just 36 molecules of ATP.

homeostasis. The series of reactions in the respiratory chain do not occur unless there is a need to replenish supplies of ATP. The whole sequence is almost self-regulating in this respect. If exercise or other events use up ATP and leave ADP and inorganic phosphate,[1] P_i, then the long series of reactions is automatically called into play to put ADP and P_i back together again. It is very much like a thermostat.

Thermostatic action in heat control	Homeostatic action in ATP synthesis
The temperature drops; a signal results.	ATP-consuming work is done; ADP + P_i form.
This starts the heater, and it sends out heat until	This starts the respiratory chain, and and it makes fresh ATP until
. . . the temperature rises, and a signal is generated which shuts the heater off.	. . . the ADP and P_i are mostly used up, and the respiratory chain slows down or stops.

In engineering, this is called an inverse feedback mechanism. In molecular biology, it is called *homeostasis,* and it is used to describe the behavior of an organism to stimuli that off-balance it by starting a series of reactions that restore the system to normal. Several conditions in the body are so constant that diseases may be diagnosed if changes occur in them. Body temperature is an obvious example. The pH of the blood, its white cell and red cell counts, and the "blood levels" (concentrations) of other components are others. Mechanisms that work to keep these constant are called homeostatic mechanisms.

It is far beyond the intended scope of this text to take up the individual reactions in the respiratory chain. Many of the details are not known anyway. Only a selected portion will be presented in a most simplified form to provide a general picture.

---

[1] The symbol, P_i, will be used to represent inorganic phosphate without any specification of the state of ionization. Depending on the pH, inorganic phosphate exists as a mixture of varying amounts of HPO_4^{2-} and $H_2PO_4^-$ plus trace amounts of PO_4^{3-} and H_3PO_4. The symbol, P_i, represents this mixture, whatever its composition.

what the respiratory enzymes do. Suppose we have some organic intermediate that can be made to give up the pieces of the element hydrogen. We shall keep the discussion general and represent such an intermediate simply as MH_2 (M for metabolite). The first enzyme in the respiratory chain in our selected portion of its sequence has as its coenzyme nicotinamide adenine dinucleotide, or simply NAD^+. (We now place the net positive charge by NAD. It has been there all the time, but now for the first time we need to know about it.) NAD^+ can react with MH_2 in the following manner.

$$M \overset{H}{\underset{H}{\cdots}} + NAD^+ \longrightarrow NAD\!:\!\underline{H + H^+} + M\!: $$

here are our pieces
of the element hydrogen

This could also be symbolized as follows:

$$M \overset{\cdot H}{\underset{\cdot H}{\cdots}} \quad NAD^+$$
$$M: \qquad NAD\!:\!H + H$$

("Reading" from left to right: the
conversion of MH_2 to M: is accomplished
by the conversion of NAD^+ to $NAD\!:\!H$
+ H^+.)

The next enzyme in the branch of the respiratory chain we are considering is one of having riboflavin as part of its coenzyme, and we shall refer to it simply as FAD (for flavin adenine dinucleotide). Its service is to accept the hydrogen just removed, and to pass it on again.

$$NAD\!:\!H + H^+ + FAD \longrightarrow NAD^+ + FAD \overset{\cdot H}{\underset{H}{\cdots}}$$

Or, to use a better display of this reaction while combining it with what happened just before it and setting it up for what is to come:

$$M \overset{\cdot H}{\underset{\cdot H}{\cdots}} \quad NAD^+ \quad FAD \overset{\cdot H}{\underset{H}{\cdots}}$$
$$M: \qquad NAD\!:\!H + H^+ \qquad FAD$$

This, then, is the pattern. Some metabolite, which can give up hydrogen, does so. The NAD^+-containing enzyme accepts it and passes the two electrons and the two protons on to an enzyme which actually is physically located next to it in the "team," the FAD-containing enzyme. The rest of this segment of the chain is illustrated in Fig. 18.2.

mitochondria. All the respiratory enzymes of Fig. 18.2 are organized together into tiny particles that occur by the thousands on the inner and outer surfaces of mitochondria (Greek *mitos*, a thread; *chondros*, a grain.) A cutaway

the metabolism of carbohydrates

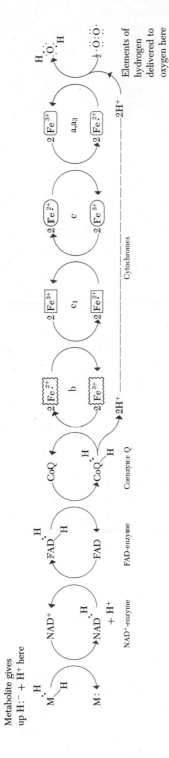

Fig. 18.2 A portion of the respiratory chain. Two protons and two electrons are removed from some intermediate, MH_2, furnished indirectly by the food we eat. These are passed along a succession of coenzymes which are part of the respiratory enzymes until they are made to combine with oxygen from the air we breathe. Water is the chemical product, but more importantly, this electron-transfer chain of reactions powers the synthesis of ATP as discussed in the text in connection with Fig. 18.4.

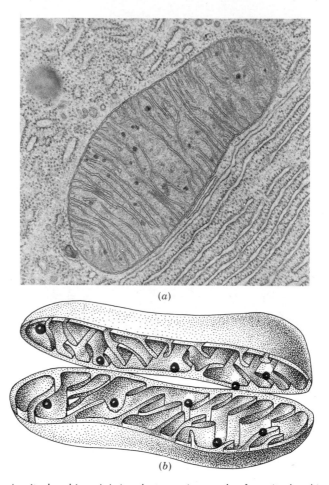

(a)

(b)

Fig. 18.3 A mitochondrion. (a) An electron micrograph of a mitochondrion in a pancreas cell of a bat ($\times$ 53,000). (b) Perspective drawing of an "opened" mitochondrion. The dots represent units of mitochondrial activity. Larger granules of uncertain composition are also present. (Micrograph courtesy of Dr. Keith R. Porter. Drawing courtesy of G. E. Nelson, G. G. Robinson, and R. A. Boolootian, *Fundamental Concepts of Biology*, 2nd edition, 1970, page 49. John Wiley & Sons, New York, 1970. Used by permission.)

drawing of one of these subcellular granules is shown in Fig. 18.3. They occur by the hundreds, sometimes a few thousand, in each cell with the number depending on the kind of cell. Sometimes called the "powerhouses" of cells, the mitochondria are the primary sites of ATP synthesis. The individual particles on their surfaces are units of mitochondrial activity, and they not only serve a catalytic function, they also are an integral part of the structure of a mitochrondrion.

The cytochromes shown in Fig. 18.2 are complexes involving iron ions (shown) and molecules (implied) that are very much like the heme portion of hemoglobin (see Chapter 20). The last enzyme in the chain, cytochrome oxidase, is the specific catalyst for the reduction of oxygen.

coupling oxidation with ATP-synthesis. The heavy dots in Fig. 18.2 are drawn that way to help you see the respiratory chain as a tiny electric current. Electrons are actually transported from place to place, not exactly as in a metallic wire, but more as a "bucket brigade," which goes extremely rapidly and in which the electrons are passed from one chemical to another. However the current flows, we know that a flow of electricity can be made to do work. The work we want done in this case is the conversion of ADP and P_i into the higher energy form, ATP. We want to "lift" the lower energy molecules of ADP and P_i up an "energy hill." Figure 18.2 does not show *how* this is done. We are at the frontier of science in this region with this question. References at the end of this chapter will tell you about some of the current speculation. Only the most general pattern will be described here.

There are three places along the respiratory chain where chemical energy is tapped for the synthesis of ATP. Figure 18.4 indicates where these are. The wide, heavy arrows actually represent a series of reactions. These reactions, according to the thinking that has dominated research in this field for years, involve the enzymes already mentioned plus at least two other enzymes—a *coupling enzyme*, which can pick up an inorganic phosphate unit, and a *transfer enzyme*, which can accept the P_i and catalyze its transfer to ADP to regenerate ATP. (There are some highly respected scientists who dispute this view; but the controversy is beyond the limited needs and goals of our present study.)

Thus, it is finally electrochemical energy, which resides in the electron-nuclei arrangements of organic intermediates and oxygen molecules, that provides the energy needed to couple P_i to ADP. In a general way, we have connected the consumption of oxygen with the synthesis of ATP. We next turn to the connection between our foods and ATP.

The principal supplier of the intermediates that can give up the pieces of the element hydrogen to the respiratory chain is a series of reactions known as the citric acid cycle. Its steps are summarized in Fig. 18.5. In this sequence, **the citric acid cycle; aerobic sequence**

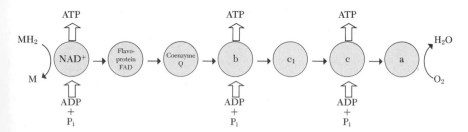

Fig. 18.4 Coupling the electron flow in the respiratory chain to the synthesis of ATP from ADP and P_i. The energy provided by the transport of electrons in the respiratory chain is made available via enzyme systems (implied by the heavy vertical arrows) to the energy requirements of putting relatively lower energy ADP + P_i back into the relatively higher energy form of ATP.

433
the citric acid cycle; aerobic sequence

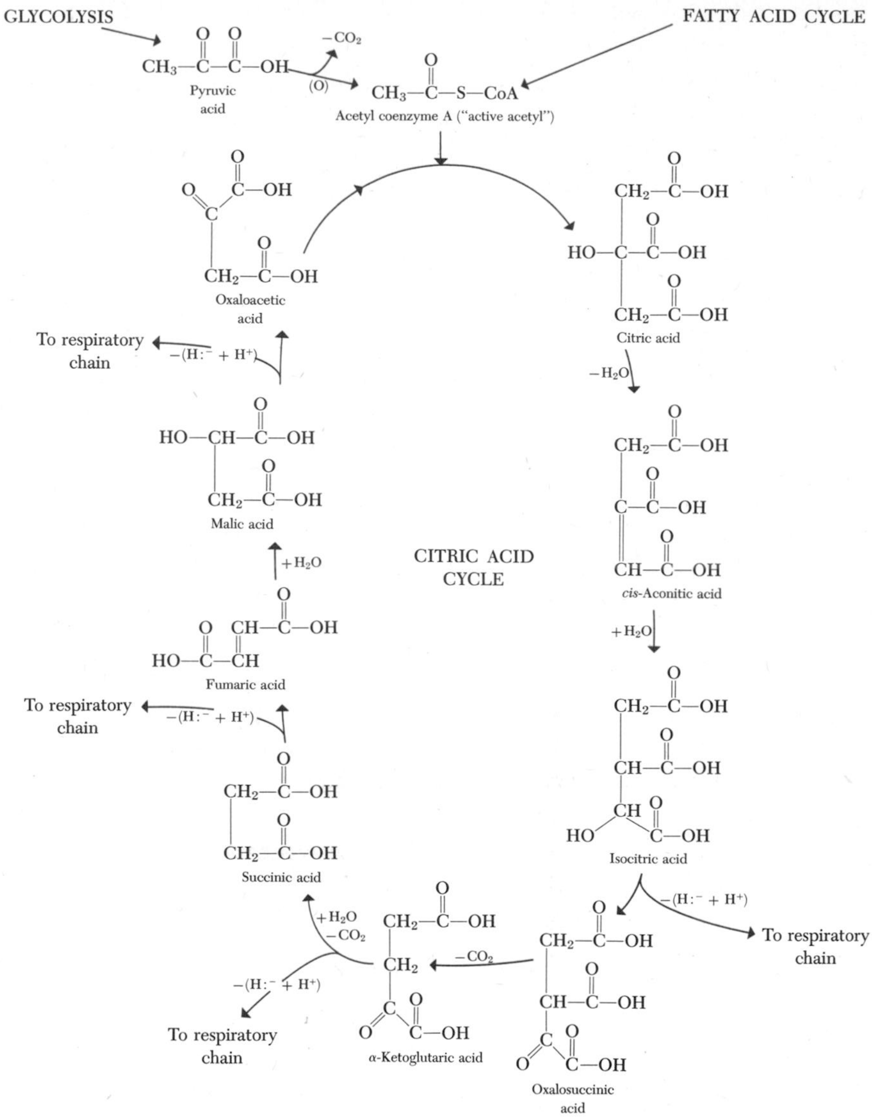

Fig. 18.5 The citric acid cycle. Acetyl groups from acetyl coenzyme A are fed into the cycle in the conversion of oxaloacetic acid to citric acid. By a succession of steps, two carbons are broken off (as carbon dioxide) and four units of hydrogen (H:⁻ + H⁺) are sent on to the respiratory chain. Finally, another molecule of the carrier, oxaloacetic acid, is generated for another turn of the cycle.

a four-carbon "carrier" molecule, oxaloacetic acid, picks up a two-carbon acetyl unit. The product is the six-carbon citric acid, and it is degraded step-wise, delivering the pieces of hydrogen to the respiratory chain and discarding carbon dioxide, until another molecule of the four-carbon carrier is produced for another turn of the cycle.

the metabolism of carbohydrates

We have not studied enough organic chemistry to take this cycle up in detail, but several steps should be familiar. The dehydration of an alcohol occurs as well as the addition of water to a double bond and the oxidation of an alcohol (twice). To fuel the citric acid cycle, acetyl units must be furnished, and this is where glucose and the fatty acids enter the picture. They are the chief suppliers of acetyl groups. (The involvement of fatty acids will now not be further considered until the next chapter.)

The citric acid cycle coupled to the respiratory chain is frequently called the aerobic sequence of glucose catabolism. *Aerobic* refers to the fact that unless the respiratory chain is run with its accompanying consumption of oxygen (from air), the citric acid cycle largely stands idle. It requires oxygen for its running even though no intermediate in this sequence reacts directly with oxygen. To credit the events of the citric acid cycle solely to glucose catabolism, however, does the fatty acids an injustice. The cycle "belongs" in the metabolic pathway of any chemical which the body can degrade to acetyl units (and this even includes several amino acids from proteins).

The conversion of a molecule of glucose into acetyl units takes another series of reactions, and until the very last step this pathway can run without oxygen. It is anaerobic.

Glycolysis is a series of reactions whereby glucose is broken into two molecules of lactic acid. ("Glycolysis," *glycose-lysis*, or glycose-loosening; it could also mean "glycogen-loosening.") Oxygen is not required, and still the sequence manages to synthesize a small but important amount of ATP independently of the respiratory chain. The overall result from a glucose molecule is:

glycolysis; the anaerobic sequence of glucose catabolism

$$C_6H_{12}O_6 + 2ADP + 2P_i \longrightarrow 2CH_3-\underset{\underset{OH}{|}}{CH}-CO_2H + 2ATP$$

Glucose   Lactic acid

If the starting point is a glucose unit in glycogen instead of free glucose, then three ATP molecules are made per glucose unit. The intermediate steps in glycolysis are shown in Fig. 18.6.

There are times when ATP-demand in certain tissues, particularly muscles, is higher than the supply immediately available from operating their respiratory chains. If oxygen cannot be delivered to respiratory units of mitochondria rapidly enough, ATP production by the respiratory chain slows down. Its rate must adjust to the rate of oxygen supply. The energy-output of a long distance runner, for example, is limited primarily by the rate at which oxygen can enter his lungs and be distributed (assuming he is in good physical shape otherwise). The reactions of glycolysis provide an emergency source of ATP when bursts of energy are needed and the cells cannot get delivery of oxygen fast enough. Lactic acid, of course, is produced, but as soon as the oxygen

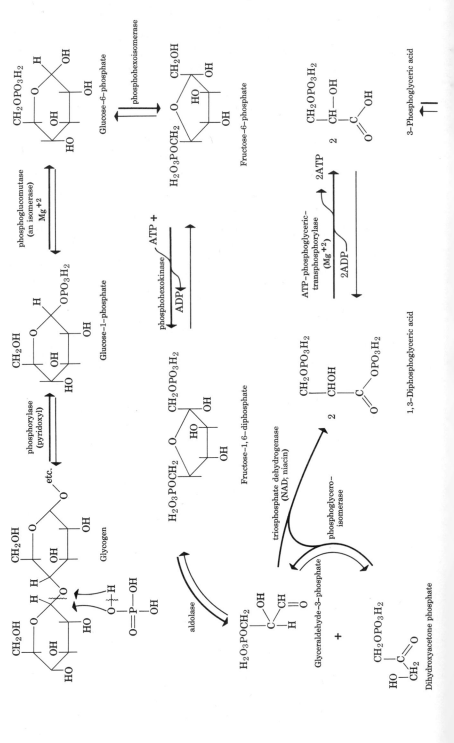

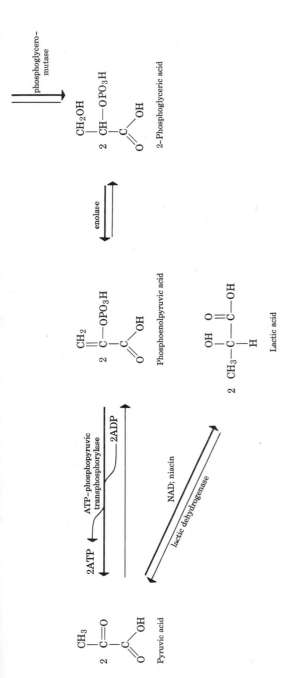

Fig. 18.6 Glycolysis, the anaerobic sequence in the catabolism of glucose, showing here the steps from a glucose unit in glycogen to lactic acid.

supply is restored lactic acid can be broken down to acetyl units that are fed to the citric acid cycle and the respiratory chain. To the extent that lactic acid accumulates, an *oxygen debt* is said to exist. Heavy breathing following strenuous exercise repays this debt by bringing in oxygen to metabolize the lactic acid. (We shall continue this discussion in Chapter 19.)

"active acetyl." The connecting chemical links between the anaerobic sequence and the citric acid cycle are displayed in Fig. 18.7. Lactic acid is dehydrogenated, with the elements of hydrogen going to the respiratory chain. (This step assumes that oxygen is available again.) Then the product, pyruvic acid, interacts with an important coenzyme called *coenzyme A*, to form carbon dioxide and the acetyl derivative of coenzyme A. Acetyl coenzyme A is something like an ester except that there is a carbonyl-to-sulfur bond instead of a carbonyl-to-oxygen bond. Unlike an ordinary ester, this *thio*ester linkage in acetyl coenzyme A is rated a very high-energy bond. From here on, through the citric acid cycle and the respiratory chain to ATP, carbon dioxide, and water, in energy terms it is "downhill" all the way. Acetyl coenzyme A, often called "active acetyl," stands at one of the major metabolic crossroads in the body. Fatty acids are richer sources of active acetyl than glucose, and their catabolism is an even more important source of energy (ATP) than carbohydrates. Figure 18.8 illustrates in broad outline the convergence of the pathways that are the major sources of ATP.

glycogenesis. Lactic acid is something like molecular rummage. There is a lot of "good" (chemical energy) left in it, and the body conserves it as best

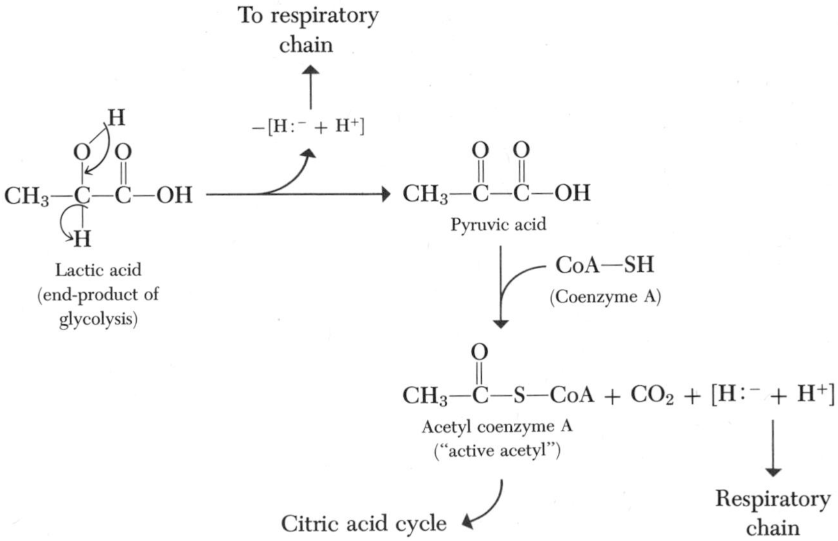

Fig. 18.7 Connecting glycolysis to the citric acid cycle; the conversion of lactic acid into acetyl coenzyme A.

the metabolism of carbohydrates

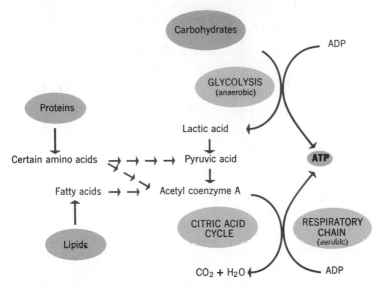

Fig. 18.8 Showing the major sources of chemical energy for making ATP.

it can. The lactic acid has to be removed, but to do that the body does not just degrade *all* of the lactic acid to carbon dioxide and water, especially not if there is no particular need for the ATP that would also be made by this process. In these circumstances, the body converts most of its lactic acid back to glycogen for eventual reuse!

This reconversion is (and must be) an energy-demanding process. (If the sequence from glycogen to lactic acid releases ATP, the reverse must require some, according to the law of conservation of energy.) To supply this energy *some* of the lactic acid is oxidized to carbon dioxide and water via the citric acid cycle and the respiratory chain. About one-sixth of the lactic acid supply is used up this way to furnish enough ATP to carry the remaining five-sixths back to the glycogen stage. Most of this activity occurs in the liver and kidneys, and the overall change is called glycogenesis ("glycogen creation").

the cori cycle. Glycogen is stored principally in the liver, the kidneys, and the muscles. When muscle glycogen is used up, it is replenished by the migration of glucose molecules from the bloodstream. These, in turn, may have come either from the digestive tract or from *glycogenolysis* (glycogen-lysis), i.e., from the hydrolysis of glycogen that is stored elsewhere. Muscle cells do not convert lactic acid to glycogen. The lactic acid produced from muscle glycogen during muscular work migrates out of the muscle cells and is transported to the liver and kidneys where most of it is converted back to glycogen. A cyclic change is obviously operating here, and the relations within the cycle are best seen by means of a Cori cycle, as illustrated in Fig. 18.9.

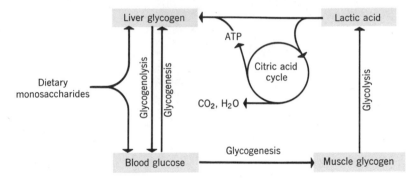

Fig. 18.9 Modified Cori Cycle, showing relations between glycogenesis, glycogenolysis, glycolysis, and the citric acid cycle.

blood-sugar level The concentration of glucose in whole blood remains fairly constant at a value known as the *blood-sugar level*. It is expressed in milligrams of glucose per 100 cc of blood. After 8 to 12 hours of fasting, the blood-sugar level of a normal adult is usually in the range of 60 to 100 mg per 100 cc. This range is called the *normal fasting level*.

Hypoglycemia is a condition wherein the concentration of glucose in the blood is below the normal fasting level. Concentrations of blood glucose above the fasting level constitute a condition of *hyperglycemia*. If the blood-sugar level is too high, the kidneys begin to transfer some of the excess glucose to the urine. The blood-sugar level above which this occurs is called the *renal threshold* for glucose. It is normally at about 140 to 160 mg of glucose per 100 cc of blood, sometimes higher. Whenever detectable quantities of glucose appear in the urine, a condition of *glucosuria* is said to exist.[2]

The only nutrient that the brain normally uses for energy is glucose taken directly from the bloodstream. The brain does not store glycogen as do muscles. Severe hypoglycemia, therefore, starves brain cells. Severe disorders of the central nervous system, such as convulsions and shock, can occur. Even mild hypoglycemia may be accompanied by dizziness and fainting spells.

Prolonged hyperglycemia at a glucosuric level is not itself immediately serious, but it indicates that the body is not able to withdraw glucose from the blood in a normal fashion.

The proper control of the blood-sugar level by the body is a measure

[2] The terms in this paragraph can be easily mastered if meanings for the following word parts are noted:

hyper-, above, excessive (hypertension)
hypo-, below, subnormal (hypoglycemia)
glyco-, referring to a "glycose" (generic name for a monosaccharide)
gluco-, referring to glucose
-emia, referring to blood
-uria, referring to urine

of its *glucose tolerance;* that is, its ability to utilize glucose in a normal way. This control is exercised in two ways:

1. There is a hormonal control. Insulin, a hormone, functions to assist withdrawal of glucose from the bloodstream. (Other hormones are also involved.)
2. Cells normally withdraw glucose from the bloodstream at a faster rate, the higher the blood sugar level, without regard to hormonal influences. Figure 18.10 shows the general fate of blood glucose at various concentrations.

We shall explore these related topics in some detail in this and the next chapter for two reasons. First, roughly one person in five is apparently genetically predisposed toward becoming diabetic. Not all do, but a large section of the population is directly or indirectly touched by this disorder. The incidence of diabetes makes it a particularly relevant choice for illustrating some aspects of the molecular basis of a disease. Second, one of the problems of untreated diabetes is acidosis, a condition that can arise from a number of causes and one that is therefore very relevant to health in general.

insulin, glucose tolerance, and diabetes mellitus

insulin. This hormone, a protein, is manufactured in and released (on demand) from the pancreas. Its molecules act as "gatekeepers" at cell walls and they facilitate the passage of glucose from the bloodstream to the interiors

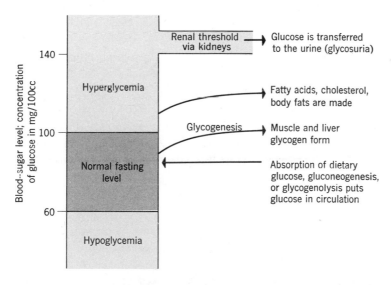

Fig. 18.10 Reduction of hyperglycemia. Glucose not needed to replenish glycogen reserves at muscles or the liver or to supply needs for the brain and the central nervous system is mostly converted into fat. Normally, the renal threshold for glucose is not exceeded and glucose is not found in the urine. In diabetes mellitus, however, glucosuria is standard. (Gluconeogenesis means the synthesis of glucose from molecular fragments obtained from proteins and lipids. "Neo-" is a word part of "new." Gluconeogensis refers to the making of "new" glucose.)

of cells. Not all types of tissues are made of cells needing insulin's services. Cells of the brain, the kidneys, and the intestinal tract, for example, can obtain glucose without insulin. Cells in skeletal and cardiac muscles as well as the liver need insulin to receive glucose. The cells most sensitive to insulin are those in adipose tissue, the tissue that handles the storage of fat in the abdominal regions, around internal organs, and beneath the skin (Chapter 19).

Because glucose is so important in metabolism in all tissues, any loss in its normal availability for whatever reason (including starvation) may be expected to result in a variety of subsequent problems. Given the great importance of glucose it should be no surprise that the living system has evolved mechanisms that give to glucose roles as both a nutrient and a messenger. As a messenger it says something to certain tissues telling them to activate support systems that glucose will need to get its various other jobs done. Its major message is to the beta cells of the pancreas, cells whose sole function is to release insulin. These cells may get that message from molecules besides glucose (e.g., certain amino acids; oral diabetic drugs such as tolbutamide), but glucose says it with greatest impact. When the blood sugar level rises sharply as after a carbohydrate-rich meal, the beta cells are stimulated by glucose to dump into the bloodstream their ready-to-go loads of insulin. The freshly released insulin then helps the glucose to enter cells where glucose is needed, and this brings the blood sugar level back down.

glucose tolerance test. In Fig. 18.11 the lower curve shows how the blood sugar level changes with time following the eating of a large amount of glucose (e.g., 100 grams or more). The data for plotting such a curve would typically be obtained during a *glucose tolerance test,* a standard test that begins with ingesting that much glucose and that is usually given when an individual appears to have some impairment in his use of glucose. (Glucose in the urine may have been discovered, for example.) An individual with moderate to severe diabetes mellitus will typically display the poor glucose tolerance revealed in the data of the upper curve in Fig. 18.11. (This is not true of every diabetic, and many other symptoms are involved.)

diabetes mellitus. The name of this disorder comes from the Greek, *diabetes,* to pass and *mellitus,* honey-sweet, together signifying passing urine containing sugar (glucose). We shall call it diabetes for short.

Diabetes is a disorder about which there is so much that is puzzling that experts still do not completely agree even on its definition. Most, however, will accept a purely clinical definition leaving open questions about what causes diabetes at the cellular, subcellular, and genetic levels. Clinically defined, diabetes is a disorder associated with a blood sugar level that is too much above normal for the existing metabolic situation in the individual. Its diagnosis is based mostly on showing that during a period of fasting and/or

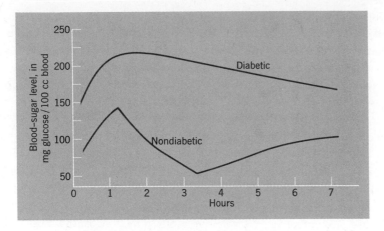

Fig. 18.11   Glucose-tolerance curves.

following the eating of a large amount of glucose the individual responds with a blood sugar level that climbs and remains high for a few hours.

Some individuals contract the severe, *juvenile onset* form of diabetes, and these (according to some scientists) probably inherited the defective sets of genes from both parents. A larger proportion of the population of diabetics have the *adult onset* (or the maturity onset) form. They acquired the clinically recognized symptoms usually after age 30 or 40 (and sometimes much older). For them the genetic disposition to diabetes probably came from one parent.

The nature of the genetic defect is not known, but it probably involves a number of genes. How that defect is *initially* expressed and in what tissue or tissues is still a subject of uncertainty. The orthodox view among specialists on diabetes is that the *primary* genetic disarray surfaces in the beta cells of the pancreas. There is little doubt that the beta cells in both the diabetic and prediabetic individuals respond sluggishly to signals by glucose molecules to release insulin. In severe cases there may be no response. In mild, undetected cases the insulin-releasing system may work well enough for years. Then an unusual or prolonged stress may occur and thereafter the beta cells may suffer a more or less gradual loss of their abilities to function. The latent diabetic then changes over to a clinically recognized diabetic. One stress is obesity. The obese individual has a "diet" that places inordinate demands almost continuously on the insulin-secreting abilities of the beta cells. If these cells are predisposed toward diabetes, under such a stress they may finally give up. Another stress would be an infection in the pancreas. To some a stress occurs during pregnancy.

In juvenile diabetes the problem (clinically) is usually a severe or total deficiency of insulin. Artificial administration of insulin is mandatory. In adult-onset diabetes the degree of insulin insufficiency varies from individual to individual. There may even appear (from blood analyses) to be a normal

insulin, glucose tolerance, and diabetes mellitus

amount of insulin, but for reasons not yet understood this insulin is more or less ineffective in controlling the blood sugar level. Insulin therapy is required in about 20% of those with adult-onset diabetes. The rest manage by watching their diets, exercising, and/or by using an oral diabetic drug such as tolbutamide that can also signal beta cells to release insulin.[3]

Associated with diabetes are problems in the vascular system—the entire network of veins, arteries, tubules, and capillaries that carry blood. The major unorthodox view of diabetes is that the primary expression of the genetic defect responsible for diabetes is in the vascular system; that eventually the capillaries in the pancreas are affected; and that this is what begins to close down the beta cells' service of releasing insulin. In severe diabetes, vascular problems may become so serious that gangrene develops.

Before insulin therapy became available in the 1920s, the most frequent ultimate problem for diabetics was the slow development of acidosis, an acidosis that eventually caused coma and death. We have to defer the rest of the discussion of this aspect of undetected and uncontrolled diabetes until the next chapter because the metabolism of lipids is involved.

hyperinsulinism. When too much insulin appears in the blood, a condition of *hyperinsulinism* is said to exist. The result is an excessive removal of glucose from the bloodstream by any or all of the several processes of glucose utilization, and the blood-sugar level drops. The ensuing hypoglycemia may cause malnutrition in the brain, and since brain cells depend directly on blood glucose, hyperinsulinism may produce convulsions and "insulin shock." The remedy is the immediate ingestion of some readily digestible carbohydrate, such as sugar in a candy bar, syrup, or honey.

Severe hypoglycemia can occur in diabetic people if too much insulin is inadvertently injected. Hypoglycemia of a more moderate nature, with attendant mild disorders to the central nervous system, may occur in people who have nothing but black, sugared coffee and heavily sugared rolls or doughnuts for breakfast. The glucose-tolerance curve of a nondiabetic person (Fig. 18.11) shows that about three hours after a heavy ingestion of sugar, with mild overstimulation of insulin secretion, the blood-sugar level drops slightly *below* the fasting level. Therefore, about three hours after such a breakfast, a person feels groggy, irritable, and bleary eyed, because his blood-sugar level is too low to satisfy energy demands in his brain cells. (If

---

[3] As of early 1970 roughly a million and a half diabetics were using oral diabetic drugs of which tolbutamide and phenformin were common examples. In 1970 and 1971 medical reports from the University Group Diabetes Program, an eight-year study of several hundred patients with adult-onset, noninsulin-dependent diabetes, cast some doubts on the safety of these drugs. Diet plus tolbutamide (or phenformin) is no more effective than diet alone in prolonging the lives of those with this mild diabetes. The Council on Drugs of the American Medical Association urges that a careful diet with exercise be used by those having mild diabetes; and where this is ineffective, insulin therapy should be added. If insulin therapy is deemed inadvisable, the physician may have to prescribe an oral diabetic drug. (*J. Am. Med. Assoc.*, August 9, 1971, page 817; *Diabetes*, November 2, 1970, page vi.)

he is a student, he may fall asleep in class.) Unhappily, most people with a mid-morning "sag" rush to the nearest coffeehouse for another round of sugared coffee and pastry, and the dreary cycle repeats itself. There is a temporary lifting of spirits as the blood-sugar level rises and meets again the requirements of the brain cells for glucose. At the same time, of course, the pancreas is once more stimulated to overproduce insulin. The blood-sugar level plummets back to a hypoglycemic level, and grogginess reappears.

The most important meal of the day is breakfast, which should be rich in proteins with some fat and carbohydrate. Proteins and fat tend to moderate the speed with which glucose leaves the digestive tract. Instead of glucose pouring suddenly into the bloodstream, it enters over a longer period, and overstimulation of the pancreas is avoided.

Several hormones besides insulin regulate glucose catabolism, and epinephrine is one that is particularly important in emergencies. This hormone of relatively simple structure is manufactured by the cells of the adrenal medulla. In times of danger or stress, epinephrine is discharged into the bloodstream in minute amounts.

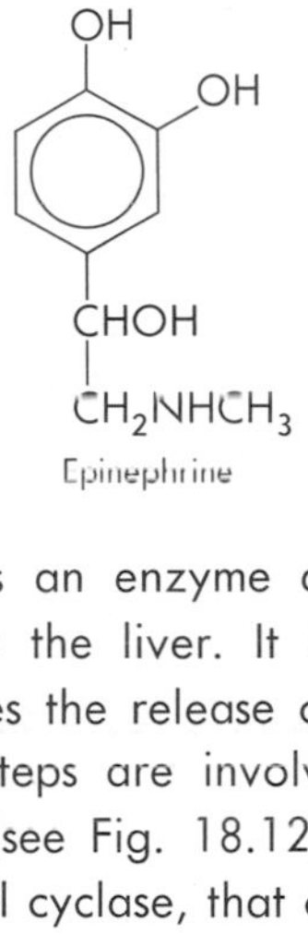

epinephrine ("adrenalin")

Epinephrine

Functioning, it is believed, as an enzyme activator, it promotes prompt glycogenolysis of glycogen in the liver. It has been estimated that one molecule of epinephrine causes the release of about 30,000 molecules of glucose. Several very rapid steps are involved in this *cascade* effect of epinephrine. Its direct action (see Fig. 18.12) may be the activation of a cell-wall-bound enzyme, adenyl cyclase, that catalyzes the conversion inside the cell of ATP to a cyclic phosphate ester, $3',5'-$AMP:

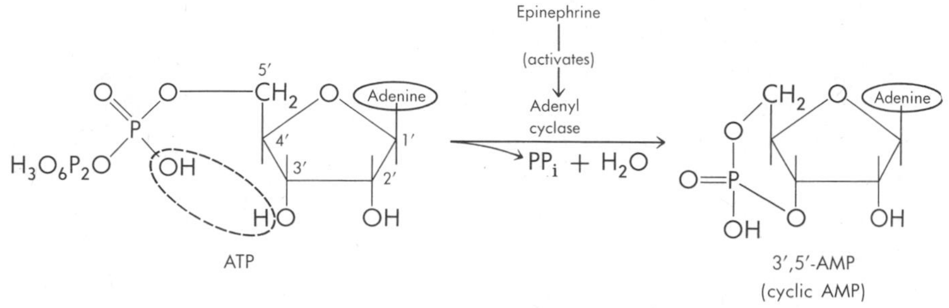

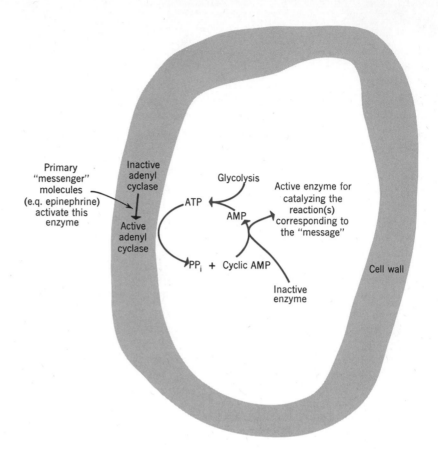

Fig. 18.12 According to one theory, primary chemical messengers (e.g., but not limited to hormones) may deliver their message at the target cell by activating the enzyme adenyl cyclase. This enzyme then catalyzes the conversion of ATP to cyclic AMP which then activates an enzyme that will catalyze the reaction(s) corresponding to the "message."

When formed, molecules of cyclic AMP activate molecules of another enzyme, which do the same, in turn, to still another enzyme until the hydrolysis of glycogen can be catalyzed. Thus a minute trace of epinephrine causes a rapid multiplication of effects similar to the work of tubes and transistors in the amplification of radio signals.

The released glucose appears in the bloodstream in such quantities that the blood-sugar level may rise to glycosuric levels. This sudden appearance of blood glucose makes available to the body, particularly the brain, an important nutrient precisely at moments when it may be required to meet a threatening situation. Epinephrine also stimulates the breakdown of stored fat, and fatty acids are released into circulation to serve as another important source of energy.

the metabolism of carbohydrates

Developments in the last few years point to cyclic AMP as an almost universal secondary chemical messenger. (The several hormones are among the primary messengers.) In an extremely active field of research scientists have found that the effects of some hormones on their target organs can be duplicated by simply adding cyclic AMP to the target organ instead. Hormones that have been studied include epinephrine, glucagon, ACTH, vasopressin, and prostaglandin.

According to Swedish diabetes specialists E. Cerasi and R. Luft the message that glucose gives to beta cells in the pancreas may be mediated by cyclic AMP. According to their tentative (1970) theory, glucose molecules interact with a signal receptor site on a beta cell. The receptor molecule responds by activating adenyl cyclase. This enzyme then catalyzes the formation of cyclic AMP that then activates the insulin releasor system. Whether this theory will hold up remains to be seen, but it is very obvious now that cyclic AMP has emerged as another of the very important molecules in living systems.

Selected Reading List

Books

1. A. L. Lehninger. *Bioenergetics*. W. A. Benjamin, Inc., New York, 1965. The flux of energy from one storage form to another is discussed in this paperback.
2. D. E. Green and H. Baum. *Energy and the Mitochondrion*. Academic Press, New York, 1970. A brief exposition of the major nontraditional theory of how ATP is made along the respiratory chain.
3. E. Cerasi and R. Luft, editors. *Pathogenesis of Diabetes Mellitus*. John Wiley & Sons, Inc., New York, 1970. The papers delivered at the 13th Nobel Symposium in Stockholm are contained in this reference.
4. L. L. Langley. *Homeostasis*. Reinhold Publishing Corporation, New York, 1965. The author attempts in this short paperback a survey of several important examples of homeostasis in both plants and animals.

Brief Summary

1. One of the most important metabolic sequences in the body is the conversion of the chemical energy of foodstuffs and oxygen into another storage form—ATP.
2. When ATP is used in energy-demanding processes (e.g., muscular work), it is degraded slightly to adenosine diphosphate (ADP) and inorganic phosphate (P_i).

3. The principal pathway for putting ADP and P_i back together again is the respiratory chain.

4. The respiratory chain shuttles pairs of electrons and protons from organic chemicals produced largely in the citric acid cycle to oxygen brought in by breathing. Powered by this electron-flow, teams of enzymes coupled to those of the respiratory chain cause the formation of ATP from ADP and P_i.

5. By a "chemical thermostat" or a homeostatic mechanism, the respiratory chain runs when it is needed (i.e., when ATP supplies have become depleted).

6. The citric acid cycle is a series of reactions that accepts acetyl units from the catabolism of fatty acids, certain amino acids, or glucose and converts them to carbon dioxide while sending elements of hydrogen down the respiratory chain until water is formed and ATP is made.

7. The body can make some ATP in the absence of oxygen by a series of reactions known as the anaerobic sequence or glycolysis starting either from glycogen or from glucose.

8. Some of the lactic acid produced by glycolysis is catabolized to furnish the ATP to carry the remaining lactic acid back to glycogen, and the Cori cycle describes the equilibrium between blood sugar and the various stores of glycogen.

9. Maintenance of the blood-sugar level—glucose tolerance—depends on a delicate balancing of glycogenolysis, glycogenesis, and glucose oxidation.

10. Insulin helps to dispose of blood glucose by promoting its withdrawal from blood by certain cells. When there is an insufficiency of effective insulin, as in diabetes mellitus, some excess glucose is withdrawn by the kidneys (glycosuria).

11. When the blood-sugar level is high (hyperglycemia), secretion of insulin is promoted to help lower the level.

12. In hypoglycemia, which may be promoted by hyperinsulinism, cells of the brain may become starved for glucose.

13. Epinephrine acts to accelerate glycogenolysis and thereby raise the blood-sugar level when a rich supply of this nutrient may be needed in times of danger or stress.

14. It is believed that several hormones may activate the enzyme adenyl cyclase, incorporated into cell walls of target organisms. This enzyme then catalyzes the formation of cyclic AMP inside the target cells which, in turn, activates other enzymes. In this way, cyclic AMP may be a secondary chemical messenger.

Problems and Exercises

1. Carefully define each of the following terms:
   (a) blood-sugar level   (d) hypoglycemia
   (b) renal threshold   (e) hyperinsulinism
   (c) hyperglycemia   (f) glucosuria

(g) glucose tolerance

(h) glucose-tolerance test

(i) normal fasting level

(j) glycogenesis

(k) glycogenolysis

(l) glycolysis

(m) respiratory chain

(n) mitochondria

(o) homeostasis

(p) cellular respiration

2. What general purpose does each of the following have in the production of ATP?

(a) glycolysis

(b) coenzyme A

(c) citric acid cycle

(d) NAD^+

(e) FAD

(f) respiratory chain

(g) cytochrome oxidase

3. Write the following in the form of an equation.

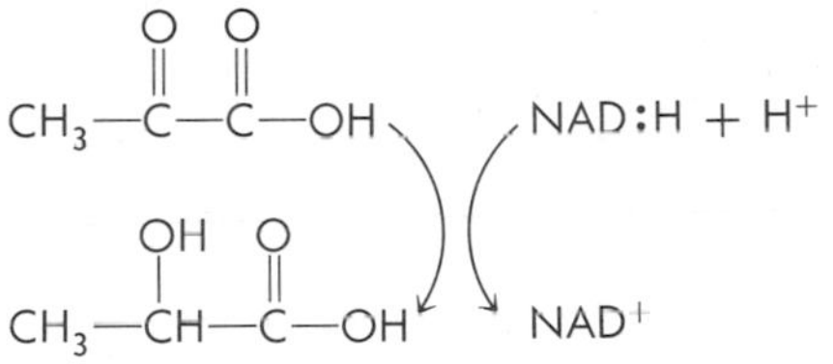

$$CH_3-\overset{\overset{O}{\|}}{C}-\overset{\overset{O}{\|}}{C}-OH \qquad NAD:H + H^+$$

$$CH_3-\overset{\overset{OH}{|}}{CH}-\overset{\overset{O}{\|}}{C}-OH \qquad NAD^+$$

4. Write the following equation in the form shown in Exercise 3.

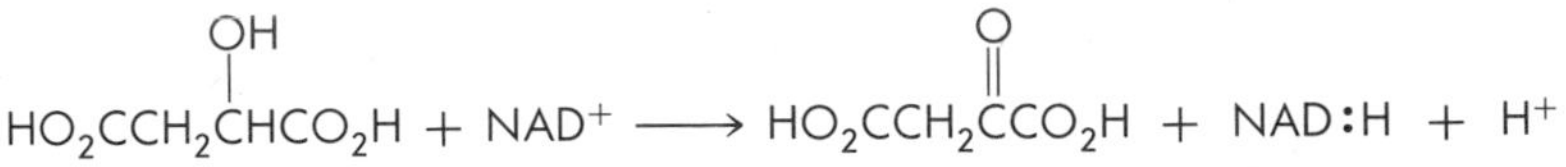

$$HO_2CCH_2\overset{\overset{OH}{|}}{CH}CO_2H + NAD^+ \longrightarrow HO_2CCH_2\overset{\overset{O}{\|}}{C}CO_2H + NAD:H + H^+$$

5. Why is hypoglycemia serious?

6. Describe how the body maintains a fairly constant blood-sugar level even though it ingests glucose only two or three times a day.

7. In periods of fasting, would you expect the amount of glycogen in the liver to increase or to decrease? Why?

8. Why does severe hyperinsulinism lead quickly to "insulin shock," whereas the absence of insulin, at least for a short period, is not so serious?

9. Is glycosuria always caused by diabetes mellitus? If not, how else might it arise?

10. How does the fact that a *trace amount* of epinephrine is effective support the theory that it acts as an enzyme activator?

chapter 19 the metabolism of lipids

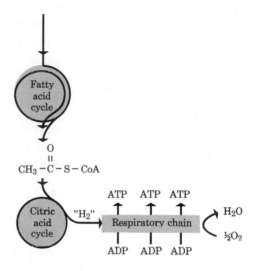

$$CH_3 - \underset{\underset{O}{\|}}{C} - S - CoA$$

The sweets of yesterday's menu often become the fat of today's waistline. The body converts non-lipid foods into fats with astonishing ease. However, body fats are not all bad. Indeed, a certain amount is vitally necessary, and in this chapter we shall study how the body makes and uses lipids.

absorption of digested lipid material. The complete digestion of simple lipids produces water-soluble glycerol and a mixture of fatty acids, which are highly emulsified by bile detergents. Complete hydrolysis of all ester links in a triglyceride is not necessary before absorption of lipid material from the digestive tract can occur. Mono- and diglycerides can also be absorbed.

Most—virtually all—lipid material is absorbed through the lymphatic network, and it enters the bloodstream in the thoracic duct. The process of absorption is accompanied by extensive resynthesis to triglycerides in route. By the time the lipid-digestion products are presented to the lacteals of the lymph system, virtually complete resynthesis to triglycerides has occurred. These enter systemic circulation as microdroplets.

function of bile salts in absorption of lipids. In lipid absorption, bile salts serve a purpose as important as their roles in lipid digestion. This function is primarily a detergent action that assists slightly soluble molecules across the intestinal barrier. Not only is this vital to lipid absorption, but it is equally significant for the successful absorption of vitamins that are water insoluble and substantially hydrocarbon-like, the so-called fat-soluble vitamins, vitamins A, D, E, and K. Their structures are given in Table 16.2.

distribution of absorbed lipids. Blood, which is an aqueous medium, could not handle the transportation and distribution of lipids were it not for the water-soluble plasma proteins. These form plasma-soluble complexes with lipids called *lipoproteins*. It is principally in this form that lipids are carried in the blood. Virtually no free, unassociated lipid is found in blood plasma. Fatty acids in circulation are also bound to proteins.

storage of lipids; adipose tissue. Lipids are deposited in nearly all parts of the body, but a specialized connective tissue called adipose tissue is the principal "depot." It occurs as subcutaneous tissue in the abdominal area and around certain organs (e.g., kidneys). "Depot fat" located in these areas cushions organs against sharp jolts and bumps and insulates them against sudden variations in temperature. It was once thought that subcutaneous adipose tissue provided insulation much like an ordinary blanket—passively. It is now known, however, that the analogy with an electric blanket is nearer the truth. Metabolic activity in the cells of this tissue generates a small amount of heat which helps offset losses of heat when the outside temperature drops. Wherever adipose tissue is found, it is quite active metabolically. Its cells have large numbers of mitochondria, nerves extend in and amongst them, and the bloodstream pushes its capillary network deep within it. One of the problems associated with obesity is the extra load placed on the heart not only to help in moving the extra weight around but also in pumping blood throughout a much, much larger and widely extended capillary network.

In the average adult human male who has received an adequate diet, there is enough lipid in the reserves to sustain his life for 30 to 40 days, assuming that he has enough water. Perhaps in primitive, prehistoric times, this supply was necessary for survival, but in developed countries it is obviously more than needed. Starvation, however, does not have to occur before the fat reserves are tapped.

After a few hours without food, the body's glycogen reserves will be gone. The lipids in actual circulation plus the blood sugar could sustain metabolic activity only a few minutes. The fat in storage in the liver is good for about an hour. Other, larger, reserves are obviously needed, and the body normally has two. One is the unabsorbed food still in the digestive tract. It is a temporary reserve to be sure, but it is important and much-used for people fortunate enough to eat regularly. The other reserve is adipose tissue.

The lipids on deposit in adipose tissue come largely from the carbohydrates and the lipids of the diet. About 30% of the carbohydrate ingested in a normally fed individual is converted to fat, and all of this conversion takes place right within the cells of the adipose tissue.

The conversion of glucose into fatty acid costs some energy (ATP), and about a quarter of the glucose supply is sacrificed to furnish it. If 30% of the carbohydrate taken in is changed into lipids, and if another 25% is used to power this change, it is apparent that a significant portion of all oxygen-consumption and heat-production in the body goes into just this operation.

There are distinct advantages to the individual in storing chemical energy as lipid rather than as carbohydrate. Lipid has a much higher "energy density." It stores more calories per gram of tissue. When glucose is stored as wet glycogen, it takes about 0.6 gram to yield one kcal. But when glucose is converted into glycerides, only about 0.13 gram is needed to yield one kcal.

When our energy requirements are "balanced" by our food intake, the amount of lipid present in the body remains fairly constant. This does not mean that depot fat just "rests" in inert storage. A constant coming and going of the molecules of depot fat occurs. Newly arrived molecules are deposited in storage as those that have been in storage are removed. A state of dynamic equilibrium exists unless a person eats too much in relation to his energy demands. Since there is no direct way to excrete excess lipid, and since lipids can be synthesized from glucose in the body, too much eating with too little exercise makes people fat. A small percentage of overweight people have hormonal troubles. Dieting is an unavoidable part of losing weight. It should by all means be done under the supervision of a physician. Those who flit from one fad diet to another prescribing for themselves an assortment of well-advertised diet pills are tinkering with their health, both physical and mental.

To mobilize the energy reserves in adipose tissue, several steps must take place, and they are outlined in Fig. 19.1.

1. Triglycerides in adipose tissue (or other "depots") must be hydrolyzed to produce free fatty acids (FFA) and glycerol. (The expression "free fatty acid," or FFA, means largely *non-esterified acids*. They may be bound to plasma proteins, however.)

2. These products must be borne in the bloodstream to sites of oxidation—principally the liver.

(a) Glycerol can enter the glycolysis pathway (by reactions that we shall omit).

3. Fatty acids are broken down two carbons at a time to provide units of acetyl coenzyme A for fueling the citric acid cycle and the respiratory chain. ATP is thereby produced.

Although the main site of fatty acid oxidation is the liver, fatty acids and smaller fragments produced from fatty acids can be used for energy in the heart and in skeletal muscles. In fact, *most of the energy needs of resting muscle are met by intermediates from fatty acid catabolism.* The degradation of fatty acids occurs by a repeating series of steps known as the Fatty Acid Cycle, or Spiral (Fig. 19.2).

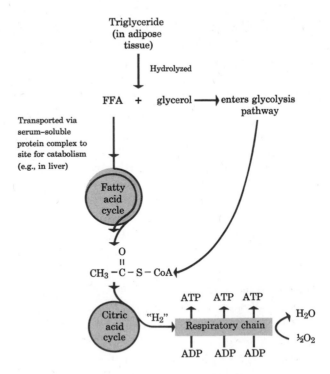

Fig. 19.1 Mobilization of the energy reserves in triglycerides. (FFA stands for free fatty acid. "H_2" stands for the elements of hydrogen, $H:^-$ and H^+.)

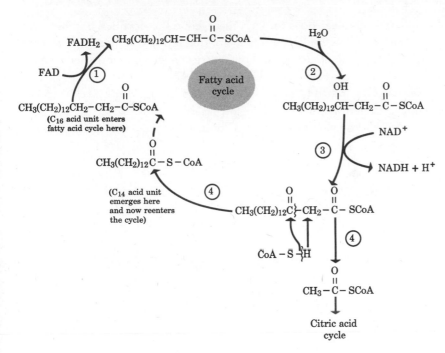

Fig. 19.2 Fatty acid cycle. Beta oxidation. The circled numbers refer to textual discussion of this cycle. It is a cycle not in the sense that the same intermediates reoccur.
Only types of them do, and types of reactions reoccur. The C_{14} acid unit produced
at ④ will next be dehydrogenated to give a C_{14} unsaturated acid. This will be hydrated, ②, and oxidized, ③. This sequence has the net effect of oxidizing the beta
(β)-position of the fatty acid chain to a ketone group. The bond from carbon-α to
carbon-β is now weakened. In step ④ it is cleaved to produce a C_{12} acid unit and
another acetyl coenzyme A. Seven turns of the cycle would be needed to break the
original palmitic acid (C_{16}) into eight acetyl CoA units.

fatty acid cycle. beta (β) oxidation. Before a molecule of a fatty acid can
yield ATP, it must be activated, and this consumes ATP. The price is small
for the return is great.

$$R-\overset{\overset{\text{O}}{\|}}{C}\underbrace{-OH + H}-SCoA + ATP \longrightarrow R-\overset{\overset{\text{O}}{\|}}{C}-SCoA + AMP + PP_i^1$$

Coenzyme A   Acyl coenzyme A

Once this initial activation is achieved, a series of reactions occurs that clip
two carbons at a time from the fatty acid unit. When two carbons have
been removed, as an acetyl unit in acetyl coenzyme A, the remainder of

[1] This is a rare example of a reaction of ATP in which it is cleaved to produce not simple
inorganic phosphate, P_i, but the diphosphate (or pyrophosphate) ion, here symbolized simply
as PP_i. The conversion of ATP to cyclic AMP (Chapter 18) is another example where PP_i splits
from ATP.

the original fatty acid goes through the cycle again to have another acetyl group removed. This continues until the original fatty acid has been cut down to the size of a final acetyl group. The acetyl groups normally enter the citric acid cycle as diagrammed in Fig. 19.1.

The steps in the fatty acid cycle, outlined in Fig. 19.2, are as follows, where the circled numbers refer to this figure.

① Dehydrogenation from the α- and β- carbons. FAD is the hydrogen acceptor.

$$CH_3(CH_2)_{12}\overset{\beta}{C}H_2-\overset{\alpha}{C}H_2-\overset{O}{\overset{\|}{C}}-SCoA + FAD \longrightarrow$$

Palmitic acid CoA: a C_{16} acid

$$CH_3(CH_2)_{12}CH=CH-\overset{O}{\overset{\|}{C}}-SCoA + FADH_2$$

An α,β-unsaturated acid derivative of coenzyme A

FAD

$[H:^- + H^+]$

Respiratory chain

$\frac{1}{2}O_2$

H_2O

ATP

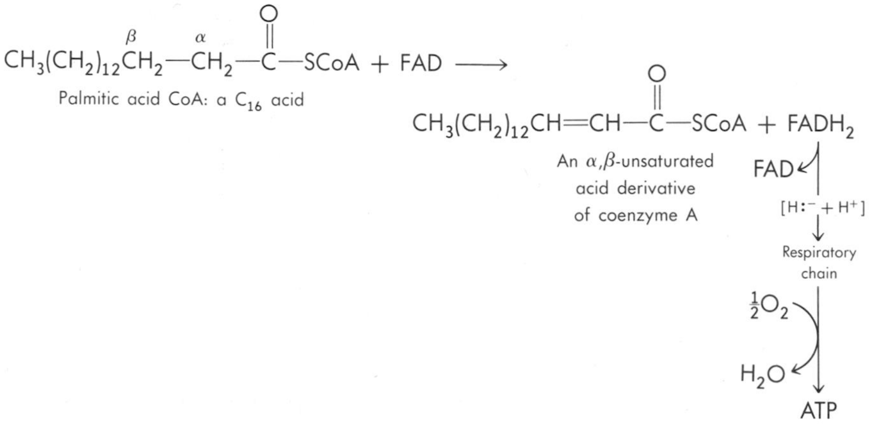

Several flavoproteins with FAD as the coenzyme act as catalysts, each specific FAD-enzyme differing in the size of the fatty acid unit it acts on.

② Addition of water to the double bond.

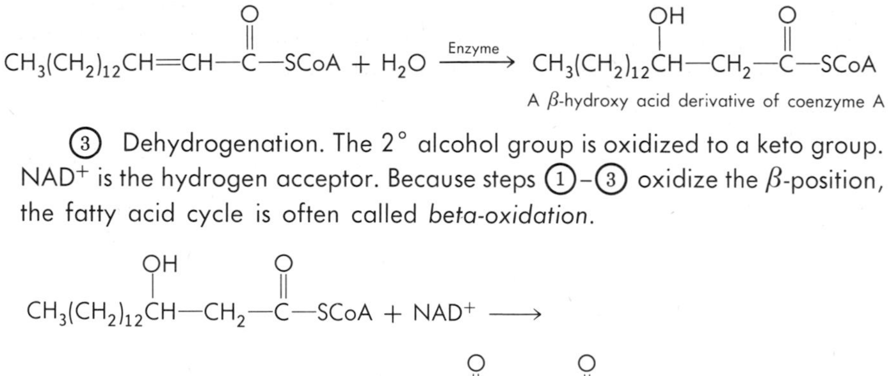

$$CH_3(CH_2)_{12}CH=CH-\overset{O}{\overset{\|}{C}}-SCoA + H_2O \xrightarrow{Enzyme} CH_3(CH_2)_{12}\overset{OH}{\overset{|}{C}}H-CH_2-\overset{O}{\overset{\|}{C}}-SCoA$$

A β-hydroxy acid derivative of coenzyme A

③ Dehydrogenation. The 2° alcohol group is oxidized to a keto group. NAD^+ is the hydrogen acceptor. Because steps ①–③ oxidize the β-position, the fatty acid cycle is often called *beta-oxidation*.

$$CH_3(CH_2)_{12}\overset{OH}{\overset{|}{C}}H-CH_2-\overset{O}{\overset{\|}{C}}-SCoA + NAD^+ \longrightarrow$$

$$CH_3(CH_2)_{12}\overset{O}{\overset{\|}{C}}-CH_2-\overset{O}{\overset{\|}{C}}-S-CoA + NADH + H^+$$

A β-keto acid derivative of coenzyme A

NAD^+

$[H:^- + H^+]$

Respiratory chain

$\frac{1}{2}O_2$

H_2O

ATP

$$CH_3(CH_2)_{12}\overset{\overset{\displaystyle O}{\|}}{C}-CH_2-\overset{\overset{\displaystyle O}{\|}}{C}-SCoA \xrightarrow{\text{Enzyme}} CH_3(CH_2)_{12}\overset{\overset{\displaystyle O}{\|}}{C}-SCoA + CH_3\overset{\overset{\displaystyle O}{\|}}{C}-SCoA$$

$$+ \; CoA-S-\{H$$

A C$_{14}$ acid
derivative of
coenzyme A

Citric acid
cycle

ATP ⟵ Respiratory chain

The intermediates in this catabolism normally do not accumulate to any significant extent. As soon as they form they react further. When the acetyl CoA stage is reached, several options are available. One of them has an important bearing on the synthesis of cholesterol. Another is particularly ominous in undetected diabetes mellitus and in periods of prolonged fasting or starvation.

general view. As we have noted before, acetyl coenzyme A stands at one of the most important metabolic intersections in all of body chemistry. Figure 19.3 is a reminder, and it serves to summarize some features not yet noted. The ready interconversion of acetyl coenzyme A to an acetoacetyl CoA

metabolic fates of acetyl coenzyme A

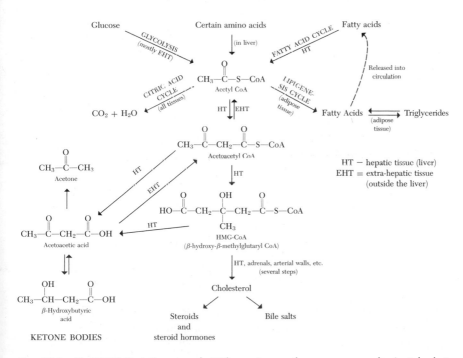

Fig. 19.3 The HMG-CoA "crossroads." The various pathways occur predominately, but not exclusively, in the tissues indicated.

(something like a reverse of step ④, Fig. 19.2) leads to another important crossroad. The formation of β-hydroxy-β-methylglutaryl CoA (let's just call it HMG-CoA for our limited needs) makes possible the subsequent synthesis of cholesterol, possibly the steroid hormones, and the bile salts; or it makes possible production of a set of three compounds somewhat inaccurately called the *ketone bodies*.

Our background in the mechanisms of organic reactions is not deep enough to arrive at an understanding of *how* molecules of acetyl coenzyme A might be put together until the HMG-CoA stage of Fig. 19.3 is reached. Therefore, only the following general summary, in the form of "word equations," will suffice for our needs.

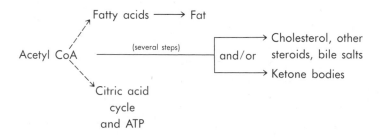

With the formation of the ketone bodies—acetoacetic acid, β-hydroxybutyric acid, and acetone—we can return to our discusssion of some aspects of the molecular consequences of undetected diabetes.

In the most general terms, the sequence of events in undetected (and, therefore, untreated) diabetes may be summarized as follows.

The relative lack of effective insulin, a major defect in diabetes, is accompanied by—

—excessive release of free fatty acids from adipose tissue, which is accompanied by—
—increased fatty acid oxidation in the liver, which leads to—
—the production of acetyl coenzyme A at a rate faster than it is normally handled, which leads to—
—an overproduction of the ketone bodies (which we shall soon identify with the term *ketosis*), which leads to—
—a lowering of the pH of the blood (acidosis), which—
—inhibits the transport of oxygen by hemoglobin, which causes—
—coma and ultimately—
—death . . . unless corrected by insulin therapy.

the ketone bodies. It has been traditional to call the three compounds—acetoacetic acid, β-hydroxybutyric acid, and acetone—the *ketone bodies*, even though one does not have a keto group. Collective analysis of the three of them is possible, and the ketone body concentration is usually expressed in terms of β-hydroxybutyric acid. The presence of these compounds is normal. They are formed slowly but relatively continuously in the liver and released into general circulation. Yet, the ketone body "level" in venous circulation in an adult is roughly only 1 mg per 100 ml of blood. This low level is maintained partly because two of the three ketone bodies, the two acids, serve as sources of energy in many tissues. Muscles, for example, obtain much of their ATP for "resting functions" from acetoacetate units, which can supply acetyl groups for acetyl CoA and the citric acid cycle as indicated in Fig. 19.3. The heart uses acetoacetate. The brain, which normally uses glucose exclusively for energy, during prolonged starvation can adjust to acetoacetate for fuel. The kidneys can remove ketone bodies, and about 20 mg per day of these substances are excreted via the urine.

When the ketone body level in the blood rises, a condition of *ketonemia* exists. When, as a result of a high ketonemia, higher than normal concentrations of these compounds are found in the urine, a condition of *ketonuria* exists. Usually "ketone-breath," the detectability of the odor of acetone on the breath, is by now noticeable. These three conditions—ketonemia, ketonuria, and ketone breath—are collectively called *ketosis*. The situation is now dangerous. Unchecked, ever-rising ketosis means death by means we shall study soon. Unchecked ketosis leads to acidosis. (When its origin is ketosis, it may be called ketoacidosis.)

Two of the ketone bodies are carboxylic acids. Persistent overproduction   acidosis
of them, therefore, is eventually bound to overtax the buffer systems of the blood. The pH of the blood slowly starts to drop. We have learned that this drift in the pH of the blood toward a pH of 7, or lower (as measured at room temperature), is called *acidosis*. As the pH drops, buffers in the blood act to neutralize the acids. One of the affected buffers is the H_2CO_3/HCO_3^- system. Bicarbonate ions are neutralized, and the excess carbonic acid is broken to water and carbon dioxide, which is expelled at the lungs. Normally, the level of bicarbonate ion in blood is 22 to 30 millimoles per liter. (For bicarbonate ion, 22 millimoles are equivalent to 1.85 g sodium bicarbonate.) This drops to 16 to 20 millimoles in mild acidosis; 10 to 16 in moderate acidosis; and below 10 millimoles bicarbonate ion per liter in severe acidosis.

Acidosis is serious for many reasons, one being that it disrupts the mechanism for transporting oxygen (Chapter 17). In moderate to severe acidosis, the difficulties in taking in oxygen at the lungs are so great that the individual experiences severe "air hunger," and breathing is very painful and difficult (a condition called dyspnea). By the time the bicarbonate level in blood has dropped to 6 to 7 millimoles/liter in the adult, coma has set in.

A consequence of even moderate acidosis is excessive loss of body fluids via the kidneys. To put the salts of the carboxylic acids (from two of the ketone bodies) into the developing urine, large quantities of water must be removed, too. The individual experiencing this suffers from a general dehydration. This coupled with disruption to his ability to transport oxygen normally will result in depression of the central nervous system. Even in mild acidosis, the individual experiences fatigue, indisposition, a desire to stay in bed, lack of appetite, nausea, headache, reduced power of concentration, lack of desire to converse, and difficulty in making even simple decisions.

We have gone into this matter of acidosis in some depth because it is instructive to realize how much of human well-being depends on the control of the pH of the blood. Acidosis is much more common than a healthy person might realize. Anyone experiences it briefly after severe physical exercise.

lactic acid acidosis and athletic accomplishment. We learned in Chapter 18 that glycolysis becomes an important source of ATP under anaerobic conditions and that glycolysis produces lactic acid. When lactic acid forms faster than it can be "removed" (converted to glycogen at the expense of some of it), its level in the blood will rise, the level of bicarbonate ion will drop and so will the pH of the blood. Acidosis from any source is acidosis; it is the nature of the treatment that varies. The lactic acid level in blood may rise from its resting level of 1 to 2 millimoles per liter to 10 to 12 millimoles per liter after hard work. This will cut the bicarbonate level roughly in half, to a level of 12 to 14 millimoles per liter, meaning that the moderate form of acidosis results. All athletes have experienced the violent dyspnea, the difficult, painful, gulping air hunger that accompanies maximum effort in a contest. When the lactic acid level is about 10 millimoles per liter, further work is rendered virtually impossible regardless of "will power." This is obviously a limiting factor in the further improvement of athletic records.

Lactic acid acidosis may arise during milder exercise if the supply of oxygen drops. Men living in lower altitudes who fancy themselves the rugged outdoor types come out of even brief hikes at high altitudes in the mountains with severe pains in the chest and the ego. Neither is serious. Recovery from lactic acid acidosis merely takes rest.

Most young people acquire the physical stamina and endurance usually attributed to middle age by the time they are 25 to 30 years old. Not being athletes they undervalue fitness. Being physically fit and being an athlete are not the same things, however. All sports require talents and skills and some sports require great muscle power. But to anyone, athlete or otherwise, the heart is the most important muscle in the body. Good lung capacity is also essential for fitness. If you improve your heart and your lungs—your entire respiratory system—you will handle the lactic acid generated by exertion much, much better. To get rid of lactic acid rapidly you must be able to distribute oxygen and remove carbon dioxide rapidly. The stronger your heart and lungs the better you will be able to do this and the more fitness and endurance you will have for activity. To improve your heart and lungs (and keep them in shape) you must put demands on them (working up slowly and carefully if you are now out of shape). Running, swimming and biking or games that involve these activities as well as a good, balanced diet are your best insurance for physical stamina all your life.

causes and prevention of ketosis. We have seen that acidosis may lead to coma and death. To check acidosis originating from untreated diabetes, it is ketosis that must be prevented or controlled. The cause of ketosis may be understood in terms of the several pathways indicated in Fig. 19.3. The ketone bodies are made, indirectly, from fatty acids and if fatty acid catabolism is accelerated more and more ketone bodies will be made. Our next question is why fatty acid catabolism should increase in diabetes.

In diabetes, cells of adipose tissue do not take in glucose as rapidly as normal. Insulin, now in short supply, is the hormone needed to assist in transporting glucose through the walls of these cells. They, therefore, do not *make* lipids as rapidly as normal. This unbalances an equilibrium between the formation of fat and the hydrolysis of stored fat into glycerol and free fatty acids. The result is a rise in the rate of release of fatty acids into circulation (which also puts some burden on the circulatory system). These fatty acids are picked up by liver cells and catabolized. While all this is happening, there is operating still another factor that increases the rate of mobilization of fatty acids (and amino acids, too).

When it is difficult for glucose to penetrate cell walls the cells of some tissues work to make glucose, and some of this glucose is put into circulation. This activity is done primarily in the liver, and we shall have to omit the details. In general terms, this synthesis of "new" glucose requires amino acids (primarily for carbon skeletons) and fatty acids (for their hydrogens). Thus, again, fatty acids are mobilized; they are catabolized faster than normal; ketosis may result. Figure 19.4 has an outline of these general events.

starvation and acidosis. Acidosis can arise from starvation[2] and the solution, although obvious, is not always available. In starvation, the glycogen stores of glucose units disappear. The system works to make glucose itself, but as indicated in Fig. 19.4, the body must take amino acids from its proteins and it must mobilize its fatty acid reserves. The system also needs a source of ATP, and when glucose is gone (or in short supply) it turns to its stores of lipids. Thus, lipids are metabolized ever more rapidly, acetyl coenzyme A production rises, and ketosis appears. It may lead to acidosis. When it does, all aggressiveness leaves the individual. Whereas in early stages of mass starvation, whole populations will rise up and riot for food, in its later stages they become passive.

[2] Starvation is here defined as total fasting whether voluntary or involuntary. It is distinguished from undernutrition in which acidosis is seldom observed. (Ancel Keys found during the course of the "Minnesota Experiment" that ketosis was essentially absent in volunteers who for six months were given a daily diet of only 1500 kcal, in contrast with an estimated daily intake in the United States of over 3000 kcal per capita. During this time they lost a fourth of their weight.)

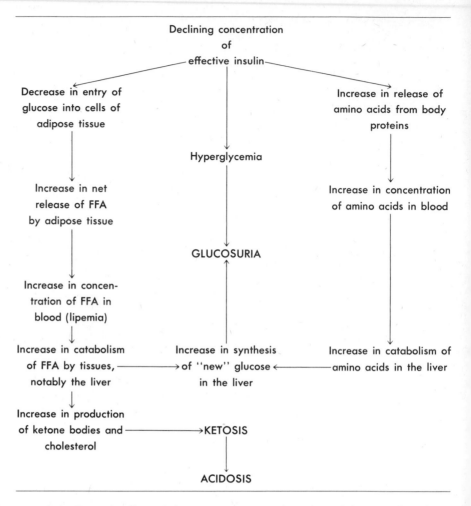

Fig. 19.4 General outline of the main sequences of events in diabetes mellitus. (FFA stands for free fatty acids.) (Adapted from Alexander Marble and G. F. Cahill, *The Chemistry and Chemotherapy of Diabetes Mellitus*, 1962. Courtesy of Charles C Thomas, Publisher, Springfield, Illinois.)

conversion of carbohydrates to lipids

Just as fatty acids are degraded two carbon units at a time, so the body can synthesize them two carbon units at a time. Plants and animals in general can take acetyl units and join them to form long-chain fatty acids. A two-carbon building block, of course, results in fatty acids of even carbon numbers, and it is precisely those acids that are found abundantly in nature.

The oxidation of glucose generates acetyl coenzyme A in the step just before the citric acid cycle. Three fates await it, as shown in Fig. 19.3. If the body seriously needs energy, it enters the citric acid cycle to generate ATP. If the body does not need energy, the acetic acid unit may be shunted into a reaction that leads to the synthesis of steroids or long-chain fatty acids

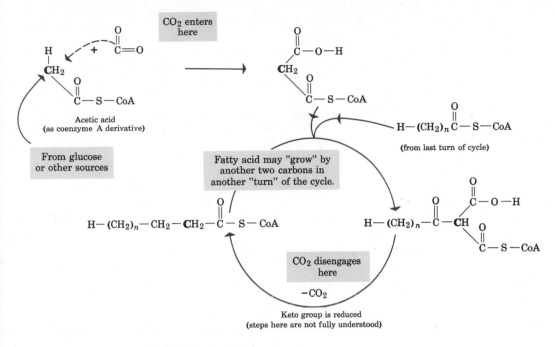

Fig. 19.5 The lipigenesis cycle.

and eventually fat. If you eat much sweet food and exercise little, the sweets inexorably become fats, as you probably well know.

An outline showing how the body manufactures fatty acids from acetic acid units—*lipigenesis*—is depicted in Fig. 19.5. Lipigenesis is a cyclic process that repeats itself as the chain grows. It is especially noteworthy that carbon dioxide is necessary to the cycle; it is not just a waste product. Among the vitamins that are essential to coenzyme systems for the cycle are biotin, niacin, and pantothenic acid.

Selected Reading List

Books (See also the references for Chapter 18.)

1. A. E. Renold and G. F. Cahill, Jr., section editors. *Handbook of Physiology. Section 5: Adipose Tissue.* American Physiological Society, Washington, D. C., 1965. A thorough, technical discussion of this important tissue.

2. Jean Mayer. *Overweight.* Prentice-Hall, Englewood Cliffs, N. J., 1968. A nutritionist discusses obesity from both a biochemical and physiological point of view.

3. A. E. Renold. "Intermediary Metabolism in Diabetes Mellitus." Chapter 7 in *The Pathology of Diabetes Mellitus,* S. Warren, P. M. LeCompte, and M. A. Legg, editors. Lea and Febiger, Philadelphia, 1966.

Articles

1. H. S. Mayerson. "The Lymphatic System." *Scientific American,* June 1963, page 80. The structure and functions of this important system are beautifully illustrated and clearly described.

2. D. M. Gibson. "The Biosynthesis of Fatty Acids." *Journal of Chemical Education,* Vol. 42 (May 1965), page 236. A survey of how fatty acids are made.

Brief Summary

1. Fatty acids and glycerol produced by lipid digestion are recombined into triglycerides as they move away from the digestive tract toward their entry into the lymph system.

2. Bile salts facilitate lipid absorption.

3. Lipids are transported in the bloodstream as complexes with plasma proteins called *lipoproteins.*

4. The body stores lipids as depot fat in order to provide insulation and protection against mechanical shock to certain organs and in order to reserve a rich source of energy.

5. Fatty acids may be oxidized in the liver through the fatty acid cycle. This feeds acetyl units to the citric acid cycle or to the synthesis of steroids.

6. If fatty acids are oxidized more rapidly than normal, ketosis may develop.

7. Ketosis, the presence of excessive amounts of ketone bodies in the blood and in the urine, with detectable amounts of acetone on the breath, originates when fatty acid oxidation produces ketone bodies faster than they can be used up.

8. Ketosis may arise from prolonged starvation.

9. Since two of the ketone bodies are acids, they tend to depress the pH of the blood toward 7, a condition known as acidosis.

10. Acidosis impairs the blood's ability to carry oxygen and may lead to death.

11. Acidosis may also develop from severe exercise.

12. The body manufactures fatty acids from acetic acid units obtained as intermediates in glucose oxidation.

Problems and Exercises

1. Carefully define each of the following terms:
   (a) depot fat   (c) lipoprotein
   (b) ketone body   (d) ketonemia

(e) lipemia   (j) ketosis
(f) insulin   (k) acidosis
(g) ketonuria   (l) lipigenesis
(h) fatty acid cycle   (m) dyspnea
(i) fat-soluble vitamin

2. Discuss the functions of adipose tissue.

3. Compare and contrast the availability of chemical energy stored as glycogen and as depot fat.

4. In what two ways is glucose used to make depot fat?

5. Discuss the mobilization of chemical energy from depot fat. How is the citric acid cycle necessary to it?

6. Starting with lauric acid, write equations for all the reactions that take place as it is degraded through the fatty acid cycle to acetic acid units.

7. Starting with the coenzyme A derivative of n-butyric acid, write reaction sequences that show how its catabolism can lead to the ketone bodies.

8. What are the three principal ways by which acetyl coenzyme A is used?

9. Under what circumstances will fatty acids and amino acids be used to make glucose?

10. What causes lactic acid acidosis?

11. What happens during a rest period to correct lactic acid acidosis?

12. Why does the liver make "new" glucose in diabetes?

13. How does starvation cause ketosis?

14. Describe how lack of insulin may lead to acidosis and thence to death. Pay particular attention to the connection between insulin and ketosis and between ketosis and acidosis.

chapter 20 the metabolism of proteins

Cats do not eat worms, but they do eat birds and when they do they care little about what birds eat. So it is in nature. Today's bread was yesterday's wheat. Yesterday's wheat was the carbon dioxide, water, minerals, and sunlight of the day before. The bird, the cat, and we human beings cannot manufacture all the needed amino acids within our bodies from fats, carbohydrates, and simple inorganic nitrogen compounds alone. In the "balance" of nature, animals rely largely on weaker or less alert animals or on plants for their supply of amino acids that they then use to make distinctive muscles, tendons, skin, enzymes, hormones, antibodies, and hemoglobin, to list but a few proteins. In this chapter and the next, we shall study how this is done.

Nitrogen nuclei are essential in the makeup of all living things, but we as human beings, who live and move in an atmosphere that is roughly 80% nitrogen gas, have no ability to appropriate nitrogen directly from the air. To be of use to us, nitrogen nuclei must be a part of derivatives of ammonia such as proteins and amino acids. We simply lack the enzymes needed to catalyze the reduction of elemental nitrogen to ammonia or to use oxides of nitrogen, nitrates or nitrites.

Fortunately, among the scores of millions of microbes to be found in each gram of most topsoils, there are many nitrogen-fixing types, i.e., those that can reduce N_2 to ammonia (NH_3) or something like ammonia. Some, like *Clostridium pasteurianum* and *Azotobacter vinelandii*, are free-living bacteria. Others, such as those in the genus *Rhizobium*, are parasites of certain plants. Still others are yeasts and blue-green algae. By steps not yet fully understood, *Clostridium* and *Azotobacter* can reduce nitrogen to ammonia; and once this compound forms, the routes are open to amino acids. These bacteria and many plants have enzymes that can use ammonia to convert ketone groups to amino groups:

$$\underset{\text{ketone group}}{-\overset{\displaystyle O}{\overset{\|}{C}}-} \;+\; NH_3 \quad \xrightarrow[\text{(including reduction)}]{\text{several steps}} \quad \underset{\substack{\text{amino group}\\\text{of an amino acid}}}{-\overset{\displaystyle NH_2}{\overset{|}{C}}H-} \;+\; H_2O$$

Bacteria of the genus *Rhizobium* have a relationship with legumes such as alfalfa, clover, soybeans, and peas by which, working together, they fix nitrogen from the air. The bacteria alone cannot do this, nor can the legume acting without the bacteria. Working together through the plant's root system, they reduce atmospheric nitrogen to hydroxylamine, NH_2OH, instead of to ammonia. But this compound can also be used to make amino groups. Thus the overall effect is the same as having ammonia the reduction product. The living together of widely differing organisms in a mutually beneficial way, as illustrated by *Rhizobium* and legumes, is called *symbiosis*. With favorable conditions legumes and *Rhizobium* can put as much as 200 pounds of fixed nitrogen per year into an acre of soil.

Atmospheric nitrogen is converted to other forms, to nitrates and nitrites, by oxidation. The daily worldwide production of nitric acid by electric discharges during storms and possibly by solar radiation is estimated to be hundreds of thousands of tons. (This is still only a small percentage of the nitrogen fixation accomplished by organisms.) Upon entering the soil, nitrates and nitrites become raw materials for many microorgansims and higher plants that can convert these ions into ammonia and thence to amino acids.

The higher animals, including man, are absolutely dependent on the soil bacteria and the plants to provide amino acids. By eating plants or by eating animals that feed on plants, the higher animals obtain the dietary proteins which, when digested, give the inventory of amino acids the particular species must have for life. When plants and animals die, decay processes return their nitrogen to the soil and atmosphere. There exists, therefore, a nitrogen cycle in nature, illustrated in Fig. 20.1, that also includes nitrogen-fixing activities of man.

According to ecologist C. C. Delwiche, before the development of modern agriculture, the earth's natural nitrogen-fixing systems annually fixed about

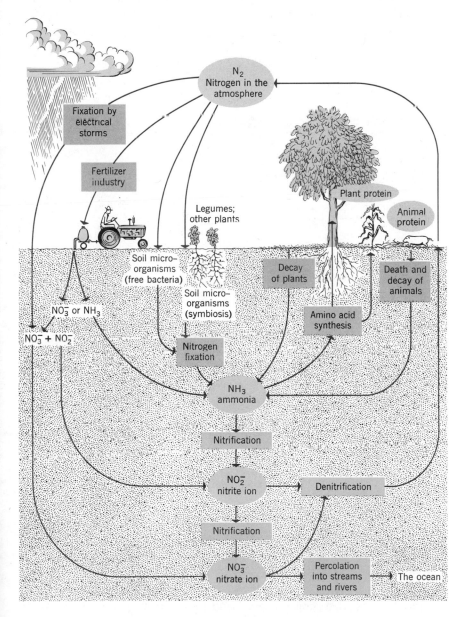

Fig. 20.1 The nitrogen cycle over land.

30 million tons of nitrogen to the soils. By the use of inorganic fertilizers based both on ammonia and nitrates we now add to the soils of our planet more than that, over 30 million tons of nitrogen a year—to what ecologic consequence we do not (yet) know. (By 2000 A.D. this may well be 100 million tons a year.)

By nitrogen fixation, soil microorganisms transfer nitrogen nuclei from the atmosphere to the soils and waters of the globe, and some of their species also help to return these nuclei to the air. In addition to reducing nitrogen to ammonia, soil bacteria participate in the nitrogen cycle in the following additional ways.

Nitrification: the oxidation of ammonia to nitrite ion and then to nitrate ion.

$$\text{Overall: } 2NH_3 + 3O_2 \xrightarrow{\text{several steps}} \underset{\text{nitrite ion}}{2NO_2^-} + 2H_2O + 2H^+$$

Then, by another microorganism:

$$2NO_2^- + O_2 \longrightarrow \underset{\text{nitrate ion}}{2NO_3^-}$$

These reactions release energy, and a few soil organisms use the oxidation of ammonia or of nitrite ion instead of the oxidation of organic compounds as their sole source of chemical energy.

Denitrification: the reduction of nitrate or nitrite to a variety of compounds including nitrogen gas and nitrous oxide (N_2O). The reactions are multistep and complicated, but they amount to using nitrate or nitrite ions instead of gaseous oxygen as electron acceptors in respiratory chains. One kind of denitrification may be represented as:

$$\underset{\text{glucose}}{5C_6H_{12}O_6} + \underset{\substack{\text{nitrate} \\ \text{ion}}}{24NO_3^-} \longrightarrow 30CO_2 + 18H_2O + 24OH^- + 12N_2$$

In the absence of oxygen, some soil bacteria get all their energy this way. From each mole of glucose 570 kilocalories are available when nitrate ion is the oxidizing agent as compared to about 680 kilocalories when oxygen is used.

The nitrogen cycle reveals once again how interdependent are all living things on our planet. Soil microbes and plants could get along quite well without man. Considering all the chemical poisons we dump onto our planet, they would get along better. But man cannot make it without plants, even the lowly microorganisms of the soil. They are indispensible to our supply of amino acids, and we now turn to a study of how we use these compounds in the body.

The end products of protein digestion, amino acids, are rapidly absorbed through the walls of the small intestine. They enter general circulation almost wholly at the portal vein. Although the exact nature of the process is not yet known, absorption of amino acids does not take place simply by ordinary dialysis. It is believed to involve actual chemical reactions in cells of the intestinal mucosa as amino acids are passed from point to point. Some absorption of simple peptides also occurs. Occasionally, especially in the very young, intact native proteins are absorbed. These "foreign" proteins often invoke an allergic response that plagues the victim for his life.

    Usually, one of the following fates awaits any amino acid:

1. It may be used to synthesize tissue protein, either to make new tissue or to repair old.
2. It may be used to make nonprotein compounds that contain nitrogen, such as nucleic acids, heme, and creatine.
3. It may be catabolized.
    (a) Its amino group may be removed as a molecule of ammonia, a process called *oxidative deamination*. The ammonia is converted into urea and excreted via the urine.
    (b) Its amino group may be transferred to a different molecule to make a new amino acid, a process called *transamination*. In this way, the body can make certain amino acids from others.
    (c) It may be degraded to carbon dioxide and water or to other nonnitrogenous compounds the body can use. Certain amino acids can be used to make carbohydrate and lipid material in the body.

On a proper diet, when a healthy person excretes as much nitrogen as he takes in, he is said to have a *nitrogen balance*. This balance is preserved by a combination of factors. The absorption of dietary amino acids delivers them to what is called a *nitrogen pool*. The nitrogen pool is not a specific depot but may be considered to consist of all amino acids wherever they are found in the body (e.g., bloodstream, intercellular and extracellular fluids) and other simple nitrogenous substances. Amino acids may enter this pool from body tissues that constantly undergo degradation and resynthesis, for most tissue proteins are in a dynamic state. They experience a constant turnover of the amino acids of which they are made. The turnover is fairly rapid among proteins of the liver and blood plasma; it is very slow among muscle proteins.

absorption of amino acids

nitrogen balance and the dynamic state of body proteins

471

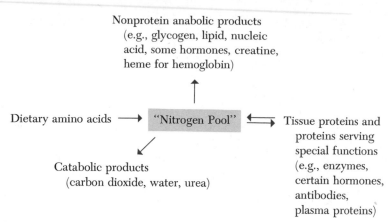

Fig. 20.2 The nitrogen pool.

The body has no mechanism for the temporary storage of amino acids, as it has for glucose (glycogen) and lipids (depot fat). Maintenance of the nitrogen balance normally requires that amino acids in the nitrogen pool be catabolized and that nitrogen be eliminated. The interrelationships that involve the nitrogen pool are summarized by the diagram of Fig. 20.2.

the synthesis of urea. Urea, the major end product of nitrogen metabolism in human beings, is made in the liver. From this organ it is carried in the bloodstream to the kidneys which remove it and place it in the urine being formed. Urea is made from carbon dioxide and ammonia. The net equation is as follows, although a few steps are required to achieve synthesis (Fig. 20.3).

$$2NH_3 + CO_2 \longrightarrow NH_2 - \overset{\overset{\displaystyle O}{\|}}{C} - NH_2 + H_2O$$

$$\text{Urea}$$

essential amino acids. Although the body has the capacity to use some amino acids to make others, a few cannot be synthesized this way. Unless they are present in the proteins of the diet, the nitrogen equilibrium is upset and the nitrogen balance becomes negative. Presumably human metabolism cannot form these amino acids from the carbon skeletons and the amino groups of other intermediates, and for this reason they are said to be *essential* (see Table 20.1). The *nonessential amino acids*, also listed in Table 20.1, can be made in the body. (Nonessential, in this context, means *temporarily* dispensable. Obviously all the amino acids listed are used by the body, and protein synthesis could not proceed without them.) Dietary proteins that contain all the essential amino acids are called *adequate proteins*. Gelatin without tryptophan and zein (protein in corn) without lysine are inadequate proteins.

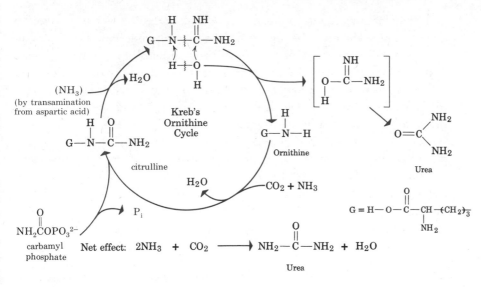

Fig. 20.3 Urea synthesis.

kwashiorkor. In parts of Latin America, Asia, and Africa the death rate among children is several times that in developed, industrialized societies. Children by the thousands are doomed to short lives with bloated bellies, patchy skin, and discolored hair. As long as they are nourished at their mother's breast, they enjoy health. When the second child comes and displaces the first, the symptoms appear in the first child. The disease is called kwashiorkor, a name taken from two words of an African dialect meaning "first" and "second"—the disease that the first child contracts when the second one is born. The diet of the firstborn, instead of milk, is now starchy

Table 20.1 Amino Acids, Classified as Nutritionally Essential or Nonessential in Maintaining Nitrogen Equilibrium in an Adult Man

Essential	Nonessential
Isoleucine	Alanine
Leucine	Arginine
Lysine	Aspartic acid and asparagine
Methionine	Cystine
Phenylalanine	Glutamic acid and glutamine
Threonine	Glycine
Tryptophan	Histidine
Valine	Hydroxyproline
	Proline
	Serine
	Tyrosine

Data from W. C. Rose, *Federation Proceedings*, Vol. 8, 1949, page 546.

and contains inadequate protein. Hardly recognized until the 1940s, the ailment is now known to be a protein deficiency disease. Both undernutrition and malnutrition are responsible. The initial symptoms are a loss of appetite and diarrhea—both of which lead the mother to reduce the amount of food she gives the child, thus hastening the onset of additional complications. In the weakened state the child is even more susceptible to the diseases that are a constant hazard in the tropics.

Efforts to improve both the quality and the quantity of protein in the diet of people in these regions have been intensive. A team led by Norman Borlaug (Nobel Peace Prize, 1970) developed high-yield strains of wheat that made possible dramatic improvements in the food supplies for parts of Asia and Latin America. His work purchased perhaps one to two decades of time in the struggle against the population explosion of these regions. Research is being conducted to develop a hybrid corn that produces an adequate protein.

The sea contains protein-rich fish, and groups in several countries have developed fish meal flour. Plankton, seaweed, and algae are also being investigated. However, Biologist J. H. Ryther (Woods Hole Oceanographic Institution) believes that 90% of the oceans are "biological deserts." The food-producing regions of the oceans are largely confined to the continental shelves already being overfished. Moreover, as oil spills and land fills continue, the nurseries of the ocean's food fish, the estuaries, bays, and rivers, will become sterile (unless people rise up and say "enough!").

synthesis of nonessential amino acids
The body can make some amino acids from molecular parts contributed by carbohydrates, lipids, and the amino acids that it cannot make, the essential amino acids. Pathways for passing the nitrogen of an amino group from amino acid to another molecule exist.

transamination. Transferring an amino group from one molecule to another is called *transamination*. The body contains a family of enzymes called *transaminases* that catalyze the reaction:

$$R-\overset{\overset{O}{\|}}{C}-\overset{\overset{O}{\|}}{C}-OH + R'-\overset{\overset{NH_2}{|}}{CH}-\overset{\overset{O}{\|}}{C}OH \rightleftharpoons R-\underset{\underset{NH_2}{|}}{C}HCOH + R'-\overset{\overset{O}{\|}}{C}-\overset{\overset{O}{\|}}{C}-OH$$

α-Keto acid   α-Amino acid   New α-amino acid   New α-keto acid

Several intermediate steps occur, and vitamin B_6 (pyridoxal) is apparently the essential coenzyme for all the transaminases.

Glutamic acid serves as a common provider of amino groups; most of the nonessential amino acids can be made from it as indicated in Fig. 20.4.

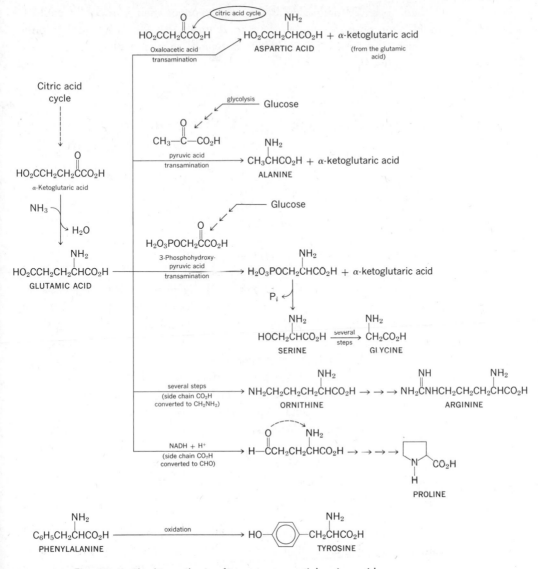

Fig. 20.4 The biosynthesis of some nonessential amino acids.

By a variety of experimental techniques (use of radioactive isotopes as labels; effects of certain diets) we now know that the majority of the amino acids can be converted into glycogen (with excretion of urea). The catabolism of a few amino acids leads to ketone bodies. Since glycogen can be converted into lipids and since amino acids can be made into glycogen (gluconeogenesis), molecular parts can obviously undergo considerable shuffling in the body.

catabolism of amino acids

With over 20 amino acids, the discussion of their catabolism could fill books. Our purpose, however, is to illustrate the general rather than to document the particular. *Oxidative deamination* is one of the pathways of breaking amino acids down:

$$\underset{\substack{| \\ NH_2 \\ \alpha\text{-Amino acid}}}{RCHCO_2H} + NAD^+ + H_2O \xrightarrow[\text{Steps}]{\text{Two}} \underset{\alpha\text{-Keto acid}}{\overset{\overset{\displaystyle O}{\|}}{RCCO_2H}} + NH_3 + NADH + H^+$$

$NH_3 \downarrow$ Urea

$NADH \downarrow \rightarrow (H:^- + H^+)$

NAD^+

Electron transport chain

Figure 20.5 is a general summary of how some of the amino acids fit into the metabolic picture of the citric acid cycle and gluconeogenesis. The major entry points are pyruvic acid and oxaloacetic acid, the second being a key intermediate in gluconeogenesis because it serves as a way station for converting pyruvic acid back to the very high-energy phosphoenolpyruvic acid. Pyruvic acid cannot be converted directly back to this precursor. In the normal functioning of the citric acid cycle, oxaloacetic acid is also an intermediate. A four-carbon "carrier" molecule that picks up an acetyl group to form citric acid, it is later regenerated. Any *extra* oxaloacetic acid that the system may produce, such as from the catabolism of amino acids, is a net gain and may be used to make "new" glucose. That is, gluconeogenesis may occur. As indicated in Fig. 20.5, aspartic acid can be converted to oxaloacetic acid, and valine, proline, and glutamic acid also lead to this intermediate. Several other amino acids can be converted to pyruvic acid, which can also be made into glucose.

Some amino acids lead to acetoacetic acid or acetyl coenzyme A. You must realize, of course, that these are by no means the only reactions of the amino acids. Amino acids are used principally to make or to replace tissue proteins, enzymes, some hormones, and other nitrogenous substances needed for life and health. Gluconeogenesis is important primarily in periods of inadequate diet, fasting, starvation, diabetes, and wasting diseases. It is now clear that if the body is to make "new" glucose, it must sacrifice some of its proteins (as well as some of its fatty acids).

hemoglobin **function and structure.** Hemoglobin is the protein of blood that carries oxygen from the lungs to other parts of the body. It consists of a simple protein portion, *globin,* that is linked to a nonprotein molecule, *heme* (Fig. 20.6).

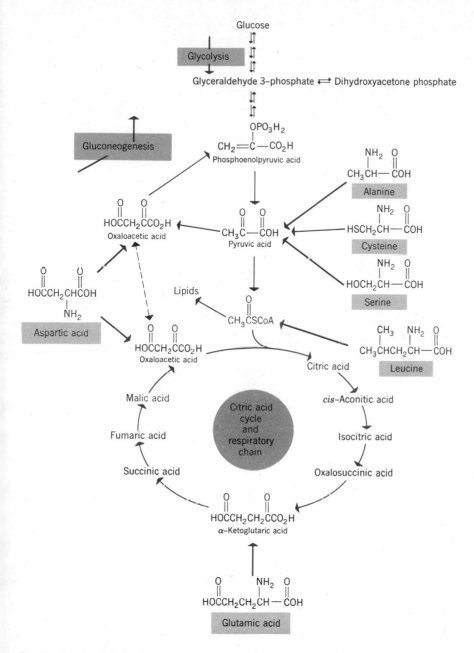

Fig. 20.5 Catabolism of some amino acids, illustrative examples. Several amino acids can enter the gluconeogenesis pathways. A few produce acetyl coenzyme A, and from it lipids, including cholesterol and steroids, can be made.

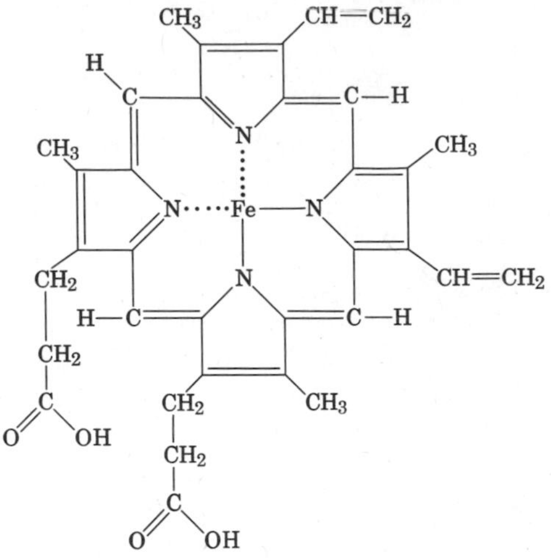

Fig. 20.6 Heme.

It is the heme portion of hemoglobin that is capable of holding molecules of oxygen.

catabolism of heme. Erthrocytes have a life span of only about 120 days. After circulating for that period, they split open. The hemoglobin that spills out is then degraded, and its breakdown products are eliminated through the bile in the feces and, to a slight extent, in the urine. The characteristic colors of bile, feces, and urine are caused by partially degraded heme molecules, the tetrapyrrole pigments or bile pigments.

The degradation of heme begins before the globin portion breaks away. One of the carbon "bridges" is removed, and we then have a linear chain of small rings rather than a large ring:

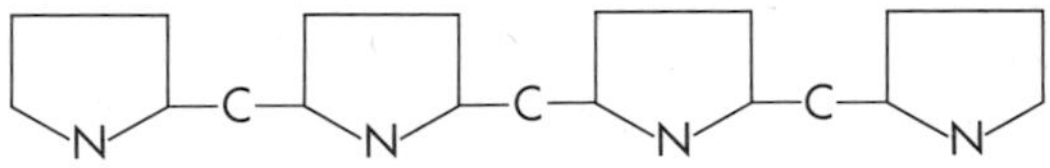

Carbon skeleton of bile pigments

The slightly broken hemoglobin molecule (now called *verdohemoglobin*) then splits into globin, ferrous ion, and the greenish pigment, *biliverdin* (Latin *bilis*, bile + *viridus*, green). Globin enters the nitrogen pool. Iron is conserved by the body in the form of a storage protein, ferritin, and is reused. In human beings biliverdin is converted by enzymes in the liver to a reddish-orange pigment called *bilirubin* (Latin *bilis*, bile + *rubin*, red). Bilirubin is not only made by the liver but is also removed from circulation by the liver, which transfers it to bile. In this fluid it finally enters the intestinal tract.

The pathway from hemoglobin to bilirubin after the rupture of erythrocytes (hemolysis) and the fate of bilirubin is shown in the schematic diagram of Fig. 20.7.

Bilirubin is the principal bile pigment in human beings. Routine flow of bile brings it to the intestinal tract, where bacterial action converts it to a colorless substance, *mesobilirubinogen*. This is further acted on to form "bilinogen," which usually goes by other names signifying differences in destination rather than structure. Bilinogen that leaves the body in the feces is called *stercobilinogen* (Latin, *stercus*, dung). *Urobilinogen* is the same compound, but it exits with the urine. Likewise, "bilin," a reoxidized bilinogen, is properly called stercobilin or urobilin, depending on its destination. Because some bilinogen is reabsorbed from the intestinal tract through the bloodstream, small amounts of it appear in the urine. The characteristic brown color of feces and urine is caused by the presence largely of stercobilin or urobilin.

jaundice. Jaundice (French *jaune*, yellow) is a condition that is symptomatic of malfunction somewhere along the pathway of heme metabolism. If bile pigments accumulate in the plasma in concentrations high enough to impart a yellowish coloration to the skin, the condition of jaundice is said to exist. Jaundice may result from one of three kinds of malfunctions.

hemolytic jaundice. This results when hemolysis takes place at an ab-

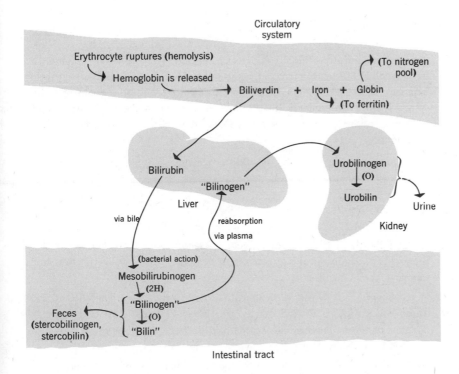

Fig. 20.7   Elimination of hemoglobin-breakdown products.

normally fast rate. Bile pigments, particularly bilirubin, form faster than the liver can clear them.

hepatic diseases. If the liver itself is not able to remove bilirubin, it remains in circulation, and a jaundiced condition ensues. Hepatic diseases such as *infectious hepatitis* and *cirrhosis* may be responsible. The stools are usually clay colored, since the pyrrole pigments do not reach the intestinal tract.

obstruction of bile ducts. Should the ducts that deliver bile to the intestinal tract become obstructed, the tetrapyrrole pigments in bile cannot be eliminated. Under these circumstances, they tend to reenter general circulation. The kidneys remove large amounts of bilirubin, but the stools are usually clay colored. As the liver works harder and harder to handle its task of removing excess bilirubin, it may weaken and become permanently damaged.

interrelations among protein, carbohydrate, and lipid metabolism

The main aspects of the principal metabolic pathways are summarized in Fig. 20.8.

Selected Reading List

Book

1. Paul Ehrlich and Anne Ehrlich. *Population, Resources, Environment.* Freeman, San Francisco, 1970. Woven around basic information from food and agriculture sciences, ecology, and demography are assessments and predictions of a rather gloomy future for mankind. The earth just does not have the resources to support a high standard of living everywhere even if there were no further growth in population.

Articles

1. C. C. Delwiche. "The Nitrogen Cycle." *Scientific American,* September 1970, page 137. Included in this article are a number of informative figures, tables, and charts.
2. A. H. Boerma. "A World Agricultural Plan." *Scientific American,* August 1970, page 54. The plan, worked out by the United Nations Food and Agriculture Organization, is aimed at closing the gap between the population growth and the food supply by 1985.
3. A. M. Altschul. "Food: Proteins for Humans. *Chemical and Engineering News,* November 24, 1969, page 68. (Available in reprint from ACS Publications, 1155

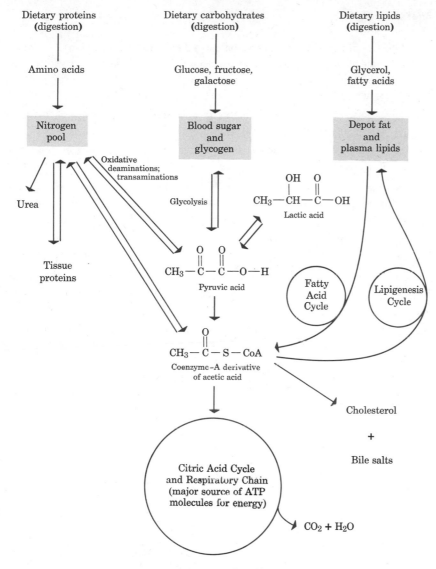

Fig. 20.8   Interrelations of metabolic pathways.

16th St., N. W., Washington, D. C. 20036. 50¢.) A discussion of meeting the world's needs for adequate protein.

4. L. R. Brown. "Human Food Production as a Process in the Biosphere." *Scientific American*, September 1970, page 161. Soil is a limited and nonrenewable resource. Brown discusses how we use it and waste it as we struggle to feed our growing population.

5. H. Brown. "Human Materials Production as Process in the Biosphere." *Scientific America*. September 1970, page 195. Basic materials such as metals and many nonmetals must be cycled or they will, through use, be so scattered as to be unrecoverable. Harrison Brown discusses this problem.

Brief Summary

1. In the flux of nitrogen nuclei between air and earth and back again—the nitrogen cycle—elemental nitrogen is fixed by electrical storms, by man (in the fertilizer industry), and by soil microorganisms sometimes together with certain plants. Atmospheric nitrogen may enter the soil as ammonia, nitrate ion, or nitrite ion.

2. Plants use soil ammonia and minerals to make amino acids, and higher animals get their amino acids from plants.

3. Soil bacteria can oxidize ammonia (nitrification) and reduce nitrates and nitrites (denitrification).

4. The digestion of proteins in animals produces amino acids that enter a general "nitrogen pool," a word symbol that represents all amino acids and other small nitrogenous molecules wherever they are found in the body in whatever fluids.

5. Tissue proteins are in a dynamic state as they undergo a constant turnover of the amino acids that comprise them.

6. The nitrogen balance of an organism is maintained by regulation of all reactions that eliminate nitrogen to match the nitrogen intake. The principal end-products of protein catabolism are urea, water, and carbon dioxide.

7. Through transaminations, an organism can synthesize some of its required amino acids. Those that it cannot make, the nutritionally essential amino acids, it must obtain in its diet.

8. Intermediate products of amino acid catabolism may enter pathways leading to lipid or glycogen synthesis.

9. The catabolism of hemoglobin presents partly degraded heme molecules, in the form of biliverdin, to the liver for clearance from the body. The iron of heme is reused. Globin, the wholly protein part of hemoglobin enters the nitrogen pool.

Problems and Exercises

1. Discuss ways in which the nitrogen cycle would be disrupted, and the implications for man of such an event, if we managed to distribute some synthetic chemical that killed or seriously interfered with soil microorganisms.

2. The nitrogen cycle cannot stand alone. Everything in nature is connected to everything else. Where and how does the nitrogen cycle "connect" with the oxygen-carbon cycle?

3. Why is it important for nutritionists to have methods for analyzing proteins for their amino acid content?

4. In one food fad diet, the only source of protein is gelatin. How is this diet dangerous?

the metabolism of proteins

5. One of the principal amino acids the body uses to make hemoglobin is glycine. Why is it not on the list of essential amino acids? (That is, what determines membership on the list?)

6. What amino acid would be necessary to yield pyruvic acid through a transamination? Where does pyruvic acid fit into carbohydrate metabolism? Is it possible for the body to use the amino acid precursor of pyruvic acid to make glycogen? Fatty acids? ATP?

7. If aspartic acid suffered loss of its amino group through a transamination, would the molecule left behind (write its structure) be able to enter the citric acid cycle?

8. Discuss the significance of a jaundiced condition from a diagnostic viewpoint.

9. Define each of the following terms:
   (a) nitrogen cycle
   (b) nitrification
   (c) nitrogen fixation
   (d) denitrification
   (e) nitrogen pool
   (f) essential amino acid
   (g) adequate protein
   (h) kwashiorkor
   (i) heme
   (j) verdohemoglobin
   (k) biliverdin
   (l) bilirubin
   (m) ferritin
   (n) "bilinogen" and its relation to stercobilinogen and urobilinogin
   (o) "bilin" and its relation to stercobilin and urobilin
   (p) jaundice
   (q) hemolysis

chapter 21 the chemistry of heredity

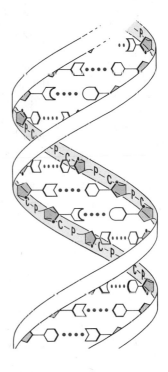

A healthy, living organism requires energy, building materials, and information. Our sources of energy are principally carbohydrates, lipids and oxygen, but if we push it back far enough we know that the energy stored in the foods came to us from the sun. For building materials we rely principally on proteins, but both carbohydrates and lipids are important, too. Plants need carbohydrates to make cell walls. Lipids are found incorporated into membranes of many types of cells. In few places do we see the remarkable unity of all living things more clearly than in the fact that from the lowest to the highest forms of life the same molecules, with some exceptions and many variations, provide energy and building materials. From the cowbird to the cow; from an amoeba to an aardvaark; from a hippo to a human, roughly twenty to twenty-six amino acids, a handful of fatty acids, glycerol, glucose, and phosphates dominate the molecules of life. If we are to understand how living things can be different while they share so many features in common we must turn to the molecular basis of information.

Among the higher animals the physical links between one generation and the next are the sperm cell of a male organism and the egg cell of the female of the species. When these two cells unite, a series of chemical events is initiated. If a baby animal is to have fur rather than feathers, at its conception a sequence of chemical reactions is triggered that will lead to the production of fur proteins rather than feather proteins. Radically different pathways are taken by different species in spite of the fact that they often eat the same or similar foods.

We have learned that nearly every reaction that occurs in a living organism requires special enzymes. These act uniquely on the fairly common molecules—glucose, fatty acids and glycerol, and amino acids, for example. Each species possesses its own peculiar set of enzymes. Fur-bearing animals have enzyme systems that catalyze the ordering of amino acid sequences resulting in that peculiar substance we call fur. Feathered creatures have different enzyme systems. Drawing on somewhat the same amino acids as furry animals do, their enzymes generate distinctively different amino acid sequences that become feathers. Whatever the genetic message may be, such as a "command" to develop as a camel and not as a goose, it seems likely that the message concerns the development of distinctive enzyme systems. It is therefore reasonable to insist that any theory concerning the chemical basis of heredity should explain how a species acquires and reproduces its special set of enzymes. Before studying such a theory, it would be well to review certain features of the physical basis of heredity.

In a typical animal, union of a sperm cell from the male with an egg cell from the female produces a new cell called a *zygote*. This cell proceeds to multiply. In a change called *mitosis* the nucleus of the cell divides and then the cell divides. The new cells divide, in turn, and an embryo gradually takes form. Early in this stage of the development, two fundamentally different kinds of cells can be distinguished: *germ cells*, which will give rise either to sperm or eggs, and *somatic cells,* from which will form all the myriad tissues and organs unique to the body of the species. The germ cells are cells set apart, protected from change and unaffected by the tremendous variations taking place among the somatic cells. When the somatic cells have proceeded in their development enough so that the gonads are fully elaborated and sexual maturity is reached, the germ cells become active. They develop sperm or eggs, depending on the sex of the individual. If the sperm and the egg of the parents contained the essentials to produce a unique enzyme system, then the germ cells of the children must possess these essentials too in order that they, in turn, may pass them to the next generation.

chromosomes and genes. The cell is the structural unit of life, and chemicals associated with living things are, by and large, organized in these units. All the material comprising the cell is called the *protoplasm*. Discrete "bodies" exist in the protoplasm, the most important of which is the cell nucleus (see Fig. 21.1). The cell nucleus contains a fluid in which twisted and intertwined filaments called *chromonemata* exist. These chromonemata apparently bear strings of the basic units of heredity, the *genes*. Chromonemata and their gene strings constitute individual *chromosomes*.

In the preliminary stages of mitosis, the chromonemata and the genes produce exact duplicates of themselves. The final cell division, then, separates duplicated chromonemata and gene strings into the individual nuclei of two new daughter cells. The division of one parent cell involves one duplication of each gene. Reproductive duplication is called *replication*. Figure 21.2 illustrates the chief stages in cell division.

If the genes furnished by the two parents for the zygote replicate in the development of germ cells in the offspring, then there is a basis for understanding how the units of heredity can be transmitted faithfully from one generation to the next.

The genes carry the heredity instructions, the genetic message. The message must be characteristic of the species; it must pass faithfully from generation to generation; yet it must be capable of evolutionary change. To understand how genes handle this assignment, scientists long ago turned to examining the chemistry of genes.

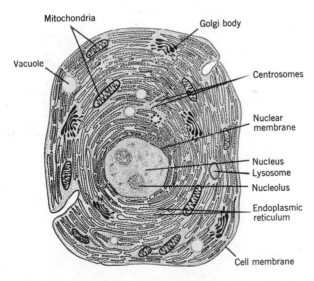

Fig. 21.1 A generalized animal cell. Cells vary greatly from tissue to tissue, but most have the common features shown here. In this chapter, we are most concerned with the nucleus and ribosome-studded endoplasmic reticulum. (From "The Living Cell" by Jean Brachet. Copyright © 1961 by Scientific American, Inc. All rights reserved.)

487
physical basis of heredity

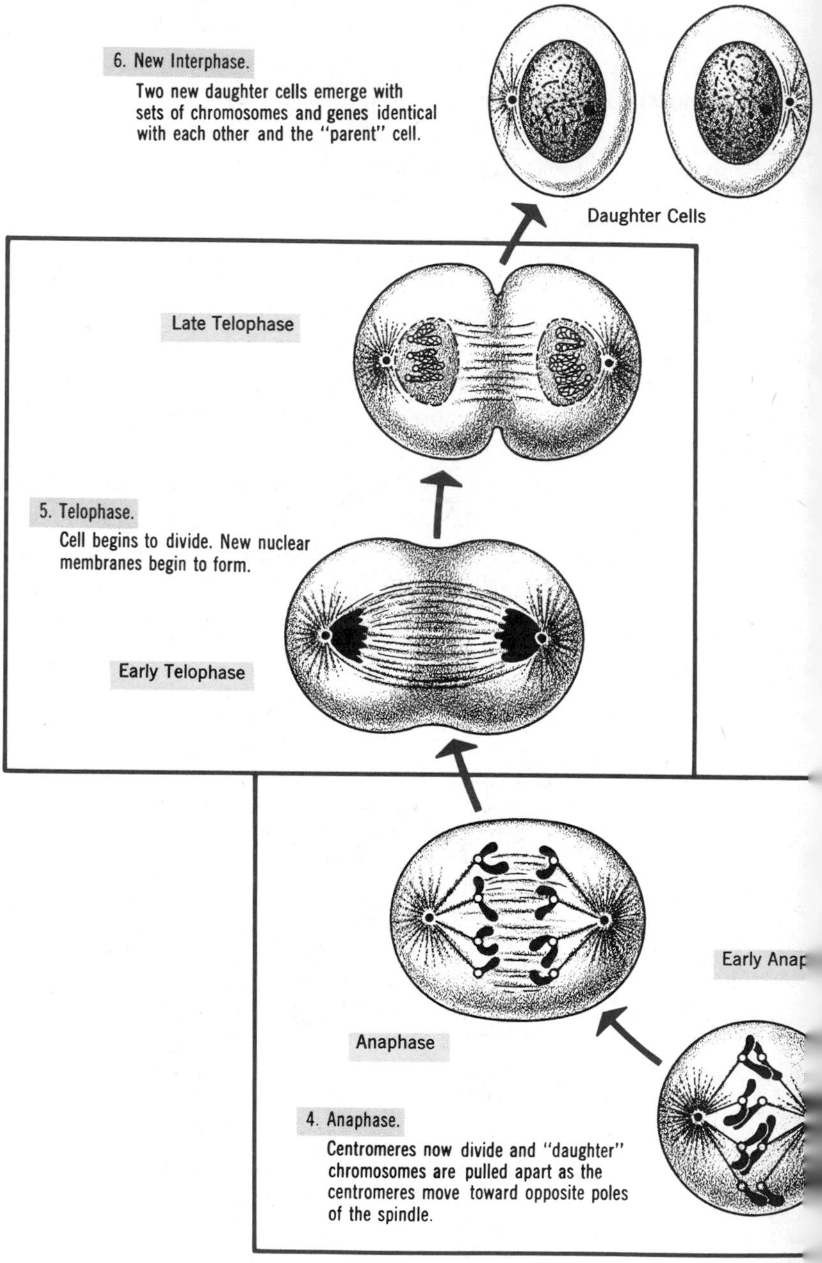

6. New Interphase.

Two new daughter cells emerge with
sets of chromosomes and genes identical
with each other and the "parent" cell.

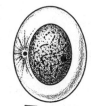

Daughter Cells

Late Telophase

5. Telophase.

Cell begins to divide. New nuclear
membranes begin to form.

Early Telophase

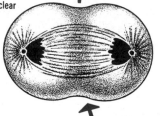

Early Anap

Anaphase

4. Anaphase.

Centromeres now divide and "daughter"
chromosomes are pulled apart as the
centromeres move toward opposite poles
of the spindle.

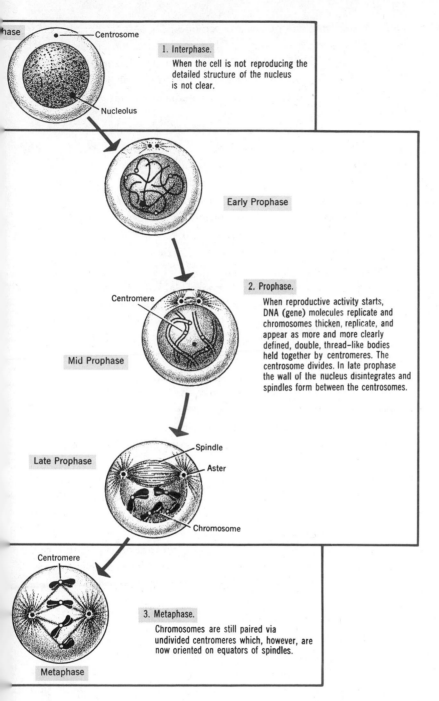

1. Interphase.

When the cell is not reproducing the detailed structure of the nucleus is not clear.

Centrosome

Nucleolus

Early Prophase

2. Prophase.

When reproductive activity starts, DNA (gene) molecules replicate and chromosomes thicken, replicate, and appear as more and more clearly defined, double, thread–like bodies held together by centromeres. The centrosome divides. In late prophase the wall of the nucleus disintegrates and spindles form between the centrosomes.

Centromere

Mid Prophase

Late Prophase

Spindle

Aster

Chromosome

Centromere

3. Metaphase.

Chromosomes are still paired via undivided centromeres which, however, are now oriented on equators of spindles.

Metaphase

Fig. 21.2   Mitosis. This sequence applies to animal cells. Plant cells show a different mitotic sequence, especially in the telophase. (Cell structures from: E. J. Gardner, *Principles of Genetics*, third edition, page 28. John Wiley & Sons, New York, 1968. Used by permission.)

It has long been known that cell nuclei are rich in a polymeric material known as deoxyribonucleic acid, abbreviated DNA. *DNA constitutes the actual chemical of genes.* In 1953, F. H. C. Crick and J. D. Watson proposed a structure for DNA that correlated its chemical and physical properties as a chemical with its apparent properties as the chemical of genes. Let us see what DNA is.

nucleic acids. Deoxyribonucleic acid, DNA, is a member of a family of polymers called *nucleic acids.* Their monomer units are called *nucleotides,* and, unlike the monomers of other polymers we have studied, the nucleotides can be hydrolyzed. As illustrated in Fig. 21.3, the hydrolysis of a mixture of nucleotides produces three kinds of products—inorganic phosphate, a pentose sugar, and a group of heterocyclic amines.

Four important heterocyclic amines are obtainable from nucleic acids: adenine, guanine, cytosine, and thymine (Fig. 21.3). Two pentoses are produced: ribose and deoxyribose ("de-" means "lacking;" "deoxy-" means "lacking in an oxygen atom found in a close structural relative"). Nucleic acids are either based on ribose, in which case they are called *ribonucleic acids,* abbreviated RNA, or on deoxyribose, in which case they are called *deoxyribonucleic acids,* DNA.

In Fig. 21.4, there is shown the assembly of a typical nucleotide monomer from phosphoric acid, a sugar, and an amine. The nucleotides of RNA are built from ribose; those of DNA, from deoxyribose.

How various monomer units—nucleotides—are assembled into nucleic acids is illustrated by Fig. 21.5. Like the formation of nucleotides, the formation of nucleic acids involves nothing more than the splitting out of water. The phosphoric acid unit on one nucleotide splits out water with an alcohol unit of the next nucleotide to form a phosphate ester linkage or bridge between the two nucleotides. The process is repeated until hundreds of nucleotide units are incorporated into the polymer.

The "backbone" of a nucleic acid consists of alternating phosphate and pentose units. Projecting from this backbone are various heterocyclic amines. When this is recognized, it is possible to condense the structure of a nucleic acid, as illustrated in Fig. 21.6. The distinctness of any one nucleic acid (e.g., any one gene) lies in the order in which the nucleotide units are assembled and which ones are selected.

Nature was not capricious in her selection of the heterocyclic compounds that project from the backbone of a nucleic acid. Their functional groups and geometries are such that they fit together in pairs by means of hydrogen bonds. Analysis of DNA, for example, reveals that adenine and thymine are present in a ratio of 1:1. This ratio suggests that the two somehow may be "paired" in DNA. When models of these compounds are examined, it is seen that they have functional groups situated in precisely the proper locations to make hydrogen bonding between them possible. They "fit" together quite nicely, as illustrated in Fig. 21.7.

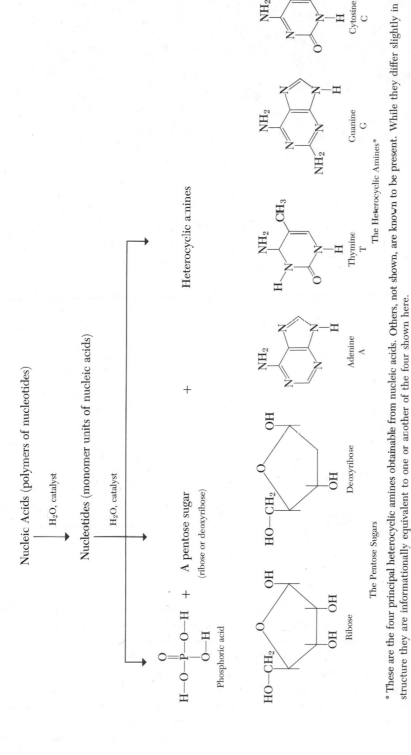

Nucleic Acids (polymers of nucleotides)

H_2O, catalyst

Nucleotides (monomer units of nucleic acids)

H_2O, catalyst

Phosphoric acid

$+$ A pentose sugar
(ribose or deoxyribose)

$+$ Heterocyclic amines

Ribose

Deoxyribose

The Pentose Sugars

Adenine
A

Thymine
T

Guanine
G

Cytosine
C

The Heterocyclic Amines*

* These are the four principal heterocyclic amines obtainable from nucleic acids. Others, not shown, are known to be present. While they differ slightly in structure they are informationally equivalent to one or another of the four shown here.

Fig. 21.3   Hydrolysis products of nucleic acids.

491

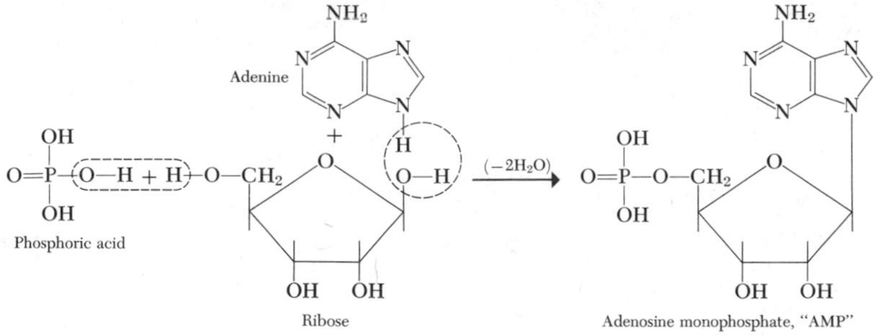

Fig. 21.4 A typical nucleotide.

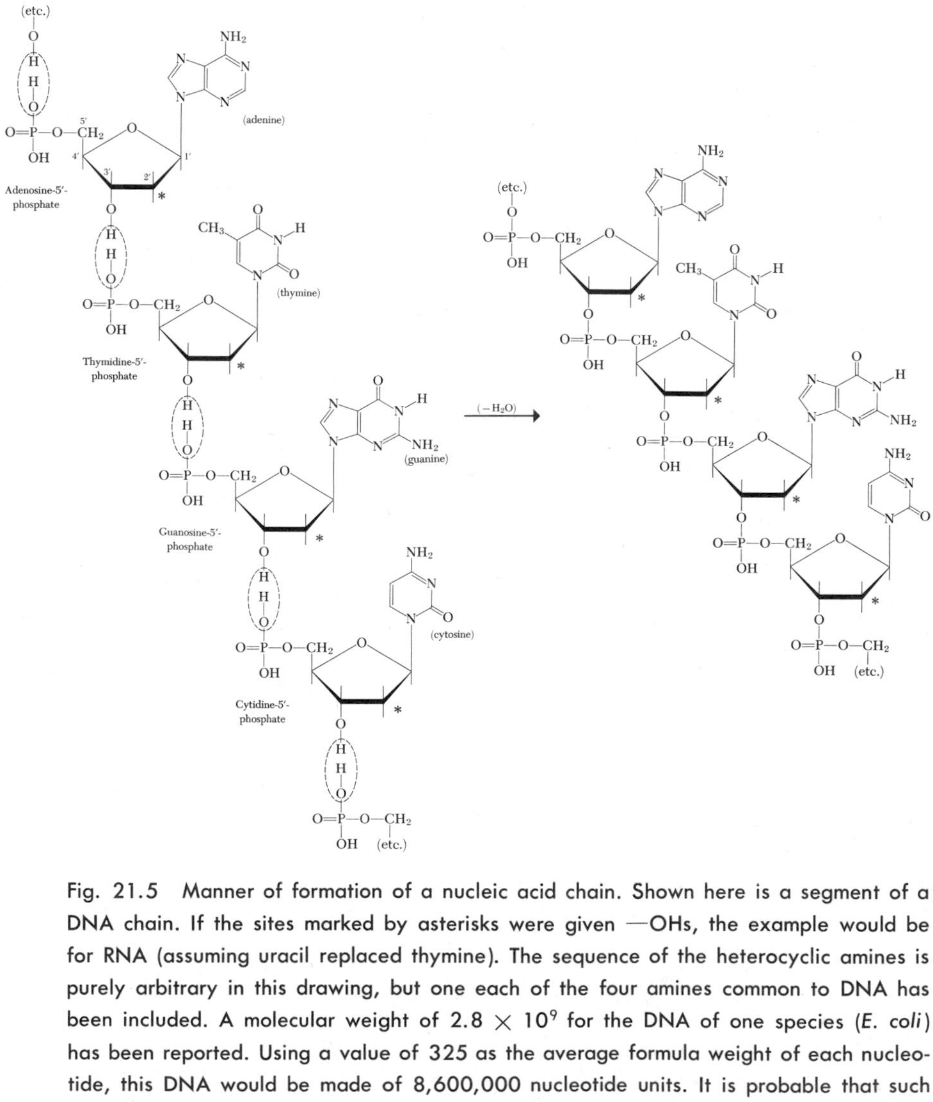

Fig. 21.5 Manner of formation of a nucleic acid chain. Shown here is a segment of a DNA chain. If the sites marked by asterisks were given —OHs, the example would be for RNA (assuming uracil replaced thymine). The sequence of the heterocyclic amines is purely arbitrary in this drawing, but one each of the four amines common to DNA has been included. A molecular weight of 2.8×10^9 for the DNA of one species (*E. coli*) has been reported. Using a value of 325 as the average formula weight of each nucleotide, this DNA would be made of 8,600,000 nucleotide units. It is probable that such a DNA molecule would make up a collection of genes rather than just one. Genetic studies indicate that the average gene size is 1500 nucleotide pairs (of a double helix).

the chemistry of heredity

```
etc.
 |
 O        Amine
 ‖         |
O=P—O—pentose
 |         |
 OH        O       Amine'
           |         |
        O=P—O—pentose
           |         |
          OH         O       Amine"
                     |         |
                  O=P—O—pentose
                     |         |
                    OH         O
                               |
                              etc.
```

or

= pentose

—⟨ = amines

P = phosphate

Fig. 21.6   Condensed structural representations of nucleic acids.

Crick-Watson theory. The "pairing" of heterocyclic units in DNA preparations, plus extensive study of X-ray data obtained from DNA, led Crick and Watson to propose that the DNA chain is coiled. Furthermore, they proposed that two coiled chains intertwine to form a double helix. In this *double-helix theory* of Crick and Watson, the two strands intertwine in such a way that a thymine unit of one chain fits, via hydrogen bonding, with an adenine unit exactly opposite it on the second chain. Likewise, guanine of one chain pairs, via hydrogen bonds, with cytosine of the second chain. Thus it is that one of nature's weakest recognizable bonds, the hydrogen bond, provides the structural stability to one of nature's most important kinds of chemicals, the DNA double helix, the chemical of genes.

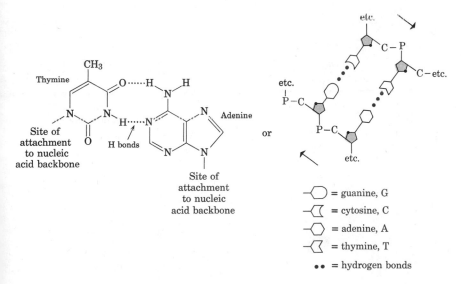

= guanine, G

= cytosine, C

= adenine, A

= thymine, T

•• = hydrogen bonds

Fig. 21.7   Suggested pairing of thymine with adenine units and of guanine with cytosine units of two different DNA chains.

The DNA double helix is represented in Fig. 21.8, which shows it standing on end. It is reminiscent of a spiral staircase, in which the steps are the paired heterocyclic amines projecting toward each other from the backbones. These relationships and analogies are a little clearer in the schematic representation of Fig. 21.9 of the DNA double helix. Another feature of the DNA double

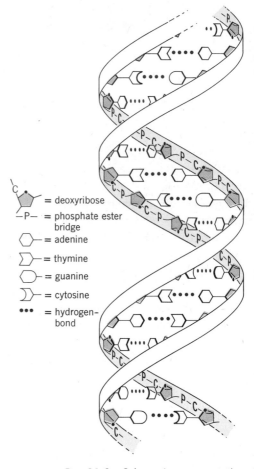

= deoxyribose

−P− = phosphate ester bridge

= adenine

= thymine

= guanine

= cytosine

••• = hydrogen–bond

Fig. 21.9 Schematic representation of a DNA double helix.

Fig. 21.8 Scale model of a DNA double helix. (Nova Research Group, Davis, California.)

helix, shown in Figs. 21.7 and 21.9 and amplified in Fig. 21.10, is that the backbones of the two strands run in opposite directions.

In spite of about two decades of the most intensive research, the question of how genes are replicated is still (1971) incompletely solved and remains one of the most important questions in molecular biology. Many facts about DNA replication are known. It occurs by a *semiconservative* process (Fig. 21.11), which means that each of the two, new "daughter" double helices has one of the original strands intact and entwined with a newly made, complimentary strand. It is also known that replication is extraordinarily accurate and that the accuracy depends partly on the replicating enzymes but mostly on the opportunities for "fitting" of adenine to thymine or of guanine to cytosine. The replicating enzymes, however, have not been fully characterized and the questions of how they work and how they are regulated are not yet resolved.

There is some evidence that a group of enzymes participates in replication and that these enzymes coexist as an easily destroyed complex, possibly as part of a structural unit in the cell. If true, efforts to study individual enzymes may be stymied if enzymic activity depends on the intact complex and cannot

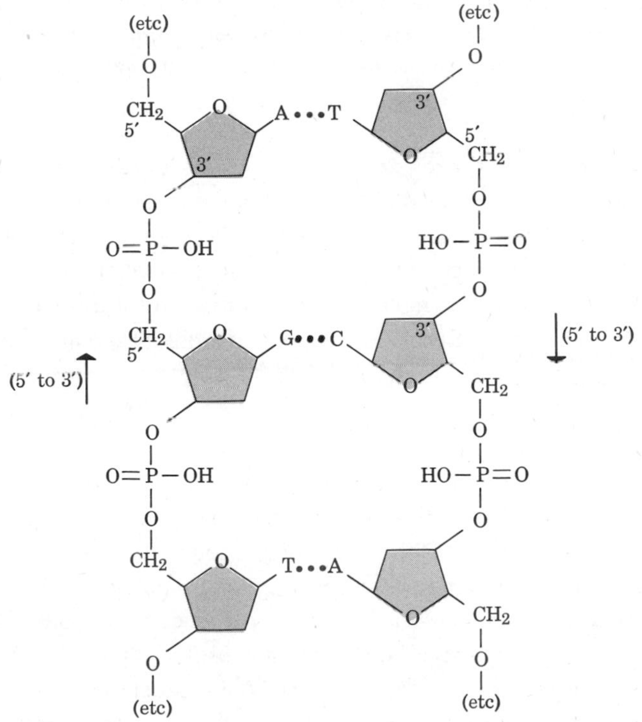

Fig. 21.10 The strands of a DNA double helix are aligned in opposite directions. (A = adenine; T = thymine; G = quanine; C = cytosine.)

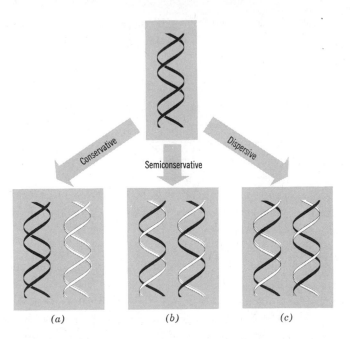

Fig. 21.11   Three possible outcomes of replication. (a) In the conservative mode both the identities and the pairing of the two parent strands would be conserved. (b) In the semiconservative mode, the mechanism that actually operates, the identities of the parent strands are preserved but they are no longer paired. Each is entwined with a new, complementary strand. (c) In the dispersive mode the parent strands would be broken up into pieces and these would be incorporated somewhat at random in the new double helices.

exist if the complex is broken up. In view of the uncertainties over details of DNA replication we shall do no more here than study a general picture that accounts for the accuracy of the event and its semiconservative character. Figure 21.12 illustrates how these features of replication come about. According to the theory shown in Fig. 21.12 the two strands of the parent double helix are forced apart as the new strands are built. Figure 21.13 is a better illustration of this aspect of the theory.

embryonic development and RNA

DNA molecules as bearers of the genetic code.   Since an individual gene is a hereditary unit, a DNA molecule somehow must be "coded" for a specific genetic message. Since all DNA molecules appear to have the same phosphate-deoxyribose backbone, differences between individual DNA molecules (*genes*) rest on the *order* in which the heterocyclic amines are strung along that backbone. *It is this order of amines that constitutes the code of the genetic message a given gene bears.* We now ask, "What exactly is this code?" Genes are chemicals, not telegraph operators. How is the code translated into genetic control of biochemical processes in cells?

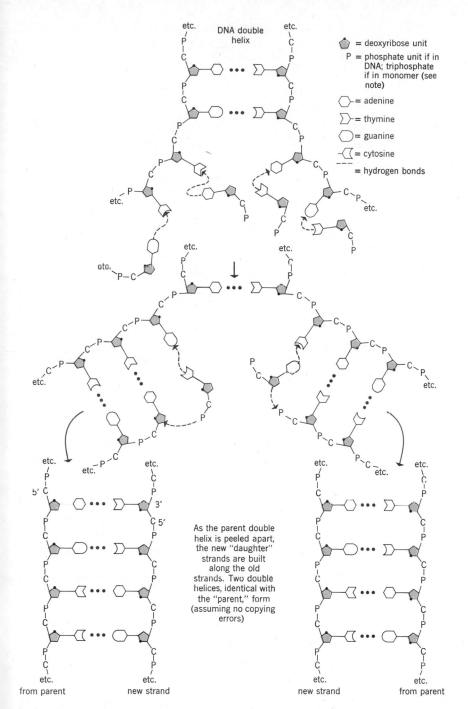

Fig. 21.12 The replication of DNA. Note: There is some question about the nature of the monomer unit, whether it is a triphosphate ester or not. It may well be a specially activated monophosphate. (*Nature*, Sept. 17, 1971, page 163.)

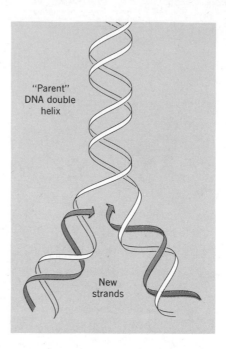

Fig. 21.13 In one theory of DNA replication, as the new DNA strands are built the old strand is forced to separate.

transfer of the genetic code to RNA molecules. We saw earlier in this chapter how the code, whatever it specifically is, is transmitted from one generation to the next through DNA replication. The use of the genetic code to direct other events is understood in terms of a similar process. DNA molecules in cell nuclei of somatic tissues serve as "molds," or "templates," for the synthesis of RNA molecules. These, in turn, help to control the synthesis of specific polypeptides which will serve as enzymes. Of the two DNA molecules intertwined in a double helix only one of them is coded for making enzymes. Our next task is to see the connection between DNA and enzymes.

DNA and the synthesis of enzymes. The general scheme connecting DNA to polypeptides (enzymes, usually) is outlined in Fig. 21.14. In the rest of this section, we shall discuss it in more detail. The immediate task of chromosomal DNA is to participate in and to determine the nucleotide sequence of RNA.

Three types of RNA are known, and we must first distinguish among them. All three types are synthesized under the control of DNA. (A fourth type of RNA associated with virus particles is also known.) For the discovery of an enzyme, *RNA polymerase*, which made possible the *in vitro* synthesis of RNA, Severo Ochoa (N.Y.U.) shared the 1959 Nobel Prize in physiology and medicine with Arthur Kornberg (then at Washington University). At least two

the chemistry of heredity

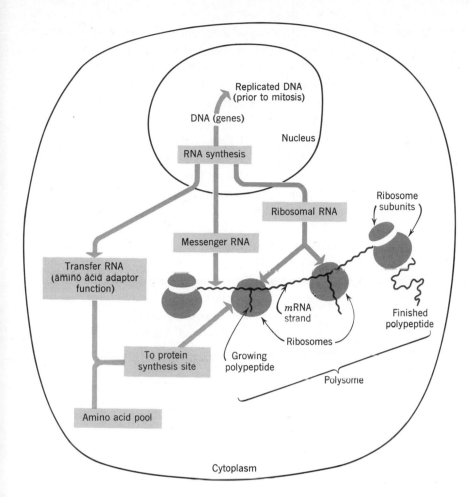

Fig. 21.14 The relations of DNA to various RNAs and protein synthesis.

RNA polymerases (possibly three) are now known to exist in a wide range of both animal and plant cell nuclei.

ribosomal RNA (rRNA). The main structural framework of a cell in any higher organism is the *endoplasmic reticulum,* a series of canaliculi and cisternae that interconnect and that permeate most of the cytoplasm. See Fig. 21.1. Studding portions of the endoplasmic reticulum are granules that might vary from 70 to 200 Å in diameter. Called ribosomes, they are sometimes found free in the cytoplasm. They are made of RNA and protein, about 50% of each, and they contain most of the RNA in the cell. Subunits of ribosomes, as indicated in Fig. 21.14, go together to form a complex with messenger RNA, the second type of RNA we shall study. Ribosomes are the sites of protein synthesis, and yet the RNA in a ribosome does not itself appear to direct this work. Messenger RNA does this. When we go into the details of polypeptide synthesis later, we shall learn that ribosomal RNA helps to stabilize a temporary union between messenger RNA and the third type we shall study, transfer RNA. It is known that ribosomes from a common source are alike. Therefore, they must serve some function that is common to the synthesis of all the proteins (enzymes) made by that source.

messenger RNA (*mRNA*). Messenger RNA molecules vary considerably in length, and they account for about 5 to 10% of the total RNA in a cell. They are not very stable and are remade as needed. As we shall see, *mRNA* molecules also bear the genetic code because they are synthesized under the direct supervision of DNA. A very general picture of how this is brought about is given in Fig. 21.15. Once made, *mRNAs* move out of the nucleus into the cytoplasm where they hook ribosomes to themselves at intervals along their chains. Such an assembly of many ribosomes along an *mRNA* chain is called a *polysome* (poly-ribosome). A molecule of *mRNA* can dissociate from ribosomes and ribosomes can associate with different *mRNA* molecules of different molecular weight. There is evidence that a ribosome moves along an *mRNA* chain while the synthesis of a polypeptide, directed by the *mRNA*, takes place. We shall return to this later. Protein synthesis requires, of course, that amino acids be brought to the *mRNA* site in the order in which they are to appear in the final polypeptide. For this task, the cell uses the third type of RNA.

transfer RNA (*tRNA*). There are believed to be at least twenty different species of *tRNA* molecules, one for each of the some twenty amino acids. The function of *tRNA* is to attach to itself the particular amino acid for which it is coded, carry it to a protein-synthesis site on a polysome (specifically, an *mRNA* site in contact with a ribosome) and there give it up to the growing end of a polypeptide chain at just that moment called for by the genetic code.

Transfer RNA molecules are the smallest of the RNAs. The first ones to be characterized had from 70 to 80 nucleotide units. Being small, *tRNAs* are more soluble and more mobile in the cytoplasmic fluid. (Until recently they were commonly called soluble-RNA or sRNA). They contain some nucleotides not common to the other nucleic acids, and their molecules are folded and partly coiled in a manner illustrated in Fig. 21.16. Each *tRNA* has an amino acid binding site and an *mRNA* coding site called an anticodon, also indicated in Fig. 21.16.

codons. It is obviously impossible to translate directly from a four letter alphabet (the four nucleotides) to a twenty letter alphabet (the amino acids). There are not enough "letters" in the one to match on a one-to-one basis

the chemistry of heredity

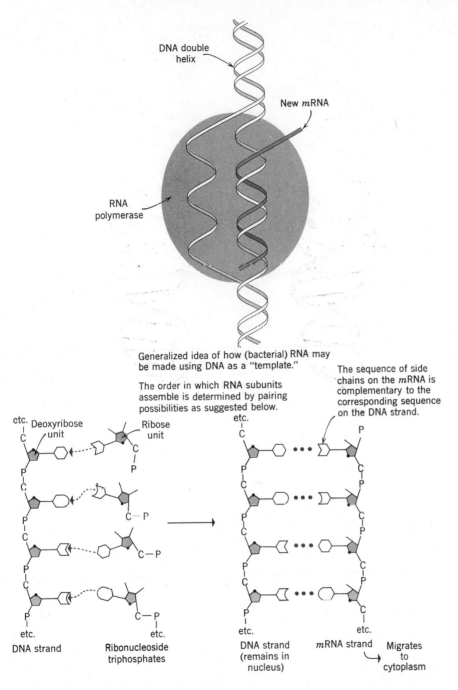

DNA double helix

New mRNA

RNA polymerase

Generalized idea of how (bacterial) RNA may be made using DNA as a "template."

The order in which RNA subunits assemble is determined by pairing possibilities as suggested below.

The sequence of side chains on the mRNA is complementary to the corresponding sequence on the DNA strand.

etc.
Deoxyribose unit
Ribose unit

etc.

DNA strand

Ribonucleoside triphosphates

DNA strand (remains in nucleus)

mRNA strand

Migrates to cytoplasm

Fig. 21.15 One theory of the transmission of the genetic code from DNA to mRNA in cell nuclei. The ribonucleotide "pool" consists of the triphosphate forms of the nucleotides. The symbols are the same as those in Fig. 21.9, except that in RNA uracil replaces thymine (▷—). Although structurally different, uracil and thymine are informationally equivalent. The newly made mRNA strand carries the genetic message of the gene to the protein synthesis site in the cytoplasm.

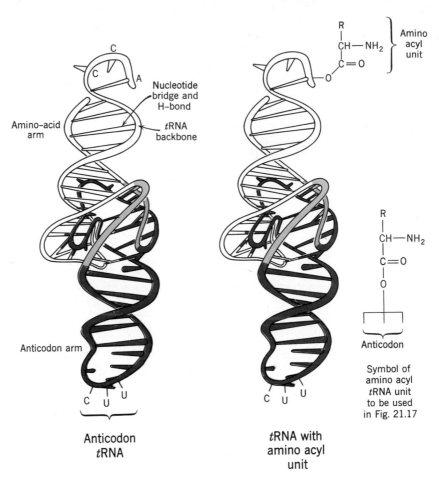

Fig. 21.16 A model of a *t*RNA molecule proposed by M. Levitt (Cambridge, England). The upper end is the amino acid acceptor site; the lower end is the anticodon arm. At the bottom of that arm are three nucleotides that can "recognize" the corresponding codon on an *m*RNA strand at a polysome. (Redrawn from *Nature*, Vol. 224, page 760; Nov. 22, 1969. Used by permission.)

with the "letters" of the other. But if the four letters of the smaller alphabet are used in varying groups of at least three, then there is possible at least one unique group of three nucleotide "letters" to code for each amino acid. Three-letter "words," i.e., groups of three nucleotides, are the fundamental amino acid message units. Wherever such a triad occurs in a messenger RNA molecule we call it a *codon*. The set of three nucleotides complementary to a codon, when found on a DNA strand, is called an *anti-codon*. Suppose, for example, that there is an anti-codon sequence of cytosine-thymine-thymine on a gene. Transcription of this into *m*RNA would give a sequence of guanine-adenine-adenine, or GAA. The GAA sequence of the *mRNA* is the codon.

$$\text{Anti-codon} \left\{ \begin{array}{l} \text{—C} \\ \text{—T} \\ \text{—T} \end{array} \right. \xrightarrow[\text{(mRNA synthesis)}]{\text{Transcription}} \left. \begin{array}{l} \text{G—} \\ \text{A—} \\ \text{A—} \end{array} \right\} \text{Codon}$$

Section of
DNA strand

Sequence of bases in
mRNA determined by
complementary sequence
on DNA

polypeptide synthesis. the one-gene–one-enzyme relation. An outline of the relation between a gene and a polypeptide was given in Fig. 21.14. The new polypeptide, whose amino acid sequence is determined by a gene, may be an apoenzyme or one of a group of small proteins that make up a multipolypeptide group which is, as a whole cluster, one enzyme. The idea of a one-gene–one-enzyme relation was first advanced (with convincing evidence) in 1941, well before the Crick-Watson theory, and it earned for its proponents—George Beadle and Edward Tatum—shares in the 1958 Nobel Prize in physiology and medicine.

The theory that enzyme synthesis depends on a special messenger RNA was advanced in 1961 by F. Jacob and J. Monod of France (Nobel Prizes, 1965). In connection with Fig. 21.15 we have seen a plausible description of how a nucleotide sequence on DNA might insure a complementary sequence on *mRNA*. We shall next inquire into the way *mRNA*, ribosomes, and *tRNA* translate a nucleotide sequence into an amino acid sequence.

The first stage of polypeptide synthesis, following the synthesis of the appropriate *mRNA* molecule, is the union of the amino acids to their particular *tRNAs*. Activating enzymes are needed as well as a source of energy (ATP). The following steps are believed to occur.

1. Activating enzyme + amino acid + ATP $\longrightarrow$
   activating enzyme-amino acyl~AMP + diphosphate ion

2. The amino acyl group is transferred to a specific *tRNA* molecule (the same enzyme serves):

Activating enzyme–amino acyl~AMP + *tRNA* $\longrightarrow$

aminoacyl~tRNA +   AMP   + activating enzyme

Will migrate	To be "recharged"	To be
to mRNA to	to ATP *via* the	reused
incorporate the	respiratory	
amino acid into	chain	
a polypeptide		

(An amino acyl group would be of the form: $R-\underset{\underset{NH_2}{|}}{CH}-\overset{\overset{O}{\|}}{C}-$, and AMP is adenosine monophosphate.)

To get the right amino acid attached to the right *t*RNA molecule, the activating enzyme is crucial. It has to be able to bind not only to just one specific amino acid but it must also be able to bind to the *t*RNA "adapter" molecule. Thus, some twenty specific enzymes (polypeptides) are needed, but it is not hard to imagine this number each with secondary and tertiary structural features that can "recognize," on the one hand, an amino acid and, on the other hand, at some other part of the enzyme, a *t*RNA molecule. The "lock-and-key" theory of enzyme action that we have studied serves well here.

In the *t*RNA portion of the aminoacyl-*t*RNA complex, we have the recognition site for a codon on an *m*RNA molecule. This recognition site would also have to be a sequence of three bases, and if the codon were GAA the recognition site would have to have the complementary sequence, CUU, (not CTT: U replaces T in RNA).

The next stage is the assembling of the polypeptide. The rest of the description of polypeptide synthesis involves such an intertwining of text and figure that all of it is in Fig. 21.17 to which you should next go.

enzyme induction and repression. The discussion incorporated into Fig. 21.17 left at least one major question unanswered. What switches enzyme synthesis on or off? Each cell nucleus in each kind of tissue presumably carries the entire set of genes originally present in the first fertilized cell of the organism. Obviously not all of the genes in the cells of a particular tissue can be active. Most of the genes in, say, a muscle cell must be switched off. A muscle cell does not need all the same enzymes as, say, a pancreas cell does. The question, again, is what keeps some genes switched off? And how are other genes turned on? As these questions concern higher organisms and man we know very little. There is some evidence that one or a few steroid hormones are gene activators. The liver, the organ that gets the first "look" at any new influx of nutrients (or poisons) from the digestive tract, has several known enzymes that can be induced into activity (or repressed) by certain chemicals, including both steroid hormones and protein hormones (e.g., insulin). Barbiturates are powerful inducers of certain liver enzymes, those that handle oxidations of drugs and poisons preparatory to their excretion. Chlorinated hydrocarbon insecticides such as DDT and dieldrin will induce these enzymes also, but in birds the activated enzymes attack some of the bird's sex hormones faster than the poisons and the bird's hormonal balance is upset. The result is poorer success in breeding.

A great deal is known about enzyme induction and repression in some of the planet's lowest forms of life which have served very long and well in research into the biochemical secrets of all of life's forms. The bacterium, *Escherichia coli,* a one-celled organism of the coliform group commonly found in the intestinal tract of man, is probably the most studied and the best understood organism in nature. It has no membrane around any well-defined nucleus.[1] Its only membrane is its cell wall. It has one large chromosome. Our best insights into enzyme repression and induction have come, thus far, from studies on *E. coli.* What will now follow will be a brief discussion of how one enzyme in this organism is controlled. The control is through control over the *synthesis* of this enzyme, a synthesis that cannot take place as long as the gene for it is switched off. The theory that follows was proposed in 1961 by F. Jacob and J. Monod of France.

The enzyme is β-galactosidase and it catalyzes the hydrolysis of those disaccharides (and related compounds), which can yield galactose by hydrolysis, e.g., lactose. Neither the enzyme nor its corresponding *mRNA* are

[1] Cells without definite nuclei are called *procaryotic;* those with discernable nuclei are *eucaryotic.*

Fig. 21.17 Polypeptide synthesis at a ribosome. The theory presented here is fairly well-established for the bacterium *Escherichia coli.* Most of its features appear to apply to higher organisms but much is yet to be learned.

We shall represent the entire *tRNA* molecule simply as:

Anticodon
triplet

Amino acid
carrier

The first amino acid that will be put in place (at least in *E. coli*) is a close relative of methionine called N-formyl methionine. Although it is not entirely clear why, the methionine unit is changed into a formyl derivative before it can be accepted by the *mRNA* and the ribosome:

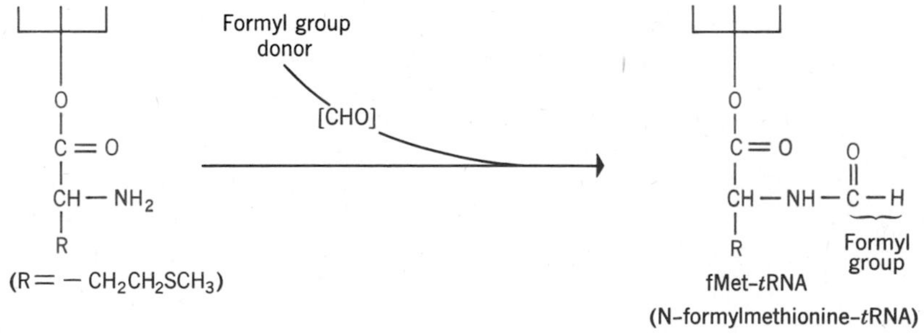

Formyl group
donor

[CHO]

$$O$$
$$|$$
$$C=O$$
$$|$$
$$CH-NH_2$$
$$|$$
$$R$$

$(R = -CH_2CH_2SCH_3)$

$$O$$
$$|$$
$$C=O \qquad O$$
$$| \qquad\quad \|$$
$$CH-NH-C-H$$
$$| \qquad\qquad\quad$$
$$R \qquad\quad\text{Formyl}$$
$$\text{group}$$

fMet–*tRNA*
(N–formylmethionine–*tRNA*)

505

embryonic development and RNA

A formyl unit at the amino end of methionine makes it look more like an amide (peptide), and that may be important to its being accepted by the ribosome. The donor of the formyl group is a derivative of folic acid, one of the vitamins we need if we are to grow and, later, to avoid certain types of anemia. At the end of polypeptide synthesis the formyl group will be removed if the N-terminal amino acid is to be methionine; if not, then the entire N-formylmethionine unit will be clipped off.

At the start of polypeptide synthesis an initiation complex forms between the smaller of the ribosome subunits, the mRNA, the fMet-tRNA unit, and other factors. Triphosphate is needed for energy. Then the larger of the ribosomal subunits joins the complex and polypeptide synthesis proceeds.

As indicated by the shaded areas, there are two kinds of binding sites at a ribosome and at least one kind of catalytic activity, *peptidyl transferase* activity to hook a growing polypeptide chain to a newly arrived amino acid unit. At least one other enzyme is needed, *translocase* activity to move a group from the acceptor site to the donor site. This enzyme appears to be in the surrounding medium.

stage 2
elongation
of the
polypeptide
chain

When the larger ribosome subunit joins the system everything is available for making the polypeptide chain. In a pattern that will be repeated often, the newly arrived fMet-tRNA unit is translocated to the donor site, $1 \rightarrow 2$.

A tRNA bearing another amino acid, the second to go into place, now is accepted at the vacated acceptor site, $2 \rightarrow 3$.

Under the influence of the peptidyl transferase (and energy from a triphosphate), the "peptide" (actually, at this stage, merely the N-formylmethionine) is transferred to the newly arrived amino acid and a new peptide bond is made, $3 \rightarrow 4$.

Not counting the N-formyl unit, we now have a dipeptide clinging to the acceptor site of the ribosome, and it is next moved to the donor site, $4 \rightarrow 5$. The first tRNA is now also released and it may be reused (or degraded).

The next tRNA bearing its amino acid goes to the freshly vacated acceptor site, and the cycle of events occurs again and again until the polypeptide change is finished.

stage 3
termination of
polypeptide
synthesis

The ribosome unit has now arrived at the other end of the mRNA strand, or it has come to a "nonsense" codon. In either case no more amino acids can be added. Some trimming, however, is now needed. Either the formyl group is removed or the N-formyl methionine group is taken off. The polypeptide is now complete and it automatically adopts whatever final folded and coiled form it naturally has in the medium in which is has been made. It is now ready to function in an enzyme system.

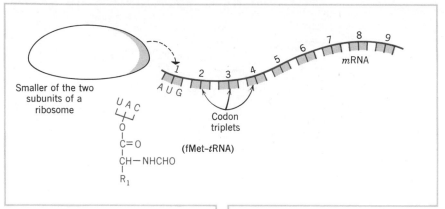

Initiation complex forms.

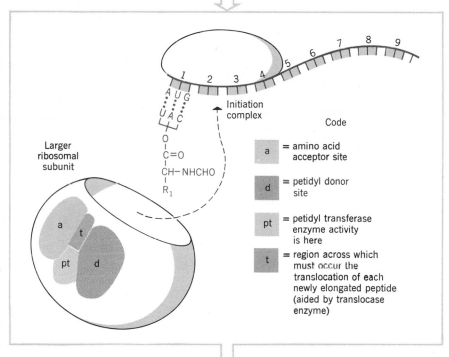

Code

a = amino acid acceptor site

d = petidyl donor site

pt = petidyl transferase enzyme activity is here

t = region across which must occur the translocation of each newly elongated peptide (aided by translocase enzyme)

stage 2

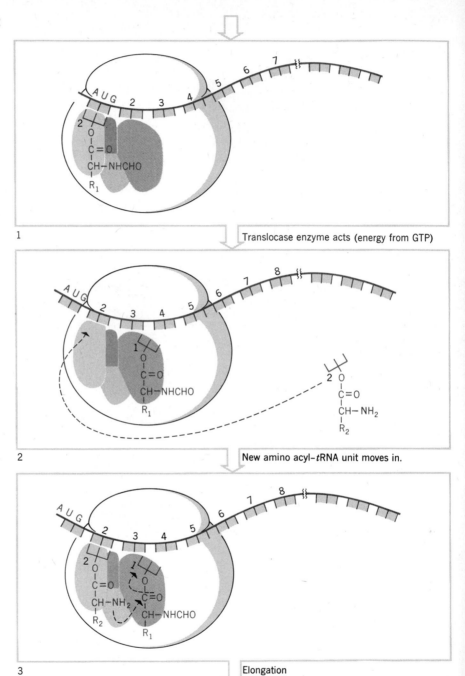

1   Translocase enzyme acts (energy from GTP)

2   New amino acyl-tRNA unit moves in.

3   Elongation

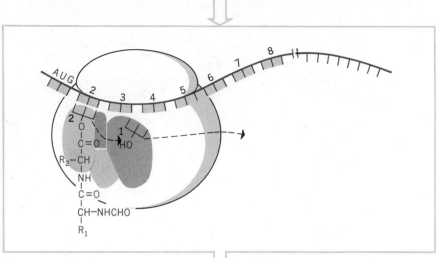

4   Translocation

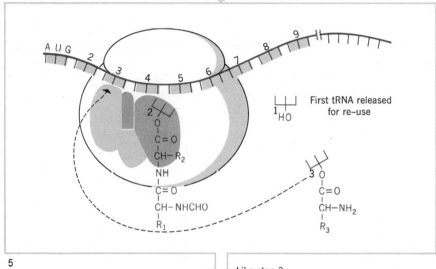

5

Like step 3
Like step 4
Like step 5, etc.

stage 3

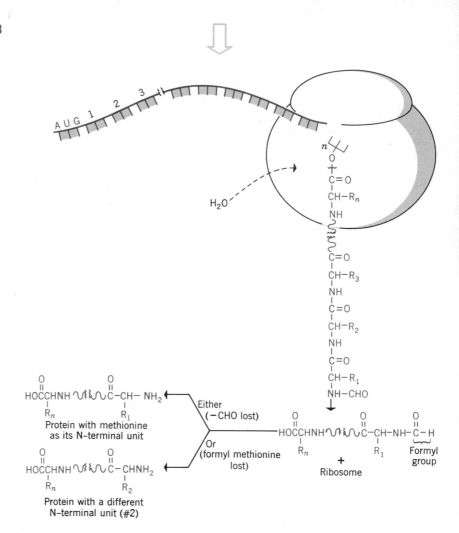

Protein with methionine as its N-terminal unit

Protein with a different N-terminal unit (#2)

Either (−CHO lost)

Or (formyl methionine lost)

Formyl group

+ Ribosome

permanent components of the cell. They break down and have to be remade, but only as needed.

Jacob and Monod proposed that the *repression* of the synthesis of an enzyme is the normal state of affairs in a cell until the gene corresponding to the enzyme is released from this repression. According to the Jacob-Monod model, there are three types of genes lying next to each other in a chromosome and all are involved in the synthesis of the specific enzyme under discussion. See Fig. 21.18. Because it specifies the structure of an enzyme, one is a *structural gene*. It is the nucleotide sequence of this gene that is translated into the sequence of amino acids of the corresponding enzyme. Next to the structural gene on the chromosome is an operator gene, which can be in one of two states—open or closed. If open, the neighboring structural gene is free to operate, free to direct the making of mRNA which, in its turn, will help make the enzyme for which the gene was coded. An

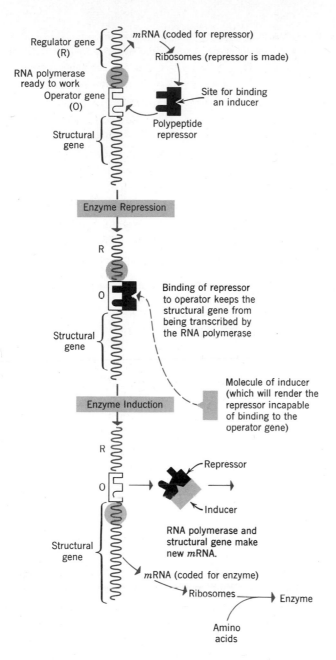

Regulator gene
(R)

*m*RNA (coded for repressor)

Ribosomes (repressor is made)

RNA polymerase
ready to work

Operator gene
(O)

Site for binding
an inducer

Structural
gene

Polypeptide
repressor

Enzyme Repression

R

O

Binding of repressor
to operator keeps the
structural gene from
being transcribed by
the RNA polymerase

Structural
gene

Molecule of inducer
(which will render the
repressor incapable
of binding to the
operator gene)

Enzyme Induction

R

O

Repressor

Inducer

RNA polymerase and
structural gene make
new *m*RNA.

Structural
gene

*m*RNA (coded for enzyme)

Ribosomes ⟶ Enzyme

Amino
acids

Fig. 21.18 Enzyme repression and induction. In *E. coli* an enzyme (β-galactosidase)
needed if the bacterium is to use lactose as its source of carbon is repressed by a small
polypeptide made under the control of a regulator gene (top). The binding of the repressor to the operator gene (middle) keeps the structural gene switched off. But lactose,
acting as the inducer (bottom) can bind to the repressor, change its shape, and cause it
to drop away. The structural gene can now help make the enzyme needed for the metabolism of lactose. This structural gene was isolated in 1969 by a team at Harvard headed
by Jon Beckwith.

open operator gene means a working structural gene, and this means enzyme synthesis. A closed operator gene means a switched-off structural gene and no enzyme synthesis. (Thus when we speak of "enzyme activation" in this example it means making a fresh batch of enzyme rather than doing something to change an inactive form of an existing enzyme molecule.)

Normally, the operator gene is kept closed, and what closes it is a small protein molecule called a *repressor*. The repressor is made directly at a ribosome-mRNA complex whose mRNA was made under the supervision of Jacob and Monod's third type of gene, a *regulatory gene*.

To recapitulate briefly (see Fig. 21.18), the regulatory gene is coded to make a repressor molecule. The repressor binds to the operator gene. As long as it is bound there, the neighboring structural gene will not work. Our next task is to see how the repressor might be forced away from the operator gene. This event would amount to enzyme induction, because it would free the structural gene to do its part in making fresh enzyme.

To allow the structural gene to work, to induce it to go ahead and direct the synthesis of an enzyme, Jacob and Monod proposed that an *inducer* binds to the repressor in such a way that the repressor will no longer fit (as in "lock and key" theory) to the operator gene. The repressor falls away. The neighboring structural gene, coded for the enzyme, is now free to make the necessary mRNA for enzyme synthesis. The inducer may be a relatively small molecule, even a molecule whose further biochemical transformations depend on inducing the synthesis of the enzyme needed for the next metabolic step. Thus lactose is an inducer in *E. coli* of the galactosidase needed to hydrolyze lactose. This is but one example of enzyme induction (and repression) in a simple cell. Some of its features may apply to higher organisms but much more research (in progress) is needed before we know how enzymes are regulated in man.

codon assignments. The triplets of nucleotides that code for specific amino acids have been worked out by the efforts of several laboratories. Marshall Nirenberg and J. H. Matthaei (National Institutes of Health) discovered that if an artificial messenger RNA made only of uracils as the bases (and called poly-U) were mixed with a DNA-free extract of *E. coli* that included ribosomes, enzymes, and triphosphates (for energy), the protein that was made contained only phenylalanine units. Evidently the code for phenylalanine was at least one uracil-based nucleotide, or a sequence of such units. A number of experiments of a similar nature disclosed the triplets of RNA bases that code for specific amino acids, and these codon assignments are listed in Table 21.1. Most amino acids correspond to more than one genetic code word, and the significance of this is not entirely clear.

The assignments given in Table 21.1 were determined for *E. coli*, but of the roughly five dozen codon assignments investigated among higher organisms every one has been identical to those for the bacteria. There is

Table 21.1   **The Genetic Code**[a]

First	Second				Third
	U	C	A	G	
U	phenylalanine	serine	tyrosine	cysteine	U
	phenylalanine	serine	tyrosine	cysteine	C
	leucine	serine	ochre	CT	A
	leucine	serine	amber	tryptophan	G
C	leucine	proline	histidine	arginine	U
	leucine	proline	histidine	arginine	C
	leucine	proline	glutamine	arginine	A
	leucine	proline	glutamine	arginine	G
A	isoleucine	threonine	asparagine	serine	U
	isoleucine	threonine	asparagine	serine	C
	isoleucine	threonine	lysine	arginine	A
	methionine, or formylmethionine	threonine	lysine	arginine	G
G	valine	alanine	aspartic acid	glycine	U
	valine	alanine	aspartic acid	glycine	C
	valine	alanine	glutamic acid	glycine	A
	valine	alanine	glutamic acid	glycine	G

[a]These codon assignments have been obtained largely from research with *E. coli*, but there is mounting evidence that they apply universally to all organisms. Thus the codon UUC, one of two that specifies phenylalanine, would specify this amino acid in any organism. GGU is one of four codons for glycine. The codons designated *ochre*, *amber* and CT specify, when encountered on an *m*RNA strand during polypeptide synthesis, that the chain should be terminated. The codon that specifies formylmethionine, at least in *E. coli*, is needed to start polypeptide synthesis. For speculations about the fact that the same amino acid may be specified by more than one codon see this reference (the source of the data for this table): J. M. Lewin. *The Molecular Basis of Gene Expression*, page 81 and following. Wiley-Interscience; New York, 1970. Used by permission.

essentially no doubt about it (as of early 1971); in nature the genetic code is universal.

genetic activity outside the nucleus. The nucleus of a cell in higher organisms does not have the complete set of genetic instructions for new daughter cells. Two kinds of very small organelles—mitochondria in both plants and animals and chloroplasts in algae and higher plants—also contain DNA, RNA, and other materials needed to make polypeptides. In the last few years more and more molecular biologists have been leaning toward the view that these organelles eons ago were free-living organisms something like bacteria. As evolution progressed they were "adopted" by larger cells and the two, organelle and cell, settled down to a cooperative living arrangement. In return for a vital function—providing ATP to the cell—the cell protects the organelle. Neither can now get along without the other.

Following by five years the announcement in 1953 of the famous Watson-Crick model of DNA structure, a structure that permitted for the first time a coherent explanation of the relation of nucleic acids to genetic information, F. H. C. Crick put forward in 1958 what has come to be known as the central dogma of molecular biology:

> "Once (genetic) information has passed into protein it cannot get out again."

With the help of Fig. 21.19, let us see what this means.

It is possible for genetic information to be passed from DNA to new DNA (replication). Genetic information can flow from DNA to RNA (transcription). It can move from RNA to protein (translation). All of these events can occur in all cells. In a few cases involving cells infected by viruses it is known that genetic information can flow from one RNA to a new RNA. In 1970, in separate laboratories, H. M. Temin and D. Baltimore launched another furiously moving bandwagon in molecular biology with the discovery that a particular tumor virus had RNA that could direct the synthesis of DNA. By early 1971 reports came from various laboratories that some types of normal (not virus-infected) human cells have an RNA that can direct the synthesis of an enzyme that, in turn, catalyzes the synthesis of DNA. Thus it is possible for genetic information, in at least some instances, to flow seemingly backwards from RNA to DNA. However, no one has (yet) observed any instance whereby a protein molecule specifies a particular building-block sequence either for another protein, for RNA, or for DNA. Molecular biologists

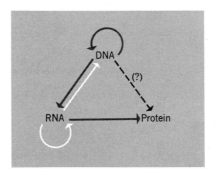

Fig. 21.19 Illustrating the *central dogma* of molecular biology as proposed and modified by F. H. C. Crick. The heavy arrows signify general transfers of genetic information that have been observed in all cells studied from the lowest organisms to the highest. The light arrows designate information transfers of a special type observed only in certain cells infected by viruses. The dotted arrow indicates a flow of information thus far seen only in a cell-free system. The central dogma holds that no arrow can lead away from protein, either to other protein or back to nucleic acid; the genetic information in a protein is not in a form any cell can use to specify new protein or new nucleic acid. (Reference: F. Crick. *Nature*, 8 August 1970, page 561. Used by permission.)

agree that should any of these transfers of information be discovered, the entire theoretical foundation of molecular biology would be severely shaken. So important to this foundation is the notion that "once genetic information has passed into protein it cannot get out again," it is referred to as the "central dogma" of molecular biology.

About 2000 diseases in man are believed to be caused directly or indirectly by a genetic disorder. Cystic fibrosis is one of the most common. It is estimated that one person in twenty carries the gene for this disease. It hits about one baby of every one thousand born. Sickle-cell anemia, a condition almost entirely confined to the population of Negroes, afflicts roughly 300,000 people in the United States. It is widespread in certain parts of Africa (particularly Ghana) where, at least among those with mild forms, it seems to have some benefit; it provides some protection against malaria. Sickle-cell anemia is the result of a defective gene.[2]

In albinism the pigments normally giving distinctive colors to hair, skin, and eyes do not get made because one gene is defective, the gene that directs the synthesis of an enzyme needed to make the pigments.

In phenylketonuria, or PKU, one defective gene results in the absence of an enzyme needed to handle the amino acid phenylalanine. As a result another metabolic event occurs to phenylalanine more frequently than normal, its conversion to phenylpyruvic acid:

$$\underset{\text{phenylalanine}}{C_6H_5CH_2\underset{|}{\overset{NH_2}{CH}}-\overset{O}{\overset{\|}{C}}-OH} \qquad \underset{\text{phenylpyruvic acid}}{C_6H_5CH_2\overset{O}{\overset{\|}{C}}-\overset{O}{\overset{\|}{C}}-OH}$$

Phenylpyruvic acid builds up in the bloodstream and since it is a ketone that has a phenyl group, the condition is called phenylketonemia. Eventually the renal threshold for phenylpyruvic acid is reached and the kidneys put increasing quantities of this material into the urine—a condition called phenylketonuria, or PKU for short. If not discovered shortly after birth, a phenylketonuric infant will become permanently mentally retarded. How this happens in humans is not clear, but it may be caused by a reduced rate of protein synthesis in the developing brain. At least it is known that when PKU is experimentally induced in young rats, the polysomes in their brains (but not in their livers) are broken back to their separate ribosome units and mRNA, an event that would certainly affect the synthesis of enzymes the

[2] In one of the more startling developments in medicine in 1970, Michigan scientists led by R. M. Nalbodian (Grand Rapids' Blodgett Memorial Hospital) announced that small, daily doses of pure urea (found in blood and urine) will check sickle cell anemia's crisis stages. It is mixed with invert sugar, and since urea can also be a poison, its use must be supervised by a physician. A sickle-cell anemia crisis, usually brought on by exercise, involves severe pains, huge swelling of legs and hands, and may progress to shock, stroke, and death.

brain needs. Congenital heart disease and microcephaly (small head) can also result.

A simple blood test taken four or five days after birth will detect PKU. The treatment of PKU has been through the control of the diet in such a way that the infant gets proteins especially low in phenylalanine. This is extremely difficult (one slice of bread has all of this amino acid a PKU infant can handle), and therefore potentially dangerous itself. It is a situation calling for the most expert of medical service, but if the infant can be brought through the most critical periods of rapid brain growth and development, the prospects for a normal later life are quite promising.

Cystic fibrosis, sickle-cell anemia, albinism, PKU—the list could be extended—are all dramatic examples of the dependence of physical and emotional health on events at the molecular level where information for living is translated and transcribed. The next and final goal of our work is to study the dangers (and benefits) of atomic radiations if they impinge on the information systems of living cells. For this study we need first to learn about atomic radiations and radioactivity in general, the topics of the next chapter.

Selected Reading List

Books

1. A. L. Lehninger. *Biochemistry.* Worth Publishers, Inc., New York, 1970. Among the many texts in biochemistry that could be a reference for our course of study, this relatively recent book has a particularly outstanding treatment of the chemistry of heredity.

2. J. D. Watson. *Molecular Biology of the Gene,* 2nd edition. W. A. Benjamin, New York, 1970. A beautifully illustrated and detailed account of molecular biology by one of the coauthors of the Watson-Crick theory (paperback).

3. J. D. Watson. *The Double Helix.* Atheneum, New York, 1968. A highly personal account of the discovery of the structure of DNA, a book that is a delight to read (and which raised many eyebrows in the scientific establishment).

4. B. M. Lewis. *The Molecular Basis of Gene Expression.* Wiley-Interscience; New York, 1970. An integration of the data and ideas of molecular biology that covers the literature to the start of 1970.

Articles

1. J. D. Watson and F. H. C. Crick. "A Structure for Deoxyribose Nucleic Acid." *Nature,* Vol. 171 (1953), page 737. "Genetical Implications of the Structure

of Deoxyribonucleic Acid." *loc. cit.,* page 964. These are the landmark papers of the Crick-Watson theory, and they are easy to read.

2. F. H. C. Crick. "The Genetic Code." *Scientific American.* October 1962, page 66. This article and the next two have the advantage of elegant illustrations plus easy accessibility in nearly all school libraries.

3. M. W. Nirenberg. "The Genetic Code: II." *Scientific American.* March 1963, page 80.

4. F. H. C. Crick. "The Genetic Code: III." *Scientific American.* October 1966, page 55.

5. C. Yanofsky. "Gene Structure and Protein Structure." *Scientific American.* May 1967, page 80. The final demonstration of a linear correspondence between a nucleotide sequence in a gene and an amino acid sequence in a protein is described.

6. B. F. C. Clark and K. A. Marcker. "How Proteins Start." *Scientific American.* January 1968, page 36. A discussion of the role of formylmethionine in protein synthesis.

7. M. Ptashne and W. Gilbert. "Genetic Repressors." *Scientific American.* June 1970, page 36. A discussion of how the gene for galactosidase in *E. coli* is switched on and off.

8. U. W. Goodenough and R. P. Levine. "The Genetic Activity of Mitochondria and Chloroplasts." *Scientific American.* November 1970, page 22. A discussion of the genetic equipment in these organelles and how they might synthesize protein.

Instructional Model

1. T. P. Bennett. *Elements of Protein Synthesis.* W. H. Freeman and Company. San Francisco, 1969. Using the instructional booklet and the pieces of this model, stamped in color on very heavy cardboard, you will be able to see very clearly how ribosomes, *m*RNA, *t*RNAs, and amino acids cooperate to make a polypeptide.

Brief Summary

1. The requirements of a successful genetic apparatus are the following.
   (a) It be capable of faithful reproduction for transmission to succeeding generations and to new somatic cells that result from mitosis.
   (b) It be able to direct and control the development of an authentic member of the species.
   (c) It can undergo evolutionary change.

2. Deoxyribonucleic acids, DNA, have structural and therefore chemical properties that correlate with their apparent properties as the specific molecules of genes.

3. The transmission of hereditary traits occurs through the replication of genes (and chromosomes) that precedes cell division.

4. Genetic control over embryonic development occurs through DNA molecules in cell nuclei. These determine how ribonucleic acids, RNA, in the cell are structured.

5. There are three types of RNA:
    (a) ribosomal RNA (rRNA), which makes up much of individual ribosomes;
    (b) messenger RNA (mRNA), which carries the principal genetic message from the gene in the nucleus to the cytoplasm, and which can hook ribosomes to themselves to form polysomes; and
    (c) transfer RNA (tRNA) of which at least twenty kinds are known, one for each amino acid.

6. When messenger RNA is made it enters the cytoplasm and attaches to itself a succession of ribosomes each of which helps to transcribe the mRNA into polypeptides as they move along the mRNA strand.

7. Aided by enzymes and triphosphates (for energy), tRNA molecules bring amino acids to mRNA codon sites where the amino acids are joined to a growing polypeptide molecule.

8. The succession: DNA (gene) to RNA to sequence of amino acids in an enzyme, links genes to enzymes.

9. According to the central dogma of molecular biology genetic information cannot be made to flow from a protein to another protein or back to any form of nucleic acid.

10. Genes that are coded for mRNA molecules may be switched on by an inducer-caused change in a repressor molecule. The repressor is made under the supervision of a regulatory gene; it normally binds to an operator gene thereby preventing the operation of the structural gene. The inducer may be a small molecule whose metabolism requires that the enzyme be made.

11. Each species possesses its own peculiar set of enzymes. If a defective gene (disordered DNA molecule) appears, it may fail to produce a key enzyme, and the organism suffers from a defect that usually will be transmitted to succeeding generations.

Problems and Exercises

1. Define each of the following terms:

(a) zygote	(e) chromosomes	(i) nucleic acid
(b) mitosis	(f) genes	(j) DNA
(c) germ cells	(g) replication	(k) RNA
(d) somatic cells	(h) nucleotide	(l) rRNA

(m) *m*RNA	(r) codon	(w) repressor
(n) *t*RNA	(s) anticodon	(x) inducer
(o) ribosome	(t) genetic code	(y) operator gene
(p) polysome	(u) enzyme induction	(z) structural gene
(q) base pairing	(v) regulator gene	

2. How are all DNA molecules structurally alike?

3. How are differences between DNA molecules related to their structures?

4. How are all RNA molecules structurally alike?

5. What is the main structural difference between RNA and DNA?

6. What is the relationship of a nucleotide to a nucleic acid?

7. What function does hydrogen bonding have in the chemistry of heredity?

8. How did Crick and Watson explain the relation of gene *structure* to gene *function?*

9. Discuss the relationship between *r*RNA, *m*RNA, and *t*RNA.

10. Discuss the relation between *m*RNA, ribosomes, and polysomes.

11. Explain in your own words, with suitable illustrations, the "one-gene–one-enzyme" concept. (That is, explain how one gene could determine the synthesis of one unique enzyme.)

12. What is the "central dogma" of molecular biology?

13. What is the enzyme induction and how is it made to occur (at least in one example in *E. coli*)?

chapter 22 radiations and human health

Before his rhapsody on the inexpensive joys of a day in June, the poet James Russell Lowell in *The Vision of Sir Launfal* reminded us that "Earth gets it price for what Earth gives us . . ." Because some of its elements are radioactive, the earth has given us an almost unlimited source of electrical power. Some radioactive elements are valued by doctors and patients in their fight against cancer. But the price of what the earth has given us is very real. For an increasing number it is leukemia; for many, shortened lives; for some in generations yet unborn, hereditary defects. Having just studied the molecular basis of heredity we are now in a position to understand how atomic radiations affect body chemicals and how these radiations can both serve us and hurt us.

The spontaneous changes in nature are our sources of useful energy. Certain spontaneous events arise from universal gravitation (e.g., a waterfall). Others, such as the combustion of fossil fuels, stem from rearrangements of outer-shell planetary electrons into more stable configurations about atomic nuclei. Chemical energy, in general, is possible because certain configurations of planetary electrons are not as stable as they could be given the particular environment of the moment. Atomic energy, on the other hand, is possible because certain configurations of particles in atomic nuclei are not as stable as they could be. Atoms that possess these nuclei are said to be *radioactive*, because in the spontaneous change they undergo to achieve nuclear stability they emit streams of radiations. The term *radiations,* ordinarily used in connection with light, is appropriate because, like light, these streams can affect photographic film. In fact, that is how radioactivity was discovered.

In 1896, the French physicist, A. H. Becquerel, chanced to store some photographic plates in a drawer containing samples of uranium ores. His film became "fogged." (Fogged film is film that, without any exposure to light, will develop as if it had been exposed to a dimly lit fog-like atmosphere.) Becquerel might have blamed the accident on faulty film or careless handling had it not been for the fact that X rays, discovered the year before by Wilhelm Roentgen, were known to be very potent film foggers. Becquerel's "accident" proved to be caused by a natural source of radiation that resembled X rays.

Intensive experimentation by Becquerel revealed that these radiations were emitted by any compound of uranium, but most intensely by uranium metal itself. They were not produced by a chemical reaction, because the usual conditions that influence the speed of this type of change—temperature, pressure, state of chemical combination—had absolutely no effect on the intensity of the radiation.

After several years of research two British physicists, Ernest Rutherford and Frederick Soddy, were able to explain radioactivity in terms of events happening in atomic nuclei. Certain kinds of nuclei are unstable. In acquiring stability, they undergo small disintegrations, and tiny nuclear bits or fragments, such as protons, electrons, and helium nuclei, are thrown out into space. An X-ray-like radiation sometimes appears also.

If an atomic nucleus loses (or gains) any protons as a result of decaying, its atomic number changes. It becomes the nucleus of an entirely different element. Planetary electrons make necessary adjustments, and different elements form. Radioactive decay, therefore, is accompanied by *transmutation* of an element.

Three kinds of radiations from various natural sources on our planet are known: alpha rays, beta rays, and gamma rays. (They were named before scientists knew what they were.) Another radiation, cosmic rays, comes to us from the sun and outer space. Although not from our planet, cosmic rays affect us and are therefore included in our study.

alpha rays. Alpha rays consist of particles moving with a velocity almost 1/10th the velocity of light. Each particle is a tiny cluster of two protons and two neutrons and is, therefore, identical with the nucleus of a helium atom. If alpha rays travel in air, collisions with air molecules stop them in a few centimeters. They cannot penetrate cardboard. Should they strike *outside* the body, they are harmless, for they cannot get through the outer layer of dead cells on the skin. (An intense dose could cause a burn.) If they get inside the body, through the lungs, for example, that is another story, to be told later.

One source of α-rays is the most common isotope of uranium, the isotope designated as uranium-238 or $^{238}_{92}U$. When an atom of $^{238}_{92}U$ ejects an alpha particle, it drops 2 units in atomic number and 4 units in atomic weight. In changing its atomic number from 92 to 90, it becomes an atom of thorium. In changing its atomic weight from 238 to 234, it becomes specifically the 234-isotope of thorium. Such changes as these are common among *nuclear reactions*. Chemical reactions, by definition, do not involve changes in nuclear composition.

The shorthand expression of a nuclear reaction is a *nuclear equation*. To avoid confusing nuclear equations with chemical equations, since they are written very much alike, atomic numbers and weights are shown, as in the equation for the decay of uranium-238:

$$\text{Atomic weight} \searrow \quad \text{Atomic number} \nearrow \qquad ^{238}_{92}U \longrightarrow {}^{234}_{90}Th + {}^{4}_{2}He$$

Alpha particle

The "balance" of a nuclear equation is checked by the principle that nuclear particles—protons and neutrons—are said to be "conserved." The total number of protons and neutrons, respectively, in all particles of the products must add up to the numbers of each in the original material. In this equation, for the proton balance, we note that $90 + 2 = 92$. The conservation of neutrons is evident from the atomic-weight balance: $234 + 4 = 238$.

beta rays. Beta rays are also streams of particles. They are actually electrons produced within and then thrown out of the nucleus. Being more than seven thousand times smaller than alpha particles, they more easily penetrate matter. Beta particles can penetrate into living cells of the skin, which will appear "burned," but they cannot reach internal organs *from the outside*.

When a beta particle, an electron, is emitted, the net effect to the nucleus is conversion of a neutron into a proton. In fact, it was once thought that a neutron was nothing more than a proton and an electron held together. According to this view, beta emission would be simply loss of the electron, leaving the proton behind. Even though this picture is much oversimplified,

radiations from natural sources. nuclear reactions and equations the *net effect* of beta emission is still the same—a change of a neutron into a proton. The thorium isotope produced by decay of uranium-238 is a beta and gamma emitter:

$$^{234}_{90}\text{Th} \longrightarrow ^{234}_{91}\text{Pa} + ^{0}_{-1}\beta + \gamma$$

[Note that neutrons and protons are "conserved." The proton balance, for example, is $91 + (-1) = 90$.]

gamma rays. Gamma rays do not consist of particles; they are identical with powerful X rays. The latter are man-made, whereas gamma rays are from natural sources, but that is the only difference. Gamma rays usually, although not always, accompany the emission of alpha and beta rays. Like powerful X rays, they are extremely penetrating.

The composition and symbols of the three rays thus far studied are summarized in Table 22.1.

cosmic rays. Their existence suspected since the 1910s and finally confirmed in 1929, cosmic rays are streams of particles that pour into our atmosphere from the sun and outer space. They come in showers whose intensities are highest during periods of solar flares. Cosmic rays that first encounter the atmosphere—the primary cosmic rays—are largely high-speed protons together with small amounts of alpha particles, electrons, and the nuclei from elements of atomic numbers as high as 26. When they descend into our atmosphere, the particles in cosmic rays encounter increasing concentrations of atmospheric gases. Collisions, becoming ever more frequent, produce the secondary cosmic rays that reach us at ground level. All of the known elementary particles—electrons, protons, neutrons, positrons, various mesons, etc.—are in the secondary rays, but the nuclei of the heavier elements have been broken up by collisions in the outer atmosphere. One of the kinds of collisions provides our atmosphere with its supply of carbon-14 which, in the form of carbon dioxide, is taken up by plants via photosynthesis. It is this isotope

Table 22.1 Natural Radioactive Radiations

Ray	Composition	Charge	Atomic Weight (amu)	Symbols
Alpha ray	Nuclei of helium atoms (2 protons + 2 neutrons)	$+2$	4	α, $^{4}_{2}\text{He}$
Beta ray	Electrons	-1	$\frac{1}{1823}$	β, $^{0}_{-1}\text{e}$, $^{0}_{-1}\beta$
Gamma ray	Energy of the X-ray type	0	0	γ

that makes possible radiocarbon dating of wooden artifacts in archeological finds.

Alpha, Beta, Gamma, X, and Cosmic Rays Are Ionizing Radiations. The source of the danger to living things posed by radiations is their ability to generate strange, unstable, highly reactive ions as they plow into tissue. That is why these (and similar) radiations are called *ionizing radiations*. (Neutrons, for example, that would escape in nuclear accidents are ionizing.)

Before we go any farther into the effects of radiations on cells let us see how radiations are described. We shall now enter an area where the topics could be made as technical and complicated as we please. At the risk of sacrificing complete security from possible misinterpretations, we shall try to keep the discussion as simple as possible. These topics cannot be avoided if we are to follow intelligently the public debates and controversies about radiation protection standards. (In some courses where the schedule is particularly tight, however, the next unit may be omitted without creating serious problems in the study of succeeding units.)

A number of units have been defined for describing the intensity, the energy, the dose and the biological effectiveness of any given radiation. Each unit arose in response to a question. Let us let these questions provide us with a broad overview before plunging into the details.

units of radiation measurement

How much energy do the particles in the stream of radiation have? One way physicists answer that is in units of *electron-volts*. (A simple conversion factor changes an expression in electron-volts into one stated in calories.)

How intensely active is a particular source? That is, how frequently are nuclear disintegrations occurring within a sample? The answer to that is given in *curies*.

How intense is a given exposure to X rays or gamma rays? That is answered in units of *roentgens*, the unit for *exposure*.

How much energy does a radiation deposit per unit of path length as it courses through matter? In answer to this, radiations may be described in terms of their linear energy transfer values or LET.

How much energy has been absorbed by a unit mass of tissue? The unit used for this is the *rad*, the unit for *absorbed dose*.

How can we take into account the fact that an absorbed dose delivered by one kind of radiation does not necessarily produce the same result in the tissue as the same absorbed dose delivered by another radiation? The *rem* unit is used for this; it is the unit for *dose equivalent*.

How can we compare the effectiveness of different radiations in causing a particular biological result? To make such comparisons radiobiologists speak of the *relative biological effectiveness* or RBE values of the radiations.

How might the toxicity of doses of radiations be described? One of several units is the $LD_{50}/30$-days value.

electron volts. You are asked to accept without the background details that, in terms of the basic dimensions of physical quantities, when you multiply the *charge* on an electron by *volts* the product will have the dimensions of energy. A volt is to the flow of electricity what pressure is to the flow of water. When one electron is made to accelerate under the influence of one volt its increase in energy is called one electron-volt. This unit of energy, useful whenever we deal with electrically charged particles in motion, is extremely small. It takes almost Avogadro's number of electron-volts to have one kilocalorie. More exactly,

$$1 \text{ eV} = 3.8 \times 10^{-20} \text{ calorie (where eV} = \text{electron-volt)}$$

Particles in radiations usually have thousandfold and millionfold multiples of the electron-volt in energy and that is why the following units are useful:

$$1000 \text{ eV} = 1 \text{ KeV} \qquad 1 \text{ million eV} = 1 \text{ MeV}$$

Even the MeV is extremely small in terms of calories, and yet an important gamma ray source used in radiation therapy, cobalt-60, delivers gamma rays of only slightly more than 1 MeV in energy. We see, then, that it obviously cannot be the heat energy that might be generated by atomic radiation that kills but the way that radiations tear molecules apart in cells that is dangerous. An electron may be made to transfer from one molecule to another to give a pair of strange, unstable ions. Bonds may be broken to produce, again, pairs of unstable ions. The alpha particles emitted from radium have approximately 5 MeV of energy. Associated with diagnostic X rays is energy of about 0.09 MeV (90 KeV). Primary cosmic rays sweep into our atmosphere with energies ranging roughly from 200 MeV to 200 BeV (billion electron volts).

the curie (Ci). Used to describe how active a particular sample of radioactive material is, the *curie* (symbol: Ci) is defined as 3.7×10^{10} disintegrations per second. This is the rate of disintegration exhibited by the amount of radium, together with its radioactive decay products, present in a one-gram sample of radium.

$$1 \text{ millicurie} = 10^{-3} \text{ Ci} = 3.7 \times 10^{7} \text{ disintegrations/sec}$$
$$1 \text{ microcurie} = 10^{-6} \text{ Ci} = 3.7 \times 10^{4} \text{ disintegrations/sec}$$
$$1 \text{ picocurie} = 1 \text{ micromicrocurie} = 10^{-12} \text{ Ci} = 3.7 \times 10^{-2} \text{ disintegrations/sec}$$

To illustrate, a hospital might own a cobalt-60 source rated as 1.5 Ci. This means that the source delivers $1.5 \times 3.7 \times 10^{10} = 5.55 \times 10^{10}$ disintegrations per second. The rating says nothing about the mass of the sample, although for naturally radioactive sources there will usually be a simple relation. The curie is a unit of *activity*, not of *quantity* of radioactive material.[1]

the roentgen (R). This unit is used to describe exposure of X-ray or gamma-ray radiation. (The common word *exposure* has a technical meaning in radiation biology. It means specifically the dose delivered by X or gamma radiation, and the unit of exposure is the roentgen. The common word *dose* also has a specific meaning in radiation biology. It means energy *released in tissue* by ionizing radiation, but such a definition is not specific enough and, therefore, a quantity called the *absorbed dose* is defined. See under *rad,* below.)

One roentgen of X ray or gamma ray is defined as that which will produce ions bearing an aggregation of 2.1×10^9 units of electric charge in one cubic centimeter of dry air at normal temperature and pressure.

This definition is not in obvious units of energy, but there is a relation between the ability of any beam of X or gamma rays to generate ions in air and the energy associated with that beam. (We shall not go into that relation.) To give a rough idea of magnitudes, if each person in a large population of people were exposed to 650 roentgens, half would die in 1 to 4 weeks.

absorbed dose. The Rad (D). The roentgen, by definition, is limited to X rays or gamma rays and to their effect in air. What happens in various tissues is what finally matters, however. That is why we need a unit for *absorbed dose,* not just for exposure. And for that we want a unit that is not restricted to just two of the ionizing radiations. The *rad,* which stands for *radiation absorbed dose,* is that unit; its symbol is D, and it is defined as:

$$1 \text{ rad} = 100 \text{ ergs of energy absorbed per gram of tissue}[2]$$
$$1 \text{ millirad} = 1 \text{ mrad} = 10^{-3} \text{ rad} = 0.1 \text{ erg absorbed per gram of tissue}$$

A total body absorbed dose of about 600 rads of gamma radiation would be lethal for most people. Yet, according to a calculation reported by physicist

---

[1] In the early days of uranium mining a different definition of the curie came into use, a definition carried over, with some changes, to describing freshly extracted thorium. We leave the details to advanced references and make this mention only to warn you that if you ever have occasion to look up data on activity for natural uranium or thorium you must check what definition of curie is used.

[2] This makes the rad an extremely small unit if we were to think of one rad only in terms of heat energy. The erg, a unit of energy familiar to physicists, is so small that 42 *million* ergs are needed for only 1 calorie (the small calorie). But the heat potentially available from radiations is usually the very least of our worries. It is their ability to generate unstable, reactive ions that is dangerous.

H. F. Henry, this dose absorbed by water would cause the ionization of only one water molecule for every 36 million molecules present. Clearly the trigger effect of unnatural ionizations within cells is vastly greater than the energy that causes it.

The roentgen and the rad are quite similar in magnitude. One roentgen of X ray or gamma ray will deliver very nearly one rad when it is absorbed in muscle tissue. The gamma radiation from such sources as radium decay products, cesium-137, or cobalt-60, all delivering gamma rays at about 1 MeV in energy, is equivalent to 0.96 rad in muscle tissue and 0.92 rad in compact bone.

the Rem. In terms of what they may do biologically to an organ in man, the energy of a one-rad dose of one radiation is not necessarily identical with a one-rad dose of another source. There are other factors that influence the biological effects in man, factors not always easy to identify and describe. Neutrons, one of several sources of danger in nuclear accidents, and gamma rays have effects in man not easily compared in terms of rads. But in the science and technology of protecting people from radiations of any type, it is obviously important to have one scale that can be used for numerical comparisons. For this reason a quantity called the *dose equivalent* (DE) is defined. It is numerically equal to the dose in rads multiplied by fractions called modifying factors that apply to the particular radiation in question and that take into account properties, beside the energy of the radiation, that contribute to biological hazards in man. The unit of dose equivalent is the *rem*. Its name is derived from *r*oentgen *e*quivalent for *m*an. One rem of any given radiation is that quantity that causes, when absorbed by man, an effect equivalent to the absorption of one roentgen. A useful subunit is the millirem or *mrem*. 1 mrem $= 10^{-3}$ rem.

The value of the rem (or mrem) unit is that doses to man expressed in rems are additive whereas doses expressed in rads are not necessarily additive. If an organ receives 5 mrem of neutrons and 10 mrem of gamma rays it has taken 15 mrem of total dose equivalent. (For purposes of developing radiation protection systems where we want large cushions against error, the dose equivalent in rems is taken to be numerically identical to the absorbed dose in rads and the exposure in roentgens.

linear energy transfer. LET. When a radiation courses through air or through tissue it loses its energy to the matter as it goes. The energy lost per unit path length is called the *linear energy transfer* or, simply, the LET of the radiation. The LET of a given radiation depends on the target, and the effective LET within the target depends on how deeply the radiation has penetrated. Generally, alpha particles and neutrons are high LET radiations. Gamma and X rays generate low LET paths. Damage done in tissue by sublethal doses of low LET radiations are more likely to be repaired by the organism than damage caused by radiations of high LET, which deposit their energy in a tight, dense volume along their paths. The effects of low LET radiation are distributed more widely and less densely around their paths.

One of the lessons to be learned from these considerations is that the dangers associated with a source of radiation are not solely a matter of how active the source is in curies. The kinds of radiations sent out, their energy, whether they penetrate intact skin or enter the system on dust and food, and their LET values in their targets are also important factors. (Also of tremendous importance is the possible concentrating effect a foodchain may have on a radioactive isotope. We shall explore this more later.)

relative biological effectiveness. RBE. The biological effectiveness of a radiation means its ability to produce a specified effect in a given tissue. Some radiations are more effective than others and the concept of relative biological effectiveness has been devised to provide radiobiologists with a means for comparing them. It is abbreviated RBE.

The standard for comparison of RBE is gamma radiation from cobalt-60 (or equivalent X rays). The RBE of a radiation is defined as the ratio of the absorbed dose delivered by gamma rays of cobalt-60 to the absorbed dose delivered by the radiation in question when both are compared in producing the *same* biological effect. For example, if a given biological effect is created by 1 rad of alpha radiation and it takes 10 rads of the gamma radiation from cobalt-60 to cause the same effect, then the alpha radiation has (with respect to that particular biological effect) an RBE value of 10. This is not the RBE value for alpha radiation for all circumstances. Its RBE varies with the dose rate, the total dose, and the tissue in addition to the particular biological effect being studied. RBE usually (but not always) increases regularly with increasing LET. (It is beyond the scope of this book to go into more detail than this.)

LD$_{50}$/30-days. One of the ways of expressing radiation toxicity is in terms of the *30-day medium lethal dose equivalent*, abbreviated LD$_{50}$/30-days, the dose equivalent (in rems or mrems) that will kill 50% of the exposed individuals within 30 days. Some of these values for various species are given in Table 22.2. It should be noted that the death rate for man may remain high for as much as 60 days following exposure. Cells do have considerable capacity for repair, and experimental animals can survive with negligible deaths following the absorption of doses as high as 200 rads. However, not all the effects of radiation appear in the first weeks after exposure. Some appear years later and radiations have a life-shortening effect, as well as other effects soon to be studied.

half-life. The half-life or $t_{1/2}$ is one of the oldest methods for describing how relatively stable a particular radioactive element is. It does not say

529
units of radiation measurement

Table 22.2   LD$_{50}$/30-Day Values in Rems for Some Animals

Animal	Rem
Man	500 (estimated)
Mouse	600
Rat	700
Dog	300

Data from: K. Z. Morgan and J. E. Turner, editors, *Principles of Radiation Protection*. John Wiley & Sons, Inc., New York, 1967, page 429. Used by permission.

anything *directly* about activity (as does the curie) or exposure (as does the roentgen) or absorbed dose (as does the rad), but the half-life of a radioactive element does tell us something about its relative stability.

The time that it takes for an initial quantity of radioactive material to decay to one-half this amount is defined as its half-life. The half-life of uranium-238 is about five billion years. This means that, if the initial amount of $^{238}_{92}$U is, say, 100 grams, after five billion years 50 grams will remain. The rest will have decayed and transmuted to other elements.

The isotope of radon, $^{222}_{86}$Rn, has a relatively short half-life, about 4 days. Of an initial 100 grams of radon-222, only 50 grams will remain after 4 days. After the next 4 days, half of 50 grams, or 25 grams, will be left. In another 4 days, 12.5 grams will remain. Thus, after three half-life periods of 4 days each, only 12.5% of the original will remain.

The enormous variations in nuclear stabilities are seen in the data of Table 22.3, which lists some common, naturally occurring isotopes and their half-lives. There are some rare isotopes whose half-lives are fractions of seconds.

One of the strategies used to reduce radioactive emissions from nuclear power plants is to hold gaseous effluents for a period of time to permit at least some significant decay of the isotopes of short half-lives before the gases are released. This still leaves some radioactive releases, and it leaves the major problem of safely disposing of longer-lived radioactive wastes scrubbed from effluents and produced in the reactor cores. As a rule of thumb, such wastes should be kept away from living things until their isotopes have gone

Table 22.3   Half-Lives and Radiations of Some Naturally Occuring Isotopes

Element	Isotope	Half-Life ($t_{\frac{1}{2}}$)	Radiations
Potassium	$^{40}_{19}$K	200 million years	Beta, gamma
Radon	$^{222}_{86}$Rn	3.82 days	Alpha
Radium	$^{226}_{88}$Ra	1590 years	Alpha, gamma
Thorium	$^{234}_{90}$Th	25 days	Beta, gamma
	$^{230}_{90}$Th	80,000 years	Alpha, gamma
Uranium	$^{235}_{92}$U	800 million years	Alpha, gamma
	$^{238}_{92}$U	4.7 billion years	Alpha

through at least twenty half-lives. For strontium-90 ($t_{1/2}$ 28.1 years), one of the common and biologically most dangerous of the radioactive wastes, this means safe storage for a minimum of almost 600 years during which time the bureaucracy for monitoring and guarding the storage systems must survive.

Since the five senses of man cannot detect the presence of ionizing radiations, it is necessary to have instruments that respond to radiations in ways we can see (or hear). Radiologists and health physicists have developed a number of instruments for different applications.

scintillation counters. Some instruments depend on electrical magnification of scintillations (tiny light flashes) produced when radiations impinge on surfaces coated with special chemicals. For example, a zinc sulfide phosphor is effective for alpha particles. (A phosphor is a salt with a trace impurity of some transition metal ion. It will "glow" when exposed to light.) The aromatic organic compound, anthracene, is useful for detecting beta rays. The pulse measured by the instrument is proportional to the energy of the particle stopped by the chemically coated surface. Scintillation counters are probably the most widely used instruments for measuring dose-rates and counts of radiation.

methods based on the electrical conductivity of a gas. Imagine a thin-walled, gas-filled glass tube, as illustrated in Fig. 22.1, in which an electrical voltage can be applied in increasing intensity between the central wire (one electrode) and a metal plate fitted to and forming part of the tube (second electrode). At zero voltage, obviously no current can flow even if, say, X rays are focused on the interior of the tube. But as soon as a small voltage is applied, then the ions produced by the X rays will carry a small current between the two electrodes. Let us follow by means of Fig. 22.2 the rise in the amount of current between the two electrodes as the voltage is increased. (We need not be concerned here about the units of current and voltage.)

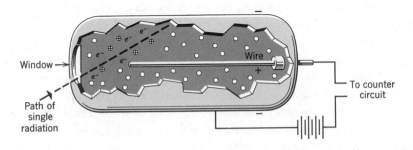

Fig. 22.1   Basic features of a gas-ionization radiation detection tube.

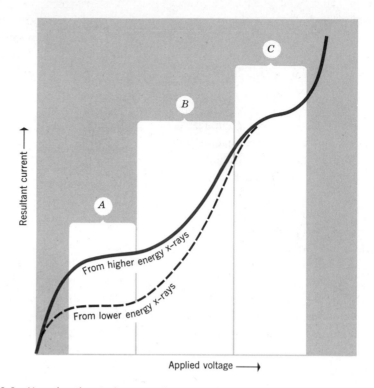

Fig. 22.2 How the electrical current changes with the applied voltage in a gas-ionization radiation detecting tube during exposure to radiation. Region (A) is the saturation region where ionization chamber devices operate. Region (B) is the proportional region used by proportional counters. Region (C) is the Geiger plateau where the Geiger-Müller counters operate. (H. F. Henry. *Fundamentals of Radiation Protection*. Wiley-Interscience; New York, 1969. Page 204. Used by permission.)

For X rays of one particular energy the curve will reach a region, (A), where further increases in the applied voltage cause no further increases in current. This is the *saturation region* for X rays of *that energy* in that tube. However, within this region at any given voltage *the amount of current is proportional to the energy of the X rays*. With many variations in the design of the tube, instruments operating at voltages of the saturation region are called *ion chambers*. Depending on the design and circuitry, ion chambers can be used to measure either the total exposure dose or the dose rate.

Leaving the saturation region (and moving into region (B) of Fig. 22.2) higher and higher voltages to the electrodes begins to *accelerate* the movement of ions to them. As the moving ions accelerate (move faster and faster) they become more and more energetic. Therefore, as they collide with gas molecules in the tube, they are more and more able to produce even more ions than were created by the initial radiation. Hence the current is more than it could be at lower voltages. The current is now proportional to the applied voltage (the cause of the acceleration of the initially formed ions), and this is the *proportional region* Ⓑ of Fig. 22.2. As the voltage is increased it becomes less and less important how energetic are the invading X rays (or other rays) as long as they do enter the tube and cause some initial ionization. By operating an instrument at the voltages of the proportional region, we can detect pulses of radiation of energies much lower than those detectable in the saturation region.

Moving from the proportional region (and into region Ⓒ of Fig. 22.2) we enter what is called the *Geiger plateau*. As long as a particle of radiation gets into the tube and produces ions, a pulse of current will flow. Now the energy of the radiation does not matter at all, as long as it enters the tube and can make an ion. A tube operating under these circumstances is called a *Geiger-Müller tube*. Devices for detecting beta and/or gamma rays commonly use this tube.

There are many other types of radiation detectors and monitors (e.g., photographic films).

The decay of an atom of uranium-238 to thorium-234 does not answer the need of its nucleus for stability. The nucleus of thorium-234 is not stable either. It decays, and still a stable nucleus is not formed. In fact, starting with $^{238}_{92}U$, a whole succession of radioactive disintegrations takes place until a stable isotope of lead, $^{206}_{82}Pb$, forms. This succession, called a *radioactive disintegration series,* is shown in Fig. 22.3.

radioactive disintegration series

There is no escaping radiations. About 50 of the roughly 350 isotopes of all elements in nature are radioactive. On the average the top six inches of soil on our planet has 1 gram radium per square mile. Radioactive materials are in the soils and rocks on which we walk and from which we make building materials. They are in the food we eat, the water we drink, and the air we breathe. They enter us with every X ray we have taken. They come to us in cosmic ray showers. Although this background radiation represents very small exposures, there is no known threshold exposure below which no adverse biological effect can be produced. It is the absence of an exposure threshold that is largely responsible for the great concern expressed by many scientists and interested laymen over additions to the human exposure burden caused by atmospheric testing of nuclear weapons, by leaks from underground tests, by effluents from nuclear power plants and the foodchains those effluents enter, and by many other proposed peace-time uses of atomic energy (such as digging huge canals by atomic explosions). We cannot escape the background radiation; why add to it is the issue.

Just how large is the background radiation? It varies widely from place to place on our planet, and only estimates (which vary with the estimator)

background radiations

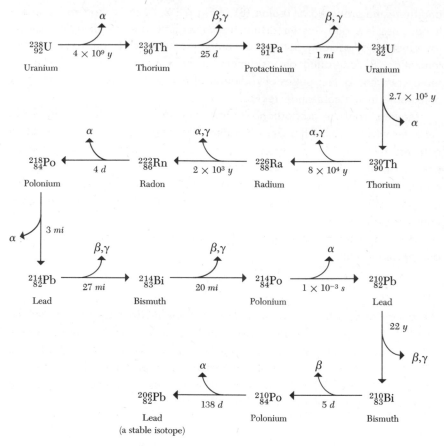

Fig. 22.3 Uranium-238 radioactive disintegration series. The number beneath each arrow signifies the half-life of the preceding isotope; *y* = years; *m* = months; *d* = days; *mi* = minutes; *s* = seconds. The small arrow that curves away from each main arrow indicates the kind (or kinds) of radiation emitted by the preceding isotope.

are possible. Table 22.4 gives the averages of radiations from various sources for the U. S. population.

The thousands of people in certain areas of the Travancore region in eastern India live on active monazite sands and receive annual doses as high as 1500 mrad. The same sands occur in certain states in Brazil, and thousands of Brazilians receive annually anywhere from 500 mrad to 1600 mrad. Citizens of Denver, Colorado, live at higher altitudes than most in this country and are therefore more exposed to cosmic rays. Their background radiation is about 170 mrem.

artificial radioactivity Artificial radioactivity is not fundamentally different from natural radioactivity. The term is used sometimes when speaking of the decay of isotopes made by induced transmutations.

Table 22.4 Dose Equivalents (in mrem) Received Annually by the Average General U. S. Population from Various Sources

Source	Dose Equivalent (mrem)
Natural Background (whole body dose equivalent)	100–140
Medical Sources	
Diagnostic X rays	20–50
Therapeutic X rays	3–5
Radioisotopes	0.2
Other Sources	
Fallout (from atmospheric testing, 1954–1962)	1.5 (5 mrem maximum in early 1960s)
Radioactive pollutants introduced into the environment from nuclear power plants (1970), U. S.	0.85
Miscellaneous	2.0[a]
Maximum Annual Limit proposed for the average, general population (by the International Commission on Radiological Protection, 1970), from all sources exclusive of medical and background	170
LD_{50}/30-Day Value for Man (Table 22.2)	500,000 mrem

[a]The one-pack-a-day smoker's lungs get at least 40 mrem per year more dose equivalent. Naturally occurring radon, a radioactive, gaseous decay product of naturally occurring radium, decays to radioactive lead that deposits on earth and foliage (including broad-leaf tobacco plants).

    Data and format from J. B. Little, *The New England Journal of Medicine*, Vol. 275, pages 929–938, 1966 (used by permission); with additional data from *Technology Review*, October/November 1970; and from *Nuclear Power and the Public*, H. Foreman, editor, University of Minnesota Press, 1970.

induced transmutations; interaction of radiations with atomic nuclei. Occasionally, as decay particles penetrate through matter, they chance to be on collision course with the nucleus in another atom or molecule. If angles and energies are just right, the particle buries itself within the target nucleus, and, in so doing, it may expel a small fragment.

Lord Rutherford, a British physicist, was the first to observe an event of this type. When he let alpha particles from a natural source stream through nitrogen, Rutherford noted the production of high-speed protons. From his data, he was forced to conclude that alpha particles, in some instances, had penetrated nitrogen nuclei. It was later shown that the other product was an isotope of oxygen. This was the first artificial transmutation of an element. The nuclear equation summarizes the event:

$$^{14}_{7}N + \,^{4}_{2}He \longrightarrow \,^{17}_{8}O + \,^{1}_{1}H$$

    High-speed α-particles   High-speed protons

The oxygen isotope that formed in Rutherford's experiment was nonradioactive. Since 1919, hundreds of artificial nuclear reactions have been achieved. Most of them have produced radioactive isotopes, and a total of about 1000 isotopes have been made. Many of these transmutations were possible only because scientists found new particles for nuclear bombardments, or they found ways to accelerate and thereby give greater impact energy to their nuclear "bullets."

The neutron is an example of a new particle capable of nuclear bombardments. When alpha particles are focused on an isotope of beryllium, ^9_4Be, the following nuclear reaction occurs:

$$^9_4Be + ^4_2He \longrightarrow ^{12}_6C + ^1_0n$$

α-Particles   Stable isotope   Neutrons
of carbon

The reaction makes available high-speed neutrons for transmutation experiments. The nucleus of an isotope of hydrogen, deuterium, is another useful bombarding particle. It is called a deuteron, and its symbol is d or ^2_1D.

interactions of
radiations with
living cells

Ionizing radiations of any type are potentially dangerous both to the individual now living and to succeeding generations. Yet virtually all people would accept some of the risks of radiations if a particular benefit is valued highly enough. It is usually impossible to make cold, analytical, quantitative evaluations of benefits (or risks); we lack too much information concerning what radiations will surely do to man to lift our decisions very much above the level of hunches, wishful thinking, and at best, educated guesses. But who, with a possible brain tumor, would not want a radiologist to use X rays and radioactive isotopes to find it and help the surgeon get it out. Even among the very large group of concerned scientists and laymen who oppose building nuclear-powered electrical generating plants, most stand opposed *at this time* but not necessarily forever. We can afford to wait, they argue, until our scientists, engineers, and business managers give us nonpolluting nuclear power plants. Radioactivity and atomic energy are sources of great benefits. Before we study some of them, let us first look at some of the risks we run to our health, longevity, and future generations.

radiation-sickness. The largest-scale results of exposure to large doses of radiations are a group of physiological responses that add up to radiation sickness. Typical symptoms are given in Fig. 22.4. Even patients given deep X-ray or cobalt-ray treatment experience gastrointestinal disturbances and a falling white cell count.

These conditions are of such different natures that it hardly seems possible that one cause can have such diverse effects. Within the last decade, however, scientists have done much to provide a chemical basis for understanding radiation sickness.

As we have learned, when radiations penetrate living cells, they leave in their tracks a mixture of strange, unstable organic ions. As these seek

Lapsed Time from Exposure	Amount of Absorbed Dose		
	1000 rad	500 rad	200 rad
First day	Nausea and vomiting and a drop in the supply of white blood cells		
First week	Nausea, vomiting, fever, diarrhea, throat inflammation,		
Second week	dehydration, prostration, emaciation —leading to death		
Third week		General poor feeling, loss of appetite, pallor, diarrhea, fever, hemorrhage, throat inflammation; loss of hair; emacia-	Loss of appetite, pallor, diarrhea, throat inflammation; loss of hair
Fourth week		tion—leading to death in 50% of those exposed	
			Unless there are complications such as infectious diseases, recovery begins. Other symptoms may appear years later or in progeny

Fig. 22.4 The symptoms of acute radiation sickness. (Adapted from "Radiation Biology" by A. C. Upton and R. F. Kimball; Chapter 12 in *Principles of Radiation Protection*, K. Z. Morgan and J. E. Turner, editors. John Wiley & Sons, Inc.; New York, 1967, page 427. Used by permission.)

stability, covalent bonds within them may break permanently. The ions may recombine either with themselves or with neighbors. New molecules, foreign to the cell, form.

Suppose that all this happens to a nucleic acid within a cell nucleus? We learned in Chapter 21 that these giant molecules simply cannot suffer structural changes and remain true to the genetic messages they bear. If a DNA molecule, a gene, is structurally altered, at the very least, mutant daughter cells will form when the cell divides. At the worst, and this is common, the cell will not be able to divide at all. It will be reproductively dead. If the cell is not made reproductively dead, any altered DNA will also produce altered RNA, possibly of all types. Faulty enzymes may be made, or one or more enzymes may not be made at all.

Since the primary site of radiation damage is the genetic apparatus of a cell, the symptoms of overexposure will appear first among cells that most frequently undergo division. Cells in bone marrow are in this category. Since they are responsible for making white cells, it is not surprising that an early sign of radiation illness is a drop in the white cell count. As other cells, less frequent in dividing, reach their time for division, damage to them will be apparent. Whatever tissue they constitute will suffer. Of course, if the exposure was severe enough initially, enough cells in enough parts of the body may be rendered reproductively dead to produce all effects of radiation illness quickly.

Damage to the contents of cell nuclei in *germ cells,* cells that produce sperm or eggs, can result in mutations in offspring. Whether or not these actually occur, and how important the changes will be, depends on the extent of the damage and on many other factors beyond the scope of this book.

radiations and cancer. Surgery and X rays have been classical methods for the treatment of cancer. Surgery works well if the cancer has not undergone metastasis,[3] and if the affected tissue is not absolutely essential to life. For forms of cancer for which surgery is not practical, ionizing radiations such as X rays or gamma rays from radioactive sources are used. If the cells damaged as a result of deliberate exposure to radiations are cancer cells, then the cancer is halted. High doses of radiation carefully aimed at cancerous cells during a reasonably short period halt cancer.

Radium therapy is not fundamentally different from X-ray treatment, since both involve ionizing radiations. Radium-226 is an alpha and gamma emitter. In practice, it is placed in a hollow platinum needle, which not only holds the radium (usually as one of its salts), but also stops radium emitted particles and confines the gaseous, easily diffused, intensely radioactive "daughter" of radium, radon. Placing the needle into or next to the cancerous growth effects an accurate and simple focus of ionizing radiations.

In recent years, an isotope of cobalt, $^{60}_{27}$Co, has been widely used. It is a powerful beta and gamma emitter with a half-life of 5.3 years. (In use, the beta rays are shielded out.) One of its principal virtues is its inexpensiveness, compared with radium. Not only can it be made in a cyclotron, but also its shorter half-life means that it can be used in much smaller amounts than radium to achieve the same radiation intensity.

Iodine-131, a beta and gamma emitter with a half-life of 8 days, is of value in treating cancer of the thyroid gland because this gland naturally concentrates iodide ion to make a hormone. Even if thyroid cancer has undergone metastasis, its transposed cells wherever they are will still absorb radioactive iodide ion. Radiation therapy for cancer of the thyroid is accom-

[3] Metastasis is the breaking off of malignant cells from a primary cancerous growth and their distribution to other parts of the body, where they may initiate secondary cancerous growths. Unless all malignant tissue is removed, a cancer may be slowed, but it is not cured.

plished simply by giving the patient a carefully measured drink of water containing radioactive iodide ion from iodine-131.

While it is a blessing that radiations can help in the fight against cancer, "earth gets its price." Radiations, besides causing mutations, can also cause cancer. If exposure to ionizing radiations is relatively mild and over a general area, damage to genes in cell nuclei is less likely to be profound. In fact, chromosomes and genes are capable of considerable self-repair. Minor changes that do remain are not likely to prevent cell division, but they may cause mutations. In future divisions, these mutations may take the form of uncontrolled cell divisions characteristic of cancer. Thus it is that repeated low exposures to radiations might induce cancerous growths in otherwise healthy tissue. Even the extremely low level of radiations from the operation of nuclear power plants has caused much concern.

Except in treating certain forms of cancer, the less frequently the body is exposed to ionizing radiations, the better. When a physician uses radioactive isotopes in diagnostic work, he deliberately places this material within the body only because its presence in any particular part, or in all parts, can be very simply determined by some types of counters. Otherwise, the radiations of the isotope are undesirable. To minimize radiation damage to the patient, a physician or radiologist will select an isotope that has a short half-life. He will use it in the form of a compound that will be quickly eliminated from the body. As a further precaution, he will use the smallest possible amount that can be accurately detected. Attention to these details ensures that, if some of the isotope remains in the patient, it will be only a trace amount that will decay quickly.

The person who uses radioactive sources of X rays or gamma rays in medical work will also protect himself from exposure. The easiest step is to get out of the way, to stand back. The intensities of radiations diminish with the *square* of the distance from the source. (If the intensity at a point 1 foot from the source is, say, 8 units, then at two feet from the source the intensity will be, not one-half, but $1/2^2$ or one-fourth; i.e., 2 units.) Another step is to wear protective clothing or get behind shields. Even very thin sheets of lead will stop all alpha and beta rays, and lead attenuates X rays and gamma rays very well, as the data in Table 22.5 show.

the use of technetium-99^m. All known isotopes of technetium are radioactive and all must be artificially produced. One particularly unstable form, technetium-99^m (m for metastable) or $^{99m}_{43}$Tc, has a half-life of only 6.1 hours, and it decays almost entirely be emitting gamma rays without releasing beta or alpha rays.

$$^{99m}_{43}\text{Tc} \xrightarrow[t_{1/2}6.1h]{} {}^{99}_{43}\text{Tc} + \text{gamma ray}$$

radiations and medical diagnosis

Table 22.5 Penetrating Abilities of Some Common Radiations

Type of Radiation	Common Sources	Approximate Energy When From These Sources	RBE (approximate)	Approximate Depth of Penetration of Radiation into:		
				Dry Air	Tissue	Lead
Alpha rays	radium-226 radon-222 polonium-210	5 MeV	10	4 cm	0.05 mm (not through skin)	0
Beta rays	tritium strontium-90 iodine-131 carbon-14	0.05 to 1 MeV	1–2	6 to 300 cm	0.06 to 4 mm (not through skin)	0.005 to 0.3 mm
				Thickness to reduce initial intensity by 10%		
Gamma rays	cobalt-60 cesium-137 decay products of radium-226	1 MeV	1	400 meters	50 cm	30 mm
X Rays						
Diagnostic	—	up to 90 KeV	1	120 meters	15 cm	0.3 mm
Therapeutic	—	up to 250 KeV	1	240 meters	30 cm	1.5 mm

From J. B. Little, *The New England Journal of Medicine*, Vol. 275, pages 929–938, 1966. Used by permission.

The product, technetium-99, decays extremely slowly by beta emission to a stable isotope of ruthenium.

$$^{99}_{43}Tc \xrightarrow[t_{1.2 \times 10^5 y}]{} {}^{99}_{44}Ru + {}^{0}_{-1}\beta$$

Technetium-99^m in the form of sodium pertechnetate, NaTcO$_4$, has been found extremely valuable as a scanning agent for a number of organs, particularly the brain. Biochemically, the pertechnetate ion, TcO$_4^-$, behaves in a manner similar to that of the halogens. When used for brain scanning, sodium pertechnetate is administered in isotonic sodium chloride solution, usually by intravenous injection. Cells in brain tumors absorb the pertechnetate ion to a degree different from that of normal cells. About an hour after a small dose of sodium pertechnetate is administered (recommended maximum: 10 millicuries), scans of the brain are started. From the results, radiologists can determine the presence, the size, and the location of brain tumors or a number of other kinds of pathological conditions in the brain.

the use of iodine-131. Iodine-131 is a beta and gamma emitter with a half-life of 8.0 days, so that in less than 2 months it decays more than 90%. It is used to test thyroid function. The thyroid gland is the only important user of iodine in the body. When a malfunctioning thyroid is suspected, the patient is given a drink of water containing sodium iodide, in which some of the iodide ions are from iodine-131. A Geiger-Müller tube is then placed in the neck region close to the thyroid gland. A normal gland will take up about 12% of the radioactive iodine within a few hours. An overactive gland—a condition known as hyperthyroidism—will absorb a much larger percentage in a shorter time. Then the overactive gland will incorporate the iodide into radioactive thyroxin, a hormone, and will quickly discharge it into general circulation again. If the thyroid gland is underactive—a condition known as myxedema—very little of the radioactivity will be detected in the gland. A myxedemic thyroid has practically no ability to take up iodide ion from circulation.

By studying how rapidly iodine-131 moves through the heart after intravenous injection, it is possible to make fair predictions of future heart attacks.[4] About 60% of cardiovascular failures ("heart attacks") are caused by a myocardial infarct, i.e., by deterioration of part of the heart's muscle when its blood supply drops after a clot forms in the coronary artery. Following injection of 20 to 30 microcuries worth of iodine-131 in human serum albumin, the passage of radioactivity through the heart is monitored by a scintillation counter placed on the chest. The data are used together with information of normal blood volume, its flow rate and the heart volume to calculate a figure called the prognostic index. When the index is greater than 7, there is roughly a 60% incidence of myocardial infarction in six months as compared to about a 10% incidence when the prognostic index is less than 7.

radiations and plant breeding

One of the least heralded contributions made by radiations has been their successful use in plant breeding. Strains of a number of grain and cereal crops have been developed in the last 40 years that are more resistant to diseases, mature earlier, and give greater yields with improved protein content. Similar results of crop improvements have occurred with vegetables, flowers, fruits and ornamentals. X rays and gamma rays (mostly from cobalt-60 sources) are used to produce mutants, and from these improved strains are selected and nurtured. The castor bean in India normally took 270 days to mature, and crops often did not mature before the rainy season. Radiations helped develop a new variety that matures in 120 days, and Indian farmers can now count on a crop every year and employ the same land for the remaining days for another crop. The highest yielding variety of rice in Japan was developed through the use of cobalt-60's gamma rays. A rice strain in Hungary matures three weeks earlier than normal. Strains of durum wheat developed from neutron-produced mutations are so superior that the United Nations Food and Agricultural Organization has recommended that some countries put their entire wheat acreage into the new mutants.

[4] G. Sevelius. *Isotopes and Radiation Technology.* Fall 1970, page 111.

All operating nuclear power plants today employ atomic fission reactions. *Fission* is the disintegration of a large nucleus into smaller fragments with the release of neutrons, radioactive isotopes and enormous yields of heat. In the light water reactors in use today the heat generates steam that drives electric turbines. (The problem of waste heat and thermal pollution was introduced in Chapter 4.)

The uranium-235 isotope is the only naturally occurring isotope that will spontaneously fission when it captures a slow (thermal) neutron. Its nucleus absorbs the neutron and then splits apart. It can split in a number of ways giving different products. E.g.,

$$^{235}_{92}U + ^{1}_{0}n \xrightarrow[\text{capture}]{\text{neutron}} ^{236}_{92}U \xrightarrow{\text{fission}} ^{141}_{56}Ba + ^{92}_{36}Kr + 3^{1}_{0}n + \gamma + \text{heat}$$

More neutrons are released than are used up. Hence one fission event produces particles that can initiate more than one new fission. In other words, a nuclear chain reaction takes place. A reactor operating on this principle is called a *burner* reactor. (The *breeder* reactor will be discussed later.)

The new isotopes produced by fission are radioactive, and their decay leads to some of the radioactive pollutants of chief concern—principally strontium-90 (a bone-seeking element in the calcium family), iodine-131 (a thyroid-gland-seeker) and cesium-137 (in the sodium family). The Atomic Energy Commission has set limits on the release of each radioactive isotope into the air and cooling waters of nuclear power plants. The decade of the 1960s witnessed an intense debate over what those limits ought to be, and in mid-1971 the Atomic Energy Commission moved to reduce sharply its allowances on emissions to concentrations and rates roughly 1 percent of the levels allowed under the former standards. Nuclear power plants operating in compliance with the new standards would expose people living near them to an extra dose no more than 5 percent of the dose they normally receive from background radiations. (All but two or three of the nearly two dozen nuclear power plants operating in the United States in 1971 already had achieved performances better than the new standards.)

The great debate over radioactive emission standards for nuclear power plants involved two important questions that have been and perhaps always will be part of any controversy involving public policy and the fruits of science and technology. One question is scientific; it can and must be handled by the most sophisticated tools of science—"What are the actual risks, statistically, of adopting a particular action?" The other question is altogether a moral one—"What are the *acceptable* risks?" Risks that are purely personal, solely voluntary; risks whose consequences are limited almost entirely to the one taking them (e.g., taking a plane trip; smoking; skiing; watching a color television set; scuba diving) are in a different category than risks of an essentially involuntary type (or at least avoidable only at major expense and trouble). These, for example, would include having to earn your living in an urbanized and therefore polluted environment. Highly trained scientists are no more competent (and no less competent) to deal with the question, "What are *acceptable* risks?" than any other group of people with a sense of moral concern. Why, ask AEC critics, should the AEC be, in effect, the sole judge of what is acceptable?

We all seem to agree that if we adopt as a matter of public policy a course of action that will *impose* risks on individuals, such risks must be much, much lower than risks we might be willing to take on a personal, voluntary basis. The controversy involving the AEC, however, has been going beyond that. The rather easily and widely accepted distinction between private, voluntary risks (which may be high) and public, imposed risks (which, public morality seems to insist, must be kept far lower)—is relevant to the living. But with the problems of nuclear power we have to ask what we may be doing to *people who have yet to be born*. The setting of standards of radioactive emissions that we judge to be acceptable is a wholly moral act. Even trace increases in exposure to radiations can be expected to affect someone, somewhere, sometime. Science may tell us what the risks are; morality must struggle with what is acceptable (meaning that people from all walks of life must struggle with it). The trend in the great debate over emission standards is that of demanding that the risks we impose on those yet to be born be far, far lower than those we accept for the presently living, lower even than the risks we accept for involuntary actions.

the breeder reactor. Uranium-235, the only naturally occurring fissile isotope, is not much more than a trace isotope (0.711%) in natural uranium. Uranium-238 is the abundant isotope (99.283% in natural uranium). According to M. King Hubbert, a geophysicist with the United States Geological Survey, the nuclear power industry with its present reactors and those being built and planned is and will be using uranium-235 at such a rate that by 2000 A.D. there will be a critical shortage. Were it not for one real possibility, electricity from nuclear power would not be available for very long. By the mid or late 1980s, however, nuclear scientists expect to have developed working *breeder reactors*.

A breeder reactor is one in which fissile material (U-235) acts on *fertile* material to make more fissile material. Uranium-238 and thorium-232 are the two important isotopes that are relatively abundant, relatively long-lived, and fertile, i.e., either can be converted by neutron capture and subsequent decay into new, man-made fissile isotopes. Uranium-238 can be changed to plutonium-239 ($^{239}_{94}Pu$):

$$^{1}_{0}n + {}^{238}_{92}U \longrightarrow {}^{239}_{92}U \xrightarrow{{}^{\;\;0}_{-1}\beta} {}^{239}_{93}Np \xrightarrow{{}^{\;\;0}_{-1}\beta} {}^{239}_{94}Pu$$

Thorium-232 can be changed to uranium-233:

$$^{1}_{0}n + ^{232}_{90}Th \longrightarrow ^{233}_{90}Th \xrightarrow{^{0}_{-1}\beta} ^{233}_{93}Pa \xrightarrow{^{0}_{-1}\beta} ^{233}_{94}U$$

The hope of those working on the breeder reactor is that by placing either uranium-238 or thorium-232 in a reactor core together with uranium-235, the neutrons released by fission of the latter will change the fertile but nonfissionable isotopes into new, fissile ones. Much less of the earth's small supply of uranium-235 would, presumably, be required to generate nuclear power. If the breeder reactor can be developed, the energy from known supplies of accessible uranium and thorium, according to Hubbert, would be hundreds of times, probably thousands of times, greater than represented by the world's reserves of petroleum and coal. (Hubbert estimates those reserves as capable of handling the bulk of the world's electric power needs for about three centuries.)

radiomimetic substances. chemical mutagens, carcinogens, and teratogens

There are many chemicals that will cause the same kinds of damages in tissue as ionizing radiations. Because they mimic radiations they are called *radiomimetic*. Chemicals that will cause mutations in experimental animals are called *mutagens*. Those that cause any form of cancer are *carcinogens*. Some chemicals will produce birth defects in offspring and are called *teratogens*.

The first compound discovered to cause chromosome abnormalities identical with those produced by X rays was mustard gas.

$$Cl-CH_2CH_2-S-CH_2CH_2-Cl$$
mustard gas

This compound is a strong alkylating agent, i.e., it will undergo a substitution reaction in which one chlorine atom (or both) is displaced and the molecule becomes attached instead to some other molecule. The heterocyclic amines that are the side-chain groups on nucleic acid strands are particularly susceptible to alkylation, and if this happens genetic transcription and translation errors are certain to happen. Some of the most potent mutagens are alkylating agents.

Other types of mutagens are also known, and how they work varies. One of the reasons the nitrite ion should be kept out of food is that in the stomach it becomes nitrous acid, HNO_2, a compound that reacts with organic substances to insert nitroso groups ($-N=O$). Nitrous acid is known to be a mutagen in many lower organisms. Yet its use as a preservative in foods and a color enhancer in sausage meats, frankfurters, smoked ham, and other meat products has gone on for years.

Between 1959 and 1962 from 2000 to 3000 babies were born in Germany with phocomelia ("seal limbs") because their mothers had taken a sedative called thalidomide during the first twelve weeks of pregnancy. In phocomelia the principal defect is a shortening or absence of the limbs, but defects in the ears, eyes and digestive tract are also common. This spectacular drug catastrophe alerted scientists and doctors to the possible dangers of new drugs to the fetus. What the mother eats, drinks, and breathes is taken much more seriously since the thalidomide disaster. Even exposure to pesticides should be avoided. Many are known mutagens in experimental animals. Some (or their impurities) are known to be teratogens. The 2,4,5-T (a potent herbicide or weed and tree killer) scattered so heavily over vast areas of Vietnam during the first decade of the Vietnamese war exposed at unknown levels untold numbers of Vietnamese women to the very powerful teratogenic effects of a trace impurity called dioxin.

One of the major problems in this area is testing, screening, and interpreting data obtained with lower organisms and experimental animals and judging what such data mean for man. We do not (deliberately) do these tests on people; nearly all our evidence comes in other ways. Thus there is room for argument, and we again have a question involving science and public policy over which experts disagree and the layman stirs uneasily. Increasingly society's wish, as we run "risks," is to err on the side of being more and more careful. The study of the molecular basis of life, both in man and in the interactions between man and the environment, that we have just concluded supports the wisdom of that trend.

Selected Reading List

Books

1. A. Romer. *The Restless Atom*. Anchor Books (S12), Doubleday and Company, Garden City, 1960. In an almost "you were there" treatment, Dr. Romer has written a delightful and illuminating book about the experiments and the people who pioneered on the frontier of physics where those restless atoms that are radioactive occur.

2. K. Z. Morgan and J. E. Turner, coeditors. *Principles of Radiation Protection*. John Wiley & Sons, New York, 1967. Although this is an advanced text of health physics, chapters on radiation biology, effects of overexposure in man, and "maximum permissible exposure levels" are both informative and easy to understand.

3. H. F. Henry. *Fundamentals of Radiation Protection*. Wiley-Interscience, New York, 1969. This is a less technical discussion than the above, but very informative.

4. Arthur C. Stern, editor. *Air Pollution,* 2nd edition. Academic Press, New York, 1968. Merril Eisenbud's chapter in the first volume (of three) of this nearly classic compendum is entitled "Sources of Radioactive Pollution."

5. H. Foreman, editor. *Nuclear Power and the Public,* University of Minnesota Press, Minneapolis, 1970. The late 1969 symposium on which this book is based brought together both supporters and critics of the Atomic Energy Commission. (Among the critics present were Arthur Tamplin and Barry Commoner.) On the subject of the title, this book is one of the most balanced as well as informative available.

6. Preston Cloud, editor. *Resources and Man.* W. H. Freeman and Company, San Francisco, 1969. The chapter "Energy Resources" by M. King Hubbert surveys the planet's supplies of various fuels and other sources of energy. Other chapters examine our resources of food and minerals.

7. National Council on Radiation Protection and Measurements (NCRP), 4201 Connecticut Ave., N. W., Washington, D. C. The NCRP publishes a number of pamphlets concerning strategies for protecting people in the health sciences and medicine from radiations. Their report No. 39, "Basic Radiation Protection Criteria," January, 1971, includes a list of their other reports.

Articles

1. J. W. Gofman and A. R. Tamplin. "Radiation: The Invisible Casualties." *Environment,* April 1970, page 12.

2. H. J. Sanders. "Chemical Mutagens." *Chemical and Engineering News,* in two parts: 19 May 1969, page 50, and 2 June 1969, page 54. (Available as a reprint for 75¢ from ACS Publications, 1155 16th St., N. W., Washington, D.C., 20036.)

3. K. Z. Morgan. "Never Do Harm." *Environment,* January/February 1971, page 28. A discussion of hazards of medical X rays.

4. "Energy and Power." *Scientific American,* September 1971. The entire issue is devoted to these very important aspects of our environmental problems.

Brief Summary

1. Atoms of radioactive elements have nuclei that are unstable. Their spontaneous breakdown is called radioactive decay, and the change produces various rays: alpha rays (helium nuclei), beta rays (electrons) and gamma rays (like high-energy X rays). All are dangerous because they create ions in their wakes.

2. Coming to us from the sun and outer space are cosmic rays which originally are mostly high-speed protons with some electrons, alpha particles, and other

atomic nuclei. By the time they reach us collisions with air molecules have produced a large number of subatomic particles.

3. Radioactive decay results in the transmutation of one element into another.

4. Radiation measurements may be expressed in the following units:
   (a) The electron-volt or multiples, KeV (thousand electron-volt) and MeV (million electron-volt), to describe the energy of the radiation itself. 1 eV $= 3.8 \times 10^{-20}$ calorie.
   (b) The curie, to describe the activity of a radioactive source. (One curie, the equivalent of the activity of one gram of radium, is 3.7×10^{10} disintegrations per second.)
   (c) The roentgen, to describe how powerful a dose of X rays or gamma rays one might be exposed to. A one roentgen dose produces ions in dry air with aggregate charges of 2.1×10^9 units.
   (d) The rad, to describe the effect in tissues of an exposure to radiation. An absorbed dose of one rad means an absorption of 100 ergs of energy per gram of tissue. (And this is not much different from the effect of 1 roentgen when it is absorbed by tissue instead of air.)
   (e) The rem, to describe for any radiation absorbed by man how many roentgens it is equivalent to.
   (f) The LET, to describe energy deposited per unit path length by radiation.
   (g) RBE, to compare the effectiveness of various radiations to cause changes in tissue with gamma rays being the standard.
   (h) $LD_{50}/30$ days, one of many ways to describe the toxicity of radiation.
   (i) Half-life, to describe how relatively unstable a given radioactive isotope is.

5. To detect, measure, and monitor radiations we have scintillation counters, photographic materials, and devices such as ion chambers and Geiger counters.

6. The natural background radiation received annually by people in the United States is an average of about 100 to 140 mrem per person. Another 20 to 50 mrem, on the average, is absorbed from diagnostic and therapeutic X rays. The $LD_{50}/30$-day value for man is an estimated 500 rem (500,000 mrem). The maximum annual limit proposed for the general population from all sources over and above the background is 170 mrem.

7. The primary site of radiation damage is the cells' genetic apparatus.

8. There is no threshold of radiation absorption below which no damage of any kind can possibly occur.

9. High doses of radiation produce a collection of symptoms called radiation sickness.

10. The result of even very low doses of radiations may be cancer, particularly leukemia. Well-focused high doses will halt cancer.

11. A number of chemicals are radiomimetic. They can produce changes in cells indistinguishable from those caused by radiations.

12. Radioactive isotopes of all the common elements are now available through induced transmutations. Many of these have been used in medical research, diagnosis and therapy, in agriculture, and other industries.

13. Nuclear energy available today for generating electric power depends on naturally occurring uranium-235. When it is hit by a neutron it fissions and produces smaller, radioactive isotopes, neutrons and heat. The newly released neutrons carry on the chain reaction.

14. In the proposed breeder reactor, naturally occurring fissile isotope (U-235) will change nonfissionable but fertile isotopes of uranium or thorium into man-made fissile material.

Problems and Exercises

1. Define each of the following terms:

(a) alpha particle	(k) roentgen (R)	(t) scintillation counter
(b) beta particle	(l) absorbed dose	(u) radiomimetic
(c) gamma ray	(m) rad	(v) fissile isotope
(d) cosmic rays	(n) dose equivalent	(w) fission
(e) radioactivity	(o) rem	(x) fertile isotope
(f) transmutation	(p) LET	(y) breeder reactor
(g) half-life	(q) RBE	(z) mutagen
(h) electron-volt	(r) LD_{50}/30-days	(aa) carcinogen
(i) curie	(s) Geiger-Müller tube	(bb) teratogen
(j) exposure		

2. Explain the paradox that ionizing radiations can both cause cancer and arrest it.

3. Explain the difference between "exposure" (or "exposure dose") and "absorbed dose."

4. Strontium-90 is a β-emitter. Write the nuclear equation for its decay.

5. Gadolinium-148 is an α-emitter. Write the nuclear equation for its decay.

6. Supply symbols for the bombardment particles used in the following transmutations:

$$(a) \, ^{27}_{13}Al + \underline{\hspace{2cm}} \longrightarrow \, ^{30}_{15}P + \, ^{1}_{0}n$$
$$(b) \, ^{32}_{16}S + \underline{\hspace{2cm}} \longrightarrow \, ^{32}_{15}P + \, ^{1}_{1}H$$

7. When nitrogen-14 is bombarded with alpha particles to produce oxygen-17 and protons, it is believed that an intermediate atom forms with a "compound nucleus" that then decays to the observed products:

$$^{14}_{7}N + \, ^{4}_{2}He \longrightarrow \underline{\hspace{2cm}} \longrightarrow \, ^{17}_{8}O + \, ^{1}_{1}H$$

Write the atomic symbol for this intermediate. Show its atomic number and atomic weight.

8. When boron-10 is bombarded by alpha particles, nitrogen-13 forms:

$$^{10}_{5}B + \, ^{4}_{2}He \longrightarrow \, ^{13}_{7}N + \, ^{1}_{0}n$$

Nitrogen-13 is also radioactive ($t_{1/2}$, 10 minutes). It decays to yield carbon-13 plus a particle called a positron:

$$^{13}_{7}N \longrightarrow \; ^{13}_{6}C + a \text{ positron}$$

Figuring from the equation given, what is the electrical charge on a positron? Its mass? Compare it with an electron.

9. If the half-life of thorium-234 is 24 days how much thorium-234 will be left in a sample that initially had 12 grams of this isotope after 72 days.

10. The intensity of the radiation from, say, 1 gram of a β-emitter of very short half-life is greater than that from the same amount of a β-emitter of long half-life. Explain why this should be. Why then are isotopes of short half-life still used in diagnosis? Why are trace amounts used? How are isotopes useful in diagnosis? In cancer therapy?

11. A radioactive source of 1 curie produced a radiation intensity of 16 units (arbitrary units) at a distance of 2 feet. What is the intensity at
(a) a distance of 1 foot?
(b) a distance of 4 feet?

appendix

IUPAC Nomenclature for Common Oxygen Derivatives of Hydrocarbons

Alcohols

   Parent compound: The longest continuous chain of carbons that includes the hydroxyl group. Replace the terminal "-e" of the corresponding alkane by "-ol." In the case of diols (dihydroxy alcohols) or higher, retain the terminal "-e" but add "-diol," or "-triol," etc.

   Numbering: Number the positions of the chain to give the alcohol group the lower number. (It has precedence over alkyl groups.)

   Examples:

CH_3OH CH_3CH_2OH $CH_3CH_2CH_2OH$ $CH_3\overset{OH}{\underset{|}{C}}HCH_3$ $CH_3CH_2\overset{CH_3}{\underset{\underset{CH_3}{|}}{\overset{|}{C}}}CH_2OH$

methanol   ethanol   1-propanol   2-propanol 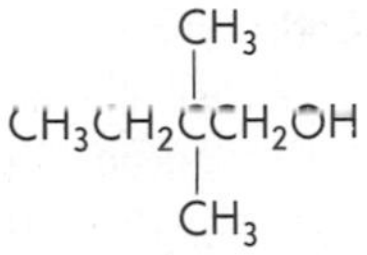   2,2-dimethyl-1-butanol

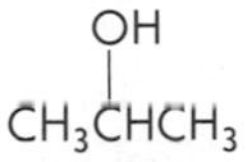

$HOCH_2CH_2OH$ $HOCH_2\overset{OH}{\underset{|}{C}}HCH_2OH$ $CH_3\overset{Cl}{\underset{|}{C}}HCH_2OH$

1,2-ethanediol   1,2,3-propanetriol 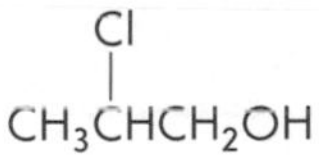   2-chloro-1-propanol 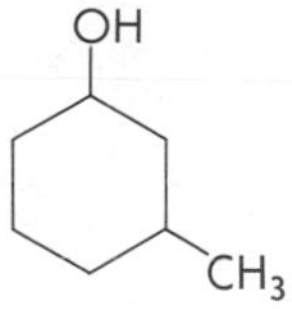   3-methylcyclo-hexanol

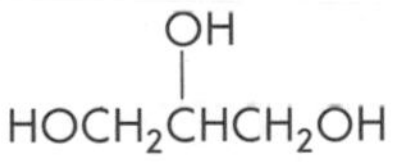

Aldehydes

   Parent compound: The longest continuous chain of carbons that includes the aldehyde group. Replace the terminal "-e" of the corresponding alkane by "-al."

   Numbering: The carbon of the aldehyde group is given number 1. (It has precedence over alcohol groups or double bonds.)

   Examples:

$CH_2{=}O$ $CH_3CH{=}O$ $CH_3CH_2CH{=}O$

methanal   ethanal   propanal

$CH_3CH_2\overset{CH_3}{\underset{|}{C}}HCH{=}O$ $CH_3(CH_2)_4\overset{CH_3}{\underset{\underset{CH_3}{|}}{\overset{|}{C}}}CH_2CH{=}O$

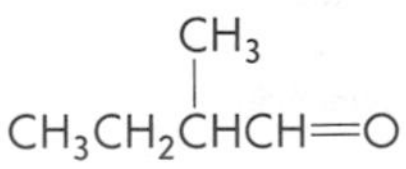

2-methylbutanal 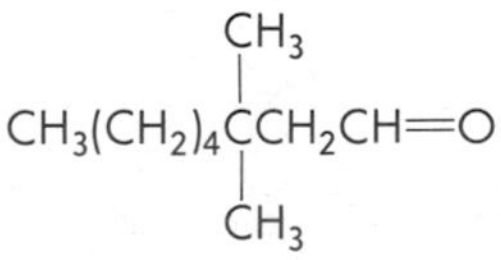   3,3-dimethyloctanal

Ketones

   Parent compound: The longest continuous chain of carbons that includes the ketone group. Replace the terminal "-e" of the corresponding alkane by "-one."

Numbering: Number the chain to give the ketone group the lower number. (It has precedence over alkyl groups.)

Examples:

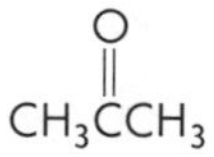

$$CH_3\overset{O}{\overset{\|}{C}}CH_3 \qquad CH_3\overset{O}{\overset{\|}{C}}CH_2CH_3 \qquad CH_3\overset{O}{\overset{\|}{C}}CH_2CH_2CH_3 \qquad CH_3CH_2\overset{O}{\overset{\|}{C}}CH_2CH_3$$

propanone 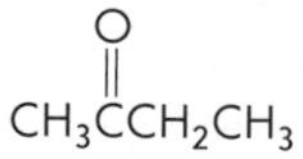   butanone    2-pentanone 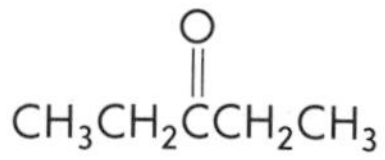   3-pentanone

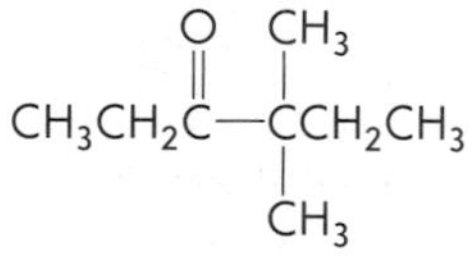

$$CH_3CH_2\overset{O}{\overset{\|}{C}}-\overset{CH_3}{\underset{CH_3}{\overset{|}{\underset{|}{C}}}}CH_2CH_3 \qquad C_6H_5CH_2\overset{O}{\overset{\|}{C}}CH_2CH_3$$

4,4-dimethyl-3-hexanone 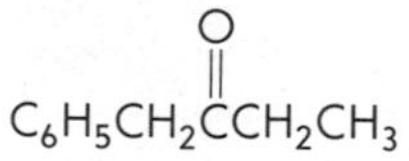   1-phenyl-2-butanone

Carboxylic acids

Parent compound: The longest continuous chain of carbons that includes the carboxyl group. Replace the terminal "-e" of the corresponding alkane by "-oic acid."

Numbering: Number the chain to give the carbon of the carboxyl group number 1. (It has precedence over all other oxygen functions.)

Examples:

$$HCO_2H \qquad CH_3CO_2H \qquad CH_3\overset{CH_3}{\overset{|}{CH}}CO_2H$$

methanoic acid   ethanoic acid   2-methylpropanoic acid

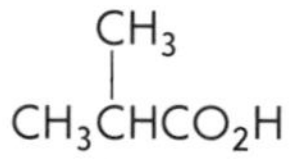

Carboxylic Acid Derivatives

Parent compound: The name of the parent acid is determined first; then, depending on the derivative, one of the following operations on that name is made.

Carboxylic acid salt: Change the "-ic acid" to "-ate" and precede this word by the name of the ion (as a separate word).

Examples:

$$CH_3CO_2^-Na^+ \qquad CH_3\overset{CH_3}{\underset{CH_3}{\overset{|}{\underset{|}{C}}}}CO_2^-K^+$$

sodium ethanoate   potassium 2,2-dimethyl propanoate

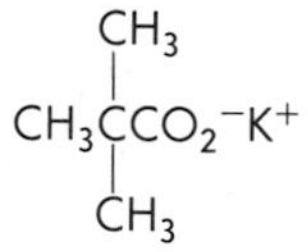

Amides: Change the "-oic acid" to "-amide".

Examples:

$$CH_3CONH_2 \qquad CH_3CH_2\overset{CH_3}{\overset{|}{CH}}-\overset{CH_3}{\overset{|}{CH}}-CONH_2 \qquad CH_3CH_2CONHCH_3$$

ethanamide   2,3-dimethylpentanamide   N-methylpropanamide

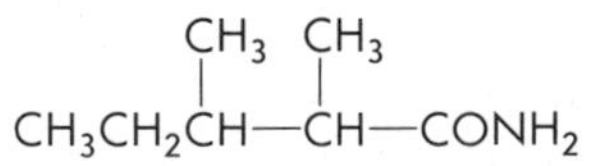

Esters: Change the "-ic acid" of the parent acid to "-ate" and precede this word
by the name of the alkyl group (as a separate word).

$$CH_3CH_2CO_2CH_3$$

methyl propanoate

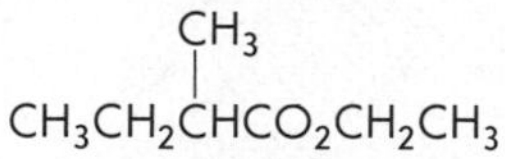

$$\overset{\displaystyle CH_3}{\underset{\displaystyle }{CH_3CH_2\overset{|}{C}HCO_2CH_2CH_3}}$$

ethyl 2-methylbutanoate

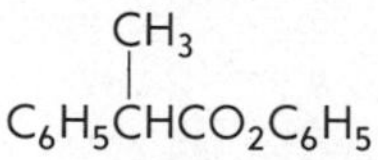

$$\overset{\displaystyle CH_3}{\underset{\displaystyle }{C_6H_5\overset{|}{C}HCO_2C_6H_5}}$$

phenyl 2-phenyl
propanoate

index